WITH BEST WISHES
FROM YOUR CONGRESSMAN.

B. F. Sisk

88TH CONGRESS, 1ST SESSION, HOUSE DOCUMENT NO. 29

The
Yearbook
of
Agriculture
1963

A

Place

to Live

The Yearbook of Agriculture 1963

The United States Department of Agriculture

Washington, D.C.

THE UNITED STATES
GOVERNMENT PRINTING OFFICE

FOR SALE BY THE
SUPERINTENDENT OF DOCUMENTS
WASHINGTON, D.C., 20402
PRICE $3

ORVILLE L. FREEMAN
Secretary of Agriculture

FOREWORD

THIS is a time and this is a book that call for discussion, cooperation, and vision to channel great forces of change in directions that ensure that America will always be a good place to live.

The signs of change are everywhere. We see them in the growth or decline of communities, the building of highways and other facilities, the moving of people to new homes and jobs, the renewal of cities and the growth of suburbs, the enlargement of some farms and the disappearance of others, questions about the place of family farms as a dynamic force in agricultural production, shifts in the uses of land, and changes in our human relationships, institutions, and aspirations in rural and urban America alike.

But the meaning and the relentless force of the changes and their diversity become fully clear only if we fit them into a broad perspective, just as we need a map of all major highways, not only the roads in our own county, when we start a long trip.

A perspective, such as this book aims to give, discloses that a new economic order is taking shape on American farms, in rural America, and in cities. It is a product of a technological-scientific revolution, which began 200 years ago and has speeded up tremendously in the past few years.

Its effect on agricultural production has been almost beyond belief. Its effect on farmers and communities that could not keep up with its fast pace has been sorrowful. It has made agriculture miraculously successful, but it is a warning signal if the changes, like an automobile out of control, are so fast, so undirected, or so unmindful of traffic signs and lights as to jeopardize the well-being of people.

I give some examples. The farmer whose fields are too small or too rugged or too poor for machines cannot compete with bigger farmers. Economic slowdown has hurt some rural communities. Many of the people who have quit farming since 1950 have moved to cities. But cities, too, have had problems, and many of their residents have gone to suburbs to seek a better place to live. Nationally a new situation has arisen, compounded of changing and growing needs for more land for industry and more water for everybody; for more and better community services; for a reevaluation of the uses of land; and for plans for the wise, enduring use of land, water, forests, open spaces, air, rivers, and seashores.

All such changes are challenges to direct American energy, American dynamism, American ability, and, yes, American humanitarianism toward a greater fulfillment of the American goal.

We have an opportunity to bring closer together all parts of our population, our economy, and our geography and so to help us realize that the prosperity of city people is tied closely to the well-being of rural people, that many traditional distinctions between city and country no longer are true, and that the United States is one Nation, indivisible.

Another opportunity, related to all the others, is to plan for our future and the future of later generations as individuals, as communities, and as a Nation: How can we best use our abundance for the good of all?

We can extend and speed up our efforts to conserve our wealth of human and physical resources for tomorrow's needs and today's unmet needs. As President Kennedy said, "In the work of conservation, time should be made our friend, not our adversary. Actions deferred are frequently opportunities lost, and, in terms of financial outlay, dollars invested today will yield great benefits in the years to come."

Of all our resources, the most valuable are people. Changes in rural America left many rural people disadvantaged. Less than a third of our population now is rural, but more than half of the 8 million American families whose yearly incomes are below 2,500 dollars live in rural areas. More than one-fifth of the 22 million youths who live in rural America are members of poor families. Many of our people are unemployed. Many are underemployed. Many need training for new work. Many need help.

To help people, the Department of Agriculture, which has a long and glorious history of service to all Americans, has embarked on Rural Areas Development programs. Their aims are to revitalize and recapitalize town and country, to improve or redevelop physical resources, to put the resources to work for all America, and to provide new or improve public facilities and new economic opportunities.

They will have a great and good effect on our family farms, which as productive units have met the test of time but which have been threatened by forces outside of farming. As I said in a statement before the Subcommittee on Family Farms of the House Committee on Agriculture on July 11, 1963: "I believe the family farm system is worth preserving because it has social worth as well as economic value. But if we are realistic, we must recognize that the family farm will continue only if it is an efficient producer of agricultural products in terms of current scientific, technological, and management practices. . . . Most of the people on these farms want to be farmers. It is their chosen profession. They want to stay on the land and in their community. We should help them realize their desire, but where the farming resources are clearly inadequate, we should make available additional opportunities so that such families can have a decent American standard of living.

All America will benefit in many ways. It is in the spirit of the American tradition of giving every man a chance.

We have also the opportunity to assess the function of government in the work before us. I, myself, believe the Federal Government must take a leading part in rural economic development because of its wide scope. But the work also requires investment capital and the help of commerce and industry. It will require the resources of State and local government, but it can succeed only with the initiative and leadership of local people.

To the fulfillment of these opportunities, we commit our imagination, technical skills, and powers. Let us not seek tasks to fit our talents. Let us rather pray that our talents fit the obligations before us.

ALFRED STEFFERUD
Editor of the Yearbook

PREFACE

THE suggestions we sent in June 1962 to the writers of this book included this statement: "Our purpose is to inform all Americans about the effects of urbanization and industrialization on rural America and the need for plans and action so that people will have a proper place to live. Many of the forces of change are most apparent in the urban-rural fringe, but our interest is in functional, rather than geographic, aspects—in the interaction of rural and urban influences wherever they occur.

"The changes affect the welfare of everyone. City people and country people have a stake in the maintenance of healthy conditions in country and city. Because a progressive, viable rural economy and the full use of its resources benefit the entire Nation, we stress the unity of our interests. What kind of rural America do we want, and how do we get it? What changes are needed in attitudes about resources? What tools of government need to be revamped to meet modern challenges? How must Federal, State, and local governments work with people to develop programs that will meet our goals for improved living and working conditions? What are our goals, values, objectives?

"This book will be especially timely and necessary because of the emphasis being placed by this Department on rural development and land and water policies and because of the growing number of persons who live on farms but do not farm. This Yearbook should be a contribution to general knowledge of the significance of agriculture in an increasingly urban civilization such as ours in the United States. At the same time it would have special interest and help to small farmers, part-time farmers, owners of suburban property, State and county planning boards, and country dwellers who work in the cities.

"We aim to acquaint city people with some farm problems; give useful information to consumers; tell more Americans about our programs of conservation, Rural Areas Development, Extension, and others; demonstrate the breadth of the Department's activities and responsibilities in its many fields other than commercial agricultural production; and set forth the social and economic aspects of the movement to and from farms. The book should also have substantial practical material in keeping with the historical function of the Yearbooks."

Now, after months of thinking about our subject and writing, editing, and publishing the book, we see no reason to change even a comma of the statement, although we might have put in a stronger sentence, emphasized by italics and an exclamation point: *No subject is more momentous than this to Americans!*

The statement gave us our title, *A Place to Live,* which embodies the yearnings of many of us for a clean, orderly, happy, secure home, where we can rear our children, make a living, and enjoy our blessings.

The statement had another—an unexpected—use. It was intended only for the guidance of the contributors, but others read it, quoted it, and so enlisted the interest and efforts of more citizens in a movement of planning and action that affects us all. The book itself, we hope, will further that momentum by providing some of the information people need to chart a course, marking some of the shoals, and pointing out some of the lighthouses along the way.

For help with the book, many persons have our thanks—the contributors; Members of the Congress, who appropriated the money for its publication, who distribute most of the copies, and who pass the national laws that make it possible to achieve a proper place to live; and the 1963 Yearbook Committee, who outlined its content.

CONTENTS

LAND

WATER AND AIR

FARMING

COMMUNITIES

GOVERNMENT

RECREATION; RE-CREATION

WHAT TO DO

EXAMPLES

THE 1963 YEARBOOK COMMITTEE

Harry A. Steele, *Economic Research Service,* CHAIRMAN
Hugh A. Johnson, *Economic Research Service,* SECRETARY
John L. Creech, *Agricultural Research Service*
Frederick D. Stocker, *Economic Research Service*
Phillip F. Aylesworth, *Federal Extension Service*
Mrs. L. M. Alexander, *Federal Extension Service*
Philip S. Brown, *Farmers Home Administration*
C. B. Gilliland, *Office of Rural Areas Development*
Albert A. Klingebiel, *Soil Conservation Service*
George A. Selke, *Office of the Secretary*

A Place to Live

CHANGES IN PEOPLE

*ALL history, all problems, all plans, all changes have
meaning only in terms of people, of me and my family and
my neighbors: How and where we live, what we think, how
we act, how we get along in life. People are not norms
and statistics, but norms and statistics are an index
of a population that is becoming more urban, more
industrialized, more mobile, older, more harried, more
questioning, more urbane, further away from tradition.
What remains of their old values? Were those values
good? Which values should we try for? Two points stand
out: "To build an economic democracy that will match
our political democracy, people must have the facts."
"The new and as yet uncharted lines of human endeavor,
fulfillment, and adventure open to the rural community and
agriculture are bound to find men and women willing
to chance it as our sodbusting ancestors did a generation
ago." To chance it, yes: To face boldly the need for institutions and actions that meet the demands of a changing
economy and a new evaluation of social policies.*

ROY C. BUCK

AN INTERPRETATION
OF RURAL VALUES

T HE 1940 Yearbook of Agriculture, *Farmers in a Changing World*, gave major attention to cultural and philosophic themes upon which the rural community and the agricultural industry were believed to be based. In a foreword to the hefty, 1,215-page book, Henry A. Wallace, Secretary of Agriculture, observed: "To build an economic democracy that will match our political democracy, people must have the facts."

But then (as now) there was an uneasy feeling among many of the writers that facts do not speak for themselves but must have meaning—which involves judgment, value, and certain presuppositions—assigned to them.

Now, 23 years later—23 years of warfare, burgeoning technology, and an almost overwhelming onrush of change—I, too, tackle the problem of meaning, hoping that something of the "value climate" of rural people can be sensed.

I use as my "text" the closing paragraphs of one chapter, "Beyond Economics," in the 1940 Yearbook of Agriculture, by M. L. Wilson, then Director of Extension Work, who summarized the value problem as he saw it:

"It is perhaps the greatest tragedy in American history that there has not been in this country a fully developed and distinctly indigenous philosophy of

social reform that is applicable to the industrial situation that dominates so much of our modern social problems. The result of this lack has been that an unduly large share of socially minded Americans have attached themselves to creeds and doctrines that may suit the situation elsewhere but are rigid and unrealistic here.

"Yet all the while there were in the United States the materials for just the kind of social philosophy that has been most needed. Those materials are to be found in the philosophy of pragmatism, in the economic thought of the so-called 'institutionalists,' and in the concept of culture. The philosophical pragmatism of William James, George Herbert Mead, and John Dewey considers rationality as an instrument for the prediction and control of experienced facts rather than as a device for grasping realities hidden from the or-

1

dinary methods of science, as was typically assumed by some of the older philosophers.

"Institutionalist economics, inspired by pragmatism, developed out of the perception that many observed economic facts did not jibe with accepted economic theory. As a consequence, among institutionalists emphasis came to be placed upon the observation and description of economic institutions as they actually exist rather than upon the elaboration or application of theories and principles conceived in the abstract. . . .

"The essence of all of these philosophical concepts is an underlying sense of the relativity of things, a belief that the most ambitious hope that men can hold for their power of understanding is that it serve them well in the particular age and circumstance in which they live. We live upon this earth but once, and at best we see but one small segment of it during a very brief existence. And what we see, we see through limited senses, clouded by the mists of the particular ideas of the culture in which we live.

"Wisdom would seem to reside in an effort to work with the materials at hand, trying to fit them together as best we may according to the needs of the moment and the powers we actually possess. In such an effort, manmade doctrines of immutable truth are likely to confuse our thinking more than they clarify it. The greatest intellectual task we have may well be that of stripping our minds of those misconceptions that prevent us from seeing things in the way that in our present circumstances would be most useful to us.

"Out of the materials of such relativistic thinking should evolve a social philosophy that is peculiarly American in origin and character. It would not be a rigid creed in any sense, unless it were in a refusal to be a creed. It would be a philosophy that left no place for personal devils or for class or racial devils. It would be democratic, not for reasons of ideological loyalty but rather as a matter of practical effectiveness.

"It would be pluralistic in rejecting cure-alls and relativistic in rejecting pretensions to absolute or static perfection. It would recognize the interdependence of social phenomena all the way from the monthly creamery check and the Monday-morning washing to the highest aesthetic or philosophic or spiritual concern. It would perceive the impossibility of sharp separation of ends and means because it would see that means tend in the long run to become ends. And it would appreciate that the material things so generally the symbols of desires really exist only for the satisfaction of psychological or spiritual needs. Such a program of agricultural adjustment and reform should be able to avoid the equal evils of rashness on the one hand and dangerous delay on the other."

Such was the thinking of a great agricultural philosopher. Dr. Wilson was uneasy with the "Old World veneer" covering what he believed to be vital elements of American character. He took seriously the New World symbol. Twenty-three years ago he was asking us to accept ourselves for what we are, a people for whom life is a journey, rather than a passive rest on tradition. Perhaps he was asking for the impossible.

Does a pragmatic culture, one concerned with practical results or values, ever make enough sense to systematize it in a philosophy and theory of human organization? Pragmatism knows many little rules of conduct, but can it be boxed in with grand theory and philosophy?

We shall not reflect on these questions. What is to follow is an attempt to carry Dr. Wilson's analysis a step or two further.

ABRAHAM LINCOLN observed in his second inaugural address: "The dogmas of the quiet past are inadequate to the stormy present. The occasion is piled high with difficulty and we must rise to the occasion. As our case is new—

so we must think anew and act anew."

Probably no other statement in American thought more succinctly lays out the pragmatic view.

To be willing to slough off that which is historically correct but immediately irrelevant, to be willing to reexamine traditional presuppositions in light of current problems, to be able to adapt to the ongoing march of civilization and not go to pieces with worry or become irresponsible, is the challenge of pragmatism.

The pragmatic view takes seriously the dictum that in the long run we are all dead. It is essentially a short-run philosophy. Pragmatic dreams are little dreams. They do not encompass a utopian view. Progress is viewed a step at a time. The faith of pragmatism is the faith in the ability of man to marshal his humanity toward realizing some measure of the good life in the here and now. "Earth is but a barren land, heaven is my home" is not the hymn of pragmatism. The pragmatic hymn is one of joy, praise, and thanksgiving directed toward God, the Creator of a world to be used and enjoyed.

Pragmatism is a philosophy born of liberty of mind and responsible freedom of action. Hampered spirits and minds weave fantastic dreams and produce grand designs. Pragmatism does not confuse man with God. It sees the careful judgment and calculated risk as responsible behavior for one less than God.

THE PRAGMATIC view is highly developed here in the United States. It is caricatured in the Yankee, Rebel, Cowboy, Businessman, Horatio Alger, and Uncle Sam. Some social critics insist that these symbols are dead. They see a certain facelessness in the American character. There may be evidence of this, but I would not assent to a wholly empty view. Although we have drifted from excesses fostered by 19th-century laissez faire spirit and provincialism, there is abundant evidence that the American can still be identified in dimensions other than a kind of generalized "well rounded-ness."

AMERICANS have a certain impatience. They tend to live as if time is running out on them. They often tackle chronic problems as if permanent solutions were possible. Americans believe in their capacity to realize some measure of the good life in the here and now.

With notable exceptions the American is up and doing—a little brash, but friendly and optimistic. He is not overly sentimental, nor is he as tough minded as he would like to believe. He is quick to give a hungry man a quarter, and his eye is cocked in the direction of a bargain. He is given to riddles. He often enjoys feigning poverty when he is "well fixed." On the other hand, conspicuous display does not always mean wealth.

Americans idealize production. The pile at the end of the day is one good American measure of a man's worth. In fact we would claim that conspicuous production is at least as treasured a value as conspicuous consumption as a status-giving element in the American's list of satisfactions.

THE COUNTRYSIDE and Main Street were the traditional habitats of the American. Here his energy and point of view were most telling. Out of a wilderness, he carved with amazing success a new way of life. He leveled forests, turned over expanses of virgin sod, mined mountains of minerals, threw up railheads, and opened banks, schools, and churches with reckless abandon. Out of a lush natural larder flooded products to whet the appetites of world markets. To get there "fustest with the mostest" was a life principle as well as battle cry.

More cautious scholars would pale at these admitted overgeneralizations, but I must defend them in the interest of being at least vaguely correct rather than being cautiously irrelevant or dully repetitive. I outline and caricature American pragmatism

in order to dispel somewhat the traditional image of rural life as being wholly rooted in a European peasantry and "Elysian bliss" or an erosion of this once-upon-a-time mentality.

American scholarship on rural life has been reluctant to accept the observations of Count Alexis de Tocqueville, the French historian who toured the continent a century and a half ago and observed even then the forces of freedom, the belief in the dignity of the common man, unbounded energy and optimism, a tendency to organize power to push for change and progress, and the element of tempered ruthlessness.

His observations, recorded in *Democracy in America: 1835–1839*, and those of other early observers from the "outside" are useful sources of insight into the foundation of the American character. They perhaps were less driven to make the New World fit Old World philosophic and social systems. They did not have to be defensive or apologetic for what they observed. They did not have the personal concern for fitting what they observed to preestablished schemes of thought. They saw America as something new and were eager to record this newness in its raw state.

Traditional scholarship has tended to look at the American community through stereotypes growing out of European thought. Peasantry is often a presupposition in looking at the farmer. Nobility is likely to feed the stereotypes used to understand the business community.

We fail to see the American as a cultural hybrid, a union of peasant and noble; a kind of shirt-sleeved lord of all he surveys. With reasonable caution I view the rural community as a product of this hybrid mentality and vigor.

The United States is not a continuation of Old World institutions so much as an object lesson in their transformation to meet the needs of a pioneer people eager to capitalize on abundant natural resources and a new taste of freedom. I recognize that in this generalization there are significant exceptions.

An observer from Sweden, touring the North Central States in the 1950's, remarked that he found communities more Swedish than Sweden. Amish communities, with their emphasis on separation, also are exceptions. One finds in large cities little pockets of homeland culture where the emphasis is on holding on to things as they were at the time of immigration. Despite these and other instances of continuing Old World customs, I concur with Frederick Jackson Turner's conclusion that the United States harbors a unique character in the world scene, The American.

ADJUSTMENT and changes demanded by major wars, continuing cold war, general prosperity, little recessions, unparalleled scientific and technological advancement, and the increasing linkage of all aspects of American society into one vast network of interdependency have left their marks on rural communities. We are in the midst of all the projections made in the 1940 Yearbook of Agriculture and many more that were not anticipated then.

Rural communities have become "electrified, telephoned, and televised." All-weather roads and superhighways lace all the countryside. Consolidated schools offer comprehensive education. Drowsy villages have become industrial towns, military base towns, resort towns, superhighway interchange towns, and suburban resident developments.

Other towns, away from main lines of transportation and development, have declined in population and vitality of social and economic life. For them, the recent past has meant stalemate and loss of significance. In a society geared to progress and development, these towns, off the beaten track, are not attractive to teachers, ministers, businessmen, and others generally inclined toward a progress psychology.

How to service economically and socially declining communities is a worrisome question for public and private agencies and institutions.

TRAILER PARKS, a new form of community life, dot the rural landscape and ring centers of rapid expansion. They house a new category of migrant worker. They gather heavy-construction workers, military personnel, young couples, retired people, and a motley assortment of persons who enjoy the freedom and autonomy of temporary residence. Established community institutions, which assume permanency of residence as a criterion for participation and service, are frustrated by the trailer community.

The trailer resident symbolizes the growing mobility of our population. Movement, a characteristic traditionally reserved for city "n'er-do-wells" and country "no accounts," is becoming an accepted life norm. Community institutions, rooted in a philosophy of owner occupancy of land, long residence, and minimum spatial mobility, are slow to adjust to this increasing mobility.

The demands of an economy that seems to be more and more observing the laws of comparative advantage of place will increase mobility of all walks of life. Ownership of real property, historically a treasured value, may very well decline as people adjust to movement as a way to capitalize on economic opportunity.

This shift will have far-reaching effects. We need to assess critically our calendar-picture image of the rural community as a cluster of like-minded people hemmed in by hills and local communication and focused on a white church steeple and "our" school.

Traditional means of expressing community loyalty and pride will change. People will be less motivated by personal involvement in local institutions. Localism will have less functional utility as mobility increases. Means of expressing responsibility in a place-released society have yet to be worked out.

Local institutions must find ways of vitally serving mobile and potentially mobile people. Here is a high-priority problem, for if our institutions fail to meet the demands of an economy that places increasing value and reward on willingness to move, what happens to the notion of the responsible man voicing his concern through the traditional channels of democracy?

ADVANCEMENTS in science and their quick transfer to technological and organizational improvements have altered rural values. Agricultural magic, folk medicine, primitive religious rites, and other aspects of rustic lore are set aside as useful remedies and practices. Where they are retained, they often are considered only as a "psychic security."

The scientific mentality, fostered by the various agencies of the Department of Agriculture and nearly the whole of contemporary society, makes probability and relativity central themes around which values cluster. While many segments of the rural population would seem to cling to old ways, a ready market generally exists for improvements in farm practices, and community leaders often are eager to have interpretations of findings in the social sciences.

The quick transfer of scientific findings into production and organization ability is a commentary on the pragmatic mind. If science is good, it must be good for something. That we continue to study adoption and diffusion of improved practices in agriculture and community organization is evidence of belief in adaptability and change as life principles.

Folk practices and superstitions multiplied because of this bent of mind. As means were developed to bring the products of science into the rural community, however, a ready market was found. Old ways became subjects of rural humor, recreation, dream weaving, and mythmaking.

Retired extension agents like to tell stories of resistance to their "newfangled" ideas. They are also quick to admit that extension was easy back then. A sack of fertilizer sowed along a row or two of corn or a sprayed apple tree were convincing demonstrations. Farmers caught on. They continue to catch on when there is compelling evidence of outcome and when the agent understands and appreciates their practical turn of mind.

ONCE AN unorganized industry, farming and its related occupations constitute one of the heaviest organized industries in the economy. Nearly every commodity supports educational and promotional organizations. General farm organizations interested in broad problems of production, marketing, and consumption operate in every State. Marketing and purchasing cooperatives claim increasing memberships and volume of business.

Agriculture is an ideal climate for organization development. An expanding industry with a shrinking labor force and a relatively inelastic demand for the product of the industry favor compounding of organization. Private groups and public agencies interlace agriculture with a staggering array of points of view and programs.

The commercial farmer in the span of a generation has adopted some of the folkways of the organization man and the bureaucrat.

Bookkeeping has been transferred from his pants pocket to a desk. He keeps informed by infinite commodity publications and reports. His calendar is filled with notices of meetings, field days, committees, and appointments with income tax advisers and credit managers. He has trouble keeping up with market reports, weather predictions, spray schedules, and breeding charts, but he knows he must. All of this has to be blended with increased organization in the community. Religious, educational, and civic groups beckon him toward both membership and leadership responsibility.

But all is not harmonious. Duplication of effort and competition for membership, resources, and position are familiar problems of rural organization.

Because of the increased heterogeneity of population and the increased specialization of agriculture, rural organization is not likely to present a united front, regardless of the issue. The traditional image of the rural community as an example of unanimity of opinion centering on common goals and means for attaining them is less true now than it once was.

General farm organizations, emerging from the diversified family farm tradition of the late 19th and early 20th centuries, are challenged to speak for an ever more "intracompetitive" industry. The specialization of food and fiber production spawned commodity-related pressure groups, which tend to foster intraindustry competition. The general occupational category of "farmer" is being replaced by dairyman, poultryman, fruitgrower, graingrower, nurseryman, and so on.

Not all of the rural dwellers belong to organizations. Personal and social attributes encourage and discourage activity in them. Informal groupings suffice for some, who may feel little responsibility for voicing opinion through formal channels. When they are asked why they do not take part in formally organized groups, very likely they reply that they are not expected to. While they would not say they were unwanted, they would admit to feeling "funny" or out of place in a formal meeting.

Other nonjoiners would say that they do not have to take part. Because of their position in the community, they are something of an elite body. They have direct access to centers of decision and can bring their influences to bear directly. They are the gate-keepers of public opinion and the legitimizers of group decision. They are the group with whom officers of local organizations "keep in touch." They are the committees behind the committees whose names the newspapers print.

Group leaders and executives often find it hard to keep grassroots democracy alive. The conviction that wise policy filters up from the crossroads to centers of action seems to be weakening. While people continue to want the right to evaluate and vote on alternative policies, they depend more and more on their professional representatives to clarify positions for their consideration.

Ours is a mixed democracy. Grassroots folk democracy is combined with representative democracy in the private sector of society as well as the public sector. Full-time executive secretaries and other organization personnel are employed by an increasing number of organizations. These professionals take on duties and responsibilities traditionally accorded volunteer lay leaders. Lay leadership tends to be redefined as the role of public opinion leader, the person with whom the professional leader keeps in touch.

Community residents increasingly express views through the vote, or more indirectly through organization affiliation and informal affirmation. Direct involvement in community organization seems to be diminishing.

Critics of the contemporary scene despair over the tendency of laymen to assume the more passive function of behind-the-scenes influence and the rise of civic activity as a legitimate vocation. This tendency for democratic responsibility to be operationalized by remote control of the citizenry, it is feared, will foster individual irresponsibility. This apparent drift in organization logistics seems to be in line with American progress values.

A key symbol of advancement in the technological sphere is the development of machinery with certain built-in, self-monitoring functions. To free the worker from personal attention of the machine is viewed positively. The growing edge of machine design is generally in the area of automation. Human contact is one of programing and general surveillance. The worker's relationship with industrial production is one of declining direct involvement.

There is reason to assume that this technological ingenuity will tend to be transferred with increasing speed to the social and political sphere.

As man is faced with the necessity to redefine productive employment, so will he need to redefine his role as a responsible citizen.

How can the individual retain a significant and vital relationship with his community if it demands less of his day-to-day attention? New ways have to be found for expressing personal concern, loyalty, and responsibility for our highly developed way of life.

Here is one of the value problems facing the American community.

I HAVE TRIED thus far to sketch an image of rural life and agriculture that contradicts somewhat the romantic tendencies to idealize the countryside. I proposed that the pragmatic view and its social and economic policies are rooted in the American rural community. I hinted at contradictions between what scholars and professional workers in agriculture presuppose as rural-value orientations and those actually held by rural residents.

I advanced this thought on the assumption that the social and economic thought of Europe provides bases for academic and professional consideration of the rural community. I agree with M. L. Wilson that little has been done to systematize the thought content of American rural life. I see a gap therefore between rural community values and those postulated for it by those who would spell out its value and structural content.

Let us go on with that idea.

The family farm is held up as the archetype for American agricultural production. Innovations in agricultural technology and farm organization are often judged according to their impact on the family farm. Agricultural policies and programs are evaluated in light of their congruence with family farm ideology.

I shall not attempt to detail this ideology. Briefly, it is the belief that a farm operation should not exceed the management, labor, capital, and credit risk resources of the resident family. The labor factor is permitted some flexibility in recognition of the need for hired labor during harvest seasons and for certain types of continuous production enterprises.

To make the family farm the archetype for the whole of farming may very well frustrate values more at the heart of American character than the family farm itself. There is danger in confusing the family farm as one among several means of agricultural production and contexts for living with its being and end, in itself, to be achieved.

There is always a tendency to make absolute a form of human organization at the expense of changing human needs and satisfactions. The image makers of American agriculture and country life need to be alert to this tendency. Clergymen, politicians, national leaders in agriculture, journalists, artists, essayists, and others who explicitly and implicitly shape the image of farm life find a ready audience for family-farm talk.

There is no doubt about the continued position of preference for the family farm as a major means of agri-

cultural production. It would seem, however, wise to consider the several other means of production as legitimate and to work toward improving them in the interest of the common welfare.

I pointed out earlier that there seemed to be no one grand design giving order and meaning to American life. This I would also claim to be true for farming. Corporation farming, suitcase farming, part-time farming, tenancy, vertical integration, and others are live options.

They must not be assessed against the family-farm archetype but against moral, ethical, philosophic, and economic norms centering on continuing concern for human dignity and integrity in a changing system of human organization.

WE HEAR a lot of talk that farming is shifting from a way of life to a business. The business image is fostered as a means of "cleansing" farming of "clodhoppers and hayseeds." We encourage rationality as the central theme, forgetting that few men live by bread alone.

There is loose talk about the human factor in farm management. We know little about its role in agricultural production. We should know more.

Studies in industrial management and worker organization suggest that an efficiency model may be empty of human value other than efficiency, but it cannot be operationalized in an antiseptic vacuum. People need to like their work. Work needs to be part of their life to insure not only personal happiness but also sustained productivity. Work is part of the way of life.

There needs to be a blending of the economic, the sentimental, the artistic, the social, and the philosophic dimensions of living. To separate them and assign priority to them is easy academic analysis. To transfer this simplified approach to the management problem denies man's humanity, his basic motivation for creating and living in a multidimensional and complicated value world. These we call the human factor.

The way of easy unidimensional determinism is a burden on us all. The tendency to assign sweeping effect to neat, pointed causes is appealing at first thought. Multidimensional contexts are complicated and do not lend themselves to neat analyses and policy.

A case in point is the well-established observation that there is underemployment in agriculture. It would seem logical to move a large segment of the farm labor force into other employment. How is this to be done? This is a complicated question.

Probably in no other enterprise can a worker continue longer in uneconomic work than in farming. An older farmer on a small paid-up farm can live off the capital investment, consolidate operations, and feel no great hurt. Assets run down, and he experiences something of the well-being of retiring on the job. Economically this is wasteful.

Here is one of the major value dilemmas in the agriculture industry. The farmer may think it is sensible to mine his capital investment, but to do so is ot likely to be in the interest of the general welfare. The new man taking er the enterprise will be faced with immediate heavy capital investment to restore some measure of economic productivity. How can this cyclic tendency be diminished?

On the other hand, is there argument for subsistence agriculture in the case of older and disadvantaged workers in the farm labor force? I know this question is met with raised eyebrows in a highly developed society. Subsistence living is a mode of life not associated with an emphasis on growth.

We may need to consider an aspect of economic and social growth to be a thorough understanding of people with limited personal resources. Every effort should be made to keep a maximum of the adult population in positions of high productivity, but there will always be a certain adult "overhead." The country community and subsistence agriculture may need to be considered among options open to these

disadvantaged people. This is not to say that the rural community should become a gathering place of persons incapable of productive employment. I do suggest that for some people the rural community offers advantages not found in the city.

At one time it was believed that a person could always farm if all other lines of opportunity were closed. Our emphasis on freeing agriculture from this image cuts out this line of action. How rigid should we be in guarding land from those who are capable of little more than subsistence living without the direct benefit of social welfare programs?

Our reason for surveying several lines of thought on underemployment in agriculture is to point out how complicated a problem can become when the value question is permitted entry.

Scientific analysis is one thing. Its transfer into public policy is quite another. Our research methods can line people up like so many beads on a string. But the human capacity to behave in a complicated value field, in ways defying the assumptions underpinning scientific study, creates a wide gap between the student of rural affairs and the rural dweller.

FOLK ART and crafts once enriched rural society. The industrial revolution and commercialization of art dampened interest in the graphic and plastic arts and structural crafts. Rural people eagerly substituted machine-made and decorated household furnishings and equipment for those produced in the home or by local craftsmen.

Attics, basements, barn lofts, and dumps accumulated the "old stuff" as the products of the machine age invaded the rural home. Public auctions scattered it at almost junk prices.

In the event that the "up-to-date" rural person was motivated to decorate a piece of furniture or cloth, he no longer needed to resort to his own creativity. For a few cents a paste-on flower or a transfer pattern could be purchased. Modern weaving equipment dupli-

cated the intricate patchwork designs
of grandma's quilts. The rural homemaker was eager to display items she
bought in a store. They were evidence
of a certain affluence and keeping up
with the times.

In the past generation there has been
a renewed interest, notably among city
people, in these lost arts and the products of their early practitioners. Antique
dealers and private collectors eagerly
sort out the "trash heaps" of rural culture for specimens of folk art and crafts.
Handmade tools of daily use a century
ago are treasured now in the urban
apartment and suburban home for their
decorative value.

Suburban communities have become
veritable museums of rural material
culture. Dinner bells and kerosene lanterns have pride of place in backyard
patios. Shelves groan with the para-
phernalia of 18th- and 19th-century
farm kitchens.

To THE EXTENT that there is contemporary interest in practicing the arts
and crafts, it also is largely urban centered. Wood carving, ceramics, weaving, furniture making, and bread baking
are likely to be part of the avocational
life of the suburban and urban population. Farmers and rural dwellers often
are shocked and amazed at the eager-
ness of the white-collar worker to recapture the way of life they so willingly
gave up.

This transfer of rustic material culture and its associated values to the
urban sector is an outstanding example
of elements of a culture shifting from
utilitarian definition to symbolic definition. The utility of the past becomes
the symbolism of the present. A crudely
hewn grain shovel occupying a place of
prominence over the living room fireplace in a suburban home is no longer
a grain shovel. It is a symbol. It suggests stability in a mobile age. It links
with a past that is becoming legendary
in our society. Besides, it is economically a good investment. Neighbors
probably have left standing offers in
the event the owner decides to sell.

FOLK MUSIC has followed the same
path.

The city is the center of authentic interest in the folk song and dance. In
rural communities that continue folk
dancing and interest in folk singing, a
certain commercialism exists. Square
dances are sponsored as moneymaking
ventures. A certain deliberate quality
clusters about folk music groups in rural communities. When it is urged on
somebody by recreation leaders, youth
workers in rural churches, and others
who make a living at organization
programing, folk music loses its spon-
taneity. It becomes studied. You get
the impression that people are playing
at country life but not really experiencing it.

Tracing a commercially designed
and printed pattern with a tube of
"liquid thread" appears to be a pathet-
ic substitute for the personal creativity
evidenced in the decorative art of our
ancestors. Aluminum trays etched in
trite little patterns of leaves and scrolls
line shelves where once were arrayed
the hearty products of workers in native clays and pigments. A professionally written country song, backed up
by an electronic organ and activated
by following a numbered chart, is an
example of the pragmatic bent.

The rural community has sold,

traded, and junked its artistic heritage in an eager attempt to keep up with the times. Where it is being restored, there is commercialism and a certain evening-class quality. The effect is shallow. The authentic quality, the organic relationship, is lost.

The value problem here is not necessarily the idea of holding on to the past, but one of retaining personal creativity in a mass-producing age. What new outlets for the creative arts in daily life are open to the individual in a time when we are driven to professionalize and mechanize artistic expression? Home economics and youth workers need to be especially sensitive to this problem.

A MUSEUMLIKE motif is developing in rural areas in response to urban demand. Farmer museums are springing up across the Nation. For the price of admission, one can see a lumber camp, a country lawyer's office, an Amish farm, and a cotton plantation.

Farm wives substitute income from rooms rented to urban white-collar workers for the traditional egg money. In the summer of 1962 a Cleveland business executive purchased the right to live on a farm for a week during the blackberry season. He had not picked berries for 35 years. He was willing to pay for the opportunity. The kitchen was flooded with berries, for which the farm wife saw no particular use. She thought the fellow rather odd. She planned, however, to advertise berrypicking as an added attraction the following summer.

The museum quality and recreational value of rural areas will continue to increase. It will substantially supplement traditional sources of rural income. The transformation of selected aspects of rural life into a venture for cultural enrichment has significant noneconomic as well as economic dimensions. As authentic rural culture is used up, a new industry will be born. We shall manufacture rural culture for market! This must be done with wisdom, taste, and responsibility.

Already deliberate manufacture of both nonmaterial as well as material rural culture is taking place in various sections. American rural culture is fabricated in foreign lands and exported to our local rural communities and urban areas for sale. Amish dolls carrying a foreign label are part of farm market displays in southeastern Pennsylvania. Cowboy hats and boots made oceans away from the lone prairie are purchased at western stores on the eastern seaboard.

Because of the splendid march of agricultural science and technology, large segments of rural community resources can be set aside for the kind of need-fulfillment suggested. Values associated with legitimate human productivity and use of natural resources will need to be adapted to meet these new market demands. A whole new array of products from the rural community will soon be added to the traditional list of food, fiber, and minerals.

New meanings will be assigned to the traditional products, which will strengthen their position in the marketplace. Our parents would perhaps have smiled at people purchasing the right to pick berries. As we move toward an increasingly urban-dominated society, berry patches will take on increasing economic significance.

MY SURVEY of rural values is far from comprehensive. I have wandered widely, sampling here and there areas that I thought had special significance. My purpose was not to catalog values associated with rural life. Rather, I hoped, through an admittedly limited perspective, to raise questions that generally go by unprobed in discussions of this sort. My central theme was that Americans, especially rural Americans, were and are a fairly unique breed in the world of civilized man.

In rural America, perhaps more so than anywhere, we find the pragmatic view. Again we spell out its main features: A tendency to think and act in the short run of human events; a belief in the triumph of human ingenuity in realizing some measure of the good life in the here and now; a tendency toward relativistic thinking; an undaunted faith in the idea that the Lord helps those who help themselves.

PEOPLE WITH these themes as guides built a civilization out of a natural wilderness in a short span of human history. Is a civilization such as we have congenial to the kind of spirit that built it? This is the question for our time.

We wonder about the symbolism of a family sitting around a fireplace in a thermostatically controlled living room climate. It would seem at times that the thermostatic life has been the goal from the beginning. To build more and more sensitive thermostats into our way of life is viewed as progress.

To what extent is the American spirit frustrated by its own success? Here is another worrisome question.

Modern science, technology, and educational practices are replacing fate, faith, magic, and nerve as approaches to human risk. As I mentioned, calculated judgment and an increasingly self-regulating technology is everywhere evident. Insecticides, herbicides, contour farming, old-age pensions, credit agencies, hay dryers, tranquilizers, and zoning commissions are everyday necessities.

As we conquer one wilderness we enter another. The wilderness of Nature is nearly harnessed. The rural dweller no longer tries to attune himself with Nature's rhythms. To the extent that there are natural patterns, he capitalizes on them or alters them to meet his interests. Cows freshen over the year. Fall lambs command a better price. A regulated flow of produce on the market is diligently worked at.

I end with questions:

What are the dimensions of the new wilderness into which the pioneer spirit can stake a claim?

In the growing company of compassionate thermostats, where do we turn to give of ourselves in the interest of others as well as self?

Must we be content to play with fire in the midst of regulated warmth?

THESE, I would argue, are not strawmen to be waved aside without a second look. We seem to be nearing the end of neolithic man, man the user of tools in a permanent community.

These are gloomy thoughts? Social scientists have a reputation for being gloomy. I see no cause for gloom—perhaps a twinge of regret, but not gloom. The new and as yet uncharted lines of human endeavor, fulfillment, and adventure open to the rural community and agriculture are bound to find men and women willing to chance it as our sodbusting ancestors did a century ago.

ROY C. BUCK *is Associate Director for the Social Sciences and professor of social sciences in the Center for Continuing Liberal Education, College of Liberal Arts, The Pennsylvania State University. He was formerly professor of rural sociology in the same institution and is a past president of the American Country Life Association.*

For further reading:
Becker, Carl L., *Freedom and Responsibility in the American Way of Life.* Vintage Books, New York, 1958.
Cleveland, Harlan, and Lasswell, Harold D., *Ethics of Bigness.* Harper & Bros., New York, 1962.
Cantril, Hadley, *The Why of Man's Experience.* The Macmillan Co., New York, 1950.
Hardin, Charles M., *The Politics of Agriculture.* Free Press, Glencoe, Ill., 1950.
Iowa State University Center for Agricultural and Economic Adjustment, *Values and Goals in Agricultural Policy.* Iowa State University Press, Ames, 1961.
Moore, Edward Carter, *American Pragmatism.* Columbia University Press, New York, 1961.
Tocqueville, Alexis, *Democracy in America.* Oxford University Press, New York, 1947.
Turner, Frederick Jackson, *The Frontier in American History.* Henry Holt & Co., Inc., New York, 1920.
U.S. Department of Agriculture, *Farmers in a Changing World,* the 1940 Yearbook of Agriculture. U.S. Government Printing Office, Washington, D.C., 1940.
Weimer, David R., *City and Country in America.* Appleton-Century-Crofts, Inc., New York, 1962.
Williams, Robin M., *American Society,* Alfred A. Knopf, Inc., New York, 1960.

CONRAD TAEUBER

RURAL AMERICANS
AND THE REST OF US

ONE-THIRD of us live in rural areas. The Nation was largely rural in the early days, but as population grew the cities and their suburbs received the greater share of the increase. The census of 1910 was the last to show a majority of the population rural; 70 percent of the population was urban and 30 percent rural in 1960.

Less than one-third of the 54 million rural residents live on farms and get at least part of their livelihood from agriculture. Some live in towns and villages of fewer than 2,500 inhabitants.

Nearly 44 million live in the open country, in the small, unincorporated places, along the highways or stream valleys in settlements that resemble the line villages of some other countries, or in scattered dwellings. But the pull of the city is not lost on them. Nearly one-fourth of the total live close enough to a city of 50 thousand or more to be included within the standard metropolitan statistical area of such a city. Some of them are farmers, but most of them look to the economy of the city and its suburbs for their livelihood.

The words "rural" and "farm" often are used as though they are identical. At one time they were. As recently as 1910, approximately two of every three rural residents lived on farms, and, al-though this proportion declined, it was still more than one-half in 1940. The decline of the farm population since the midthirties has been rapid; in 1960, only about one-fourth of the rural population was living on farms.

Many rural residents no longer are engaged directly in agriculture. Some supply goods, services, machinery, feed, fuel, fertilizer, or labor to farmers. Some provide financing, marketing services, or primary processing of agricultural products and perform the many activities that are related closely to farming but no longer are done generally on farms or by persons living on farms, such as hatching chicks, dusting and spraying, custom harvesting, packing vegetables and fruit, making butter and cheese, and slaughtering meat animals and poultry. Moreover, the growing specialization of agricultural production has caused a decline in barnyard flocks, kitchen gardens, and

13

the use of woodlots. The consequence is that many farmers buy supplies that once were part of the subsistence provided by every farm.

The growth of business related to agriculture has meant a division of labor between those who produce the primary product and others who contribute to its production as well as to its ultimate disposition. This development and increases in the productivity of agricultural workers have led to a reduction in the number of farmers.

The people of the United States are not distributed evenly over the country's 3.6 million square miles. A map of the distribution of population shows large clusters in the metropolitan areas. There also are large spaces with a relatively low density of settlement; many of them have been declining in population. They make up a large part of that half of the counties that lost population during the fifties.

North Dakota, 65 percent of whose population is rural, led in the proportion of the rural population. Mississippi, Alaska, West Virginia, Vermont, South Dakota, and North Carolina were not far behind; each reported more than 60 percent rural. One-half of the population of South Carolina, Arkansas, Kentucky, and Idaho lived in rural areas.

The South, 41.5 percent of whose population is rural, is the most rural region. It includes 42 percent of the rural population of the United States, but only about 30 percent of the total population.

As a result of a substantial movement of Negroes from the rural areas of the South to the cities of the North, West, and South, the proportion of Negroes living in rural areas is now less than that of the white population. The highest proportion of rural residents for any major racial group is that for the Indians; three of every four Indians live in rural areas.

During the fifties, when the population of the Nation as a whole was increasing rapidly, the rural population registered a small decline. It failed to

share in the national growth, and it gave up population to the urban areas.

This in part was the result of the growth of cities into rural territory, because cities often take over rural area and rural population as they expand their boundaries. As urban settlement spreads, it takes over areas that formerly were rural. Land generally is reclassified from rural to urban when it is taken into subdivisions.

A substantial migration of people from rural to urban areas has been going on throughout our history. It is a moot point whether the opportunity to move to the cities or the opportunity to move West offered the biggest safety valve for the population pressure that developed in the older settled areas. The movement to cities early became the more important one in terms of numbers of people affected. The movement to the West in recent times has been largely a movement to western cities.

Birth rates in rural areas tend to be higher than those in cities. A conservative estimate is that the rural population would have increased by about 11 million persons during the fifties if there had not been a migration to cities and if the cities had not spread into what was formerly rural territory. Instead, the rural population gave up this potential growth of about 11 million persons and even registered a small net decline.

These figures are in terms of the areas in which people live. Another rural contribution to the urban segment is the growth in the number of people who commute to cities to work and thus in a sense become a part of the urban population. Fifteen percent of workers who live in rural places work outside the county in which they live; many of them no doubt work in nearby cities. In addition, many rural workers commute to a city in the same county in which they live.

An outstanding change within the rural population has been the change in the farm population.

Thirty-two million persons lived on

farms in 1910. That number had dropped to 30.4 million by 1930. It declined to 25.1 million by 1950. It was about 15 million in 1962.

During the depression years, when the normal migration from farms to cities was slowed down and there was some back-to-the-land movement, our farm population increased temporarily, but the growing demands for manpower in industry and the service occupations changed that. The rapid growth in agricultural productivity freed manpower for other sectors of the economy, and there was a large shift from agriculture to other activities.

The net migration from farms amounted to 8.9 million between 1940 and 1950, and between 1950 and 1960 it was only slightly less, 8.6 million persons. The net migration from farms during those 20 years was greater than the net immigration from overseas into this country during the peak years, 1896–1915. Many of our problems of rural and urban adjustment in recent years result from these shifts in the population.

One consequence of the relatively high birth rates among farmers is that the rural population has a larger proportion of children under 15, who accounted for 33.4 percent of the rural population but only 30.1 percent of the urban population.

Rural areas also exceed the urban in the proportion of persons 15 to 19 years old. In other words, a larger proportion of their people is in the school and preschool ages. In the later years, however, the effects of the migration from rural areas become apparent, and there is a relative shortage in each of the age groups between 20 and 64. The shortage is especially large in the age groups that are most mobile—the persons who were 20–44 years old in 1960. Young adults contribute most heavily to the migration, as is shown again in these figures.

The percentage of persons 65 years old and over in rural areas is only slightly higher than that of the urban areas. The large proportion of children

brings the average age of the rural population down to about 3 years less than that of the urban population.

Towns of a population between 1,000 and 2,500 constitute about one-eighth of the rural population. Some striking differences exist between the people who live in small towns and most of those who live in cities.

The small towns have a relative shortage of children under 10 and of adults under 55. They have a relative excess of older persons, and this excess is particularly marked for persons 65 and over. The small towns in many sections continue to provide a place to which older persons move from the open country when they retire. In the small towns, one person in every eight is 65 or over. Some midwestern small towns have taken on an even more pronounced retirement function; in Iowa, Missouri, and Nebraska, nearly one-fifth of the residents of the small towns are at retirement age.

The nonwhite farm population has a median age of only 17.4, which is about 10 years below that for the rural population as a whole. This group has a relatively high proportion of children and teenagers and a relative shortage in all other age groups.

Much the same is true of the nonwhite population in rural areas but not on farms, although for this group the relative excess of children is somewhat less than in the farm population, and the average age is 20 years.

With lower-than-average incomes, rural people have a disproportionately large number of children to be educated. As the children reach adulthood, furthermore, the probability is strong that they will move away from the rural areas in which they were reared. The better trained persons are likely to find greater opportunities in cities, and they constitute therefore a smaller proportion of the rural than of the urban population. This is particularly true of the farm population, which has only about a fourth of its share of the college graduates.

Nevertheless, rural people have high

regard for education. One indicator is the proportion of 16- and 17-year-olds who are still in school. For the farm population, the percentage was 81.8 in 1960, practically the same as that for the urban population, and for the rural nonfarm population it was nearly as large.

Advanced education, however, normally means going from country to city. The return migration is much less frequent. The traditional view that country people need less education than others was so widespread at one time that many of the older rural people had little opportunity to attend school beyond the eighth grade.

The rapid growth of high schools in rural areas came in the main after the First World War. The average number of years of school completed by persons 25 years old and over is 10.6 years for the Nation as a whole, but for rural areas it is 9.2. The people on farms have a lower average than those living elsewhere in rural areas.

White rural residents have an average of 9.6 years of schooling, but nonwhite persons have only 6.2 years— less than eighth-grade graduation. The averages are especially low for the rural farm population—8.9 years for white persons and 5.7 years for nonwhite persons. These averages have been rising and can be expected to continue to rise as the older generation with its lower educational levels is replaced by a younger generation, which has had greater opportunities to continue its education through the high school.

About a third of rural residents live on farms, but this refers to their place of residence rather than to their occupational attachment. Sixty-nine percent of the men in the labor force who live on farms and 26 percent of the rural farm women in the labor force reported that their major line of work was in agriculture. Thus nearly one-third of the men and three-fourths of the women in the labor force who live on farms are not engaged primarily in agriculture. Some farm operators and

about one-half of the hired farmworkers do not live on farms. The number of farm residents who work at nonagricultural jobs greatly exceeds the number of nonfarm residents who work at agricultural jobs.

The volume of migration from farms to nonfarm areas and from rural to urban areas is largely a matter of the ability of the urban sector to provide employment for the young people now growing up in rural areas. Nearly twice as many young farm people will reach their 20th birthday in the sixties as there are older persons who will die or reach age 65 during the decade. With the declining needs for manpower in agriculture, many of these young people will be looking for jobs in cities.

The growing specialization of agricultural production and the continued trend toward larger units in agriculture are closely related to the large outmigration that has occurred. I see no indication that these trends will not continue and have reason to expect that a substantial number of persons now living on farms will seek opportunities elsewhere in the national economy.

The most productive one-fourth of the farms in 1959 contributed about three-fourths of the total product that reached the market. Many of the other units represent uneconomic operations whose total contribution to agricultural production could readily be had with a much smaller number of units and of manpower.

There were 1.6 million farms that had a gross value of sales of less than 2,500 dollars in 1959. About one-fourth of them were units on which the operator was 65 years old and over. They represent a form of partial retirement. Their contribution to total sales was only about 1 percent. Their significance lies in the opportunities for useful work, housing, and subsistence that they provide to their elderly operators, most of whom are receiving other forms of income as well.

The operators of more than 1 million

of these farms with gross sales of less than 2,500 dollars receive most of their income from nonfarm sources, but carry on enough agricultural operations to qualify their places as farms. Their total contribution to the market was less than 3 percent. Like the part-retirement farms, the part-time farms often are carried on as supplements to other sources of income. Whether they are continued depends largely on the possibility of finding jobs with enough income to enable operators to make the part-time farming operations less attractive.

The operators of 349 thousand farms were under 65 years of age and had gross sales of less than 2,500 dollars. Farm production was their major source of income. Agricultural production would be hardly affected if they could be employed in nonagricultural activities, but retraining and relocation would present major challenges. Setting the dividing line at gross sales of 2,500 dollars is arbitrary—many farmers with a larger volume of sales would welcome alternative employment opportunities.

One indication of things to come is the age of farm operators. Farming has lost much of the attraction it once had for young men, many of whom lack the large investment required for a productive farm of adequate size. Unless a significant change comes about, the number of farm operators will decline as men now in farming die or retire.

The average age of farm operators in 1962 was about 50 years, and there were more operators between the ages of 45 and 54 than in any other 10-year age group. Not enough younger men have come forward to replace older farmers, and this has been responsible for a part of the decline in the number of farmers. The indications are that there will be a further decline in the number of farmers as older men retire or die.

Farmers on the less productive farms tend to be older than those on the more productive farms; the operators on farms with gross sales of 2,500 to 5 thousand dollars average nearly 4.8 years older than those on farms with gross sales of 20 thousand to 40 thousand dollars.

Many of the smaller farms give the present occupants an opportunity to use their labor and resources for subsistence or provide a base for substantial off-farm work. As farms, however, they make little contribution to total agricultural production, and many of them are likely to drop out of the farm inventory when the present operator can no longer continue farming.

Three of every 10 farmers in 1959 reported that they worked off the farm 100 days or more. They include young men who are trying to accumulate enough capital so they can take over a full-time farm, business and professional men who carry on highly productive farming as a sideline, industrial workers who commute from a farm which they and their families operate after normal working hours and on weekends, farm laborers who live in the country and produce barely enough products for sale to qualify their places as farms, and more like them.

The larger commercial farms are essentially full-time operations. Only about 10 percent of the operators of farms with sales in excess of 10 thousand dollars reported as much as 100 days of work off the farm. But one of every four operators in the group that had sales of 2,500 to 5 thousand dollars had this much work off the farm. A little more than one-half of the farmers with sales of less than 2,500 dollars reported work off the farm to at least this extent.

The possibilities of combining the operation of a commercial farm with work off the farm vary considerably by type of farming. On fruit and nut farms, poultry farms, and livestock ranches, about one-fourth of the operators report at least 100 days of work off the farm. Cotton or tobacco farms, dairy farms, and general farms are much less well adapted to the combination of farm and nonfarm work.

Income from sources other than the

farm include not only the earnings of the operator who also worked off the farm. They include also any other income the operator may have, such as pensions, compensation for disability, or returns from other investments, as well as the earnings and other income received by other members of the family.

Among the larger commercial farms, those with sales of 20 thousand dollars and over, only 6 of 100 operators reported in 1959 that the family income from other sources exceeded the value of sales. For the smaller commercial farms, those with sales of 2,500 to 5 thousand dollars, 27 percent reported that the family income from other sources exceeded the value of sales from the farm.

Altogether, about four-fifths of all farm operators and their families obtain some income from sources other than the farm. This applies to about seven-tenths of the commercial farms and nearly all of the other farms.

SEVEN percent of the farmers are not living on the farms they operate, and a substantial proportion of seasonal farm laborers do not live on farms. Most of these nonresident agricultural workers live in rural areas.

The proportion of nonresident farm operators is highest on the commercial farms with the largest gross value of sales, and is lowest for the commercial farms with low values of sales. The type of farm is a major element in such arrangements; one-fifth of the livestock ranches and one-sixth of the fruit and nut farms, but only one-fortieth of the dairy farms have a nonresident farm operator.

A small proportion of those who combine agricultural and nonagricultural work do so on a scale that provides relatively high incomes from each source. For the majority, however, the combination is one of relatively low income from agriculture with relatively low income from other sources. The prevalence of low incomes for families in rural areas, particularly for those

who live on the farms, has often been observed.

Even when allowance is made for housing and home-produced food and fuel, the total incomes are still low. Insofar as values can be assigned to nonmoney incomes, the amounts tend to be lower for the smaller than for the larger farms.

Money income is not the only (and often not the major) element in determining whether a person stays on a small farm or moves from it. For some persons, the freedom that comes from being self-employed in an activity that does not require full-time effort the whole year is an important perquisite that offsets some disadvantages that come from lower money income. Some gain satisfaction from working with the soil or with growing things. Others value the relative isolation from neighbors and the absence of the crowding that is usually associated with living in cities. Security from the hazards of periodic unemployment often is cited as one of the values that hold people on small farms.

The population of the United States is now growing by about 3 million persons a year. The needs of the economy and the preferences of individuals appear to be calling for increasing concentration in metropolitan areas. Even the movement of industry into open country tends to develop urban settlements in the immediate vicinity and thus to increase the urban share of the population. Nevertheless, the rural population continues to be a large part of the total.

CONRAD TAEUBER *is Assistant Director, Bureau of the Census. He was a member of the staff of the former Bureau of Agricultural Economics in the Department of Agriculture and, in 1946–1951, a statistician in the Food and Agriculture Organization of United Nations. The holder of three degrees from the University of Minnesota, Dr. Taeuber is coauthor of two books,* Rural Migration in the United States *and* The Changing Population of the United States.

LOUIS J. DUCOFF

OCCUPATIONS
AND LEVELS OF LIVING

OUR economic development during the past century is reflected in changes in the occupational structure of our labor force and the rural-urban composition of our population. Our agricultural labor force continued to grow the first 50 years of the past century and nearly doubled by 1910, but it grew at a much slower rate than the nonagricultural labor force, which had a sixfold increase from 1860 to 1910.

Employment in the nonagricultural sector in the past 50 years climbed to two and one-half times that of 1910, while agricultural employment declined, first gradually and then faster, so that by 1962 agricultural employment amounted to 5.2 million and represented less than 8 percent of the Nation's employed civilian labor force.

A parallel change was a decline in the relative size of the rural population and in the absolute and relative size of the farm population. The urban population of the United States was 70 percent and the rural population was 30 percent of the population in 1960. An increasing proportion of the rural population resides in rural nonfarm areas, and a declining proportion lives on farms.

These changes have been part of our historical economic development and could not have taken place were it not for revolutionary changes in the productivity and efficiency of our agricultural plant, which year by year has set new records in productivity per man-hour of labor and in aggregate production, more than enough to meet the needs of our growing population.

We should take a closer look at the effect our economic development has had on the occupational structure and levels of living of the rural population and the extent to which all sectors of population have shared in the gains in level of living.

First is the fact that the rapid growth of cities has meant a relative but not an absolute decline in the size of the rural population. The rural population in 1910 was 50 million. The rural population numbered 54 million in 1960. The sharp drop occurred in the farm component of the total rural population—from 32 million in 1910 to 14.3

19

million in 1962; 91 percent of the decline occurred after 1940.

We can summarize the trends in the rural labor force in terms of occupation and industry. The occupational classification relates to the kind of work people do (carpentry, plumbing, and farming, for example). The industry classification relates to the type of establishment in which a person works (for example, furniture factory, clothing store, construction firm).

Among the 54 million persons living in rural areas in 1960, 18.2 million were in the civilian labor force (the employed and those who were unemployed and looking for work). The size of the rural labor force in 1960 did not differ greatly from that in 1950, but because of the substantial increase in the urban labor force the proportion that the rural comprised of the total labor force dropped from 31.6 percent in 1950 to 27.2 percent in 1960.

With the sharp decline in farm population and agricultural employment, the occupation and industry mix of the rural labor force has changed greatly.

Farmers and farm laborers are no longer the largest occupational group among workers living in rural areas. Nearly one-half of the rural employed in 1940 were farm operators, farm managers, or farm laborers. Only one-fifth were in the agricultural occupations in 1960.

The skilled and semiskilled industrial workers have surpassed the farm occupations as the most numerous class. More than 5.5 million craftsmen, foremen, and operatives were resident in rural areas in 1960, compared to a little more than 3.5 million farmers and farm laborers. The white-collar occupations had about 4.8 million workers and thus also were more numerous than the number of rural persons in farm occupations.

Manufacturing, the single most important industry group, accounted for 4.2 million rural persons, or 24 percent of the total, compared to 3.8 million persons, or 22 percent, in agriculture in 1960. A decade earlier, agriculture ac-

counted for twice as large a proportion of the rural labor force as did manufacturing—36 percent and 18 percent, respectively. Wholesale and retail trade establishments comprised in 1960 the third most important industry group of the rural labor force. Establishments engaged in professional and related services were the fourth largest group.

Manufacturing industries increased their employment of rural persons by nearly 900 thousand during 1950–1960, a gain of 27 percent. This percentage increase was one and one-half times greater than the one in manufacturing employment among urban residents.

Large absolute and relative increases during the decade also occurred among rural people employed in professional and related services, wholesale and retail trade, finance, in insurance and real estate, and the other categories of industry.

Employment in agriculture, as I indicated, declined sharply between 1950 and 1960. Reductions also occurred in employment in the other extractive industries, mining, forestry, and fisheries, which employ mostly rural residents. The drop in mining was quite substantial, 234 thousand rural persons or a decline of 40 percent from 1950 to 1960, mainly because of the drop in coal mining.

The changes in occupation and type of industry during the decade in the rural labor force were like the change that occurred among city people, among whom the greatest relative gains occurred in the occupations connected with professional, technical, and distributive services. Nevertheless, rural people are still relatively more numerous in the skilled and semiskilled groups among occupations that require less education and formal training, but the differences between urban and rural occupational profiles are lessening.

Thus we are developing an increasingly more urbanlike occupational structure among rural people. In view of the generally higher incomes obtained in nonagricultural occupations than in agriculture, the effect of these shifts has been to increase average incomes among rural families and to raise their levels of living.

A SIGNIFICANT trend in the rural population between 1950 and 1960 was the growth of the labor force living in rural nonfarm areas as compared to the decline of the labor force living on farms. This, of course, follows from the fact that the farm population has dropped sharply while the rural nonfarm population has gone up.

The civilian labor force in the rural nonfarm population increased from 10.4 million in 1950 to 13.4 million in 1960, but the labor force in the farm population fell from 8.1 million in 1950 to 4.8 million in 1960.

A part of this large drop in size of the rural labor force is due to the more restrictive definition of farm population adopted in 1960, but a large part of it is due to the actual decline in number of farms, farm population, and agricultural employment.

The major distinction in the occupational distribution of the rural nonfarm as compared with the farm labor force is the preponderance of employment in agriculture among farm residents and the very small percentage engaged in agriculture among rural nonfarm residents. Only about 7 percent of the rural nonfarm labor force in 1960 were engaged in farming occupations, and this percentage was about the same as in 1950 and 1940. Thus, more than 90 percent of the labor force living in rural nonfarm areas customarily have been employed in occupations other than agriculture.

Most of the gainfully employed members of the farm population have traditionally been engaged in farming, but this situation has been changing over some decades, and the changes have become progressively more rapid in recent years. Thus, of the employed population living on farms in 1960 only 60 percent were engaged in agriculture and 40 percent in nonagricultural occupations. Agriculture accounted for 70 percent in 1950 and nearly 80 percent in 1940. The proportion of the employed population living on farms and working in nonagricultural occupations therefore doubled between 1940 and 1960.

LET US examine a little more closely what has been happening to agricultural employment.

The number of persons employed in agriculture between 1950 and 1960 dropped 24 percent, from 7.5 million to 5.7 million, according to estimates of the Department of Labor. Further decreases in 1961 and again in 1962 cut agricultural employment to 5.2 million. The agricultural labor force is now no larger than it was shortly after 1850, more than 100 years ago. The decline since 1950 has been greatest among farm operators themselves, following the sharp drop in the number of farms.

The decline in unpaid family workers has been roughly proportional to the decline in total agricultural employment. Among hired farmworkers, however, there has been no clear, persistent trend in either direction since the end of the Second World War. Thus, because of the decline of farm operators and unpaid family workers, the relative importance of hired farmworkers has increased, rising from approximately one-fifth of the total agricultural employment shortly after the war to one-third by 1962.

The agricultural employment has dropped in every region of the country. The South, however, experienced the largest absolute and relative drop; by 1960, the South accounted for only 40 percent of total agricultural employment in the United States, compared to 52 percent in 1940.

In view of the extensive mechanization on farms since 1940 and the sharp ₊decrease in labor requirements and labor input in agriculture, it seems rather surprising that employment of hired farmworkers has shown little change in numbers since the end of the war.

Apparently the effects of mechanization and other laborsaving practices on the employment of hired farmworkers have been counterbalanced by the increase in the number of farms with a value of sales of 10 thousand dollars and more. These farms are the principal employers of hired labor, and they increased from 484 thousand in 1949 to 795 thousand in 1959. Farms of that size accounted for 83 percent of the total expenditures for hired labor in the United States in 1959.

Changes in the level of living of farm and nonfarm families have come about partly because of the differences and changes in occupational patterns that I have discussed.

Various indicators influence or reflect the economic and social well-being of rural families. Among them are income, the possession of certain goods, the extent of educational attainment, and the availability of health services.

Median family money income increased about 80 percent between 1950 and 1960 in each of the three residence categories. A rise in living costs absorbed a part of the increase. The real increase in median family income for the United States was 50 percent, after adjusting for changes in the Bureau of Labor Statistics Consumer Price Index. The median money income in 1959 of farm families of 3,228 dollars was about two-thirds of rural nonfarm and a little more than one-half of urban families. These relationships were practically the same a decade earlier, although at lower income levels.

Nearly a third of all rural farm families had incomes of less than 2 thousand dollars, compared with less than a fifth for rural nonfarm and only one-tenth of the urban families. The proportions of families with less than 2 thousand dollars income had declined by one-half or more in the urban and rural nonfarm areas. Among farm families,• the proportion of low-income families did not decline so much.

While farm families in 1959 comprised only 7 percent of all families in the United States, they had 18 percent of all families with incomes of less than

2 thousand dollars. Thus, while substantial economic progress was made by all sectors of the population, farm and nonfarm, the wide differentials between the farm and nonfarm sectors continued to persist.

We should note that family income in the South in 1959 was substantially below that of the other regions—about 4,500 dollars, as against 6 thousand dollars in the rest of the United States. In both 1950 and 1959, about one-third of all families and more than 45 percent of all low-income families lived in the South.

In view of our interest in occupational patterns, we may also note the income differentials among major occupational groups. Of the 11 major occupational groups, farmers ranked the third lowest in 1961, farm laborers next to the lowest, and private household workers (mostly domestic servants) the lowest.

BESIDES current income, measures of level of living usually include data on the facilities available to families—such as television sets and telephones, automobiles, homefreezers, and hot and cold water in the house—which can serve, with some reservation, as partial indicators of level of living.

The ownership of television sets between 1950 and 1960 has grown remarkably among all groups, rural and urban. Only 3 percent of the rural farm households had television sets in 1950; 80 percent had them in 1960.

Almost all urban housing units but only two-thirds of the farm homes had hot and cold water in 1960, although the proportion of rural farm housing units equipped with hot and cold water more than doubled in 1950–1960.

By 1959, almost all farms were electrified; 80 percent had automobiles; two-thirds had telephones, and more than one-half had homefreezers—almost five times the proportion reporting homefreezers in 1950.

Thus, as far as the possession of these facilities reflects level of living, marked improvement can be seen in the past decade, partly because families had more money to buy them.

An index developed in the Department of Agriculture based on data of the census of agriculture to indicate variations in the level of living of farm operators by counties shows a substantial rise from a county average of 59 in 1950 to 100 in 1959. The index brings to light marked geographic variations. For example, in both 1950 and 1959, the South ranked lowest on the index and the West ranked highest.

Our information on the educational attainment of the adult population (persons 25 years old and over) suggests that the differences favoring the urban population in 1950 had persisted and in some instances widened by 1960. For example, in 1960 half of the adults in the farm population had completed 8.8 years of schooling—a gain since 1950 of only 0.4 of a year in the median grade completed; whereas the median years of school completed by the urban population of 11.1 in 1960 rose by practically a full year since 1950.

In both 1950 and 1960, the adult farm population contained the highest proportion of individuals who may be characterized as functionally illiterate (those with fewer than 5 years of school completed) and the lowest proportion of high school graduates. The proportion of farm high school graduates in 1960 was considerably below that for urban residents 10 years earlier.

Nevertheless, the decade did record educational progress in the farm as well as in the nonfarm population. The proportion of adults with at least a high school education has increased, and the proportion with very little schooling has dropped.

The future looks still more promising. Particularly noteworthy is that the proportion of farm youths of high school age enrolled in school increased substantially between 1950 and 1960 and reached the level characteristic of the urban population.

A few comments on health facilities: Despite the rapid acceptance of health insurance programs, the proportion of the farm population covered by health insurance is substantially below that of both the urban and rural nonfarm. Only about 4 of 10 farm persons but more than 7 of 10 urban persons were covered by hospitalization insurance in 1959. Also, proportionately fewer health facilities are available to rural residents than to persons in or near metropolitan areas. Partly because of rapid population growth, there was little difference in the ratio of physicians to population in 1949 and in 1959, but in both years the rural areas were at a substantial disadvantage compared with the metropolitan areas.

When we discuss occupational and level-of-living changes, we are dealing with the effects of extremely broad and pervasive forces, concerning which short-range projections are not very meaningful and long-range projections are hazardous.

Science and technology in agriculture have brought about a sharp polarization in income and competitive position between farms that are of adequate size to permit efficient family management and an adequate level of family income and farms of inadequate size.

In the readjustments that have been occurring in agriculture, the family commercial farms of adequate size have been increasing at an accelerated rate since 1950. Farms with gross sales of less than 10 thousand dollars and particularly those with less than 5 thousand dollars of gross sales have been steadily decreasing in numbers, and their rate of decrease has also accelerated. Such adjustments will continue, and bring further reductions in the total number of farms, but with an increasing number and sharp gain in the relative importance of the family farm of adequate size.

Aside from hired farm employment, which is concentrated very heavily on the farms with gross sales of more than 10 thousand dollars, the size of the total agricultural labor force and of the farm population is determined principally

by what happens to the nearly 80 percent of the farms that in 1959 had sales
below 10 thousand dollars. There can
be little doubt as to the continuing decrease in their number, with a consequent downward movement of farm
population and agricultural employment. By 1965, agricultural employment (as measured by the labor force
series of the Department of Labor) may
decline to about 4.5 million, and by
1970 to around 4.0 million, if recent
trends continue.

We should also bear in mind that
future reductions in agricultural employment, as measured by the Department of Labor, will reflect as in the
past increasing prevalence of part-time
farming. The proportion of farm operators with more than 100 days of off-
farm work has risen steadily; 30 percent
of all farm operators were in this category in 1959. (Many of them do not
report farming as their chief occupation and therefore are not counted in
agricultural employment.)

Some general observations are in
order.

We can be fairly sure of a continued
high rate of total population increase
for some decades to come.

The trend toward further urbanization for all practical purposes is irreversible, and a further shrinkage of the
rural proportion is quite certain. The
absolute size of the rural population,
however, may not drop significantly
below current level. Thus, for example,
should the rural proportion decline at
the rate of the past 40 years, then by
1980 only 20 percent of the population
would be rural, compared with 30 percent in 1960. But this 20 percent would
still be equal to at least 50 million
people under the several projections of
total population.

If our assumption as to the future
size of the rural population is tenable,
the decrease foreseeable in the farm
population and its labor force will be
offset by increases in the rural nonfarm
population.

The occupational and type-of-indus-
try attachments of the rural nonfarm

population characteristically have been
much more like those of the urban population than of the rural farm population. With declines that have occurred
in mining and some other industries
that have typically employed rural
dwellers, the rural nonfarm and urban
labor forces are tending to become ever
more similar.

As I have indicated, the farm population has also become increasingly
diversified in its occupational and industrial attachments. Nonfarm occupations already claim 40 percent of the
farm population who are gainfully
occupied, and this proportion has
shown a steady upward trend, which
is likely to continue.

The national trend of greater participation by women in the labor force
also has reflected itself in the case of
women living on farms. Thus, of all
girls and women 14 years of age and
over living on farms, the proportion
who are in the labor force has risen
from 12 percent in 1940 to 16 percent
in 1950 and to 23 percent in 1960, and
the proportion employed in nonfarm
occupations (75 percent in 1960 and 60
percent in 1950) has risen. The proportion of workers among farm women
in 1960 was considerably lower than
among urban women (37 percent) and
rural nonfarm women (29 percent).

Should employment opportunities
available to farm women expand, an
increasing number of them would undoubtedly take jobs.

The technological revolution in agriculture that has so drastically reduced
labor requirements and increased productivity per worker is thus freeing an
increasing proportion of individuals in
farm families for employment outside
of agriculture. For some it has meant
migration to rural nonfarm or urban
areas. For others it has increasingly
become a matter of commuting to their
jobs, while continuing to live on farms.
Thus the distinctions in occupational
and living patterns between the rural
and urban population and between the
rural farm and rural nonfarm segments
are rapidly diminishing.

The adjustments that still need to take place with respect to half or more of the farms and the people on those farms with units that are too small to provide a minimum adequate living from agriculture are of great magnitude and involve a long-term process of development of human and physical resources.

THE SAME THING may be said for substantial segments of the rural nonfarm population. Some of these rural nonfarm people were previously classified in the farm population under a somewhat less restrictive definition of farm population used before 1960. It is therefore well that the Rural Areas Development program does not draw sharp distinctions between rural farm and rural nonfarm low-income people who have had common problems of inadequate employment opportunities and, under existing conditions, an inadequate potential for development of their human and physical resources.

Nevertheless, it is well to recognize the more acute and special nature of the problem confronting the low-income farm families and their heavy concentration in some areas. The information presented indicates that while progress has been achieved in the improvement of levels of living of farm families generally and further progress may be anticipated, there are still wide discrepancies, not only in income between farm and nonfarm families but also in educational preparation, health facilities, and other measures of general well-being.

The farm population has a disproportionate number of its people among the poorly remunerated, the poorly educated, and the underprivileged. The agricultural wageworkers, by and large, have a more precarious and less adequate level of living than many low-income farm-operator families.

The importance of agricultural wageworkers to the operation of our highly productive sector of commercial agriculture is too obvious to need any special reiteration. Hence their needs and

well-being should be fully considered in such programs as Rural Areas Development, manpower training and development, or other programs designed to expand opportunities and raise the level of living.

We know that the requirements of the economy in years ahead will make necessary a well-trained and well-educated labor force. Those with limited education will be at a considerable disadvantage. The importance of increased investments in basic education and the continuous raising of the level of education of rural youths cannot be overstressed.

Meeting the needs for higher levels of basic educational attainment and for training and retraining of rural and urban workers in skills that are currently and prospectively in demand are problems of national proportions that can be expected to continue to receive increasing attention.

LOUIS J. DUCOFF *is Chief, Farm Population Branch, Economic and Statistical Analysis Division, Economic Research Service. He joined the Department of Agriculture as a junior agricultural economist in 1935. Dr. Ducoff is the author of a number of publications about agricultural labor, and in 1953 he received the Department's superior service award.*

For further reading:
Bancroft, Gertrude, *The American Labor Force.* John Wiley & Sons, Inc., New York, 1958.
Cowhig, James D., *Farm Operator Level-of-Living Indexes for Counties of the United States, 1950 and 1959.* Statistical Bulletin 321, U.S. Department of Agriculture, 1962.
Education, Economy, and Society, A. H. Halsey, Jean Floud, and C. Arnold Anderson, editors. Free Press of Glencoe, Inc., New York, 1961.
Iowa State University Center for Agriculture and Economic Adjustments, *Labor Mobility and Population in Agriculture.* Iowa State University Press, Ames, 1961.
Miller, Herman P., *Income of the American People.* John Wiley & Sons, Inc., 1955.
Taylor, Carl C., and others, *Rural Life in the United States.* Alfred A. Knopf, Inc., New York, 1949.
Woytinsky, W. S., and associates, *Employment and Wages in the United States.* Twentieth Century Fund, New York, 1953.

WALTER C. McKAIN, JR.

THE EXURBANITE:
WHY HE MOVED

PEOPLE move beyond the city limits to escape the insecurities of city life, to recapture a romantic ideal, to cut the cost of living, or to get a better place for their children. So they say. Sometimes their motives are not put into words, even in their own minds. The reasons for making this great change in life, whatever they are, have much to do with the families' adjustment to suburbia, determine how long they stay there, and give an enlightening view of what is happening to cities and to people.

Some parents move to the suburbs because they want to rear their children in more healthful surroundings and a better moral climate, away from city streets, city playmates, the artificiality of urban life, and the temptations that companions of differing social backgrounds and standards may place in their way. Suburbs offer more place for play and creative activity.

Children need a chance to spread out more than they can in city apartments, to have their own rooms, and to have a dog or a cat. The parents themselves get more privacy, and the father can have a workshop.

Educational facilities also are compelling reasons. New buildings suggest an up-to-date educational system that will prepare children to meet the challenges of the changing world. Parents expect that their children

will be studying and playing with the "right" kind of youngsters.

The homey virtues of rural life appeal to many exurbanites, many of whom have rural backgrounds or are only a generation or two removed from the land. Those who were born in the country recall their childhood, forget the less pleasant aspects, and develop a longing for the open spaces, the green sod, the clear skies, fresh air, and sunshine. Others have heard about it from their parents, or remember summers spent on the farm, or have read Wordsworth, Goldsmith, Robert Frost, and other romantic poets.

In their mind's eye they see an idyllic small community. Neighborly relations will replace the complexities of urban individualism. A more leisurely pace, less crowded living conditions, and the face-to-face relations in the small subur-

26

ban neighborhood will be much better than the anonymity, coldness, and impersonal character of the city. Clothes will be more casual, personal habits more informal, and friendships more lasting. The smalltown way of life brings government closer to people and may increase their participation in it. Neighbors, not political bosses, make the decisions that determine local policies and services—at least in theory.

The suburb also beckons the status seekers as a symbol of affluence, prestige, and what Madison Avenue calls gracious living. It affords a change of mental clothing for the entire family. The working woman can become the lady of the house. The breadwinner can join the country club. Music lessons and horseback riding for the children may complete the transformation. When a distance of 20 miles separates home and job, status barriers are easily broken. Suburban life has become the American ideal.

Pervasive changes in the daily routine of most urban jobs also are behind the swelling current of exurbanites. There is a monotony in specialized urban employment. Few jobs carry the reward of creative accomplishment. Unlike the farmer, the artisan, and the artist, whose labor can be seen, most persons in the urban labor force do not have a direct interest in the fruits of their labors. As a suburbanite, the urban worker can engage in activities that produce tangible evidence of his usefulness. His garden, lawn, workshop, and home improvements give him a chance to make things that others will see and appreciate. He hopes that suburban activity will compensate for the frustration of his job in the city.

The do-it-yourself craze flourishes in the suburb. Mechanical gadgets may not fit into a city apartment, but they fill the basements and garages of the suburban ranch home. The powersaw, drill, and lawnmower vie with the automobile and the boat in the affections of the exurbanite male.

Suburban homes are seldom completed. A dormer window, a recreation room, an extra bedroom, a larger garage, or a utility room in the breezeway are projects the exurbanite undertakes. Meanwhile, the normal painting and papering work must be done. Landscaping is an endless undertaking. A flower or vegetable garden, an outdoor fireplace, a swimming pool, or a rock garden consumes spare time.

Some exurbanites hope to find more economical living conditions in the suburbs. They believe that they can get more mileage from country dollars than from city dollars. The pressures for expensive living are less in rural areas. A reduction in clothing costs, entertainment expenses, medical bills, and most service costs more than make up for the added expenses of transportation.

A few subscribe to the chicken-farm myth. They hope that a small vegetable garden, a few chickens, some fruit trees, and perhaps a cow will enable them to reduce food costs to a minimum. They are confident that these ventures into agricultural production will provide healthful exercise, useful activities for their children, and a better, if not a cheaper, table.

The availability of housing at moderate prices is responsible for a large part of the suburban trend. Before the Second World War, most homes were built one at a time for their owners.

The economies of mass production have led to housing developments in which many homes are built at the same time and then offered for sale. Space for a large housing development seldom is available within the city limits, and developers have invaded the hinterland, where they have found land at reasonable prices with lenient zoning regulations and building codes.

Prospective homeowners from the city are attracted to these suburban developments, and they have shown a willingness to commute long distances. Commuting patterns were revised drastically during the war. Wartime jobs expanded normal labor market areas, and wartime housing shortages cemented this pattern. Today a family does not hesitate to select a home many miles from the place of employment.

The relatively low cost of homes in a housing development and the favorable financing plans that are now available have enabled apartment dwellers to afford a home in the country. Lunchpail suburbs have come into being, and blue-collar and white-collar workers compete each morning and evening on the highways leading to the city.

Migration in the past was tied to economic opportunities, but now most exurbanites are looking for homes, not jobs, in rural communities. They expect to work in the city, although a few and perhaps a growing number of urban residents are attracted to suburbia because of employment opportunities.

All suburbs provide some jobs, and many suburbs are gradually becoming satellite cities. The process takes this form: After the first wave of new families, a number of essential services are provided. Schools, churches, stores, and other basic commercial establishments are built. Then come more specialized shops and services. Shopping centers begin to duplicate the downtown city services. Physicians and dentists move nearer their patients. Medical specialists establish clinics in the area. Soon there is a succession of new establishments ranging from beauty parlors to funeral parlors. Small manufacturing plants and research laboratories begin to tap the suburban labor market, and soon the suburb has become a miniature city. This entire development increases the number and variety of jobs available in the suburb.

MANY OF THE problems encountered by exurbanites in their new environment may be traced to the reasons that prompted their move.

Some fled the city only to find there was no escape from urban influences. Others, attracted by the romantic ideal of rural living, discovered that the ideal state eluded them in the suburb. Very likely their expectations were unrealistic in the first place.

The truth is that suburbs are part of the metropolitan complex. They are dominated by the central city. Life in the suburb is largely urban life; only a few traces of rural living remain. An exurbanite retains many urban ties. If his office is in the city, the part of his life that is job oriented also remains there. He does not immediately sever connections with his urban friends. He returns to the city for athletic and cultural events and many specialized services. His attitudes and values, as well as those of his suburban neighbors, are urban. His loyalties are divided between city and suburb.

The rural ideal he hoped to capture is elusive.

Urban customs and urban values usually invade the suburb long before the exurbanites do. Face-to-face relationships do not develop easily, particularly at first. There is a ravine between newcomers and oldtimers; the newcomers are drawn from such a diverse set of backgrounds that common interests remain hidden. The insecurity and anonymity that plagued him in the city follow him to the suburb. A roomy lot can insulate him from neighborly contacts as effectively as a crowded apartment house.

Exurbanites who fled the city to strengthen family ties may find that dispersive forces in the suburban life have weakened life within the family. In the suburban family, mothers live in one world, fathers in another, and their children tend to seek a third world. The breadwinner becomes a nightly visitor to the home. The mother must maintain the home, do the work of both mother and father, and somehow retain her own personality. In the process, the children gravitate to their peer groups, from whom they receive recognition and a system of values. Parents complain that they have less time to spend with their children than they had in the city. Suburban life not always has fostered closer family ties; often it has made the ties more tenuous.

The do-it-yourself movement, a part

of the suburban trend, also has its shortcomings. The workshops, the barbecue pits, and the swimming pools require time as well as space, and time soon becomes precious. The father who undertakes house painting and plumbing repairs is usually a slow and inefficient worker. He soon finds that huge chunks of his leisure time have been preempted by household chores. His hobbies and avocational interests take on the urgency of regular work.

His wife may discover there is little time for gracious living in a suburban setting. The second car that was to take her to afternoon teas and bridge clubs may become her prison. She is continually on the move. Her children must be driven to school, the homes of friends, the doctor and dentist, the movies, the park, and the playground. Meanwhile, she has trips to the supermarkets, the shopping centers, the downtown department stores. Her husband has become a handyman; she has become a chauffeur.

ONLY A FEW exurbanites find that they can take an active role in the local government. The oldtimers manage to remain in power long after their numerical superiority is lost. In most rural communities, active participation in local government affairs is time consuming and thankless. Newcomers want and obtain few elective offices. One exception is the school boards, on which many exurbanites serve. Elsewhere, the exurbanite is content to let someone else worry about local politics and local government.

Most of the conflict with the rural community is in public services. Exurbanites hope to obtain the advantages of rural living without sacrificing the comforts and conveniences of urban life. The newcomers are accustomed to urban services; the oldtimers are satisfied with the status quo. Roads, schools, police and fire protection, sidewalks and street lights, trash collections, planning and zoning, industrial development, water supply, sewage, and health services can be-

come points of disagreement. Many suburban communities with a nonindustrial tax base cannot afford the kind and quality of services provided in the city. The rural resident dislikes to pay for services that he has never had and never wanted.

Commuting is a special problem. A large part of the time granted by a shorter workweek is spent traveling between residence and place of work. The early rising, the hasty breakfast, the long ride to the city, and the return late in the day become tedious and upsetting. New roads at first may relieve the congestion, but they also attract developers and a new stream of exurbanites. Highways often breed highways.

The commuter has little time to spend with his family and even less for the community. He becomes a weekend resident. He neglects local clubs, organizations, and activities, and his acceptance as a member of the community is delayed or prevented. Much of the conflict between oldtimers and newcomers can be traced to differences in their timetables.

MOST of the problems faced by exurbanites fortunately are being solved. Not all their dreams about country living have come true, but many have. The exurbanites usually are young people with enough enthusiasm and resilience to meet success and failure. They are developing a new way of life in the United States. They are the pioneers of the 20th century.

WALTER C. MCKAIN, JR., *is professor of rural sociology in the University of Connecticut in Storrs. Dr. McKain is the author of a number of bulletins and articles concerned with suburbanization. He has undertaken an extensive survey of the impact of the Connecticut Turnpike on the social and economic life of eastern Connecticut. Dr. McKain became acting director of the Institute of Gerontology at the University of Connecticut in 1961. He worked in the United States Department of Agriculture from 1938 to 1947.*

EVELYN MURRAY AND E. ELEANOR RINGS

YOUNG PEOPLE
AND THE NEED FOR PLANNING

MANY economic changes before 1970 will affect the choices of occupations of young people, the number of available jobs, and the kinds of jobs that promise the greatest opportunity. Rural boys and girls particularly will have to anticipate how the changes will affect them and the choices they must make.

A rural youth will still find, however, that he must choose at various stages between further schooling and an immediate job, just as he does today.

As he reaches the teens and nears adulthood, this one basic choice will confront him in many forms—whether to complete the final years of high school or drop out of school and go to work; whether to take the mathematics and language courses specifically required for college entrance; whether to explore the possibilities of technical courses at a nearby junior college; whether to do postgraduate work toward an advanced degree.

Each of the decisions he makes will shape his future job and will expand or limit his opportunities.

By 1970, there will be nearly one-third more young people than there were in 1961 in his age group (16–24 years) making such decisions. Nearly 32 million young persons will be enter-

ing the labor force or getting additional education. At 1961 levels, about 38 percent of these youths in 1970 will be enrolled in schools. That will mean a school population about 4 million greater than the number of 16- to 24-year-olds enrolled in high schools and colleges in 1963.

Migration from farm to city during the 1960's may change the distribution, but we estimate that about 3 million of the 32 million persons 16 to 24 years of age in 1970 will be rural farm youths. An additional 7.8 million will be nonfarm youths who live in small towns or in farming areas that are classified as rural nonfarm. Rural nonfarm youths frequently attend the same consolidated schools and find employment in seasonal agricultural jobs. Many of the same factors that affect rural farm youths also influence the occupational choices of rural nonfarm young people.

Most of the young people who did not complete high school in 1961 faced bleak employment prospects and an unpromising future in the labor market. Unemployment was greater among workers who did not finish high school than among those who did.

The situation for high school dropouts will probably be worse by 1970.

If a rural youth in 1970 decides to drop out of high school and enter the labor force, the same kinds of job opportunities will be available to him as in 1961, but the jobs requiring little or no training will be relatively less plentiful.

Dropouts who were employed in October 1961 did not have much opportunity to obtain the better paying and more attractive jobs. For example, fewer than 10 percent of the dropouts held clerical jobs, compared with nearly 40 percent of those who had finished high school.

Nobody can overstate how important it is to young people to get the basic skills and abilities that will be needed in tomorrow's world. Yet a survey in 1961 disclosed that proportionately fewer students from farm families than from other households attended college or made plans to do so by taking college preparatory courses in high school.

Today many young people growing up on farms or in small towns and rural districts can no longer expect to earn a good living by staying in their home areas. Approximately two-thirds of the net migration from farms during 1950–1960 consisted of young people under 20 years of age or those who reached age 20 during the decade. In some rural agricultural counties, the exodus of young people has so reduced the proportion of young people that deaths exceed births.

These changes in the farm population have occurred simultaneously with so many dramatic technological changes that few people growing up today can measure their significance. One good measure of the increasing productivity of American agriculture is the estimate that on the average each farmworker in the United States now produces enough for his needs and those of 26 or 27 other consumers. Nearly one-half of this gain in productivity has come since 1945.

While this represents a major asset in any summary of our total economic gains, the situation is not entirely reassuring. Research on ways to increase agricultural productivity often brings new methods and machines that require a heavy capital investment and reduce the need for farmworkers.

The amount of capital required to finance farmownership will keep many rural boys who have not inherited farms from even considering the possibility of working their own farms. The capital investment required for purchasing modern equipment may discourage other youths from retaining farms they inherit.

Agricultural economists have estimated that for the whole country not more than one person in ten now born on a farm can expect to get enough money from farming to live by minimum American standards. In this rich Nation, many will continue to earn a good living by supplying food and other agricultural products to American consumers and to the people in other lands, but the number of farm youths who can anticipate such a career will continue to decline.

To own and manage a farm today takes not only money to invest in land and machinery but business ability and technical knowledge as well as the traditional agricultural skills. The land-grant colleges prepare many young people for careers in many types of specialized farm management. They also offer training in sales and service occupations in which farmers are the customers or suppliers. In his day-to-day dealings with farmers, a graduate of such courses who has a farm background has an advantage.

Some owners of farms that are too small for profitable farming may be able to continue to live on the farm and supplement their income by developing vacation facilities for city people.

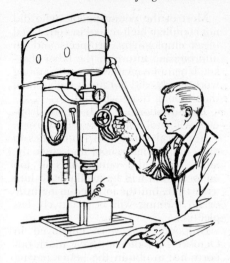

Youths seeking jobs as hired workers will find that the total numbers and the duration of such jobs, particularly for seasonal farmworkers, are declining. Many farm youths, therefore, must think in terms of alternatives to farming.

The alternatives may not entail moving out of a rural area, but they may require additional education. It is becoming increasingly possible for rural persons to commute to work in plants or offices located in the open country or in nearby towns. The job skills required in such industries, however, sometimes make it difficult for rural residents to obtain employment without special education or training.

While high school graduates have a wider range of occupational choices, the decisions they make in high school also have a direct effect upon subsequent employment. As more and more rural youths seek jobs in cities, they need more information about the whole labor market.

It is estimated that by 1970 more than 50 percent of the workers in the United States will be the blue-collar workers, and 13 percent of the labor force will be in the skilled trades and crafts. Semiskilled and unskilled workers who learn their job after a period of on-the-job training and skilled workers who usually gain their skills by serving an apprenticeship after they finish high school will be needed. Employment in clerical and sales occupations and for many kinds of services is expected to expand. The most rapid growth, however, will occur in the professional and technical occupations. Preparation for most of these jobs requires training beyond high school.

SOME OF THESE occupations we describe in more detail.

Many of the stimulating and rewarding jobs in which there was a shortage of workers in 1963 require long study and training. We have had shortages of workers in many of the sciences and in engineering, particularly in fields requiring the application of higher mathematics, such as physics and astronomy, and in agronomy, bacteriology, entomology, metallurgy, and oceanography. Work on aerospace projects and exploration of the oceans are examples of scientific programs that use teams of research workers from several fields of science and engineering.

Persons trained in the medical occupations have also been in demand.

Physicians, dentists, psychiatrists, pharmacists, nurses, physical therapists, medical librarians, dental hygienists, and supporting personnel in the medical and health professions have had little difficulty in finding jobs.

More teachers, guidance and counseling personnel, social scientists, librarians, and social workers also are needed. Many of the openings in these professions are for graduates with at least one year of training beyond the bachelor's degree. Administrative positions in hotels, hospitals, and State and local governments are open to graduates with training in business administration, public finance, or accounting.

Opportunities exist also for persons trained in conservation, forestry, and soil science, for marketing experts, and for inspectors of processing plants and warehouses where agricultural commodities are stored. Preparation for such jobs is offered in the land-grant colleges and other institutions. Professional training is also required for jobs in agricultural extension service work, for directors of 4–H Club activities, and for those employed in communications, including jobs in journalism and broadcasting. Young people graduating from agricultural colleges may also specialize in sociology and agricultural economics, banking, credit and insurance, and land appraisal. Some of these graduates are employed by public agencies in agricultural research programs.

Growing numbers of technicians and engineering aides are employed to assist professional workers in many fields. In industry, the technician often acts as a link between the scientific research and engineering staffs and the production workers. Mathematics is basic to most of the jobs for engineering aides in research laboratories.

The technician assists the professional workers by using instruments and tools to design, operate, maintain, or fabricate objects, materials, or equipment. He frequently applies the knowledge of the professional, and he studies the performance or relative costs of producing a model or design before it is adapted for mass production by assembly-line workers. An air-conditioning technician, for example, may select the equipment needed, estimate costs, and do inspection. He may supervise installations that are planned or designed by architects and engineers.

For jobs in the health fields, where technicians are being used in growing numbers, knowledge of the biological sciences and chemistry is essential. Such workers include medical secretaries, X-ray technicians, laboratory technicians, and dental technicians.

Usually a technician has to have specific training, which may vary from a few months to two or more years in a college or a technical institute. The length of training depends partly on previous education and experience and partly on the requirements for a particular occupation. Technical training is offered by some junior colleges. Some States also have

technical institutes, which offer special training for technicians.

The Manpower Development and Training Act of 1962 will encourage training in some selected occupations in which shortages exist. It contains provisions for assisting unemployed adults and youths to obtain training. Members of farm families whose annual net income is less than 1,200 dollars are considered as unemployed and will have the same priority as unemployed workers for training.

Special programs for testing, counseling, and selection of young people for occupational training and further schooling are authorized by the act. Training for occupations such as electronic mechanics, automobile mechanics, machine tool operators, welders, and stenographers and typists has been authorized.

Since the number of service jobs is increasing, training facilities for them also will have to be expanded. We have looked to Europe for chefs, bakers, and other hotel and restaurant workers, but a shortage of such workers in many countries has meant that we must now train our own service workers for hotels, resorts, restaurants, and clubs.

Opportunities also will exist for service workers in such institutions as hospitals and schools.

More policemen and firemen will be needed as the population increases and as urban communities grow.

Trade and industrial education in high school, other vocational courses, and apprenticeships can lead to many kinds of jobs in industry. Workers are needed in many labor market areas in skilled occupations, such as those of machine tool operators, machinists, automobile and airplane mechanics, electricians, plumbers and carpenters, bricklayers, welders, electronic technicians, electrical appliance repairmen, and air-conditioning and refrigeration mechanics.

We know how important the role of vocational agriculture has been in the training programs of rural high schools, and we understand the problems of providing expensive, modern high school facilities and trained personnel in sparsely settled rural areas. If rural young people are to obtain the education that fits them for one or another of a wide range of occupational choices, they must have the opportunity to attend schools that offer vocational courses in many fields. They should have the advantages of a multitrack educational program that includes a rich academic curriculum in addition to training for a range of occupations. The courses in mathematics, science, languages, the arts, and humanities in many small high schools must be enlarged and improved to insure that their graduates will have occupational mobility. Such a curriculum also provides an awareness of our cultural heritage and adds greater meaning to life.

Rural high schools have not always had teachers trained for or able to devote time to counseling boys and girls, discussing occupational goals with them, and advising them about how to obtain the essential training. The National Defense Education Act of 1958 made possible the training of more school counselors.

Trained personnel of the nationwide network of public employment offices have made their resources available for employment counseling in rural areas. There are 1,900 local offices of agencies affiliated with the United States Employment Service. Staff members worked in more than 10 thousand high schools in urban and rural areas in 1963. They interviewed seniors who were to enter the labor market after graduation.

Local employment service staff members go to the high schools to register the seniors for employment and to provide employment counseling for those who need help in making vocational choices. The number of schools covered by this arrangement varies among States, but about two-thirds of the high school seniors throughout the country were screened for employment assistance in 1963.

In some localities, employment service staff members go to outlying high schools to conduct counseling and placement interviews and to register seniors who will be seeking jobs after graduation. They often arrange for the transfer of application records to city offices where the youths may be seeking work or try to obtain employment for them in a nearby town.

YOUNG PEOPLE who live in centers where a variety of industries and trade and service outlets provide job opportunities can often find suitable work nearby, but country boys and girls often must travel long distances or relocate to a new place in order to find suitable employment. Good roads and transportation increase the likelihood that people can live in rural places and work many miles from home. As more new industries build plants in the countryside and as larger firms decentralize to locations outside the metropolitan areas, they will furnish additional jobs for rural youths who wish to live at home and obtain profitable nonfarm employment.

For those who wish to continue living where they are, the Area Redevelopment Act of 1961 provides a means for rural and smalltown youths as well as other groups to acquire new skills. Up to 16 weeks of training can be financed while people from counties designated as redevelopment areas learn marketable skills. Training projects approved under the act include clerical, trade, and service occupations, such as those of clerks, stenographers, machine tool operators, welders, riveters, automobile mechanics, electronic mechanics, nurses' aides, and waiters. Several States have also received approval for training projects for operators of farm equipment and for farm mechanics.

Increasingly, then, young people must think of the entire country, if not the whole world, as their job market. But the community still has the primary responsibilities to prepare its young people by giving them the basic education and training necessary to

move ahead in professional, technical, managerial, commercial, skilled, semiskilled, and service occupations where competent workers will be needed. Change has always characterized our country. Each generation must meet the challenge of new opportunities.

EVELYN MURRAY *is a youth employment specialist with the United States Employment Service, an agency of the Department of Labor. She has been active in the vocational guidance movement for many years. She is the author of many articles and two handbooks,* Counseling and Employment Service for Youth *and* Counseling and Employment Service for Special Worker Groups.

E. ELEANOR RINGS *is a labor economist in the Office of Farm Labor Service, the Department of Labor. She was formerly with the Scientific Manpower Program of the National Science Foundation and is the author of a number of publications, including* Employment and Unemployment *and* Education and Employment Specialization in 1952 of June 1951 College Graduates.

For further reading:
Iowa State University Center for Agricultural and Economic Adjustment, *Labor Mobility and Population in Agriculture.* Iowa State University Press, Ames, 1961.
President's Committee on Youth Employment, *The Challenge of Jobless Youth.* April 1963.

U.S. Congress, House Committee on Agriculture (87th Cong., 2d sess.), *Hearings . . . on Farm Policy Recommendations of the Committee for Economic Development,* Aug. 6–10, 28–29, 1962. U.S. Government Printing Office, Washington, D.C., 1962.
U.S. Department of Agriculture, *Career Service Opportunities in the U.S. Department of Agriculture.* Agriculture Handbook 45, 1960.
—— *Careers in Soil Conservation Service.* Micellaneous Publication 717, 1960.
—— *Choose a Challenging and Rewarding Career in the U.S. Department of Agriculture.* Miscellaneous Publication 833, 1961.
—— *Economic Research Service, Agricultural Outlook Chartbook 1963.* November 1962.
—— *Economic Research Service, Education, Skill Level, and Earnings of the Hired Farm Working Force of 1961.* Agricultural Economic Report 26, March 1963.
—— *Electrical Engineers: Make your Professional Training Count with the Rural Electrification Administration.* Miscellaneous Publication 736, 1960.
—— *Federal Extension Service, Helping Rural Youth Choose Careers.* Miscellaneous Publication 771, 1958; revised 1963.
—— *A Job with the Forest Service—A Guide to Nonprofessional Employment.* Miscellaneous Publication 843, 1961.
—— *Scientific Careers in the Agricultural Research Service.* Miscellaneous Publication 798, 1961.
U.S. Department of Commerce, Bureau of the Census, *U.S. Census of Population 1960: General and Economic Characteristics, United States Summary.* Final Report PC(1)–1C, U.S. Government Printing Office, Washington, D.C., 1962.
U.S. Department of Labor, Bureau of Employment Security, *Career Guide for Demand Occupations.* 1959.
—— Bureau of Employment Security, *Counseling and Employment Service for Youth.* Revised edition, 1962.
—— Bureau of Employment Security, *Job Guide for Young Workers.* 1963–64 edition.
—— Bureau of Employment Security, *Youth Employment Program of the United States Employment Service.* February 1962.
—— Bureau of Labor Statistics, *Employment of High School Graduates and Dropouts in 1962.* Special Labor Force Report No. 32.
—— Bureau of Labor Statistics, *Occupational Outlook Handbook.* 1961 edition.
—— Bureau of Labor Statistics, *The Employment of Students, October 1961.* Special Labor Force Report No. 22.
—— Office of Manpower, Automation and Training, *Manpower Development and Training Act; A Report and Evaluation of Research, Trainees, Training Programs, and Training Activities.* February 1963.
—— Office of Manpower, Automation and Training, *Training for Jobs in Redevelopment Areas.* 1962.

HENRY S. BRUNNER

EDUCATIONAL
OPPORTUNITIES FOR ALL

AN EXPECTED increase of 50 percent in high school enrollment and 70 percent in college enrollment in the next years threatens a shortage of classrooms, facilities, and qualified teachers. Make no mistake about the seriousness of the situation: If we are to achieve our long-run national goals, we must make strenuous efforts immediately to plan and finance the costs of construction and operation and to train teachers required for the increases in demand for education.

The challenge applies to all of the United States, but it has special significance for rural districts.

It is not only a matter of population figures, such as those that indicate the number of high school students is growing from 6.5 million to nearly 14 million and the number of college students from 2.7 million to 6.4 million in 1950–1970.

Rather, there are questions and issues that census data are not intended to include, much less to solve. These are qualitative questions—questions about whether the educational system and the educational plant are administered in a way that encourages the people to use them; whether the teaching in the system is of the kind that promotes the fullest development of the intellect with which each student is endowed; and whether the administration and the

teaching combine to provide effective and continuing preparation for the life and the kind of living the students are likely to face in their—each his own—world.

The effectiveness and therefore the adequacy of a school or school system rests on the quality of the teachers. Good education results when schools have competent and insightful teachers, men and women who are broadly educated, interested in young people, familiar with the processes of human growth and development, professionally trained in the science and art of teaching, and thoroughly grounded in the common as well as their own specialized learnings.

The better qualified teachers generally are in the larger school districts, partly—but only partly—because salaries are better. They do not remain in the smaller rural districts although they may start their teaching careers there. I cite the teachers of English as an example because all schools offer courses in English.

Studies in Michigan, Virginia, and Ohio disclosed a positive relationship between the size of the school community and the percentage of English teachers holding advanced degrees, the length of the English teachers' experience, and the number of hours of English training its teachers have had.

Those who made the study in Virginia concluded: "The fact must be faced that the education of our children suffers because of three effects which inadequate salaries have upon the teaching profession: They cause many good teachers to seek employment in more remunerative positions in business; they pose a problem of morale with those who remain in the teaching ranks; and they are very definitely a hindrance in the recruitment of the more intelligent high school and college graduates for teaching. . . ."

Dr. Donald R. Tuttle, Specialist for College English in the United States Office of Education, in a statement to support the quality education bill, said: "The English teachers in rural and village areas usually have less preparation in academic subjects . . . often have no person who knows more in their field than they do to supervise their efforts . . . have no school or village libraries with the kind of books they need to better themselves . . . and salaries so low they cannot afford to buy these books themselves. . . . Because of the small size of the school, they have to teach as many as three different subjects and consequently have more preparations to make than the teachers in larger schools. . . . Scholarships to in-service institutes, money for libraries, money for qualified supervisors, and money for research in ways of meeting their needs could do much to assist the rural teachers."

For teachers of agriculture, the captions of an exhibit on teacher educa-

tion in agriculture prepared for a national meeting of the American Vocational Association set forth several standards:

"The teacher must have a desire to teach, a willingness to work, an appreciation of scholarship, a concept of the individual, a sympathetic personality, a love for rural life, a sense of moral responsibility, a commitment to the ideals of freedom.

"The teacher must know the basic principles of science, soils and fertility, feeds and feeding, culture of crops, the livestock diseases—prevention and treatment, market demands—quality the products, management practices, budgetary analysis and financing, conservation procedures, machinery selection and maintenance, farm structures needs, leadership and citizenship qualities, the place of agriculture in the world economy.

"The teacher must understand how pupils learn, the techniques that facilitate learning, the worth of the individual and the family as a unit, the importance of encouragement, the influence of enthusiasm, youth's need for love, and the power of the spirit."

Serious attention to the proper preparation and competence of teachers in all fields might well be the most important effort that could be made to improve the adequacy of rural schools in fulfillment of the function of preparing youth for productive lives.

WE FIND evidence in census data that rural farm and rural nonfarm groups have less formal education than city people. Furthermore, although we can cite cases of young workers who have less than high school education but successfully enter the professions or become skilled workers, the level of jobs workers hold is strongly related to the amount of education they have. Young workers increasingly are expected to have at least a high school diploma; college training is necessary for many positions.

The 1950 census revealed that 49.8 percent of the urban population 25 years old and over and 43.4 percent of the rural population of the same age had completed at least the elementary grades. Only 19.2 percent of the city people did not continue beyond the eighth grade, 23.2 percent completed high school, and 7.4 percent completed 4 or more years of college. Of the rural population, 24 percent of the total did not go beyond the eighth grade, 15.7 percent completed high school, and 3.7 percent completed 4 years or more of college.

The 1960 census showed higher levels of educational attainment. Of city people 25 years old and over, 16.3 percent terminated their education with the eighth elementary grade, 25.7 percent completed high school, and 8.9 percent completed 4 or more years of college. In the rural group, the proportion terminating with the elementary grades was 20.6 percent, 21.9 percent completed high school, and 4.7 percent completed 4 or more years of college.

While the percentages of the people 25 years old and over attaining the different levels of education remained less in the rural segment than in the urban segment of the total population, the relative increases of the rural group at both the high school and the college level were greater than those in the urban group.

The remarkable increase occurred in the rural group at the high school attainment level—that is, 21.9 percent of the people 25 years old and over in the rural group had completed high school in 1960, compared to 15.7 percent in 1950, an increase of 39.5 percent in the proportion.

More detailed tabulations of the census data may show that a considerable part of this increase was in the nonfarm rather than in the farm part of the rural group. That, however, would not gainsay that the rural high schools are serving greater numbers and increasingly larger proportions of the people in their communities.

In this connection we must consider all the selective factors of migration, which include age, sex, family and economic status, psychophysical status, and intellectual performance.

Most of the migrants are 15 to 25 years old. The ones who move to cities tend to be more intelligent and to have superior school aptitudes. This factor may have a bearing on the census data that show a larger proportion of the rural than of the urban population 25 years old and over with less than five grades of schooling. It means that older persons who remain in rural communities include the people with lower school aptitudes. Furthermore, they were of a generation and a time when schooling was not expected of everyone, much less considered essential to success.

We should remember, too, that these older people are exercising the usual parental influence on their sons and daughters. Many surveys have shown that the influence of parents is the greatest single explanation of why boys and girls finish high school and go to college. Cumulatively, then, rural young people undoubtedly receive less encouragement and are subject to less insistence toward any higher educational attainment than is convenient.

Recognizing the conditions that operate to the disadvantage of rural and farm youths in the matter of education, and therefore in the matter of competition for city jobs, we should give attention to marshaling all possible educational and social forces to correct the disadvantage.

It is wrong to attribute the rural-urban differences to innate differences in intellectual ability or other potentials in the boys and girls. A broad educational effort in the schools, with the parents, and with the social organizations in the rural communities can do much to improve the situation.

For youths and adults who are out of school and need and want more education or specific preparation for a job, a program of continuing education—to include special day or evening classes in general education or in skills required for employment and to be administered by the local schools or a college—may fill the need.

Many of us do not understand or utilize the opportunities offered in correspondence or home study courses. The optional educational and training programs of the military services are based largely on these courses. Great numbers of workers in business and industry, including engineers and technicians, keep themselves up to date in this way. Many teachers take this way to meet certification standards. School systems in rural communities could greatly increase the scope and variety of their offerings to meet individual needs by offering such courses.

Teachers of vocational agriculture in nearly 10 thousand rural high schools know that only about half of the boys in their classes will have a chance to farm. They know also that those who do get into farming need a broad understanding of agricultural science and technology and a knowledge of management and financial practice in order to operate large units. In most cases, either as State policy or in local practice, the content of the courses and instructional plans have been adapted to those needs.

They have realized that the traditional program of how-to-do-it training for farming would not entirely suit the needs of the boys who would go out into nonfarming occupations but that many of these occupations would be closely related to the lives of farmers and to the business elements of farm production. It has been possible, with this in mind, to change the approach to agricultural technology, sometimes for an individual, sometimes for a small group within a class.

California provides an example of the movement toward teaching the fundamental principles of the sciences on which agriculture is based. There the teacher education division of the University of California at Davis, in cooperation with members of the staff of the California State Department of Education, have developed and used

experimentally in selected high schools an agricultural course of study built around the basic principles of biological science: "All things, living and nonliving, are either matter, energy, or a combination of matter and energy," or "The basis of classification of living organisms is the similarity of structure and function," or "All organisms derive the energy required for their processes and activities from the oxidation of simple foods within their protoplasm."

This plan requires a change in emphasis in teaching—a shift from the *product* of science to the *process* of science, but is entirely in keeping with the science-oriented base on which our society seems to be moving. The students in this plan should come to an understanding of the interrelationships of biology, mathematics, physics, and chemistry and be conditioned for similar interrelations in the sociological and economic areas of life.

A study in Illinois of future plans of high school seniors in vocational agriculture disclosed that 44.4 percent planned to enter farming, 32.2 percent had plans for further education, and 18.2 percent were going into nonagricultural occupations. The others were undecided. A higher percentage of boys with 3 or 4 years of vocational agriculture registered for further education than did those with only 1 or 2 years of vocational agriculture, and 61 percent of the college-bound seniors planned to study agriculture.

Many other studies in nearly every State have found that boys who studied vocational agriculture in high school and went on to college performed just as well as their counterparts from other high school programs in general college work and better in agricultural courses.

The difficulty often encountered in admission to college on account of requirements in mathematics has been greatly alleviated by a policy in many high schools of providing for program adjustments that allow the boys who know they are going to college to take the necessary mathematics along with vocational agriculture.

In a study in Ohio, the findings indicate that employers emphasize personal characteristics—honesty, initiative, ambition, cooperation, neatness, cleanliness, dependability, willingness to work, ability to work with others, commonsense, responsibility, and good moral character.

I think those characteristics can be acquired in a rural school perhaps better than in a large city school, because the teacher-pupil relationships are more personal in the smaller school and there is greater opportunity for involvement in the activities of school life.

The habits developed in the required work experience and the general knowledge of modern machinery are attributes cited by many employers as desirable characteristics of graduates of vocational agriculture high schools.

Another notable emphasis that has developed in the vocational agriculture program is the attention given to leadership activities. Abilities in communication—in speaking and writing—and practice in the organization of groups are a recognized part of the learning activities. This training will serve both the boys who get into farming and rural living as well as those who go into other occupations, whether in country or city surroundings.

Consideration has been given therefore to boys in high school vocational agriculture who will find themselves in occupations other than farming—those who go on to college and those who go into the branches of industry related to agriculture. Thus it is likely that the teachers are providing for these boys a kind of vocational training that they could not get in any other way in the rural schools.

Vocational agriculture is only one part of the broad vocational education offerings in 17 thousand schools and other institutions. There are nearly 2 thousand comparable programs of training for trades and industry, 1,300 programs of training for distributive occupations, and more than 11 thousand home economics programs.

The availability of training centers and their flexibility of organization make it possible to initiate or adjust training programs to meet national, State, and local needs. Important contributions to the training of manpower for the work force have been made by private as well as public institutions.

I LIST some of the principles that can guide the development and operation of vocational education programs.

The need for training is determined by school officials and competent individuals and groups representing the occupations for which training is to be provided.

The content of programs and courses is based on an initial analysis of an occupation and a periodic reanalysis and reappraisal of training needs.

Courses and programs for an occupation are designed and maintained with the advice and cooperation of representatives from the occupational field. The facilities and equipment used in instruction are comparable to those found in the occupation.

Training in a particular occupation is carried to the point of developing marketable skills and other job assets to enable students to succeed in initial employment in this occupation and to give them a basis for further education and advancement.

The principle that one learns to do by doing is applied in all phases of vocational education in order to bridge the gap between the school and the work situation.

COURSES FOR employed workers in an occupation usually take the form of short units of instruction designed to develop specific areas of skill for updating or upgrading training. Efforts are made to provide this type of training in the amount needed to meet the worker's needs at a time and a place convenient to him.

Programs of public vocational and technical education are carried on with Federal aid in regular high schools or technical or vocational high schools. They are designed primarily for students 14 to 18 years old and within the last 4 years of the typical 12-year program of public education. It is not uncommon, however, for older persons to be enrolled for preparatory training in some of these schools. The facilities of the schools are used not only for daytime preparatory training but also for evening courses for employed workers who wish to improve their competency.

An increasing number of post-high-school vocational and technical education programs are offered in public community colleges, junior colleges, technical institutes, and area vocational schools, designed entirely or partly to meet the preparatory training needs of persons who have completed the normal 12 years of public education and of others who are beyond the age of the group usually enrolled in the 12-year public education program. Their programs usually involve 2 years of training and lead to immediate employment. They reflect a growing trend of public vocational education for older students and also provide facilities for training adult employed workers.

Area vocational schools have received increasing attention and emphasis. Their purpose is to serve young people and adults within a rather large geographical area. The goal is the development of enough of these schools to give to capable students throughout the Nation the opportunity to get the vocational training they think they need.

The land-grant colleges in fulfillment of their function as "the people's colleges" have been giving particular attention to the place of rural youth in our society. In many States they have conducted organized recruitment and counseling programs in rural high schools. The agricultural colleges are adjusting to the fact that career opportunities for the graduates are no longer dominantly in farming. About 15 percent of the graduates from these colleges go into farming each year.

A study at Cornell University of the graduates with baccalaureate degrees from the College of Agriculture in 1956–1960 found 18 percent of the graduates had gone into farming and farm management; 15 percent into agricultural conservation, research, teaching, and services; 20 percent into agricultural business; 38 percent into graduate or professional study; and 9 percent in nonagricultural occupations.

A committee of the American Society of Agronomists gathered data on the first occupations of baccalaureate-degree graduates from the different curriculums in agronomy for the United States during the 5 years from 1957 to 1962. The study included those who had gone into military service (524) and an "unknown" category (259), representing together about one-fifth of the total of 3,640 graduates. Of the other 2,857 4-year graduates, 18 percent, exactly the same proportion as in the Cornell study, had gone into farming and farm management; 33 percent into publicly supported agricultural occupations; 18 percent into agricultural business, industry, and communications; 26 percent into graduate study; and 5 percent into nonagricultural situations.

The two studies are examples of the efforts administrators and faculties of the agricultural colleges are making to review and revise their aims and curriculums to meet present and prospective needs. There is general agreement among them that agriculture in our present economy must be looked upon and understood as a broad and complicated industry concerned with producing, processing, and distributing food and fiber for the United States and many other countries. Agriculture therefore needs trained youths who can work in a variety of situations and under different conditions. We look to the agricultural colleges to produce graduates equipped to adjust themselves to new ideas, handle a variety of problems, and meet unpredictable situations in on-the-farm and off-the-farm enterprises.

Curriculums are being revised in various ways. The direction has been toward a broader base, with emphasis on the basic sciences and on an understanding of the sociological and economic interrelationships of the agricultural industry with the other forces in the modern world.

Guidelines for many of the changes were given by the Committee on Educational Policy in Agriculture of the Agriculture Board in the National Academy of Sciences-National Research Council.

The Committee recommended, "as a basis for attaining the status of Bachelor of Science in Agriculture," a course requiring (when the total required for graduation is 130 credit-hours): General education, 65 credit-hours (comprising communications, 12 credits; humanities and social sciences, 18; mathematics and statistics, 9; physical sciences, 12; and biological sciences, 14 credits); major field, 26 credits; supporting courses to major field, 26 credits; and electives, 13 credits. The proportions should be the same, whether the student's area of concentration is in agricultural sciences, agricultural production, or agricultural business.

The recommendation concluded: "The Committee wishes to point out that many colleges of agriculture are now offering this type of program. The importance of this 'suggested minimum' is not that the institutional leadership is unaware of the need for a strong background in the basic sciences, humanities, etc., but that the public does not realize that agriculture colleges now offer such curricula. . . . It is the hope of this Committee that the Agricultural Board will encourage the dissemination of this information in such a way that it will help inform persons interested in the final product of agricultural colleges that there is science in agriculture, that agriculture is science."

Recognition has grown of the need to have some knowledge of business, whether to prepare for the management of a farming operation or for responsibility in an industrial organization related to agriculture.

Some institutions have a specialized agricultural business curriculum, usually offered in the department of agricultural economics and using courses from the college of business administration on a service basis. The curriculum in others is administered jointly by the college of agriculture and the college of business administration. The most significant pattern seems to be the offering of options, usually three, called business, production (or technology), and science, in each of the established departments.

All this points to a curriculum that encourages training in the scientific disciplines, a knowledge of the application of scientific principles to agriculture, something of a background in the humanities, and an opportunity for the student to think for himself.

A MAJOR question in education is how to acquaint students of all ages with the opportunities they have in occupations and careers. Effective guidance services have been set up in many schools, but not in all.

In public schools enrolling more than 50 thousand pupils, there were four times as many organized guidance programs in 1962 as there were in

1959, but only twice as many in schools of fewer than 5 thousand. The small school units of fewer than 100 pupils had 204 guidance programs in 1959 and 208 in 1962.

The discrepancy is all the more regrettable because the advice of experienced counselors about the shift in our occupational distribution from goods-producing activities to service-producing activities is needed more by rural young people than by city students, who are closer to the factories and offices that some day may hire them.

Counseling can be done by everyone qualified to contribute. Teachers of vocational agriculture and extension workers are among those who can give boys, girls, and parents a greater appreciation of the importance of education and proper preparation for an occupation. To do this effectively, however, the teachers themselves must be properly informed as to the requirements for different kinds of jobs and have a keen awareness of the economic, sociological, and all cultural interrelationships among all fields of study.

Young people are being urged by leaders in industry and education to get a broad training in English, basic science, and mathematics. Their arguments are similar, regardless of their vocation. Some suggest that all early training should be basic and that undergraduate work in college should be in the liberal arts, with any form of specialization left for graduate study.

The concern of the Federal Government for the education of all citizens has been well established. Support to the States for schools, at first in the form of grants of public lands, dates from 1787. A notable action was the Morrill Act of 1862, which provided the basis for the establishment of colleges in which instruction in agriculture and the mechanic arts ("not to the exclusion of other subjects") should be offered.

These colleges, now 67 in number, with at least one in each State, generally are known as the land-grant college system. They enroll about one-fifth of the Nation's college students and in 1961 granted nearly one-third of the baccalaureate degrees, two-fifths of all master's degrees, and more than one-half of the doctorates granted in the United States.

Provision for carrying instruction from these colleges to adults and young out-of-school groups was made in the Smith-Lever Act of 1914, broadened in its scope by amendments through the years, the latest in 1955.

In 1917 the Congress passed the Smith-Hughes Act providing for vocational education in agriculture, trade and industry, and home economics in the secondary schools. The George-Barden Act of 1946 augmented and broadened this secondary school program to include preparation for the distributive occupations.

The National Defense Education Act of 1958 included titles authorizing support for loans to college students; strengthening instruction in science, mathematics, and modern foreign languages; graduate fellowships; guidance, counseling and testing; language development; research and experimentation in new educational media; and area vocational schools.

There is also important Federal support for education in the field of medicine and health through the National Institutes of Health, for all fields of science through the National Science Foundation, and for many specialized programs, such as education for the blind, police training schools, and war orphans education.

The 87th Congress enacted the Area Redevelopment Act of 1961 (Public Law 87–27) and the Manpower Development and Training Act of 1962.

The former included provision for support of programs "to meet occupational training or retraining needs . . . for those unemployed or underemployed individuals (in the areas designated as redevelopment areas) who can reasonably be expected to obtain employment as a result of the skill which they will acquire in the training which is to be made available."

The stated purpose of the second act is to "promote and encourage the development of broad and diversified training programs, including on-the-job training, designed to qualify for employment the many persons who cannot reasonably be expected to secure full-time employment without such training and to equip the Nation's workers with the new and improved skills that are or will be required."

An underlying element in the question of the adequacy of the rural schools is the fact that the measure used has usually been the level of schooling attained by rural people, a level that is determined largely by the desires of the people themselves.

It is reasonable to assume that if rural people as individuals or as a group during the past 50 years had wanted greater educational opportunity—that is, a more adequate school system—it was theirs for the making and taking. Motivation is essential in education; growth is something a person must want for himself.

THE DANGER now, amid the preoccupation for larger administrative units, bigger school buildings, and more classrooms, is that the learning programs and the courses of study in these improved facilities may still not be adequate to prepare young men and women for the new system of life, the technological stage of civilization, in which they must live.

The planning for this adequacy must be a shared responsibility.

The family, the school, the church, and the business community must operate in a frame of mind prepared for change—change of residence, jobs, details in a particular job, and in community relationships. This will require a recognition of growing urbanization and the need for preparation for life in that environment. Schoolchildren as well as adults should have an understanding of our society and our economy.

The population of the United States may increase 18.7 percent from 1960 to 1970. This increase and expected increases in the numbers who seek education at the different levels justify projections for the same 10-year period of 20 percent greater enrollment in the first 12 grades, with 50 percent more completing high school; and double the number of college graduates, with even greater increases in postgraduate institutions.

More people to educate will certainly require more school plants, more classrooms, and more teachers, but they will not in themselves improve the adequacy of the education provided for the youth of the country.

It is the qualitative considerations that will make the difference. In the last analysis, the attitude of understanding, appreciation, and wanting education on the part of the parents and general populace that will bring the necessary high quality into reality.

HENRY S. BRUNNER *is Specialist for Agricultural Education, Division of Higher Education, in the United States Office of Education. He was formerly head of the Department of Agricultural Education in The Pennsylvania State University. He is author of* Criteria for Evaluating Programs of Preparation for Teachers of Agriculture *and* Land-Grant Colleges and Universities, 1862–1962.

For further reading:
  Brown, C. Harold, and Buck, Roy C., *Factors Associated With Migrant Status of Young Adult Males From Rural Pennsylvania.* The Pennsylvania State University, Agricultural Experiment Station, Bulletin 676, 1961.
  Clark, Lois M., *Rural Education in 1965.* National Education Association, Washington, D.C., 1960.
  National Education Association, *Rural Education: A Forward Look.* Special Yearbook, Department of Rural Education, NEA, Washington, D.C., 1955.
  U.S. Department of Health, Education, and Welfare, Office of Education, *Mechanical Technology Design and Production: Suggested Techniques for Determining Courses of Study in Vocational Education Programs.* OE–80014, U.S. Government Printing Office, Washington, D.C., 1962.
  —— *Progress of Public Education in the United States of America 1961–62.* OE–1005–62–A, U.S. Government Printing Office, Washington, D.C., 1962.

DANIEL E. ALLEGER

OLDER PEOPLE
AND THEIR PROBLEMS

THE progressive aging of our national population is a highly significant fact that bears pointedly on several realities of living, policies, and public programs. Our total population increased 78 percent between 1920 and 1963, from 105.7 million to an estimated 188.0 million. The number of Americans more than 65 years old rose from fewer than 9 million to more than 17 million, an increase of nearly 98 percent.

That number matched the combined populations of New York, Chicago, Los Angeles, Philadelphia, and Detroit or the populations of the Dakotas and the five States bordering the western side of the Mississippi River.

Only 11.1 percent of the farmers were 65 or over in 1930, compared to 16.8 in 1960—an increase of 51 percent in just one generation. During these intervening years the age profiles of farmers in every geographic division of the United States had been changing.

The directions of change were by no means alike, but the proportions of farmers more than 65 years old in 1960 tended to become more evenly distributed than in 1930.

We can understand better the proportional changes if we use index numbers, which are comparative measures of magnitude. For 1930, the index of 100 was synonymous with the 11.1 per-

cent of all American farmers who were aged. All indexes above or below 100 were proportional to the base.

New England in 1930, after nearly three centuries of agricultural settlement, contained the largest proportions of aged farmers in the Nation. Its index was 176, or 76 percent above the national average.

Indexes for the Middle Atlantic, Pacific, and East North Central States were 143, 134, and 125, respectively. The index for the South Atlantic States was 100, but within this division indexes ranged from 77 for South Carolina to 150 for West Virginia.

All other geographic divisions yielded indexes of less than 100. North Dakota and South Dakota were the lowest, with indexes of 62. New Hampshire had the highest, 204.

Remarkable changes in the population occurred during 1930–1960. Alto-

45

gether, 19 States increased and 28 dropped their pro rata share of the aged farmers. Florida alone maintained the same index in 1960 as in 1930—127—where the 1960 index of 100 was based upon the national average of 16.8 percent.

The States with highest indexes in 1930 generally dropped in their pro rata position in 1960. The reverse held for States with low 1930 indexes. The net result was that the 1960 indexes for each geographic division more nearly approached the national average than did those of 1930. The New England index was still the highest at 116, but had fallen 60 points. All other divisions also dropped 6 to 36 points, except in the South. The index for the East South Central States rose from 88 to 114; for the South Atlantic States, from 100 to 111; and for the West South Central States, from 72 to 108.

We can attribute the lower 1960 index of some of the older States, compared to 1930, largely to the fact that the proportions of aged farmers therein remain rather constant as the national percentage rises. In Maine, for example, 20.7 percent of the farmers in 1930 and 20.6 percent in 1960 were aged, yet its indexes dropped from 186 to 123 because of the overall aging of the American farmers.

Distributions of the aged farmers within States vary widely on a county basis. The factors that cause the changes are in even sharper focus there than in the bigger national picture. Forested mountains, fertile valleys, urban centers, industrial development, and mining, among other physical features, and cultural factors all impinge on the development and settlement of counties.

The older farmers of 1960 were concentrated generally in southern New England, western Pennsylvania, the Virginias, Kentucky, and Missouri. Additional concentrations existed also in parts of the South Atlantic and South Central States, New Mexico, and the Pacific States.

We can attribute the changes in the geographic distribution of the aged farmers to the complexities of historical development, changing economic conditions, and increased longevity. In the South, the rapid aging of farmers, the heavy outmigration of rural youth, the low educational attainments of the older farmers, and the changing patterns of rural living can be observed as causes.

VARIOUS State governments have come to recognize that the aged have unique claims to the planning of public policy.

All States participated through advisory committees in the 1960 White House Conference on Aging. By 1962, to meet some of the special issues of aging, at least 46 States had provided for permanent statutory bodies with budget and staff, financed wholly or partly from State funds.

The main problem is how to improve the low economic position of the constantly increasing numbers of aged persons. They may total 21 million by 1970, as estimated by T. Lynn Smith, an internationally known sociologist.

The insecurities that trouble rural families are complicated and intertwined throughout all the eastern and western cotton areas of the South, according to studies completed in 1960 and 1961 by the Southern Regional Rural Sociological Committee. Investigations in other areas substantiate the findings.

A widespread rural poverty often stems from area concentrations of aged persons with low incomes, limited cash and total assets, and inadequate housing. Because ever-larger proportions of area income are derived from public sources in the form of welfare payments, Federal insurance benefits, or the equivalent, community economic progress is threatened or halted.

Because of low incomes, levels of living drop below acceptable minimum standards of comfort and good health—conditions that tend to influence community attitudes.

If county officials and businessmen

fall largely into the brackets of the aged or aging, decisionmaking is often foreshortened. Conservatism and resistance to change become the keynote, and the result is a general reluctance to spend money for long-range developments. Moreover, local leaders often support more staunchly the proposals for health and welfare legislation that offer promise of rewards without local sacrifice.

IN THIS AGE of specialization and commercialization in agriculture, the average elderly farmer faces the same problems of insecurity and adjustment that beset older people in other walks of life.

The aged share but little in the advances that have quadrupled the American farmer's productivity, and their outlook is for security through retirement with incomes derived largely from Federal sources.

Average per capita incomes in rural areas are less than half those of urban areas. Cash assests are relatively low, and rural homes of the aged are mostly substandard, as measured by safety, convenience, and protection against hazards to health.

The elderly among the farm families suffer more disabling and longer lasting illnesses than their urban counterparts. They therefore spend higher percentages of their incomes for medical care. In time, their opportunities for emotional satisfactions diminish, forces of motivation weaken, interests and aspirations become self-oriented, and abject despondency may develop.

Society has placed high values on physical labor and income-earning activities, but has regarded recreational and cultural pursuits as trivial. Rural people, by the very nature of their employment-role activities, cannot easily engage in play, in social functions, or in cultural activities divorced from the familiar. Society, moreover, tends toward the psychological rejection of the aged, consigning them to undesired leisure-oriented existences of social dependency.

Dependency in old age is a crushing blow to human dignity. In a farm ballad of nearly a century ago, Will Carleton voiced its tragedy in these lines: "The world keeps newing so! They fashion it/So old men find no place wherein to fit."

The reality of living looms to the aged as a continuous series of inescapable confrontations. Modern rural living, which places great emphasis upon urban social patterns, uproots or threatens many of our deep-seated cultural values, which have their genesis in the country. The philosophy of independent self-sufficiency, which for centuries dominated our rural culture, no longer is an adequate base upon which the aged may build a planned program for security.

THE SOCIAL SECURITY ACT of 1935 and later amendments greatly relieved the aged from compulsion to work until physical incapacity, infirmity, or senility removed them from the labor force. For the first time in history, many workers gained assurance of a relatively secure retirement underwritten by law. Today, with the inclusion of farmers under social security coverage, more than 90 percent of all workers are protected by its insurance provisions.

The accumulation of substantial cash reserves is not a characteristic of the average farmer. As a rule, his net worth consists largely of investments (or equity) in his farm, livestock, and equipment. He relies on his property rather than on life insurance to provide an income to his widow.

Many surveys in the United States, however, indicate that the average farmer owns too little property to provide self-support in old age for himself and his wife or his widow.

Older persons are more likely to have their savings invested in their homes or businesses than in forms that can readily be converted into cash.

The Department of Health, Education, and Welfare said that 54 percent of all families with heads aged 65 or over in 1959 had bank accounts or savings bonds worth less than a thousand dollars. Average net worth was under 5 thousand dollars for 37 percent, from 5 thousand to 14,999 dollars for 34 percent, and 15 thousand dollars or more for the remainder.

Lack of savings may denote that the urge for improved living standards competes with accumulation of capital and that without public pensions most elderly country people would be in need.

Not that the 65th year is the time people must lay down the tools of their trade and become idle. In fact, one-fifth of the aged were gainfully employed in 1960.

Farmers commonly stay in farming until they reach 75. Nonagricultural workers start to withdraw from the labor force when they are 60, particularly those in hazardous and physically strenuous occupations. Some who withdraw from active nonfarm employment retire on small rural holdings.

Many retirement programs are in active operation, but 55 percent of the aged who are not confined in public institutions receive less than 1 thousand dollars in annual income; 23 percent, between 1 thousand and 2 thousand dollars; and 9 percent, between 2 thousand and 3 thousand dollars. The remainder have incomes in excess of 3 thousand dollars, according to information presented to the Senate Subcommittee on Retirement Income, at whose hearings in Sarasota, Fla., in 1961 retired persons said medical and hospital costs and inflation were the principal threats to personal security.

E. Grant Youmans, of the Kentucky Agricultural Experiment Station, reported that the median 1959 income of rural men of 60 and over in Casey County, Ky., was 815 dollars. The median income of older urban males in Lexington, Ky., was 2,256 dollars. As a rule, these incomes represented the incomes of both husband and wife. Only 3 percent of the rural and 18 percent of urban men reported incomes of more than 5 thousand dollars.

Those findings closely duplicated those I reported for Florida in 1961. For retired persons living on small farms in Florida, 66 percent had retirement incomes of less than 1 thousand dollars; 27 percent, from 1 thousand to 2 thousand dollars; and the remainder, or 7 percent, more than 2 thousand dollars.

Elderly landlords in Oklahoma who receive social security insurance benefits average close to 1,200 dollars annually in benefit payments, according to findings reported in 1962 by Ward W. Bauder, Otis D. Duncan, and James D. Tarver, of the Oklahoma Agricultural Experiment Station.

It is of public interest to recognize that none of the average per capita incomes I have quoted would approach the estimated annual budgetary requirements of 2,400 to 3,100 dollars for an aged urban couple, as developed by the Bureau of Labor Statistics. It is unlikely that budgetary needs of elderly farm couples who live under a cash economy system are much below those of urban couples.

Cash incomes and levels of living are correlated closely. Sociologists and economists recognize many differences in levels of living, but in relation to aging we are concerned chiefly with the subsistence and comfort levels.

In general, the rural areas of the South—areas that have large proportions of old people—are nearer the subsistence than the comfort levels enjoyed by nearly all other regions.

Commercial farmers—farmers who report gross sales of agricultural products in excess of 5 thousand dollars annually—generally score high on level-of-living scales. The low scorers are low-income operators, and most of the aged are low income. Their average level of living is the lowest of all.

I found in a survey in 1960 that more than half of 206 rural families whom I interviewed lived in unpainted frame houses. Nearly one-third had no running water in their homes. Fewer than one-fourth had telephones. Similar findings have been reported by research workers in other States.

HEALTH in old age is bound inseparably with the self-image of serviceability. We now know that the health of older people affects every aspect of their activities—economic, social, and psychological.

High costs of medical and hospital care pose the greatest threats to their feeling of economic security. Case histories of public welfare agencies contain many accounts of the health tragedies of the aged, of which those of the rural aged are among the most depressing.

Many kinds of data prove that our senior rural citizens who live on low fixed incomes cannot meet the costs of long or unusual medical care. The public generally concedes that a way must be found to guarantee this care to the aged. In January 1962, 31 States had the legislative authority for a program of medical assistance to the aged, but 2 of them did not provide funds for the implementation of their programs.

Costs of medical care rise with increases in age. Numbers of the aged exhaust their cash reserves suddenly when illness strikes. It is the fear of unexpected high medical and hospital costs that generates grave concern among the elderly. Proposals that their medical care be subsidized through increased social security taxation have aroused strong political controversies. It has been estimated that annual costs for a medical care program would reach 2.5 billion to 5.4 billion dollars by 1983.

According to a national survey, about 28 percent of the aged in rural areas had hospital insurance in 1959, as compared to 41 percent in rural nonfarm areas and 51 percent in cities.

Dr. Youmans reported somewhat similar findings for Kentucky in 1961 in a survey of 1,236 older persons. He found that only one in five rural persons 60 years or older had protection against medical care costs in the form of insurance, as compared to one in two of the urban persons. The proportions of males and females covered by health insurance were approximately equal in both the rural and urban areas, however.

In a 1962 report to the President of the United States, Senator Patrick V. McNamara of Michigan stated that the health insurance of farmers is of poorer quality, costs more, and pays fewer of the bills than health insurance of older city persons. Older farmers paid 23 percent higher premium costs for medical insurance (76 to 62 dollars) in 1955 than older urban residents and lacked the advantages urban citizens enjoyed through group insurance coverage. The insurance carried by the rural aged paid a smaller part of the hospital bill than insurance of the urban aged. Only 33 percent of the rural aged had some part of their short-stay hospital costs paid (1958–1960) by insurance, compared to 57 percent of the urban aged.

Heart diseases, arthritis or other rheumatic conditions, blood pressure, and diseases of the digestive system rank high among the disabling agents affecting older persons. Nationally, 48 percent of all aged rural persons have one or more chronic conditions that limit their productive usefulness.

In Florida in 1952 and 1953 I found that among rural farm retired persons the rate of disability rose from about 70 percent at age 65 to 95 percent at age 85. Dr. Youmans learned in Kentucky in 1959 that activity-role impairments of men and women at ages 60–64 were 48 percent, and at age 75 and over, 66 percent. Heart diseases and arthritis were among the leading causes of disability reported by rural people in Florida and Kentucky. Interestingly enough, poor health was a predisposing factor in retirement rather than the effect of it.

Rural areas generally lack the clinical and home health services that most urban people take for granted. During the 1950–1960 decade, Hill-Burton funds eased the hospital situation in many rural areas. Still virtually unavailable to rural people are facilities to provide intermediate hospital care at reduced costs, services of medical

social workers, outpatient services, vocational rehabilitation services, home
nursing programs, and community
mental health programs.

It is the rural aged who keenly suffer
these privations, because often they are
physically unable to commute to urban
centers to get the care they need. In
some places there is almost no public
assistance for medical care, although
in many of them six or seven of every
ten persons over 65 receive old-age
assistance.

FAITH in the morrow is strong and
compelling among older persons who
are well adjusted physically and psy-
chologically.

Age 65 and retirement are a challenge. Farmers usually pass the age
without changing employment and
without a need for physical and psychological realinement, as most people
do who retire from industry.

Most farmers apparently do not seriously consider planned retirement before they become eligible for social
security benefits.

William G. Adkins, Texas Agricultural Experiment Station, and Joe R.
Motheral, of the Department of Agriculture, reported that 78 percent of
farmers they interviewed in Texas in
1954 concerning retirement had made

no plans for it, 12 percent had made
definite plans, and 10 percent had
given the matter some thought without
reaching a decision.

"Paradoxically," they stated, "families which were in the weakest financial
position had given the least consideration to the problem."

Three-fourths of the farmers in Oklahoma do not plan to leave their farms
upon reaching conventional retirement
age, according to findings of Ward W.
Bauder, Otis D. Duncan, and James D.
Tarver, of the Oklahoma Agricultural
Experiment Station. Farmers under 65
had made no definite plans for retirement, they said, and 71 percent expected to continue farming after age
65, but on a reduced scale.

Agricultural activities provide people
from many walks of life with mental
stimulation; with opportunities to satisfy
deep-seated creative urges through the
planting and caring for flowers, ornamental shrubs, and trees; and with
time to enjoy the recreational values of
self-controlled labor. They fashion their
sentiments of fear, trust, and awe about
a supernatural world under doctrinal
rationalization.

In advanced ages their formal social
contacts center largely in the church,
Sunday school, and other religious
activities. Because of the anxiety of the
aged over approaching death, the dread
of leaving dependents unprotected and
alone, and the promise of rewards to
come, the rural church is provided with
a unique ministerial role.

Research in the South by the S–44
Southern Regional Cooperative (Rural
Sociology) Committee indicated that
high proportions of rural old persons
undergo a period of personal disequi-
librium or "normlessness." Because of
failure to attain socially acceptable
personal goals, some of the aged develop feelings of inward guilt and of
social inadequacy. Norms and goals
become unclear, the mind becomes
confused, and abject despair (anomia)
sometimes follows.

The extent to which isolation, loneliness, and enforced idleness induce

dejection is as yet unmeasured, but I have data that suggest that high proportions of older people tend to become anomic, particularly after age 75. Most data do show, however, that it is the personality of the individual that determines his adjustment to old age.

Older people as a rule are content to live without thrill—according to surveys I made in Florida—but they seek companionship with others of their age group who share similar tastes. Most of them are usually satisfied with a narrow range of social relationships, such as family visiting, relaxing in the sun, or, on hot days, philosophizing in the shade. Some are happiest in cities or towns. Others prefer small villages or the open country. Childhood memories often bear heavily on their retirement decision.

ONE IN SIX farmers in the United States (about 616 thousand) was over 65 in 1960. Nearly 404 thousand farmers were classified by the census as part-retirement farmers. Presumably most of these were aged. I think, therefore, that more than 200 thousand aged farmers remained in the active farm labor force.

Aged farmers in Louisiana in 1955 were disproportionately concentrated among the operators of small farms (under 10 acres) and of large farms (70 acres and more), as reported by Paul H. Price and Homer L. Hitt, of the Louisiana State Agricultural Experiment Station.

In low-income agricultural areas of western Florida, I learned in 1960 that nonemployed rural residents, who were mostly retired, lived on farms averaging 35 acres; commercial farms averaged 161 acres.

Poultry farming, general farming, and livestock production (except dairy) were the enterprises reported as usually followed in Louisiana by older farmers. The typical retired farmer in Florida kept 1 or 2 dairy animals or swine, or both, and 15 to 30 chickens. About 1 in 10 of those who remained on their own farms had abandoned agriculture completely.

Reduced activity seems to precede complete retirement. On the average, human efficiency is highest around the midthirties; then it declines gradually until late middle age; and thereafter it goes down rapidly.

Some retired persons live with their children. Others maintain separate homes on the land. A minority settle in crossroad settlements, villages, or towns. Sometimes father-son agreements permit the continuance of a farm as an economic unit while the parents give up active management.

In some places older farmers employ management services in order to retain their farms. In Florida, for example, 20 percent or more of the farm operators in 1960 were more than 64 years old in 26 of the State's 67 counties, yet 20 of the counties formed a contiguous block in central Florida—the citrus belt—where grove-management services were available, and annual farm incomes were well above the State average.

THE URGE to earn money becomes less of a drive in the later years. Retired persons generally treasure personal values above money if their income is ample for ordinary needs.

A conclusion Fred R. Marti and I reached in a study of retirement farming in Florida was that retirement farmers, those who engage in part-time or small undertakings, have different desires and incentives from those of commercial farmers, who are impelled by the profit motive. The retired ones seek primarily personal adjustment and security.

Retirement incomes and net farm earnings are inversely related. Low-income retired farmers usually cannot supplement fully their basic needs from farming, but high-income retirement farmers spend extra income for recreational forms of agriculture, such as growing exotic fruits and flowers or experimenting with crossbreeding.

Few retired persons go into farming

for profit, but I have many examples of old people who retired from trades and professions and became financially successful in some kind of agriculture.

The older newcomers to farming tend to overestimate their physical ability. General opportunities for farming may seem plentiful, yet the variety of opportunities actually may be limited by work capacity. Old people, for example, cannot bend their backs the long hours needed to produce, pick, and pack a commercial strawberry crop. The production of vegetable and flower plants may be practical for young farmers, but transplants that are to be marketed early in the morning may have to be gathered and packaged late into the night, a time when old people should be in bed.

Those who enter farming after years of living in cities may be surprised to discover a number of restrictions. Certain crops, such as flue-cured tobacco, are under allotment controls. States have regulations as to the production of milk and other dairy products that are to be sold. Farmers in some counties cannot market farm-dressed meat without buying a retail license, which is granted only when certain sanitary standards are maintained and authorized officials inspect the product.

Thus a number of circumstances— low income, advancing age, declining strength, and laws—may limit the retired to the production of farm products for home use.

WHETHER to live in the country, a village, or a city is a decision every retired person must make.

Most of our rural villages have all the amenities of comfortable living, but one will encounter many material and social privations in the country. The use of the village as a retirement settlement by former farmers is indicated by high proportions of older people, or one in four, who live in rural nonfarm areas.

The aged usually have no desire to be segregated, yet some do prefer to settle in retirement centers. The Housing Authority of Jacksonville, Fla., places elderly couples in accommodations best suited to their needs.

" If they like to have children around them, and many of them do," remarked Roy O. Edwards, a consultant for the Housing Authority, "they are placed in a neighborhood of families with children." Otherwise they are located in a section where they have the quiet they desire.

A plan for a sponsored neighborhood village, which would combine worthy elements of rural and urban living, for retired people was made by the Retirement Research Division of the State Improvement Commission of Florida in 1950. It would consist of 500 or more living units placed around a community center and located within the surburbs of a city of 50 thousand or more. Up to one-fifth of the inhabitants would live in apartment houses and the rest in one-story dwelling units on landscaped lawns. The center of the village would contain stores, shops, and outdoor recreational facilities. Rural-minded people would live in the periphery of the village, where they could garden and grow fruit.

The Florida plan never received legislative support, but some of its basic principles have been incorporated in nonpublic retirement village designs.

Retirement villages now dot the countryside from California to Florida. Village ownership ranges from distinctly private to institutional. Some are merely real estate ventures; others are regulated retirement centers.

Most of them support community shopping and recreational facilities. They are landscaped and have paved roads, central water supplies, and other necessary community services. Some villages restrict visits of children. Some provide life care and medical services. Others are open to the public simply as housing.

Among the nationally known private retirement village centers are Del Webb's Sun City, Fla., and Sun City, Ariz.; Port Charlotte and Cape Coral, Fla.; ranchettes in Florida and Ari-

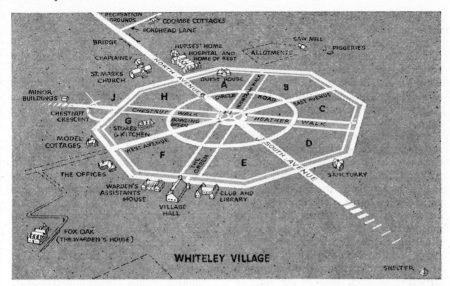

WHITELEY VILLAGE

zona; various retirement centers in California and other Southern States; numerous and widely distributed trailer parks; and fraternal and church settlements.

Interest in retirement centers is widely distributed. The Postal Colony Company acquired 1,800 acres adjacent to Clermont, Fla., about 1926. Two years later an additional 700 acres were added and sold to personnel in the Railway Mail Service, which operates much in the same manner as the Postal Colony. Penney Farms was founded by J. C. Penney and operated by the Christian Herald, and is another rural retirement project.

The Upholsterers International Union, the Loyal Order of the Moose, and Lutheran, Presbyterian, and Advent Christian churches, among others, have pioneered in retirement settlements. The basis for admission, fees charged, care given, and other requirements vary from organization to organization. Yet all villages are designed with the older person in mind and provide an atmosphere that is friendly, cheerful, and restful.

The maladjustment of many rural retired men and women is cited as an argument for developing a rural-urban type of atmosphere for country-bred people.

A similar thought prevailed in England some years ago. Out of that thinking came Whiteley Village. William Whiteley in 1910 made a grant of a million pounds to provide homes for men over 65 and women over 60 years. The 225-acre site is undulating and heavily wooded, yet it is only 2 miles from Walton-on-Thames and Weybridge. Thus it provides the amenities of urban living and retains the rusticity of the countryside. The village layout is hexagonal and has one through avenue, a circle road, and numerous named walks. It includes stores, a bowling green, and a recreation pavilion and provides stage plays, concerts, lectures, and library services. The residents include 100 men and 260 women.

FEDERAL, State, and county rural areas development committees are beginning to consider the needs of older people.

In one low-income Florida county, the rural areas development committee and the Retirement Department of the Florida Development Commission in 1961 promulgated plans, subject to financing, to build a hundred homes for the aged with better-than-average incomes.

The retirement village has been planned to occupy approximately 50 acres of land at Live Oak, Suwannee County. All living units are designed as single or duplex dwellings. Letters received by the planners indicated all homes would be quickly occupied. Nevertheless, the financing of this Rural Areas Development nonprofit project, which is supported by outside rather than local demand and which is designed to spur the local economy by imported income, encountered some difficulty, which pertained to financing construction. Moreover, community planning to provide local low-income rural people with adequate housing in an environment that adds to the value structure of their lives is not part of the present project.

Retired people in villages or suburban areas have few demands on their time. Most of them are free to do whatever they wish. Generally they enjoy television, the radio, cards, fishing, and reading. They often view the recreational aspects of gardening as superior to more formal types of activity. One measure of the importance of backyard agriculture is gleaned from reports of county agricultural agents.

In South Carolina nearly 400 thousand farm or home visits were made by county agricultural extension workers in a year; 441 thousand office visits and nearly 526 thousand telephone calls were received also by the Extension Service.

In one year in Duval County in Florida, where Jacksonville is located, 8 thousand telephone calls were received by the county agent regarding the care of lawns, and information was given to 6 thousand homeowners about flowers and shrubs. The agricultural extension services in a number of other Florida counties frequently hold clinics relating to lawns, ornamentals, and dooryard citrus. Clearly the role of the county agricultural agent assumes a new image as our aged seek adjustment in small-scale agricultural pursuits in suburbs and villages.

THE REAL HOUSING problem of the rural aged is one of limited financial resources. Healthy and still active older persons with adequate incomes and savings experience no housing problems except those common to their communities.

For those in the later years of life, according to John B. Mitchell in a 1955 Rhode Island Agricultural Extension Service bulletin, the expense of maintaining a large house often creates a serious economic situation. The family home, besides being too big for the aged parents living alone, needs more repairs since it also is aging.

Sagging porches, broken floorboards, decaying steps, and similar deterioration all add to the safety hazards of old people. The old home, with its empty rooms and hollow sounds, is often too lonely for contented living.

Special housing designs for the aged relate largely to items associated with convenience and safety.

Safety can be enhanced by emergency automatic cutoff of gas ranges, by nonslip bathtubs and conveniently placed grab bars, by doors without sills, by doorways wide enough for the passage of wheelchairs, by elimination of doorknobs, and by good lighting, with no dark halls, corners, or closets. Floors should be warm and resilient. The heating system should maintain even temperatures of 68 to 70 degrees or higher. Air conditioning should be installed in areas of high temperatures.

Housing costs for the aged are often out of proportion to income. Inadequacy of income subjects the aged to political judgment in the use of public funds for housing. It opens the question of how much social security or other types of government financing can be employed to improve their lot. What concerns the public—the taxpayer—is housing at a price to enable a low-income couple to spend the later years with dignity in a socially acceptable environment, whether in the city, the village, or the open country.

The Victoria Plaza Apartments for the aged of modest means (a maximum annual income of 3,100 dollars) in San Antonio, Tex., is another departure from conventional housing. The apartments were erected in 1960 under the San Antonio Housing Authority with funds supplied by the Federal Government. It is a 9-story building containing 185 apartments. It has many safety devices needed by old people. It achieves a feeling of warmth and hospitality through architectural design, furnishings, and administration. Companionship, recreation, consultation on personal problems, and clinical services are available. It points up one way by which the rural communities and counties, as well as cities, can provide low-cost housing, companionship, and serenity to their aged.

Many problems in financing, taxation, ownership, transfer of property (continuity of existence), and management are yet to be solved before any great number of the aged can be aided through public projects. To speed up the process through private agencies involves subsidies from public funds to insure profits, yet the aged are now subsidized under various other public programs. The issues involved impinge upon alternative costs and procedures that would enhance the general welfare.

One encouraging note is that Federal legislation has attempted to fill the housing credit vacuum for rural persons over 62 years of age. In September 1962, President Kennedy signed the Senior Citizens Housing Act of 1962, which amends title V of the Housing Act of 1949. This program is under the Farmers Home Administration.

Under the new provisions, eligible persons can buy previously occupied existing housing as well as build or improve their homes, or even partly finance a building lot. For persons who are deficient in repayment ability, co-signers may be used. All loans bear 4 percent interest, and may be amortized over 33 years.

Loans will be made from a revolving fund of 50 million dollars.

Another 50 million dollars have been made available at 3.5 percent interest to private nonprofit corporations and consumer cooperatives to provide moderate-cost rental housing and related facilities for the aged in low and middle income groups.

The act also establishes an insured loan program to assist profitmaking individuals, corporations, associations, trusts, or partnerships in providing rental housing and related facilities for older people. The interest rate varies but may not exceed 6 percent, and individual loans are limited to 100 thousand dollars.

Another program for aid to the aged functions under the Federal Housing Administration. The sum of 251 million dollars is the maximum permitted to be outstanding at any one time. In order to secure a mortgage under the program, a borrower must show he has failed to secure financing from at least two conventional financing institutions.

The programs sketched emphasize the concern of the Federal Government in adequate housing for persons in advanced years. By 1980 it is expected that 10 million persons over 62 will be living in rural areas. The new legislation will enable many of them to live with dignity in comfortable and sanitary housing.

More than two-thirds of the 17.4 million aged persons in the United States received old-age, survivors, and disability benefits in mid-1962. In all, 13.4 million persons were eligible under that program. At the same date, 2.2 million aged persons were receiving old-age assistance and just over 100 thousand received medical assistance for the aged under the Federal-State program. Other persons received payments from Government employee programs, railroad retirement, veteran, and similar sources. About 1.5 million persons aged 65 and over had no income from employment or the public programs.

Among farmers, as indicated by Roy L. Roberts, in the May 1962 *Social Security Bulletin*, social security retirement claims are proportionately higher than survivor claims in the traditionally low-income areas, and conversely in the more prosperous farming areas.

In 1956 two agricultural economists of the United States Department of Agriculture, K. M. Gilbraith and L. A. Reuss, compiled income data on 730 rural families in 25 northern counties of Florida. Farm operations contributed a little more than 14 percent and income from nonemployment about 20 percent of all family income.

More than 35 percent of all social security beneficiaries in Louisiana in 1960 were also receiving old-age assistance. For Colorado, Mississippi, Alaska, and California, the next highest States in the order named, the percentages were 21.8, 21.2, 17.1, and 15.1, respectively. The lowest was Virginia, 0.8. Collectively, 9 percent of the aged social security beneficiaries in the South were on the old-age assistance rolls in February 1960, as compared to 6 percent living elsewhere.

The number of farmers actually receiving social security from farming operations is somewhat confused by farmers who also earn social security benefits from covered nonfarm employment. However, the number of farmers of all ages covered by the social security program from farming totaled 2.2 million in 1959. This number was only 0.1 million less than the number filed under the social security program in 1955, and 0.3 million less than the number for the peak year 1956.

Meanwhile, in 1954–1959, the number of farmers dropped from 4.7 to 3.7 million. This indicates that larger proportions of the farmers were included under the social security program in 1959 than in 1955. Presumably social security will substantially replace old-age assistance among farmers in the years ahead, except for those aged with relatively high unmet needs.

The numerical, social, and political importance of the aged in our communities will continue. The penetration of urban values deep into rural areas has brought about great changes in rural value systems. Thus it is that our rural aged have become exposed to cultural shocks, to social dependency, and to frequent feelings of rejection and maladjustment.

Social changes affecting the family, particularly since the enactment of the Social Security Act in 1935, have evolved rapidly and have conspicuously modified the traditions and outlook relating to the support of the aged.

The trend today is toward dependence in old age upon government rather than self for survival and comfort, because the social security and public welfare programs tend to institutionalize the care of the aged. Public emphasis is now focused upon the elimination of poverty and improvement in the general welfare.

Economic security is the one necessary condition for effectively widening the horizons of older people. Great values can be achieved from recreational and cultural pursuits when they attain a status value equal to that of work. Because of common interests, the rural community is in a unique position to join forces with its own aged for economic and social advancement.

DANIEL E. ALLEGER *is an associate agricultural economist with the University of Florida Agricultural Experiment Station, Gainesville, Fla. He is the author of* Rural Farm Retirement, *a research bulletin published by the Florida Agricultural Experiment Station, and the editor of* Fertile Lands of Friendship. *He was chief of party of the University of Florida Agricultural Mission to Costa Rica from 1958 to 1960.*

For further reading:

Aging in a Changing Society. University of Florida Institute of Gerontology, Gainesville, 1962.

Bauder, Ward W., Duncan, Otis D., and Tarver, James D., *The Social Security and Retirement Program*. Oklahoma Agricultural Experiment Station, Bulletin B–592, 1962.

Curtis, Thomas B., "What Price Medical Care for the Aged." *Reader's Digest*, June 1962.

LAND

LAND is a many-splendored thing. Crops grow on it—on about 60 percent of the total land of the United States. We use land for homes, cities, highways, forests, junkyards, parks. To some of us, land is a piece of the earth to be cherished; to some, it is a commodity to be exploited. We have been fortunate in having much land of many types, but we have been wasteful. This section explores some of the problems that are developing and some courses of action; they are treated more fully in later chapters. Urban requirements have been relatively small, but the growth of cities eventually may impinge more seriously on other major uses. Local units of government are increasingly important in guiding the use of undeveloped lands. Economists calculate that 71 million acres should be shifted from use as cropland by 1980. We need therefore to review the potential of our land to see how well it will meet future needs for food, forest products, urban uses, and recreation and how effectively we can shift from one use to another—but we cannot enlarge the extent of our precious land. It is all we have.

673–282°—63——6

MARK M. REGAN AND HUGH H. WOOTEN

LAND USE TRENDS
AND URBANIZATION

THE land and water area of the United States exceeds 3.6 million square miles, from the Atlantic to the mid-Pacific and from the Gulf of Mexico to the Arctic. About five-sixths is in the 48 contiguous States. All but 2 percent is land. What and where it is, how it has been used since it was settled, who owns it, and how it is related to the growth of population and production bear on the country's social and economic development and future.

About 60 percent of the total land of the 50 States is used directly to produce crops and livestock. Twenty percent is used for forests. Less than 3 percent is devoted to urban and related intensive uses. Land designated as primarily for recreational or wildlife uses and those devoted to public installations and facilities account for about 5 percent. The rest, 12 percent, is mainly desert, bare rock, swamp, and other land of limited economic use.

The use of land and expansion of cities have been related closely since early settlement. Greater productivity in agriculture and growing commercialization of agriculture are an initial condition for urban expansion. A smaller number of workers needed to produce food and fiber makes more of the labor force available to produce nonagricultural goods and services. Urban expansion at the same time pro-vides the market for agricultural products and employment opportunities for released workers.

Another interrelationship is the effect of urbanization on patterns of land use within the zone of influence of cities. Improved means of transport of persons and products have extended continuously the zone of urban influence on the use of land. Also relevant is the amount of the land required to meet urban needs in relation to requirements for other major uses.

Urban requirements thus far have been relatively insignificant in the total picture, although increasing urban expansion eventually may impinge more seriously on other major uses.

BEFORE the European settlers came, the land was used largely for fishing and hunting. Almost one-half of the land area was forested. About two-

59

fifths was covered with grass and herbaceous plants. The remainder was covered with shrubs or was barren rock or desert. The forested areas formed two belts, one inland from the Atlantic and the other from the Pacific. The eastern forest covered both the valleys and the mountains of much of the humid East.

Two types of grassland formed a central belt between the eastern and western forests. The prairie, or tall grass area, was slightly larger and extended west from the eastern forest to the 100th meridian. The plains, or short grass area, extended westward to the mountains. The two grasslands occupied about 30 percent of the total land surface. Other grasses, such as mesquite, bunchgrass, and marshgrass, covered about 8 percent of the land. Desert shrubs grew in places.

Although in the first settlements dwellings were in villages, the cultivation and grazing of adjoining land was a major source of employment and income. With abundant land, a pattern of individual ownership was established as the economy evolved and agricultural products were produced for oversea markets.

The early settlements grew at an increasingly rapid rate. By the time of the first census in 1790, the population was 3.9 million. Only about 5 percent were urban. Most of the rural population engaged in agriculture. Transportation access to the Atlantic seaboard was important. Inland movements of population tended to follow navigable streams. Only land within 15 to 20 miles of navigable streams or markets generally was cropped.

Improved lands in 1790 totaled about 30 million acres. Most of the agricultural development was confined to a strip about 250 miles wide along the Atlantic Plain. Agricultural production was sufficient to meet increasing domestic requirements and to permit some exports. The 20-odd settlements west of the Appalachian Mountains accounted for less than 5 percent of the population.

Heavy immigration continued into the 19th century, and rapid settlement took place beyond the mountains. Impetus to land development and settlement stemmed from major transport innovations in the form of the steamboat, canals, and railroads. The first railroad in 1830 had 13 miles of line. Within 10 years, the total railroad mileage approached 3 thousand. Before the railroads, each city depended on local supplies of fruit, truck, and vegetables. The expansion in rail transport broke the locational advantage of the farmland along the seaboard. The production of grain, sheep, and cattle shifted westward to the frontier, and fluid milk could be supplied in place of butter and cheese.

Many implements—the cotton gin, the iron and the steel plow, harrows and seed drills, the corn planter, mechanical reapers, and a practical threshing machine—were developed. They had tremendous effect on production and the use of land.

By 1850, agriculture was spreading to the prairie lands of Illinois, Iowa, Kansas, and Texas. A few settlers had penetrated as far west as Utah, Oregon, and California. Land in farms totaled 294 million acres, of which 113 million were cropland. Most of the improved land had been carved from virgin forest. The real value of gross farm product was about four times that of 1800.

The westward migration continued throughout the second half of the 19th century. Settlement was stimulated by passage of the Homestead Act in 1862, the Desert Land Act in 1877, and completion of the first transcontinental railroad in 1869.

By 1900, farm settlement had reached the arid zone along the 100th meridian, and irrigation and dryland farming were expanding in the Pacific Coast States. Croplands totaled almost 400 million acres, of which about 7.5 million were irrigated. Cropland and farm pasture combined totaled about 600 million acres. The dominant role of the Corn Belt in the Nation's agriculture had become established. The real value of gross farm product had increased about fivefold from 1850; agriculture accounted for almost one-fourth of the gross national product and supplied about two-thirds of the total exports.

Developments in land use during the 19th century were dominated by agriculture's conquest of the wilderness. By the turn of the century, pioneer farmers had cleared more than 300 million acres of virgin forest and had plowed a like amount of virgin grassland. The development of fertile western lands was having repercussions in the East, as reflected after 1880 in the reduced acres of land in farms. While a part of the decrease may be accounted for by a shift to urban and transportation uses, much was abandoned for agricultural use.

THE FIRST two decades of the 20th century mark a turning period in trends in the use of land.

Agricultural expansion continued, largely through the development of arid, semiarid, and wet lands. But the areal expansion of agriculture was rapidly nearing completion. The peak in total cropland of 480 million acres reached in 1920 was unchanged in 1930.

This period also marks the beginning of a more rapid and different type of

areal expansion of cities. Urban population increased almost a hundredfold during the 19th century, and a corresponding increase occurred in the space occupied by cities. Although railroads and rapid-transit systems had extended metropolitan influences over broader areas, much of the development near them was still in the form of compact industrial or residential suburbs and satellite communities.

Automobiles and improved highways accelerated mobility and set the stage for more scattered and explosive types of expansion than the earlier gradual and regular growth. At the same time, working hours were being reduced, more leisure time was available, and incomes were rising. They provided the ingredients for an expansion in requirements for recreation and related types of land use.

Many of the developments since 1920 reflect the acceleration of earlier trends—the rise in the urban proportion of the population, a corresponding decrease in the rural population, a decline in the proportion of the labor force employed in agriculture, higher yields, increased mechanization, and the release of cropland formerly required to feed horses and mules.

By 1960, a population three-fifths higher than in 1920 was being provided with improved diets from less cropland. The acreage harvested declined by 34 million acres from 1920 to 1959, and by 1961 was down 54 million acres, the smallest acreage of cropland harvested in more than 50 years.

The greatest change in land use since 1920 has been the doubling of areas in special-purpose uses, such as urban areas, highways and roads, parks, and wildlife refuges.

The average rate of absorption of rural land by special-purpose uses during the 1950's was about 2 million acres a year. Cropland and grassland pasture were the source of about 40 percent of the land shifted to special-purpose uses since 1950. About 40 percent came from forest and 20 percent from idle land.

Special-purpose uses include intensive uses, such as urban and built-up areas, and extensive uses, such as areas devoted primarily to recreation and wildlife and to public installations and facilities. About 54 million acres of land were devoted to urban uses, transport, and other intensive uses in 1959.

Urban uses and highways and roads accounted for about 90 percent of this category. The area devoted to urban and other intensive uses has increased by two-thirds since 1920, about two-fifths since 1940, and by about one-fifth since 1950.

INCREASES over the past two decades in the acreage devoted to urban and other built-up areas have approximated the United States average in the Northeast, Lake States, Corn Belt, Appalachian, and Pacific regions. Increases have been considerably greater in the Southeast, Delta States, and Southern Plains regions. Practically no change occurred in the Northern Plains.

The area devoted to extensive types of special-purpose uses has about doubled since 1920 and has increased by more than 20 percent since 1950. About 62 million acres were devoted to parks, wildlife refuges, and other recreational uses in 1959. Nearly one-half of this acreage consists of reserved forest land in parks, wildlife refuges, and wilderness areas. Public installations and facilities occupied about 31 million acres, about three-fourths being in national defense areas.

THE EXPANSION of cities and increasing requirements for land for nonagricultural uses have affected strongly the use of land for agriculture. Some has shifted directly into nonfarm uses, and farming operations on the remaining agricultural land in fringe areas often have been adversely affected.

Frequently the first farms to disappear are the intensively utilized truck farms, which are shifted farther from the market of the central city. Displaced next are dairy farms, orchards, and lands devoted to the production of specialized and perishable products.

Other impacts of encroachment include higher tax burdens stemming from the need for increased public services. Tax levies in many places may be beyond the productive capacity of farmland, which then is placed on the market prematurely.

Highway improvements also have an immediate effect on the direction, rate, and nature of changes in land use. The quality and location of highways directly influence the location of residences, factories, recreation, and other land uses, where ready accessibility is a strategic consideration. In general, highways have enhanced the value and intensified the uses of adjacent land. Beneficial effects usually overshadow such adverse effects as the severing of farm operating units or the separation of parts of the service areas of communities.

The intensive type of urban-related uses generally represent higher valued economic uses of the land and water resources involved and hence have the advantage in competition with agricultural uses.

Trends and expectations indicate that continued urban expansion is inevitable.

OVER THE NEXT two decades, special-purpose uses are expected to increase by almost 50 million acres, or about one-third. Urban and built-up areas are expected to increase by almost two-fifths, and the less intensive nonagricultural uses by about 30 percent. The increases in urban and other special uses would be drawn initially from all other major types of use.

Since most of the reductions in the next two decades would likely be replaced by diversions of cropland, the ultimate incidence of the absorption by increased nonagricultural uses would be on cropland.

Because of the increased output in agriculture, the needed acreage could be shifted from crop production to meet the expanding requirements for noncrop uses.

Estimates indicate that (if trends in yields since 1950 continue) the food and fiber needs of a population that may be 45 percent higher by 1980 could be met with 407 million acres of cropland, compared with 458 million acres in 1959.

In terms of effects on total agricultural capacity, the expansion in urban and related nonagricultural requirements would appear to have no serious repercussions during the next few decades. Such shifts, in fact, would contribute toward bringing the amount of cropland devoted to agricultural production more into line with requirements for food and fiber.

THE MORE serious adverse effects are likely to occur within the immediate zones of urban influence.

More consideration needs to be given the problems that attend such expansion and to possible means for their alleviation.

Among possible avenues for promoting more orderly development and minimizing adverse impacts that need to be explored by rural and urban interests are fringe area and rural zoning, reorganization of local government and resource districts, tax assessment policy, and environmental and regional planning.

MARK M. REGAN, *an agricultural economist in the Farm Economics Division, Economic Research Service, has written a number of publications on resource evaluation, cost sharing, and other aspects of the development and use of resources. His activities include service on the staffs of several regional and national resource commissions and foreign assignments on resource problems with international agencies.*

HUGH H. WOOTEN, *an agricultural economist in the Farm Economics Division, Economic Research Service, has been engaged in farm appraisal and land utilization studies since 1926. He is author and joint author of some 70 bulletins, articles, and chapters on the major uses of land, shifts in land use, and projections of future needs for land. These publications have continued the series on the uses of land, which was started by Dr. O. E. Baker about 1912.*

For further reading:
   U.S. Department of Agriculture, *After a Hundred Years,* the 1962 Yearbook of Agriculture. U.S. Government Printing Office, Washington, D.C., pp. 536–542.
   —— *Land,* the 1958 Yearbook of Agriculture. U.S. Government Printing Office, Washington, D.C., pp. 1–62, 460–522, and 524–592.
   —— *Land and Water Resources. A Policy Guide.* Land and Water Policy Committee, 1962.
   —— *Major Uses of Land and Water in the United States, With Special Reference to Agriculture.* Agriculture Economic Report No. 13, 1962.
   Landsberg, Hans H., Fischman, Leonard L., and Fisher, Joseph L., *Resources in America's Future, Patterns of Requirements and Availabilities 1960–2000.* Resources for the Future, Inc., The Johns Hopkins Press, Baltimore, 1963. This volume of 1017 pages is of particular value and usefulness to readers of the Yearbook of Agriculture. Its three major parts are "Requirements for Future Living," "Demand for Key Materials," and "Adequacy of the Resource Base." A statistical appendix contains invaluable information. The chapters cover basic economic patterns, food, clothing and textiles, construction, transportation, durable goods, containers and packaging, paper products, military goods, heat and power, outdoor recreation, crops, lumber and woodpulp, water, mineral fuels, metals, chemicals, land, water resources, energy, and nonfuel minerals.
   Press, Charles, and Hein, Clarence J., *Farmers and Urban Expansion. A Study of a Michigan Township.* U.S. Department of Agriculture, Economic Research Service, ERS–59, May 1962.

WILLIAM H. SCOFIELD

VALUES AND COMPETITION FOR LAND

LAND is a many-splendored thing. To some, it is soil—how many bushels of corn will it raise? To others, it is a small piece of the earth's surface, rare as a gem, something to be cherished and enjoyed like an old masterpiece. To still others, it is space—something on which to build a home, an apartment, a shopping center.

More people need more space, stretching always outward into the country, along the highway, across the river, along a lake. Cover it with asphalt and concrete, clear off the trees, level a hill, fill in a draw, change it as you will, but space—land—is still there. It separates people; it brings them together. We can stretch it by building upward and compress it by high-speed highways. Tear down the old buildings; use it again and again. Space never wears out.

How do you put a price on such a commodity?

Land is an economic good—something capable of satisfying human wants. Over the past 100 years, our Nation has been transformed from a mainly rural to an urban society.

Now, 63 percent of our people live in or near cities of 50 thousand or more. The end of this trend is not in sight. Population increased only 11 percent within the central cities between 1950 and 1960, but nearly 50 percent in the adjacent fringes. The increase in the wholly rural counties was only 7 percent.

We have used land lavishly in the process of growing horizontally. Automobiles have a voracious appetite for land. A mile of four-lane divided highway built to the Federal interstate standards takes nearly 40 acres. The artistic tracings of an interchange may take another 10 acres. The parking area needed for the typical shopping center is several times the area taken up by the stores themselves. The space required for a carport or separate garage and driveway may take up as much land as the house.

The jet age of commercial aviation also consumes vastly more land for airports than in the era of the DC-3's. The new airport for Washington, D.C., takes in 10 thousand acres for its service areas and 2-mile runways. The 17-mile access road to downtown Washington took another 915 acres for the right-of-way. This combined acreage of land would accommodate 40 thousand single-family dwellings—a community of 125 thousand persons.

One's aversion to climbing stairs undoubtedly has contributed to the popularity of the one-story dwelling, but other types of construction also have followed the trend toward horizontal growth. New schools seem to stretch out endlessly as new wings are added to accommodate the increased enrollment from new subdivisions of ramblers.

The new factory buildings likewise spread out over large areas, but for good engineering reasons. The trend can be traced to the innovation of the continuous assembly line. Great gains have been made in the efficiencies of handling materials, based on the horizontal movements of raw materials through the production and assembly operations to the final product. Today, the multistory manufacturing plant is as obsolete as the whippletree and horse collar.

IT IS INEVITABLE, therefore, that the multitude of new uses and demand for land have resulted in new standards of land value that differ sharply from those long associated with land when it was predominantly a source of food and fiber. In a rural economy, land represented little else. Today, land provides an array of services that are far more difficult to measure and to value.

The problem is further compounded by the fact that many of these needs for land can only be predicted. Present values must reflect a large element of uncertainty with respect to future uses. Time is a key element in the pricing formulas.

Although more involved in actual application, the valuation of land for agricultural purposes is relatively simple. It is the present worth of the expected annual returns in the future.

Thus, land with an expected rental return of 10 dollars an acre would be worth 200 dollars if a return of 5 percent is desired. But when farmland is sold for nonfarm uses there is usually no annual income. The returns from annual appreciation are not realized until the land is sold. In the meantime the carrying costs for property taxes and interest on the original investment mount.

The eventual selling price of such land can never be predicted with certainty because its future use depends to so great an extent on events beyond the control of the landowner. The exact location of a highway, a sewer or water line, adjacent or nearby development of other land, or decisions by a zoning board may each add or substract thousands of dollars from the value of a tract of land.

It is not surprising, therefore, that the market for land in expanding fringe areas often is nebulous, capricious, and subject to wild speculation. The land booms of the past attest to this. The speculative interest in farmland in 1963 is basically similar to that which existed on the new-land frontiers a century ago. Then, unsurveyed and hostile lands were bought for a dollar or two an acre and sold for 5 or 10 dollars. Today, dealings are in terms of hundreds and thousands of dollars an acre. Million dollar transactions are by no means rare.

THE BASIC characteristics that create value for land for nonfarm uses are of two general types.

First are the physical, or the on-site, characteristics, such as topography, soil, drainage, and vegetation. These often can be modified or adapted to a particular use and are seldom the major factors that determine value.

Most important are the broader locational attributes that are less subject to change but are by no means fixed indefinitely. Thus, distance in miles to other points is fixed for each tract of land, but traveltime can be altered by highways. Likewise, the kind of development taking place on adjacent or nearby tracts may enhance or detract from the value of other tracts.

Four major types of land use are usually recognizable in any urbanized area—residential, commercial, industrial, and public. Each tends to have its own specific requirements with respect to type and location of the land to which it is best adapted and a range of values. The range within a major class, however, often may be greater than the difference between classes.

Some uses may be quite tolerant with respect to the characteristics of the land to be used. Others must have a particular characteristic. Land suitable for such commercial uses as motels and restaurants must have frontage on a highway with a relatively high rate of traffic flow. An industrial site likewise must have rail or highway transportation facilities, but traffic volume is of minor concern. On-site characteristics are important for residential uses of land, along with travel-time to centers of employment.

Public uses of land—schools, parks, golf courses, airports, highways—often claim top priority in the allocation of land uses. In addition, current concepts of urban planning stress the need for reserving even more undeveloped land for public use. More concentrated development is favored as a means of reducing urban sprawl. If future growth of cities followed this pattern, it would likely result in much sharper peaks and troughs in the profiles of land values. Lands once considered too remote from the central city for high-rise apartments could, for example, with rapid transit facilities become usable and valued for this use. Conversely, lands in the wedges between the major transportation arteries would remain in low-intensity uses.

Local units of government are playing an increasingly important role in guiding and determining the uses to be made of undeveloped lands. Decisions with respect to layout of streets, the location of sewer and water lines,

minimum sizes of lots, the uses specified under zoning regulations, tax assessment policies, and many others have varying effects on the density of urban development and land prices. Many of them are subject to change. Current values often reflect the possibility that a particular tract or even a general area may benefit from a new regulation or a modification of an existing one in the future.

Shopping centers, apartments, and subdivisions often seem to spring up like wildflowers after a spring shower. The casual observer may wonder why a tract of land that was in pasture or a cornfield only weeks ago suddenly has started to acquire a new use: How did it happen? Why was this particular tract selected from among the dozens of other vacant tracts in the same general area?

No two developments have the same history, but we can follow through a fairly typical example. The present shopping center may have had its origin 5 or 10 years ago when an investor bought a farm that appeared to be in the path of suburban growth. He probably noted nearby subdivisions that were taking shape and also knew the probable locations of new highways that were to be built. He may have operated the farm for the first few years after he bought it. At the same time, he sought to interest other persons in joining him for the eventual development of the land.

Out of such negotiations, a land syndicate could have been organized in which the landowner joined forces with a contractor, a lawyer, a real estate broker, and possibly others. Each party would thereby contribute capital and their specialized knowledge and experience. By working together, the chances of success would be greater than if one individual were to attempt to handle all of the various stages of development.

One of the first major steps to be taken by the newly formed syndicate, particularly when the proposed development is quite large, would be to make a detailed market analysis.

That operation often is performed by an expert outside the group. It consists of a detailed analysis of the many economic and demographic characteristics of the area to be served by the shopping center. The rate and direction of population growth of the central city, income levels, the size and composition of the labor force, retail sales volumes for different major items, traffic flows along the highways providing access to the tract, and many other factors are determined and evaluated. The results of this study could show, of course, that the proposed use was not warranted. Some other use, such as a subdivision, might be indicated, and the overall plans of the group would be changed accordingly.

But let us assume that the go sign is given to the shopping center. Many details still remain to be worked out before construction can start. Changes in zoning classification may be necessary. Water and sewer lines may need to be extended. Approval has to be obtained for constructing the necessary access roads from the main highway. Negotiations for tenants to occupy the new stores also would be started at this stage of development. Long-term leases with tenants having national credit ratings are most desired because they strengthen the chances of obtaining mortgage financing for the project.

Thus far, it has been all expense, and no income, and capital from the usual commercial sources either is not available or is relatively costly. National banks, for example, are specifically prohibited from making loans in excess of agricultural value on unimproved land. Federal laws also limit the amount of money that insured savings and loan associations can lend on such properties. The risks and uncertainties generally are too great for such lenders. As a result, the syndicate organizers often expand their original limited partnership group to bring in other individuals who can provide the necessary capital.

An alternative approach for raising equity capital that has become increasingly common is to offer shares in the venture to the investing public. If the public offering is made in more than one State and exceeds 300 thousand dollars in any one year, registration is necessary with the Securities and Exchange Commission. This registration requires that all relevant and material facts about the proposed venture be made available to prospective investors. The Federal regulatory agency does not express judgment as to the merits of the proposed stock issue. It is up to the prospective investor to decide, on the basis of the facts given in the prospectus.

Most States have so-called "blue sky" laws, which seek to regulate the issuance of new securities and to protect the investing public from fraud, misrepresentation, and the temptation of questionable offerings.

LEGAL EXPERTS are inclined to question whether present Federal and State regulations are adequate to protect the investing public. Some questionable real estate ventures have been launched which have yielded handsome profits to the promoters and left investors with an empty shell. Other observers note that the opportunities available to promoters for large profits may encourage overbuilding.

The income-producing real estate—apartments, stores, office buildings—is one of the few types of business that can show no taxable income year after year (even a loss) and still yield a return of 8 to 10 percent a year to shareholders. It is not done with mirrors, or disappearing ink, but legally under provisions of the present Federal tax laws. The magic is performed by utilizing two kinds of tax provisions—treatment of capital gains and depreciation allowances. Few new real estate ventures can be found today whose financial success does not rest on either one or both of these tax provisions. Real estate provides the medium to implement these provisions to a greater extent than almost any other kind of business venture.

The financial gains realizable from capital gains and depreciation have been further enhanced by strongly rising market prices since the end of the Second World War. Some evidence exists that a part of this rise can be attributed to the influx of investment capital attracted by the tax-shelter features of real estate.

How does it all work?

The Federal income tax rate on ordinary taxable income is graduated and ranged from 20 percent to as high as 91 percent in 1962. But the maximum tax rate on the profit from the resale of an asset held for more than 6 months is 25 percent. This difference in tax rates creates strong incentives to invest not only in vacant land but also in land improvements that are likely to rise in market value. The basic investment goal is the same as in the selection of common stocks with a growth potential. The investor prefers to forego ordinary income, taxable at fairly high rates, in favor of capital appreciation.

Tax savings possible from accelerated depreciation rates provide an additional incentive for the construction of income-producing real estate. Under certain conditions it is permissible to take twice the normal rate of depreciation. This practice can substantially reduce the taxable income from the property and at the same time permit tax-free returns to shareholders.

Annual returns to shareholders in real estate investments are of two types.

One is ordinary income, similar to that derived from interest.

The other consists of the pass-through of depreciation allowances. Although it is not taxed as income because it represents recovery of the original investment, it does reduce the cost basis of the share. Taxable capital gains would occur on such shares if the sale price was more than the original cost, less the depreciation allowances that had been received. The investor, however, has achieved his primary goal of converting the ordinary income into capital gains.

Although quite complex in actual practice, the tax rules governing depreciation also encourage relatively short periods of ownership. Accelerated rates of depreciation are most advantageous during the first 7 or 8 years. Thereafter their income-reducing value approximates the more usual straight-line depreciation.

More important, however, is that the sale price of a property provides a new cost for depreciation purposes.

The new owners can thus start the depreciation process all over again. As long as market prices are advancing, the new owners may be able to deduct even more for depreciation than the previous owner. Frequent turnover of property is thus encouraged. Some observers say that investors are actually "buying" depreciation allowances, not the property itself.

The investing public has had an important part in providing the equity capital for new construction, but the great bulk of the needed capital has come from the commercial credit market. Insurance companies have been one major source of such mortgage credit; they use funds obtained from insurance premiums. Thus many millions of persons holding life insurance are indirectly "investors" in urban growth.

The availability of this long-term investment capital, at fixed interest rates and at a relatively high proportion of the total construction cost, adds to the returns to equity capital.

This arises from the application of the principle of equity leverage. It means that the owners of equity capital receive the annual earnings as well as the capital gains and the depreciation allowances that accrue to the borrowed capital, as well as to the capital they have provided.

Thus the shareholders in a property, who may have contributed only 10 or 20 percent of the total price, receive the net earnings from the entire property after the interest and principal payments on the mortgage. A net income of 1 percent on the total value of a property after debt-servicing costs becomes a 5-percent return on a 20-percent equity. A relatively small total resale profit on the entire property likewise becomes a substantial profit in relation to the shareholder's contribution.

We can note several other less complex tax provisions that affect the ownership pattern of undeveloped land.

Real estate taxes and interest payments on such lands are a deductible expense for tax purposes. But the net costs of these expenses vary with the tax bracket of the individual. An individual in, say, the 50-percent tax bracket can thus afford to hold vacant land longer than can an individual with a more modest income. In addition, the prospects of capital gains are more attractive to the person with a high level of ordinary income because of the substantial difference in tax rates on the two kinds of income.

Taxes on capital gains can also serve to postpone the sale of vacant lands that may have become prime property for development. Where such property was acquired many years ago and the realizable gains have reached a high figure, the owner may feel that he cannot afford to sell. His alternative is to allow the property to become a part of his estate. The fair market value at his death becomes the new cost basis, and his heirs may then sell at this figure and pay little or no tax on the capital gains. Such a transaction, however, is not necessarily tax free because of inheritance taxes, but they normally are less than he would pay if he sold during his lifetime.

The special tax treatment given nonprofit organizations occasionally may be a factor in establishing prices of certain income-producing properties or even for vacant acreage. Schools, churches, and fraternal organizations often invest in real estate and can afford to pay more than can individuals or corporations that are subject to different tax laws.

THE DISRUPTIONS to the farm community caught in the path of urbanization often are subtle and gradual.

Initially, a new subdivision or a few scattered clusters of rural residences may cause only mild interest on the part of bona fide farmers. But gradually the consequences become apparent. Property taxes rise to finance the new schools and other public services. Farm labor becomes difficult or impossible to obtain, even at higher wages. Here and there a few farmers sell out, and the land is no longer farmed in the usual way. New voices are heard; new views are expressed at local meetings. There is talk of zoning, school consolidation, a new expressway, a new plant to be built somewhere in the community.

The pitch of sounds of commuter traffic past the farmstead gradually mounts. One day a stranger stops to inquire if the farm might be for sale. He is a little vague as to just how much he will offer, but it seems to be several times the land's worth for farming.

Should the farmer accept it? If farming is his only skill and he is still years away from retirement, he will need to find another farm if he sells. But how long can he hold out, considering the rate at which taxes are going up? Sell off a piece of land, perhaps, and delay the decision. Or should he wait for a higher price as the city grows?

The dual roles of farmer and speculator are seldom compatible. The decisions concerning major improvements to the farm, the purchase of major pieces of farm equipment, even farming practices, will be tempered by the knowledge that his stay is temporary. A well-maintained set of farm buildings will add nothing to the value of the land when he eventually sells. The buyer may reduce his offer by the cost of removing the buildings.

Several different prospective buyers are now clamoring for the farm. Some want an option to purchase at a specified price. Others offer only 10 or 20 percent as a downpayment. Still others may propose that the farmer join with them in developing the land and offer him a share of the expected profits.

The purchase option deserves a closer look, as it often is used to set a nominal, even fictitious, price for land. It is the favorite tool of the speculator who hopes to skim off the initial ripples of advancing land prices.

It is a legal instrument in which the prospective buyer makes a small payment for the right to buy the land at a specified price, within a specified time. If he fails to exercise the option by the date agreed upon, the landowner keeps the option money. On the surface, the seller risks nothing and may gain.

But the option taker has gained an important right—the right to sell the option for more than he paid for it. He may know of a new highway or an interchange to be built near this particular farm or of a builder who is searching for a tract for his next subdivision. If the land is worth more than the price stated in the option, a buyer will be willing to pay a premium to get the option. The profit to the option holder can be substantial, considering the small amount he paid for it.

Even though the option cannot be sold at a profit and is allowed to lapse, the price offered tends to set a new level of market prices for land in the area. Others owning land nearby learn of the price offered and adjust their asking prices accordingly. Such dealings often feed the upward price spiral.

The purchase option also may be used to gain time to arrange financing when the option taker has definite plans to develop the land himself.

Organizers of land syndicates frequently follow this practice when they do not have enough funds to buy the land outright.

The installment land sales contract is still another method of selling land in the urban fringe. It is a long-term sales agreement in which the seller receives a relatively small downpayment, and the buyer agrees to make periodic payments on the balance due.

One of the key features of this method of sale is that legal title to the property remains with the seller. This allows him to regain possession of the property quickly if the buyer fails to make a payment. Although State laws governing contract sales vary, in many States the seller is allowed to keep the downpayment, and any subsequent payments made up to the time default occurred. The buyer loses all that he has put into the property.

Special provisions, called partial releases, are usually inserted in an installment purchase contract involving land to be developed. They spell out the conditions under which the landowner will transfer title to the parts of the tract on which structures have been built. The builder thus can get construction loans and can sell the completed buildings later.

Selling land by means of an installment contract also can have tax advantages to the seller under Federal tax laws. If the total payments received in the year of sale do not exceed 30 percent of the sales price, the capital gains may be distributed over the life of the contract. By reporting only a part of the total gain each year, the taxpayer can often keep his total taxable income in a lower tax bracket.

There are numerous technical requirements in the tax law regarding such sales. Both prospective sellers and buyers should seek competent legal advice before entering into an installment land contract.

THE ILLUSION of insatiable demands for land and impending scarcity all but disappears under closer examination.

Prof. Mason Gaffney, of the University of Wisconsin, has documented the substantial areas of vacant lands that still exist within central cities as well as in the surrounding areas. He concludes that "urban land prices are uneconomically high—that the 'scarcity' of urban land is an artificial one, maintained by the holdout of vastly underestimated supplies in anticipation of vastly overestimated demands."

Dr. Gaffney made these observations

in a chapter in the 1958 Yearbook of Agriculture, *Land,* but evidence has continued to mount that land speculation in anticipation of future needs has become almost a national pastime.

Take Cape Canaveral, Fla., for example. The orbital flight of Col. John Glenn in 1962 gave a further boost to an earlier land boom that was triggered by the announcement that Cape Canaveral would be the launching site for the moonshot. Thousands of acres of pine and palmetto lands worth less than 50 dollars an acre for pasture have been converted into future homesites and sold readily for the equivalent of 200 to 500 dollars an acre. The fact that some of the land offered would be subject to periodic flooding by the St. Johns River, or that building permits could not be obtained from county authorities, did not seem to dampen interest.

More thousands of acres of land with little or no agricultural value have found a ready market elsewhere in Florida as future retirement homesites. Some are in well-planned communities, but others have been launched indiscriminately and reportedly promoted by highly unethical methods. Will plasterboard arches and faded signs of cities that were never built dot the roadsides a decade from now?

Arid desert and grazing lands in Texas, New Mexico, Arizona, and other Western States have also become the favorite merchandise for other land-promotion schemes. Such land has been bought "wholesale" in blocks of 5 or 10 thousand acres for 10 or 20 dollars an acre, and retailed by mail in 1-, 2-, or 5-acre blocks for 600 dollars or more. The warm, dry climate is stressed in the advertisements in big-city papers, but no mention is made that water for even household use may be unobtainable or will cost more than the lot. Schools and main roads are often miles away, and only cactus and stunted juniper make up the landscape.

The process of urbanizing the California desert is well described by Kenneth R. Schneider in the February 1962 issue of the Journal of the American Institute of Planners. The areas he studied were east of Los Angeles along the western edge of the Mojave Desert and farther south along the Salton Sea.

Both of these sections have been the scene of vigorous land-promotion schemes to subdivide and sell isolated homesites. Little actual development has occurred because of the lack of roads, water, and other public services. New problems are being created for the local units of government.

The rash of such land-promotion schemes has caused mounting concern on the part of legitimate real estate interests. It has led to public warnings from the Federal Trade Commission. But the urge still persists to have a ticket in the national land sweepstakes.

The few winners will be hailed as astute investors—the thousands of losers will shrug off their losses.

MUCH OF THE haphazard and unplanned growth around our cities— urban sprawl—can be traced to land speculation. String developments along the major highways form a thin veneer of intensive land use that hides much larger areas of undigested vacant land between the radiating spokes of the highway network. There is a strong inclination to hold such lands in the hope that they also will benefit from the high prices commanded by the more fortunately situated tracts.

Or take the widely observable tendency for leapfrog developments that add greatly to the costs of providing local services. Lands with more desirable locations often are passed over because owners want higher prices.

Much land also is literally destroyed for its best use by indiscriminate intermixing of incompatible uses. Land originally sold as "farmettes" may now be a prime location for luxury homes, but the general character of neighborhood now rules against it.

Junkyards, drive-in theaters, gravel pits, and heavy industry may have an economic role in a community. Their particular location for business reasons may be less important to the community than their possible effects upon surrounding property values. A good zoning and land use plan should seek to strike a proper balance.

The center-stage role of the suburbs in recent years should not divert attention completely from the central city. Traditionally the ultimate focus of people, commerce, and vitality, this sleeping giant has by no means remained passive to the outward thrust.

Urban renewal is one such measure being taken to revitalize the downtown business area and to create desirable residential areas where slums had developed. Similar steps are being taken also by private capital in the hope of reversing the outward flow of people and business. Billions of dollars in property values are at stake, and the winner in this gigantic interplay of economic forces is still not clear.

WE HAVE a few bits of evidence, however, that outward growth may be slower in the 1960's than in the 1950's. One is the expanding demand for apartments. The proportion of all new housing starts consisting of three or more family units rose from 9 percent in 1956 to about 25 percent in 1962.

The main reason for this trend can be found in the shifting age distribution of the population. The increased birth rate following the Second World War will be reflected in new family formations in the late 1960's and into the 1970's. Initially, such new families are likely to be apartment dwellers rather than buyers of suburban homes.

At the upper end of the age distribution, families who moved to the suburbs in the postwar period to rear a family are potential candidates for apartment living.

It is not too important from the standpoint of requirements of land whether the trend toward apartment living occurs within the central city or in the suburbs. In either instance, the land area needed per housing unit will be substantially less than for single-family dwellings.

The physical limits imposed by commuting time and distance is another factor that may slow down the outward growth of some of the larger metropolitan areas. Railroads have faced serious financial problems in providing commuter services. The alternative of publicly financed mass transportation facilities and operating subsidies had not received wide acceptance in 1963.

Still other problems arise if the highway network is expanded to accommodate the daily mass movements of people from the far-out suburbs to their work and back home again. The time individuals are willing to spend in daily travel has some upper limit.

What will our metropolitan areas look like by the mid-1970's? We can be sure that more people will be living there, both in actual numbers and in relation to the total population. Various levels of government may have a more active role in shaping the rate, direction, and characteristics of future growth. The powers to do so already exist. Whether and how to implement them is still to be seen.

WILLIAM H. SCOFIELD, *a land economist, is in charge of research work on farm real estate values and valuation in the Economic Research Service. He received his training at Cornell University, the University of Illinois, and the University of Wisconsin, and has worked in the Department of Agriculture since 1939.*

For further reading:
Berger, C. J., "Real Estate Syndication, Property, Promotion, and the Need for Protection." *Yale Law Journal*, Vol. 69 (No. 5, April 1960).
Bogue, Donald J., *Metropolitan Growth and the Conversion of Land to Nonagricultural Uses.* Scripps Foundation, Studies in Population Distribution, No. 11, Oxford, Ohio, 1956.
Clawson, Marion, Held, R. Burnell, and Stoddard, Charles H., *Land for the Future.* Resources for the Future, Inc., The Johns Hopkins Press, Baltimore, 1960.
Friedenburg, D. M., "The Coming Bust in the Real Estate Boom." *Harper's*, June 1961.
Gottmann, Jean, *Megalopolis; The Urbanized Northeastern Seaboard of the United States.* Twentieth Century Fund, New York, 1961.
Wibberley, G. P., *Agriculture and Urban Growth.* M. Joseph, London, 1960.

KARL S. LANDSTROM

GROWTH AND
THE PUBLIC LANDS

THE Congress established the General Land Office a century and a half ago to administer the landed estate of the Federal Government. The "land office," later part of the Department of the Interior, has been close to the growth and development of the country and to the people—to the relentless, often impatient, westward movement.

The story of the public lands is instinct with the ideals of freedom and individualism; hardship, heartaches, and disappointment; and often with immediate exploitation rather than ultimate conservation of resources.

The passage of the Taylor Grazing Act in 1934 culminated many years of latent awareness of the need for a comprehensive policy of land classification and management. It was not perfect, but it was an answer to the immediate problem. It was a part of a progression of events in which the land policy had passed through stages of revenue, development, and conservation into a management era.

When the Homestead Act passed the Congress in 1862, there was such an abundance of land that no need was seen for a management-classification type of administration for the public lands. At that time no great diversification of land use existed, such as de-

veloped in the latter part of the 19th century.

President Franklin D. Roosevelt in 1934 and 1935 withdrew by Executive order all unclassified land outside of Alaska from entry. Thus, for the first time in American land history, comprehensive and general authority was given for the classification of the unreserved public land according to its highest and best use and for the rejection of applications for other uses.

The Taylor Grazing Act provided not only for grazing administration but for wildlife habitat, hunting, fishing, soil and water conservation, and other land management measures. It was in fact a multiple-use act.

Further implementing the multiple-use concept, the Congress and the Department of the Interior continued to reserve substantial acreages for national parks, wildlife refuges, and recreational facilities. In all of this, the

73

General Land Office and its successor, the Bureau of Land Management, have assumed increasingly greater management responsibilities.

The term "western public lands" is not here used in a technical or legal sense. As I use it, the term embraces all lands and resources administered by the Department of the Interior through the Bureau of Land Management, except those in Alaska.

Included are about 168 million acres, located chiefly in 11 Western States, withdrawn in connection with the Taylor Grazing Act; more than 2 million acres of high-yielding forest lands in western Oregon; and some 2.4 million acres in land-utilization projects, mainly in Montana. Unreserved (vacant) lands in Alaska, nearly 300 million acres, are not included in the term because of their different tenure status.

The Bureau of Land Management is partly or wholly responsible for mineral resources on some 800 million acres (approximately one-third of the area of the United States) and has sole jurisdiction over the management and resources of some 477 million acres. The basic aim in management is the maximum use in the public interest of renewable resources on public lands consistent with the statutes governing conservation and development of productive capacity.

THE OWNERSHIP pattern of the western public lands is a conglomerate of small, isolated, scattered tracts; vast checkerboards of intermingled public and private lands; and often a number of large, consolidated blocks.

This largely unplanned pattern of tenure results from adhering to 19th-century public-land laws and policies designed primarily to promote exploration, settlement, and development of agriculture and business in the western wilderness. Many of the laws have long been inadequate to permit reconciliation of the numerous and complex use and tenure problems of modern managers of land and resources.

In the coming years, an increasing demand will be placed on the public lands to satisfy differing public and private uses. Lands for outdoor recreation and for urban expansion of cities and their industrial and transportation networks are needed even now.

The Department of the Interior works closely with State and local governments to help them meet their public recreational needs. One major means of accomplishing this is by lease or title transfer under the Recreation and Public Purposes Act. Under this law, States may purchase up to 6,400 acres a year for park purposes, and local governments may purchase up to 640 acres.

To stimulate expansion of public recreational facilities, a special pricing schedule has been adopted for public lands for outdoor recreation. State and local governments can purchase land areas from the western public lands for 2.50 dollars an acre, or lease them for 25 cents an acre per year. This price eliminates one of the major stumbling blocks to State and local recreation programs—their inability to finance expensive land acquisition plus necessary improvements and facilities.

Lands obtained under this act must be open to the public without discrimination or favor. No more than a reasonable charge may be made for use of recreation facilities, and entrance fees may not exceed those charged at similar State or local installations.

The traditional needs as to soil, water, forests, forage, wildlife, and minerals also command increasing attention. If the public lands are to receive any sound administration in accordance with modern concepts of the use and development of resources, major adjustments in land tenure, based on current inventories and a meaningful system of land classification, are necessary.

Take, for instance, the challenge of growth in a State like California. The people pour into California at a rate of more than 1,500 a day. The 1962 population of 17 million may be doubled by 1980.

Where will these people be living? Where will they make their livelihood? What does this mean for the 45 million acres of Federal lands in the State?

More particularly, what should be done with 15 million acres of public lands in the State under the supervision of the Bureau of Land Management?

California, like other Western States, needs more water for new homes, farms, and industries.

California wants more roads and highways; more areas for recreation, campgrounds, campsites.

California needs to have scenic, scientific, wildlife, and recreation areas set aside for present and future use.

Many of these needs will have to be met from the public lands.

The arrangements for all of this are bigger than any one agency alone can handle. Federal-State-local coordination is essential if the job is to be accomplished properly.

The fact that the Federal Government is the proprietor of the public lands implies at least a proprietor's care in the use and disposition of the lands for future benefits. It does not go so far, however, as to relieve the State and local governments from their responsibilities.

Comprehensive State and local development plans are essential to guide Federal actions in the management of public lands.

California has a State office of planning and development. The State development plan, and the plans of local government units, will stand as guideposts toward a comprehensive program in which the management of Federal lands may seek an appropriate place.

The increasing economic activity in California and other public-land States has caused a growing demand for land for commercial and industrial purposes, particularly for the electronics, aircraft, and the missile installations, which require large, open sites and climatic conditions of the type that exist in certain regions where a great deal of public land is situated.

No means is easily available for the disposal of public lands in tracts of sufficient size for those purposes. Cumbersome and roundabout methods have to be used, such as exchanges for the acquisition of suitable lands. Occasionally special legislation for individual sites has been sought.

A demand also has grown in connection with urban and suburban development in the periphery of cities and along highways leading from them.

The Department of the Interior often has stated that the statutes governing the disposition of public lands for occupancy purposes are inadequate to cope with the emerging situation. The Department reported to the Congress in 1961 that it had been attempting to meet this challenge with inadequate means.

THE SMALL TRACT ACT of 1938 is a general law under which thousands of promoter-inspired applications have clogged the land offices in desert States.

The homesite, headquarters site, and trade and manufacturing site laws operative in Alaska may not be in line with the growth of Alaska under statehood. Section 2455 of the Revised Statutes providing for the sale of "isolated" and "rough and mountainous" tracts contains restrictive provisions that are ill adapted to current needs for sales of public lands to accommodate rural-urban growth and development.

New rules providing for closer cooperation with local governments in sale and leasing under the Small Tract Act were placed in effect in 1962. Under the rules, the Bureau of Land Management will cooperate with local government units in classifying public lands for small tract development. The availability of public facilities, especially schools, water, roads, and electricity, will be thoroughly reviewed before any small tract communities may be developed on public lands.

With the exception of community sites, small tracts are sold at not less than their fair market value. Community sites are sold at a discount to local governments or nonprofit organizations. In such cases, the land must be permanently dedicated to the use for which it is sold.

The stability of existing economic enterprises and the protection of scenic attractions, water resources, and other interests of the general public merited attention in the rule revisions. Public use areas will be kept open for public use by preventing the sale or leasing of small tracts that would not be in the public interest.

Over the years, the Congress has enacted a series of laws providing for the withdrawal, location, use, and disposal of townsites on the public lands. The varying procedures prescribed by the laws are partly interdependent, partly alternative, and in part unrelated. Many of their provisions have become obsolete.

Development of new and better techniques for townsite planning and management have caused the public to lose interest in employing older and less advantageous techniques.

Practical experience has also revealed a number of particulars in which the existing laws are ambiguous, contradictory, or incomplete.

Several of the townsite laws, as amended, contain limitations on the size of townsites and on the area of the various types of tracts in townsites. The limitations have tended to impede normal growth of communities and the laying out of a townsite and its facilities in the most beneficial way. Some of the townsite laws contemplate a system of public sales to be followed by private sales.

One of the problems in the development of public land is that the development of mineral values often is inconsistent with the development of surface values. The development of leasable minerals, such as oil and gas, may have a limited influence on the surface of land. On the other hand, the development of other minerals, such as gold, silver, copper, and uranium, for which mining claims may be lo-

cated under some conditions, can greatly handicap or prevent the proper development of the surface.

The Small Tract Act of 1938 provides that each patent for a tract bought under that act shall contain a reservation to the United States of all the mineral deposits, together with the right to prospect for, mine, and remove them. This provision permits (after the issuance of regulations by the Department of the Interior) the development of the reserved minerals under the applicable mining and mineral leasing laws. The Department has not issued regulations.

Even though the minerals in the patented lands have not been opened to appropriation under the Federal mining laws, the possibility thereof probably has retarded the development of their full surface potential. Prospective intensive developers may well hesitate to invest the large sums for such development in the light of the possibility that surface values may be entirely destroyed by activities under the United States mining laws.

These are only a few of the limitations and pitfalls existing along the routes available today toward acquiring tracts of public land. One of the major perils is in the operations of third parties, or "agents."

The Government joins the Better Business Bureaus in alerting citizens as to unethical middlemen. The perils of dealing with a public land locator were pretty well known 50 years ago, but in the upsurge of demand for public lands today people tend to be unsuspecting.

Some promoters—not the ethical ones—prey on the natural desire of people to acquire a tract of public land and their inexperience in such matters.

By advertising widely and issuing vague promises, promoters have induced thousands of people to pay exorbitant fees for their professionally inadequate services in making out applications that have little or no chance of success.

Actions taken by Better Business Bureaus and State officials, in cooperation with Federal departments, are helping to remedy this problem, but the only certain way an individual can escape entanglements with unethical promoters is to refuse to do business with them in the first place.

This advice is offered by the Bureau of Land Management: Be cautious in dealing with strangers. Ask for printed or written details before paying any money. Note how much of the money to be paid will be retained by the service and how much will go to the Government. Find out whether the application can be made directly to the Government. Remember that State governments have laws and regulations regarding real estate brokerage transactions. If you intend to hire brokerage services, be sure that you are dealing with a licensed broker. Before signing a contract with a firm that is not known to you, seek information about its reliability.

The Department of the Interior, operating through the Bureau of Land Management, has embarked on a thoroughgoing analysis of the western public lands to evaluate the potential contribution of the lands to national programs. This is known as the "master unit" system of inventory and evaluation. For this purpose, each State is divided into "master units."

Under the existing statutes, the Bureau of Land Management has had to operate its programs largely on an uncontrolled basis, with the initiative in the hands of the general public for filing applications. The result has been sharp peaks in the numbers of applications and sharp changes in types of applications, plus a rapid development of uncontrolled backlogs and many rejections of applications, which could not be approved as not being in the public interest.

Fraudulent and unethical practices based on the application process coming to the attention of the Department increased greatly, with resultant losses to the public amounting to millions of dollars. These practices were substantially curbed during a moratorium on most types of nonmineral applications from February 1961 to September 1962.

These are the capabilities and limitations under which efforts are being directed by the Department of the Interior to meet the needs for public lands as a part of rural-urban growth and development.

As President Kennedy said in his special message on natural resources on February 23, 1961: "The Federal Government owns nearly 770 million acres of public land, much of it devoted to a variety of essential uses. But equally important are the vacant, unappropriated, and unreserved public lands, amounting to some 477 million acres— a vital national reserve that should be devoted to productive use now and maintained for future generations."

Karl S. Landstrom *became Director of the Bureau of Land Management, the Department of the Interior, in 1961 and is now Assistant to the Secretary for Land Utilization. He served in the former Bureau of Agricultural Economics in the Department of Agriculture before joining the Bureau of Land Management in 1949. He later became a member of the bar of the State of Virginia and served as consultant on Public Lands, Mines, and Mining for the Committee on Interior and Insular Affairs of the House of Representatives.*

THE POTENTIAL
OF OUR LAND

W E NEED to review the potential of our land to see how well it will meet future needs for food, forest products, urban uses, and recreation and how effectively we can shift from one use to another. Nations as they become more urban find new ways to meet their needs for land or to adjust their demands to available supplies. Space requirements may be met by increasing the height of apartments and office buildings. Food can be imported. Outdoor recreation needs can be met partly by going abroad or by more intensive use of available recreation land.

Of all these demands upon land, that for recreation is the most elastic. Demand for it rises with income and with improvements in accessibility or reduction in cost.

The United States has abundant land to supply most of its wants.

With rapidly improving technology, our cropland can furnish more farm products than we can profitably use. From 1950 through 1960, when the population increased by only 18 percent, farm output rose 20 percent. Per capita demands for farm products changed very little over this period, however. Production in recent years has outrun effective demand by about 8 percent a year. Except in years of drought and war emergencies, we have had surpluses every year since 1930.

Output per man-hour almost doubled from 1940 to 1950 and almost doubled again from 1950 to 1960, largely because of mechanization. Crop yield per acre rose only 15 percent from 1940 to 1950, but it increased by 40 percent from 1950 to 1960, because of a fourfold increase in the use of fertilizer from 1940 to 1960.

The capital investment per farm doubled between 1950 and 1960 and has increased sixfold since 1940. There also has been improvement in the productivity of capital: The productivity of each unit of the resources used in agriculture rose by 26 percent between 1950 and 1960.

Technological progress will continue, and men in the Department of Agriculture estimate that by 1980 we can meet our food needs, including exports, with 326 million acres actually used in crop production, including cropland harvested, crop failure, and fallow. That is 12 million acres fewer than were so used in 1961, when we had an additional 28 million acres standing idle in the Conservation Reserve and 25 million diverted under the emergency feed grain program.

By 1980, we expect about 17 million acres of new cropland to be developed, partly under public programs, but mostly through private initiative. This land will come out of present forest and grasslands.

Taking into account our expected acreage of cropland and our anticipated needs for its products, we figure that about 71 million acres will need to move into other uses by 1980: To offset the effect of land that will be coming out of the Conservation Reserve and feed grain program, 53 million acres; to offset the effect of new cropland development, 17 million; and to bring acreage now in crops down to needs, 12 million. We subtract a projected allowance of 11 million acres for soil improvement and idle cropland from that total of 82 million acres and have 71 million acres to be shifted from use as cropland.

Some of our present cropland can be used effectively to produce forest products, but that outlet is limited. The demand for some forest products is declining, and great improvements can be made in the productivity of existing forest lands.

We estimate that by 1980 the commercial forests can absorb 19 million acres that are now held as cropland.

We can shift some cropland into permanent pasture. Further improvements in pasture production are probable, but it seems that our grasslands could absorb 37 million acres of cropland by 1980. We also can lengthen crop rotations enough to take up an additional 4 million acres as rotation pasture.

The shifts to forest and pasture will be offset partly by later shifts out of those uses into uses for cropland, recreation, and urban needs.

About 7 million acres will be taken out of crop use by 1980 by urban expansion, or for industrial use, or for public facilities, such as highways and airfields.

The projected allowance of 11 million acres or so constitutes the acreage of cropland that is normally expected to be idle, resting, or in process of improvement for later use, either for crops or cropland pasture.

These adjustments would leave about 5 million acres of cropland that can be shifted exclusively or primarily to recreational or wildlife use. This land will be an important part of the total of 23 million acres that can be added to acreage used for recreation and wildlife.

Our major crop surpluses are in wheat and the feed grains, which are widely grown and so productive that they have intensified the need to adjust cropland.

An illustration is in the regional distribution of cropland that was standing idle under the Conservation Reserve and emergency feed grain programs in 1961, as listed in this table:

| | Acres diverted | | |
Region	Under the Conservation Reserve	Under the feed grain program	Total
Northeast	1,186,092	486,200	1,672,292
Corn Belt	2,909,499	9,141,900	12,051,399
Lake States	3,336,349	2,599,900	5,936,249
Appalachian	1,319,070	1,671,200	2,990,270
Southeast	2,324,022	1,041,800	3,365,822
Delta States	1,129,350	393,800	1,523,150
Southern Plains	5,139,101	3,117,400	8,256,501
Northern Plains	6,842,560	6,064,600	12,907,160
Mountain	3,438,726	561,800	4,000,526
Pacific	764,926	136,500	901,426
Total	28,389,695	25,215,100	53,604,795

Because much of our cropland is not far from population centers, prospects are bright for developing new uses for some for city people. Privately owned farmlands are better situated in this respect than our public lands, on which we have relied for recreation.

According to a study in 1960 by the Outdoor Recreation Resources Review Commission, the Northeast has 25 percent of the people in the United States but only 3 percent of the public recreation lands. For the North Central States, the proportions are 29 percent and 10 percent; the South, 31 percent and 10 percent; the West, including Alaska and Hawaii, 15 and 77 percent.

Our abundant supply of cropland and its mounting productivity give us an opportunity to do much more than we have done to meet city dwellers' requirements for facilities for outdoor recreation. To some extent, new recreational developments will include parks, playgrounds, and other highly specialized facilities. But to a greater extent our recreational needs can be met by adding a new dimension to production. Much of our land and water resources already serve multiple uses. An acre of forest land can provide timber, wildlife, recreation, and watershed at the same time. Crop and pasture land can produce birds and small game and open space, along with crops.

Such opportunities may exist in connection with the development of small watersheds.

Under the Watershed Protection and Flood Prevention Act, many of these are now being developed for flood control and water management.

At one time, financial assistance in the development of recreational features of these projects was not allowed.

Legislation in 1962 broadened the objectives of the program and created possibilities for recreational projects, whose aim will be to develop, with local sponsoring organizations and State agencies, plans to provide recreational storage in selected reservoirs and develop adjacent land and stream courses for recreational use.

Cooperative watershed projects may include a number of activities: Increases in the capacity and surface area of the reservoir, acquisition of adjacent land, land preparation, tree planting and seeding, and construction of sanitary facilities, boat docks, and so forth; advances of funds to local cooperators to acquire needed adjacent shorelands, rights-of-way for access roads and sites for adjacent parks, campsites, and picnic areas in order to prevent encroachment of other developments; provision of loans, as well as cost sharing, to the local organization for land acquisition, easements, construction of dams, and development of public recreational facilities such as docks, bathhouses, picnic shelters, and water facilities; intensified technical assistance and cost-sharing programs on private lands near recreational areas to encourage wildlife, stabilize streamflow and improve scenic values; encouragement of the local cooperating organization to obtain suitable zoning regulations to guide and protect area development; loans to farmers and other individuals for private, income-producing recreational developments.

Technological progress is giving city people more time to enjoy the out of doors. At the same time it makes it possible for us to shift land out of crops in order to meet growing demands for recreation. As a side effect of technological change, we are continually in need of new sources of employment and income.

The vigorous development of land-based outdoor recreation can help us to bring the production of farm products into balance with needs, while at the same time creating new sources of employment and contributing to a better living for Americans.

ORLIN J. SCOVILLE *is Chief, Agriculture Division, United States Operations Mission to Bangkok, Thailand. He formerly was a staff economist of the Staff Economists Group in the Department of Agriculture and secretary of the Department's Land and Water Policy Committee.*

WATER AND AIR

WE do not appreciate water until the well runs dry. We do not appreciate good, fresh air until smog chokes our cities and gases despoil the countryside. That has been happening and will get worse if we are not careful. An average of 30 inches of precipitation yearly falls on the United States. Water withdrawals for all purposes from all ground and surface sources have nearly doubled in a few years. Pollution of water is a growing hazard, although great efforts are made to control it, for we are coming to realize that pollution that occurs in urban areas affects long stretches of the streams and all water uses beyond the city boundaries. Extensive research into many phases of weather and water supplies is going on, but the substantial expenditures of money and effort in these directions could be profitably extended or expanded: The scientific horizon is such that the outlines can be seen of a potentiality that has high stakes. Air pollution is the result of our activities, and we—each of us, not somebody else—must accept responsibility for it. How else can we insure a good place to live?

GEORGE A. PAVELIS AND KARL GERTEL

THE MANAGEMENT
AND USE OF WATER

WATER, land, forests, and people are a fascicle of needs and uses. Three must be managed jointly in line with the regional and national, changing and competing needs of the fourth—people in cities and on the land. The oceans are the original source of all terrestrial waters and the natural reservoirs to which water not returned directly to the atmosphere and not remaining in storage in the soil ultimately returns.

Atmospheric circulation, precipitation, and conversion of salt water are the main processes whereby fresh water is provided to land.

We mention saline conversion at this early point because it bypasses precipitation and represents man's first important success in the direct management of oceanic or continental salt waters for fresh water needs. The technological feasibility of the conversion of saline water has been proved. The big remaining obstacle is the reduction of costs to levels where it can be employed economically on the scale necessary for relieving pressure on existing supplies of fresh water. Urban and rural interests coincide in this research and development work, which has become a major goal of national water resources policy in our own and other countries.

We can only speculate on the water supplies received naturally from the oceans, since an astronomical quantity of water is always in suspension as vapor in the atmosphere.

In their *Primer on Water*, Luna B. Leopold and Walter B. Langbein estimated that quantities transported yearly over the continental United States range near the equivalent of 150 inches spread evenly over the land surface.

Of this total, an average of about 30 inches precipitates and reaches the surface as rain or snow, but the amount ranges from 155 inches at a few weather stations in Alaska to less than 4 inches in parts of California, Nevada, and Arizona. This fact alone explains why we are so keenly interested in techniques for increasing precipitation.

Modification of weather and conversion of saline water are thus paired as new elements of water management pointed toward increasing the natural supplies of water.

Were it not for the fact that research and development in the modification of weather cannot be confined to laboratories or pilot installations, as in saline conversion, urban and rural interests in the testing of this new technology would be in harmony also.

A notable urban-rural weather-control controversy occurred in the Pacific Northwest in 1951, when farmers in northern Idaho and western Montana were faced with the problem of delayed harvesting because of an unusually wet summer. Quite naturally they objected to attempts of hydroelectric companies to increase rainfall in early autumn in the headwaters of the Columbia River so as to firm up the winter power output at Grand Coulee Dam and other downstream plants.

In principle, this issue might have been resolved by requiring the utilities to compensate the farmers at least for the losses resulting from further postponement of harvesting, provided the compensation added to the cost of the weather operation did not exceed the benefits of increased power, in which case the operation would have been a net gain for the region and a net loss for no one.

Solving the problem in practice, however, would have been a lot harder. One would need accurate advance estimates of all damages and project costs, and groups of utilities officials and farmers would have to be formed to negotiate and arrange distribution of the compensation.

The main point here is that urban-rural problems of water management do not involve exclusively the regulation and use of natural supplies—we must consider new technologies for increasing natural supplies when appraising the total extent of our water.

As to the use and management of existing natural supplies of water, what happens to the 30 inches of average annual rainfall that reach land or water surfaces?

Although conditions of land use vary greatly and wide differences occur region to region, we can generalize that about 21 inches evaporate directly from the surfaces or are transpired by vegetation. Most of the remaining 9 inches return to the oceans directly as surface runoff or indirectly as flow of ground water—the water that permanently saturates the earth's subsurface and is an important part of the water cycle.

Important problems of management of agricultural and nonagricultural water rise along all these routes.

A good part of the 21 inches, or 70 percent, of rainfall that never reaches streams supports forests, pastures, and crops. We do not know, though, how much represents evaporation and transpiration separately. The two processes are combined in the one term "evapotranspiration."

The significance of evapotranspiration for agriculture and forestry is indicated by the fact that roughly 80 percent of the value of all crops in the United States is produced on nonirrigated land and that nearly all of our timber and livestock (there are some important regional and local exceptions) are produced on nonirrigated land.

A further consideration for everybody is that evapotranspiration greatly influences remaining runoff, a prime source of water for irrigation and domestic use in rural areas, all urban and industrial uses, and such uses as recreation and commercial navigation, which we can call rural or urban only in specific instances.

It is in its effects on all of these factors that we regard evapotranspiration as the primary use of water and the first major point in the hydrologic cycle where management problems arise in connection with water use, because increasing or decreasing the evapotranspiration over a given area will have decreasing or increasing effects on potential runoff.

And it is the relative values attached to evapotranspiration and runoff by various individuals or groups that determine whether their interests are opposed or in harmony.

At one extreme, for example, ranchers in arid regions would prefer that evapotranspiration use of rainfall be maximized. They recognize that moisture conditions on the range improve as a smaller portion of the rainfall of an average or below-average season is permitted to reach streams through such techniques as range pitting, water spreading, and controlled grazing.

The other extreme of minimizing use by evapotranspiration would be illustrated by the municipalities or irrigation farmers in a region. They would prefer that seasonal rainfall in upland areas appear as water yield, especially in places where no recourse to ground water exists for supplying their needs.

These extremes present complex problems of urban-rural water management in themselves, but in between lie an unlimited number of other complex situations compounded mainly of geographic differences in rainfall, use of land, density of population, economic activities, and alternative sources of water supply.

Considering all rural or urban or upstream and downstream interests, we can reduce the basic watershed management problem to the question of what is the ideal amount of evapotranspiration use to permit (and consequently the ideal water yield to obtain) from a particular watershed for a given period, either by altering the extent and type of vegetation or by otherwise modifying the landscape with structures and practices to control water.

Again, in principle, such questions can be resolved by evaluating the agricultural and nonagricultural values of evapotranspiration use and later use of water yield in terms of community interests, and then managing tributary areas in the manner most consistent with these interests. We admit that is a sweeping statement, but it is the essence of many successful programs for developing watersheds and river basins that involve the cooperation of farm and nonfarm groups.

THE SUCCESS of a community approach to problems of watershed management is due to many factors other than a reconciliation of competing values of rainfall in on-site evapotranspiration and subsequent uses of water yield.

It may be based largely on common benefits from solving the problems of water management that are not related particularly to use. Major cases in point are flooding and erosion. Almost by definition, flood control and erosion control are water problems for farm and nonfarm and private and public attention.

The Department of Agriculture's National Inventory of Soil and Water Conservation Needs, completed in 1961, and other studies indicate that nearly 86 million acres of flood plain in the United States still need more or less protection.

Flood plains occupy about 7 percent, or 125.7 million acres, of the United States mainland and Hawaii. (Data are lacking for Alaska.) About 69 percent of all flood plains are in smaller tributaries. The rest are along major rivers.

Flood control has been made effective to some degree on about 27 percent of the tributary areas in need of protection, on 40 percent of downstream or main river areas, and on roughly 31 percent of all flood plains.

We lack complete information on the annual flood damage to agricultural and nonagricultural groups, but it is likely that agricultural and nonagricultural interests are about equally affected by flood damage and that about two-thirds of upstream and one-third of downstream damages are of an agricultural nature.

These data imply that agricultural interests in flood protection are not confined to small watershed projects and that urban interests are not limited to downstream water supply or flood control facilities.

Data on other remaining needs for erosion control as an aspect of water management are also available from the Conservation Needs Inventory. It shows that nearly 162 million acres—39 percent—of the 407 million acres expected to be needed for cropland use by 1980 will need protection from erosion as the primary conservation problem. About 32 million acres (6 percent) of privately owned pastures and ranges and about 12 million acres of privately owned forests and woodland may also need treatment.

Moreover, erosion problems remain serious enough on about 24 million acres of public and private land to require project-type action in addition to individual treatment. The latter acreage is a primary source of sediment damage to downstream flood plains and storage structures; the sediment causes reductions in the quality of both rural and urban water supplies.

Thus the evapotranspiration use of water in upland areas affects not only the seasonal quantities of downstream water yields but also the rates and quality of streamflow at particular points in time.

Efforts to regulate or manage evapotranspiration as a hydrologic process bring into play a large number of physical and economic variables that affect the welfare of urban and rural groups who may rely on retention of rainfall in upland watersheds or subsequently withdraw streamflow and ground water for various purposes.

A REVIEW of the supply-demand situation as it concerns the use of streamflow and ground water must note first that several uses, such as navigation, recreation, and perhaps the generation of hydropower do not involve the actual withdrawal of water; that fresh water is not required for some uses; and that a large part of the quantities withdrawn for most industrial and municipal purposes can be reused many times, although its quality may be changed considerably.

Reuse, or "recycling," possibilities are recognized by the term "consumptive use," which is the portion of withdrawn water that is returned to the atmosphere through evapotranspiration or is more or less permanently incorporated in products.

Evapotranspiration in this connection refers mainly to the evapotranspiration of irrigation water, aside from the water that otherwise leaves the landscape. It includes also such components as human and livestock biologic requirements plus evaporation in connection with various industrial processes.

We must also note that national data on water uses and supplies are probably more interesting than useful.

Regional water needs usually must be met with regional supplies. The California Water Plan—the conveyance of water from the northern to the more populated southern portion of the State—and the Fryingpan-Arkansas transmountain diversion project in Colorado are two of many instances in which strict single-basin approach to water problems does not apply.

But we can say also that national studies on the use of water and other natural resources often reveal particular regional trends and associated problems that might have gone unnoticed, since the accuracy of national statistics increases with the degree of underlying regional detail.

WE MENTIONED that about 9 inches out of the 30 inches of average annual rainfall over the 48 mainland States and Hawaii represent the Nation's known average annual continuous supply of water available for navigation, power generation, recreation, and all specific agricultural and nonagricultural withdrawal uses.

The 9 inches can be expressed as 1.3 billion acre-feet per year (an acre-foot is 1 foot of water over an acre) and can be imagined as a lake about 8 feet deep over Texas. Alaska complicates estimates of the Nation's water supply; the new State's water resources are known to be tremendous but are not completely charted.

Other difficulties involve ground water aquifers. Their adequacy as continuous sources of supply is commonly examined in terms of whether annual withdrawals are less than natural rates of replenishment, rather than whether withdrawals are less than total volumes feasibly pumped.

Many physical and economic factors determine such feasibility. One estimate is that the Nation's stocks of ground water are equivalent to 10 years of average annual rainfall, or 33 years of average annual runoff.

Because of these and other uncertainties, we compare in a general way the national situation and recent trends in agricultural and nonagricultural use and sources of water with total supplies, but we shall try to focus on management problems of surface and ground water as they concern agricultural and nonagricultural interests.

GETTING ACCURATE information on uses of water and supplies, a complex task, requires considerable ingenuity and cooperation of individuals, industry groups, and almost every level of government.

Most national statistics are prepared by such agencies as the Geological Survey in the Department of the Interior, the Bureau of the Census in the Department of Commerce, and the Public Health Service in the Department of Health, Education, and Welfare. State agencies and the Weather Bureau, the Bureau of Reclamation, the Corps of Engineers, and the Department of Agriculture contribute to these efforts, as shown in studies of the Senate Select Committee on National Water Resources of future water requirements and development potentials in each of the country's 22 major water resource regions.

Drawing from various sources but mostly from data of the Bureau of the Census on irrigated acreage and the Geological Survey on water use rates, the Land and Water Policy Committee of the Department of Agriculture estimated that water withdrawals for all purposes and from all ground and surface sources amounted to 287 million acre-feet in 1960. That is roughly 22 percent (compared to 10 percent in 1940) of the mainland's annual renewable supply of 1.3 billion acre-feet.

On a per capita basis, daily withdrawals increased from 872 to 1,425 gallons between 1940 and 1960.

Agriculture withdraws about 107 million acre-feet (37 percent of the United States total) for livestock, irrigation, and its domestic purposes. Irrigation alone amounts to 96 percent of the agricultural withdrawals and 36 percent of all withdrawals.

Agricultural withdrawals have increased by 60 percent since 1940, compared with 190 percent for withdrawals of an urban and industrial nature, an indication of a substantial decline for agriculture relative to other uses.

As projected by the Land and Water Policy Committee, agricultural withdrawals may go down to 19 percent of all withdrawals in 1980 from the 37 percent estimated for 1960. Taken alone, these agricultural-nonagricultural gross withdrawal relationships reflect the increasingly urban and industrial character of the country, but are poor indicators of future or even current competition for available water supplies.

WE GET a better insight into urban-rural relationships in the use of water by considering data on consumptive use.

On the average, about 50 percent of the water withdrawn for agricultural purposes is consumed, in the sense of not being reusable for any purpose.

Rates for different agricultural purposes in 1960 were 93 percent of withdrawals for livestock watering, 60 percent of domestic withdrawals and irrigation water actually applied to crops, and 48 percent as the average for irrigation, if computed at diversion or pumping rather than application points.

K. A. MacKichan and J. C. Kammerer, of the Geological Survey, figured that about 21 percent of the water withdrawn for irrigation was lost in transit through seepage and evapotranspiration from canal surfaces or vegetation, although some of the seepage is recoverable elsewhere.

On the other hand, overall rates of consumptive use for municipal and industrial withdrawals average around 5 percent of withdrawals.

The net result of these different rates of consumption is that, while agriculture accounts for only 37 percent of all the water withdrawn annually in the United States, it accounts for nearly 87 percent, or 52 million acre-feet, of the 60 million acre-feet consumed.

Considering the future, the Land and Water Policy Committee indicated that, while agricultural withdrawals may decline by 1980 to 19 percent from the current 37 percent of all United States withdrawals, agricultural consumption will fall to only 76 percent from the current 87 percent of total consumption. In other words, agriculture will remain the leading consumptive user of water for a long time.

We can summarize the various esti-mates we cited by saying that nationally we are withdrawing 22 percent and consuming 5 percent of our total renewable water resources of 1.3 billion acre-feet, and that even by 1980 we will be withdrawing only 51 percent and consuming around 6 percent of this total.

But the most significant conclusions drawn from such aggregate figures are their convenience for burying crucial problems of regional scarcity and their complete abstraction from nationwide problems of water quality.

We know that present water appropriations already exceed or approach the limit of available supplies in many western river basins with attendant problems of quality maintenance; that industrial-municipal and rural demands have created many supply and treatment problems in many eastern localities; and that ground water poses use and management problems of its own.

MANAGEMENT possibilities for relieving problems of scarcity in particular river basins were outlined in some detail in 1959–1960 by the Senate Select Committee on National Water Resources. Their general significance is indicated here by focusing on the group of 17 Western States.

The West is often singled out because of its following average relations to mainland totals: 60 percent of the total land and water area; 40 percent of the total annual rainfall; 28 percent of the total annual runoff; 62 percent of all water withdrawals (excluding hydropower); but 80 to 85 percent of total consumption of water.

The reason for the last is that the West and Hawaii accounted for 93 percent (33.8 million acres) of all estimated irrigation in the United States in 1963, although, according to census trends, irrigation in the 31 Eastern States increased from 390 thousand acres in 1939 to about 2.6 million acres in 1963. (Alaska had about 360 acres of irrigated land in 1963.)

WE CAN illustrate the urban-rural aspect of western water management by comparing irrigation with all other uses, since irrigation accounts for practically all agricultural consumption and because farm and nonfarm groups have common though not necessarily equal interests in water storage for hydropower, flood control, recreation, and other purposes.

Major withdrawals of western water can be listed as evaporation from manmade reservoirs and ponds and diversion or ground water pumping, with diversions including an allowance for conveyance losses en route to points of use as well as desired deliveries.

The artificial nature of storage and conveyance explains the inclusion of associated evaporation in withdrawals, while conveyance losses involve evaporation from canal surfaces, seepage, and use of water by canal phreatophytes—vegetation with high water requirements but no economic value.

Corresponding rates of consumptive use as percentages of withdrawal total 100 percent for reservoir-pond evaporation and may vary from 45 to 60 percent for diversion and pumping combined. (The 45-percent figure assumes complete recovery of canal seepage; the higher figure assumes no recovery.)

Canal evaporation and the phreatophytes are 100 percent consumptive.

Seepage varies from 0 to 100 percent consumptive, depending on recovery possibilities.

Considering all forms of water withdrawal in the West, consumptive use averages 21 percent in nonirrigation uses, from 49 to 68 percent in irrigation, and from 44 to 60 percent for the West as a whole, again with the lower and upper percentages respectively assuming complete recovery and no recovery of canal seepage. Also, the low consumption rate of 21 percent for nonagricultural uses should be qualified by the fact that much of the nonagricultural use is in coastal areas where return flows reach the ocean quickly.

Even so, these percentages suggest major possibilities for improved management of water and potential effects on the supplies available for various purposes.

First of all, a one-for-one relation exists between reductions in all forms of evaporation or phreatophyte losses and effective increases in water supplies made available for increased consumptive use in all beneficial purposes.

Considering respective consumptive use rates and even assuming no recovery of canal seepage, we can say that a saving of an acre-foot in evaporation and phreatophyte consumption would release nearly 1.5 acre-feet of water for irrigation withdrawal, 4.75 acre-feet for nonirrigation withdrawal, and an average of 1.66 acre-feet for total western withdrawal distributed as at present between urban and rural beneficial uses.

In a study of evaporation, J. Stuart Meyers, of the Geological Survey, indicated that nearly 12.3 million acre-feet of water evaporates annually from major reservoirs and regulated lakes in the West.

Various tests of chemical and other means of suppressing evaporation from reservoirs, conducted by the Bureau of Reclamation, show an average reduction of 15 percent in evaporation loss, which would amount to an average saving of 1.9 million acre-feet out of Mr. Meyers' estimate of total loss in the West. When we multiply the 1.9 million acre-feet by these release rates, we get an indication of the possible effects of a full-scale suppression program and an explanation of the obvious interest of both urban and rural groups in the Bureau's experiments.

Similar benefits are possible in reducing evaporation from ponds and small lakes, which Mr. Meyers estimated to run 3.4 million acre-feet a year.

The quantity of water wasted by phreatophytes along canals alone was estimated at nearly 2 million acre-feet per year by F. L. Timmons, of the Agricultural Research Service. And there is evidence that phreatophytes altogether may consume up to 40 percent as much water as the total volume consumed by all irrigated crops.

How do such comparisons and possibilities relate to problems of water scarcity in the West that involve farm and nonfarm groups, and particularly to possibilities for resolving such issues through improved management?

To take an extreme case, we noted that consumptive use of water in irrigation amounts to about 68 percent of withdrawals if canal seepage is figured as a complete loss, while consumptive use for nonirrigation purposes runs about 21 percent of withdrawals. In other words, an acre-foot of water goes only about one-third as far in irrigation as it does in nonirrigation uses. This is to say that, under conditions of overall scarcity and aside from quality considerations, the net economic value of an additional acre-foot of irrigation water would need to be three times its alternative net value in other uses (as it may well be) to justify the added diversion, and in economic value we include both monetary and intangible benefits.

If canal seepage could be totally recovered or prevented, irrigation water would need to be valued only at two and one-third times the competing values to justify diversion of an additional acre-foot.

These calculations may be purely hypothetical for any given river basin or other area, but they do explain current arguments for shifting water use from agricultural to nonagricultural purposes on the basis of comparative monetary values, even to the extent of modifying the historic legal doctrines governing the use of water.

But regardless of such current issues as surround water law, the elimination of consumptive waste from evaporation, phreatophytes, and seepage is clearly a management problem on which all farm and nonfarm groups can agree. No values are sacrificed aside from the costs of developing and applying control practices, and no one benefits from the uncertainty regarding eventual recovery of seepage losses. This uncertainty extends particularly to the quality aspects of water management, both in the West and the Nation.

WE CAN GAGE the significance of the quality of water if we recall that by 1980 we are expected to consume only 6 percent of our renewable water supply but withdraw 51 percent and in addition use water for recreation, navigation, and other in-channel uses. The threat to adequate water therefore may lie not so much in the small fraction consumed but in the quality of the 94 percent remaining.

If we also keep in mind that one of the major uses of streams is to receive waste discharges, we grasp the outlines of the problem of water pollution.

Perhaps "problem of the management of water quality" is a better term than "pollution problem."

If we choose to define pollution as any change in quality of water from its natural state, pollution is inevitable but not necessarily undesirable.

If we mean the indiscriminate disposal of wastes in streams and aquifers, pollution is intolerable.

In other words, we can tolerate the degree of pollution resulting from carefully monitored disposal of wastes, combined with economic treatment and coordinated with the varying quality requirements of different water uses.

Agriculture and industry both cause and suffer pollution. Agricultural pollution problems are concentrated in the Southwest, where high contents of salt in return flows from irrigation complicate critical problems of water scarcity. For example, El Paso, Tex., has been forced to pump most of its water from wells more than 500 feet deep because of the high salt content of the Rio Grande that flows past the city. Salts in the lower reaches of the Colorado River have long been a sore point in our relations with Mexico.

In all parts of the country, the expanded use of insecticides and other agricultural chemicals requires vigilance against adverse effects.

The many forms of industrial and urban pollution are more concentrated in the East and Midwest. At major centers of water use, at least the more common type of pollutants can be removed, at a cost, by water treatment.

The individual farmer or irrigator often has no choice but to stop using the water.

But perhaps the most serious rural damage of pollution, unmeasurable in money, is suffered by city dwellers—namely, the loss of an opportunity to fish, swim, or boat in polluted water.

The problems posed by pollution are stubborn and are aggravated by past attitudes and insufficient knowledge. Solutions will require much money, imaginative planning, cooperation, and intensive research.

As TO GROUND water, the idea that water is a renewable resource is only partly true—an important fact in its management.

We noted that nearly all the renewable water supply that reaches the land each year either returns directly to the atmosphere or flows into the ocean. Ground water that saturates the sands and gravels and permeable rock materials beneath the earth is part of this cycle.

Over the ages, and in amounts negligible by man's reckoning, the rate of recharge of some ground water areas has been in excess of discharge. This accumulation is the source of our underground treasure house of water, which is laid down very unevenly over the country.

Uses of ground water in 1960 were estimated at about 17 percent of all water withdrawn. More than 60 percent of the total pumped was for irrigation. Another 6 or 7 percent was taken for rural domestic and livestock purposes. In the West where surface sources of water have been more fully developed, the trend to irrigation with ground water has been continuous and accelerated by the development of modern irrigation pumps. In the Nation as a whole, there seems to be a trend away from ground water in non-farm uses.

SINCE MOST irrigated land is in the 17 western mainland States, they account for more than 85 percent of all rural ground water use. The West also accounts for some 40 percent of all urban and industrial ground water withdrawals in the Nation, a much higher proportion than the western share of all urban and industrial uses of the streamflow.

In the East, more than 90 percent of the use of ground water for irrigation and almost half of all rural uses of ground water in 1960 were in Arkansas, Florida, Louisiana, and Mississippi, the leading eastern irrigation States. Other ground water uses were also significant in those States. Just the same, however, nearly 75 percent of the urban and industrial uses of ground water in the East was in States other than them.

Pumping of ground water is most intensive in the Southwest, where also exists the greatest pressure on all water resources. Three States—California, Texas, and Arizona—accounted in 1960 for almost 60 percent of all rural uses of ground water as well as for some 25 percent of all urban and industrial ground water use.

The position of agriculture in the use of ground water and the location of many urban wells outside the main irrigated areas help explain why competition for ground water has been more prevalent within agriculture itself than between agriculture and other uses. Even in such sections as the Texas High Plains, where city and farm overpump the same underground supply, there has been little direct competition.

Moreover, a greater ability to pay for water permits nonfarm users to continue to pump deep aquifers after declines in the water table have rendered irrigation pumping prohibitive.

For example, Flagstaff, Ariz., obtains municipal water from wells 8 miles away and 2 thousand feet deep. The actual pumping lift is 1,600 feet—more than three times the estimated maximum pumping lift Arizona cottongrowers could afford.

IN MANAGING ground water, to look for rural-urban competition is to look the wrong way.

The more useful approach recognizes the unity of ground and surface water in the hydrologic cycle and considers the mutual interests of all users of water.

Some questions that will lead to constructive action in any situation:

Where and in what amounts is ground water replenished? How fast does it travel?

Are we pumping an underground treasure house with little recharge—the underflow of an adjacent river or an aquifer discharging into a more distant surface body?

How fast will the water table decline in the future, or will it merely fluctuate with rainfall?

If persistent declines are in prospect, are these general or concentrated in pockets of heavy pumping and what will be the effect on well yields?

Is there a threat of intrusion of saline water or even subsidence of the land surface as the aquifer itself is dewatered?

Is pumpage interfering with established water uses in streams or lakes? Does salt-laden drainage water from irrigation or brine from oil wells or other waste degrade the quality of ground water?

Once we know the facts, we can look for a solution that fits the situation.

Hydrologists and engineers provide us with an expanding number of tools. The economist evaluates the costs and benefit of each alternative. The lawyer appraises the legal feasibility and may work with the political scientist and legislator for needed legal reform.

The final choice is a balance of varying local and national interests.

An inventory of uses often brings to light opportunities for eliminating waste or possibly changing to a crop rotation or industrial process that requires less water. Most people do not know how much water they use. Time and again the simple step of installing watermeters has paid off by saving water and money on the farm and in the city.

In Orange County, Calif., the people have gone one step further. They have harnessed the price system to achieve economic use of water. Each user pays according to his pumpage, and the water management district uses the money to recharge the ground water reservoir from surface sources. In such situations, an opportunity also exists to draw on the stream in wet seasons and to fall back on the ground water reservoir when streams run low.

Along streams in the Southwest, ground water use could be coordinated by deliberately pumping the adjacent water table below the reach of useless streambank vegetation that waste several million acre-feet each year.

Mining of ground water should not be condemned out of hand. It is unplanned mining and ignorance of the consequences that poses the real threat.

Southern California supports a booming population, agriculture, and industry, all launched in large part by mining of ground water. This expansion grew to a scale that supports importation of distant surface waters and its evaporation-free storage in underground aquifers, with experiments in pumping water into special injection wells to form a barrier to sea water intrusion. Financing is by water tolls and property levies, so that users of water and the general agricultural and urban community shares in the financing. California's water problems are far from solved, but actions there show what can be accomplished.

THE CHOICES are fewer and harder in places where ground water is mined and no adequate alternative supply is obtainable. The choices often are between using water for the current generation or conserving it for the future. Once the area is developed and an established agriculture and the supporting economy is based on ground water, the local people understandably have been reluctant to stop pumping. Most of the West and several Eastern States, however, now have laws that control the use of ground water.

Implementation at the local level is generally encouraged by providing for establishment of ground water districts. These generally have broad powers to prevent waste and control the spacing of wells to avoid concentrated overdraft, or where feasible, induce increased recharge into the ground water reservoir. In most critical areas, all these measures cannot prolong the life of the ground water indefinitely but will permit enough time to amortize existing investments or bring in new supplies.

COOPERATION is one word with which we can conclude this discussion of water use and management as they involve rural or urban groups.

The mutuality of interests lies in joint development of water, in which are recognized such factors as the base that irrigation farming provides for the economy of several Western States.

Even the competition between farm and city will center largely on the best means for cooperating in the joint planning and financing of water resources development.

GEORGE A. PAVELIS *and* KARL GERTEL *are Leader and Research Agricultural Economist, respectively, for Water Use Investigations, Land and Water Economics Branch, Resource Development Economics Division, Economic Research Service.*

For further reading:
Colorado Ground Water Commission. Western Resources Conference. (Presentation of papers and articles read at Conference, Boulder, Colo., August 1960.)
Hughes, W. F., and Magee, A. C., *Some Economic Effects of Adjusting to a Changing Water Supply, Texas High Plains.* Texas Agricultural Experiment Station, Bulletin 966, 1960.
Leopold, Luna B., and Langbein, Walter B., *Primer on Water.* Geological Survey, Washington, D.C., 1960.
MacKichan, K. A., and Kammerer, J. C., *Estimated Use of Water in the United States, 1960.* Geological Survey Circular 456, Washington, D.C., 1961.
Meyers, J. S., *Evaporation From the 17 Western States.* Geological Survey Professional Paper 272–D. U.S. Government Printing Office, Washington, D.C., 1962.
Piper, A. M., *Interpretation and Current Status of Ground-Water Rights.* Geological Survey Circular 432, Washington, D.C., 1960.
Smith, S. C., "The Rural-Urban Transfer of Water in California." *Natural Resources Journal,* Vol. 1 (No. 1, March 1961).
U.S. Congress, *Report of the Select Committee on National Water Resources.* Senate Report 29 (87th Cong., 1st sess.), U.S. Government Printing Office, Washington, D.C., 1961.
U.S. Department of Agriculture, *Agricultural Land Resources: Capabilities, Uses, Conservation Needs.* Agriculture Information Bulletin 263, 1962.
——— *Land and Water Resources. A Policy Guide.* Land and Water Policy Committee, 1962.
——— *Major Uses of Land and Water in the United States, With Special Reference to Agriculture.* Agricultural Economic Report No. 13, 1962.
——— *Water,* the 1955 Yearbook of Agriculture. U.S. Government Printing Office, Washington, D.C., 1955.
Water and Agriculture, R. D. Hockensmith, editor. American Association for the Advancement of Science, Publication 62, 1960.
Wollman, Nathaniel, and others, *The Value of Water in Alternative Uses.* The University of New Mexico Press, Albuquerque, 1962.

EDWARD A. ACKERMAN

RESEARCH ON
THE WATER SUPPLY

A CARTOON in Punch, a British magazine, showed a hirsute but bald man in a barber chair. The barber was telling him, "Yours, sir, is not a problem of production, but of distribution." The same words describe the water supply of the world or any major part of it.

Tremendous volumes of water exist on the earth, and most of its surface is covered by water in liquid or solid form. Even parts of the land, as in the tropical rain forests, are so well supplied with moisture that their principal problems are adaptation to the overabundance of water.

The extreme conditions of a desert illustrate the problem of distribution of water in its simplest form. Man finds other resources that can help to support him or create his wealth. In the desert he must seek and distribute water in order to exploit those resources, whether they are mines or lands; otherwise they are valueless to him. All other water problems are variants of this simple illustration, where human needs are greater than can be met by local supplies.

The problem has two sides. Its extent depends on the size of the demand as well as on the size of the supply.

Except when they are reduced to the

utmost straits, men tend to think of meeting their needs for water almost always in terms of finding and distributing a supply rather than altering their demands.

Only when our technology becomes highly sophisticated do we otherwise approach the matter of supply and demand in terms of reducing the demand—even in this day, whether we are concerned with individual families, farms, great municipalities, or entire States.

Research on the water supply thus moves in a direction favored by the social and individual psychology of most men in meeting a vital problem in our society.

WE CONSIDER HERE the supply of fresh water, the water that may be found on earth and can meet man's own consumptive needs, the needs of the land plants and animals on which he depends, and the needs of the in-

94

dustries that embellish his life and improve his existence.

We seek this water in four general sources: In the streams, lakes, or ponds, which are part of the drainage system of the lands; in the percolating or stored waters under the surface of the soil; in the waters of the oceans, seas, or other surface bodies of salt water; and in the water vapor of the atmosphere.

Research investigations may look into water occurrence within any one of these four major areas quite without practical objectives or any thought of solving a water supply-demand problem. At the other extreme is the search for a better design of a mechanical device, like a pump, aimed toward the reduction of cost in lifting, moving, or distributing water to a consumer.

Both types of research are important, and as James B. Conant observed some years ago, the line dividing the two has become indistinguishable in modern times. I make little distinction in this chapter between fundamental (without an immediate practical objective) and applied research. We must assume that the web of technology, here as elsewhere, cannot be cut into pieces and always begins with the purest and most recondite of laboratory investigations.

Another aspect of the fabric of technology is what we may call the windfall effect of inventions or discoveries. Thus the invention of earthmoving and compacting equipment, a major event among the techniques of stream regulation and water storage, made possible the great, economical earthfill dams. The same may be said about the development of high-strength and other special-purpose concretes.

None of these inventions was conceived in terms of water development, but they prove a basic point: By far the best assurance of practically effective research on water supply is the existence of a healthy, well-supported, broadly interested scientific establishment in the Nation and a vigorous technology that offers maximum stimulation to invention.

Those who face problems of deficient water supply in one degree or another look first for large supplies to the atmosphere and the oceans.

The atmosphere in total contains far less water (1.15×10^{10} acre-feet) than the oceans (10^{15} acre-feet), but it is a much more attractive source because the atmosphere is everywhere, and he who finds the key to precipitating water from the atmosphere solves part of one of the most difficult tasks in supplying water to needy areas, that of transportation and distribution.

Furthermore, that water comes in the form most needed, fresh water, and there are already natural processes at work producing precipitation, albeit deficiently timed and geographically distributed. Theoretically, we have only to guide or trigger these processes to tap the cheapest source. Failing that, a capacity to forecast natural processes would be a next most desirable step to enable us to adapt our activities to the vagaries of weather with a minimum of economic loss.

A KEY POINT in the hydrologic cycle is the precipitation of moisture from the atmosphere upon the land, where it becomes soil moisture, runoff, or percolating ground water, and sooner or later stored water on the surface or underground. On the surface the storage may be in the form of snow, ice, or liquid.

Everybody knows that the volume of water received from precipitation in any locality or region may vary from season to season and from year to year. The shortest range fluctuations are of importance in that they may cause floods. The fluctuations from season to season within any given year are less important in that patterns of human activity have generally evolved in a way that accommodates to them.

The fluctuations from year to year, on the other hand, are extremely important, because human beings have a way of crowding the favorable side of these fluctuations with their water- and moisture-dependent economic activities and actions.

Societies the world over tend to be optimistic about the continuance of favorable moisture receipts in the plans they lay and the activities they engage in. Particularly in the semiarid climates of the world, this social optimism (or social necessity) frequently has led to disaster.

History is filled with the records of drought-caused famines and migrations. In more modern times, social organization has made the impact of these disasters somewhat less violent in most countries. Nonetheless, they still are of enormous financial, social, and political importance in semiarid and arid environments. Furthermore, as productive structure becomes more complex in advanced societies, even the lesser fluctuations from year to year have financial significance. The potential importance of long-range forecasting of water receipts from the atmosphere therefore is great.

On the shortest range fluctuations of importance in water receipts on the land—those of a few days—we have a reasonable ability to forecast.

An official committee of the American Meteorological Society in 1962 stated that, "For periods extending to about 72 hours, weather forecasts of moderate skill and usefulness are possible. Within this interval, useful predictions of general trends and weather changes can be made." Thus information of value in forecasting impending floods can be obtained in advance. In addition, temperature conditions for periods as long as a month can be predicted with some skill.

Beyond periods of a month, however, the committee said that forecasts must be considered as experimental; although promising study is in progress, skill has not yet been demonstrated.

Thus all of the true long-range problems of forecasting must depend on the basic data and the interpretations that climatology has provided in the past. These of course are only rough averages for any locality or region.

Attempts to forecast the season-to-season and year-to-year fluctuations have been made over many years. They generally have taken the form of the analysis of weather records in an attempt to discern simple or complex cycles, but however careful the statistical analysis and however ingenious their construction, none of the supposed cycles has been of any practical value in forecasting water receipts.

On the other hand, meteorology, physics, and other sciences have made great progress toward a better understanding of the dynamics of the atmosphere and have provided concepts and observational data that can be helpful in later attempts to arrive at long-range forecasting skills.

The great strides made in statistical analysis, the development of systems analysis, the introduction of digital and analog electronic computers, the first large-scale accumulations of data on conditions in the upper atmosphere, and other aspects of research have given us a far more sophisticated understanding than ever before of the enormous complexities that characterize the physical circulation and energy exchanges in the atmosphere up to 200 miles or more above the earth's surface.

Nevertheless, a large expanse of ground still must be covered before we will have a truly solid foundation for long-range forecasting. It is not likely to be a development of the immediate future, and the time of its realization undoubtedly will correspond to the intensity of effort in fundamental meteorological research and observation in the future.

The meteorologists most familiar with these problems feel that it will be possible to attain some skill in long-range forecasts within 10 or 20 years, assuming an adequate level of support for research toward these ends.

At the same time, there will be doubt about our capacity to make long-range forecasts until there is a much more accurate knowledge of the timing, location, and the sequential pattern of energy receipts and emission by the atmosphere in all of its layers from and to outer space. Even with the striking penetration provided by satellites, this is one problem that may well require many years of attention for a full clarification.

The unusual directions that significant research can take has been illustrated in a conclusion of E. G. Bowen of Australia. Several years ago he observed that rainfall patterns throughout the world tended to show peaks on certain days. He concluded that only extraterrestrial influences could account for them and that a possible relationship exists between the rainfall peaks and meteor showers encountered by the earth in its orbit, the dust of which could act as nuclei of condensation for rain.

Dr. Bowen found a close correlation between meteor showers of November and December and rainfall peaks in December to February, with a consistent lapse of about 30 days between the meteor showers and the rainiest days. His hypothesis is not generally accepted yet, but the importance of extraterrestrial influence on the course of meteorological events on the earth certainly is recognized, particularly in the flow of energy from the sun.

Even the orbital relations of planets may influence this flow. J. H. Nelson, of Radio Corp. of America, has calculated that the planetary configuration has a striking correlation with magnetic disturbances observed on the earth.

MEN FOR A LONG time have been intrigued by the possibilities of doing something about the weather, even if they could not predict it.

Although we again operate with far greater knowledge than at any time in the past, we still are seeking to do something about the weather, particularly to bring rainfall where and when we think it would not occur naturally.

Some years ago we thought that we had a startling new development and a valuable insight into the problem of creating rainfall artificially.

The modern version of doing something about the weather commenced with the cloud-seeding experiments of Irving Langmuir and Vincent Schaefer in the 1920's. After that time, cloud seeding waxed for some years, and a number of commercial ventures flourished in the 1950's. For a while, on the basis of statistical observations, it was thought that the benefits of seeding were definite. Since this was the cheapest possible manner of producing water, interest in cloud seeding in every water-deficient area soon appeared in many parts of the world.

The optimism about creating rainfall by cloud seeding with dry ice or silver iodide has changed since. No longer is it considered immediately possible to bring about statistically significant increases in precipitation by means of cloud seeding. Evidence pointing in this direction has accumulated from two sources: Research on the physics of clouds and the natural processes within them which produce moisture, and careful experiments to measure the effects of cloud-seeding operations.

Research on the physics of clouds suggests that the clouds that might be considered especially favorable for treatment by seeding either are infrequent or have within them such small amounts of water that significant quantities of rain could not be obtained from them.

It seems that the largest movements of the atmosphere, particularly those of rising currents of moist air, far overshadow the influence of condensation nuclei in the creation of rainfall.

These conclusions from a study of cloud physics were borne out by a 4-year series of experiments supported by the Federal Government and conducted at the University of Arizona. L. J. Battan and A. R. Kassander, employing a high-density network of rain gages, could find no statistically significant increases in rainfall from the seeding operations they measured.

Theoretically, however, some students of the atmosphere still consider effects of cloud seeding to be capable of increasing rainfall, potentially as much as 10 percent, compared to that expectable from unseeded clouds. The experiments at the University of Arizona, however, suggest that several decades of experiments might be necessary in order to measure such effects and provide conclusive proof.

That does not mean that we should abandon hope for artificial precipitation in the future. But it does mean a new appreciation of the complexity and physical nature of the processes of precipitation. The conclusions point toward increased needs for research to chart fully all these processes before science can indicate dependable means of artificial precipitation.

That is why the establishment and future operation of the National Center for Atmospheric Research in Colorado is a good long-range investment for the Nation.

SPECULATION about the alteration of weather effects on a larger scale, far from having been subdued by the doubts cast on cloud seeding for local effects, actually has increased in recent years.

An intriguing possibility lies in the possible manipulation of the tremendous energies and the vast amounts of water found in the hurricanes that visit the Eastern States in late summer and early autumn.

The late Harry Wexler of the United States Weather Bureau noted that one hurricane in 1961 precipitated enough fresh water to supply the entire needs of the United States for more than 2 months, and that the energy of its winds alone, properly harnessed, could provide the electrical energy used in the entire United States for half a year. These great storms have been seeded experimentally, and interesting effects have been observed.

In another direction, one of the world's most renowned meteorologists, Tor Bergeron, of Sweden, has hypothesized that it may be possible to extend geographically rainfall effects of a monsoon, like that found in western Africa, by enriching with moisture the airmass that moves from the sea into the continent. If costs of artificial energy are low enough, as might be supplied by future nuclear sources, sea-water-evaporation factories may be able to alter the climatology and therefore the economy of the southern Sahara.

Still other imaginative suggestions on a grand scale have been made in the past, such as Dr. Wexler's for covering parts of the polar icecaps with a dark-colored dust, like that from coal. Striking changes in the general circulation of the atmosphere theoretically could follow.

Again, these suggestions must be carefully kept in mind as speculations with enough possibility to give excellent reasons for continued, and perhaps doubled and redoubled, efforts to help us understand the mechanics of the atmosphere.

If we do learn enough eventually through research to seek key points of control in some of the large-scale precipitation-producing processes, the stakes are enormous and of the highest international concern.

Over the long range, therefore, study of the atmosphere is probably the most important field of investigation that affects water supply in the world as a whole. At the same time one can see for the immediate future only relatively small practical returns from such research. Contrary to the expectations of a few years ago, returns in the form of capacity to forecast may appear before those of ability to control weather, but both still are long range.

THE VAST SUPPLY of water in lands adjacent to the oceans has been a tantalizing subject for technological investigation.

It has long been known that fresh water could be produced through the application of heat to salt water and consequent distillation of fresh water, but only within relatively recent years have distillation processes been perfected (particularly in what is known as multiple-effect evaporation), so that salt water could be the raw material for fresh, even in areas that could stand high costs of water. Such plants are in operation almost universally on shipboard and in some desert localities with adequate energy supplies and high water requirements, as in the petroleum-refining areas of Aruba in the West Indies and Kuwait and other places on the Persian Gulf.

The costs of such water, however, are high, even in the most efficient plants. The most recent commercial plants are said to produce water from the sea at costs between 1.25 and 2 dollars per 1,000 gallons—15 to 25 times or more than the cost of irrigation water from a typical water supply in the Western States.

The commercial water distillation plants of any substantial size today employ fossil fuels. Because of their cost, the idea of solar distillation has been attractive, but the investment costs of solar stills has remained high in relation to capacity for water production.

Although such investment costs undoubtedly will be reduced, as is shown by experimentation at the University of Arizona, they appear to be promising only in places where high water costs can be borne. One advantage they have over the fossil-fueled distillation plants is that units of relatively small productive capacity may be as practical as large units and may therefore be the answer for small communities with no other source of water.

Desalinization is of substantial potential interest because of the massive bodies of ocean water that beckon for exploitation and because there are lesser but still great volumes of brackish water contained in the aquifers underlying many arid and semiarid lands, including those of the western part of the United States and Saharan Africa.

Applied research thus has been directed toward the development of still other types of processes that may reduce the salt content of these less salty but still undesirable or unusable waters.

Among those that have been experimented with by the Office of Saline Water in the Department of the Interior and by private corporations are straight freezing processes; refrigeration processes using a hydrate; a process (electrodialysis) that employs a thin membrane of hydrated organic polymers, which permit the passage of salts in solution but not water; and another process, known as ultrafiltration, in which water, but not the salt, passes through another type of thin membrane under pressure.

Of these, electrodialysis now is used commercially, but again mainly in small plants in areas or for uses that can support water production at high cost. This process appears to have its widest application where the amelioration of brackish water is desired.

I must stress that all these processes, even if they are perfected beyond their present state, would appear to reach floors in their costs at levels that still represent high-cost water, perhaps as low as four and as much as eight times typical western irrigation water costs.

By contrast, Professor Thomas K. Sherwood, of the Massachusetts Institute of Technology, has speculated that the minimum possible work energy required to separate a given volume of fresh water from sea water is only about one-half the costs of the irrigation water I mentioned. Thus there appears still to be a wide field for research, for it is the really cheap water that will be the important water in the end.

A conference sponsored by the National Academy of Sciences in 1961 emphatically described the need for more fundamental research on the physical and chemical nature of water, its performance as an electrolyte, the thermodynamic properties of sea water at high temperatures, the effect of magnetic and electrical fields on it, the performance of salt water in the presence of osmotic membranes, and a variety of other questions.

It would appear that even biology has a relevant and basic contribution to make in describing the structure of the natural membranes employed by plants and animals to control salt absorption.

Once more it would seem that we are

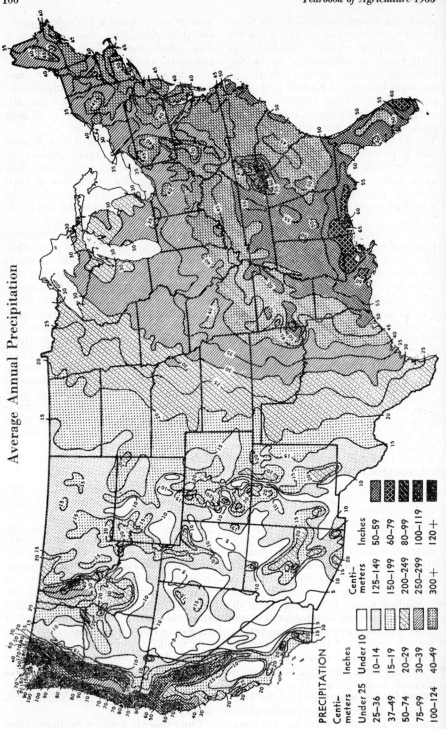

Average Annual Precipitation

PRECIPITATION

Centi-meters	Inches
Under 25	Under 10
25–36	10–14
37–49	15–19
50–74	20–29
75–99	30–39
100–124	40–49
125–149	50–59
150–199	60–79
200–249	80–99
250–299	100–119
300+	120+

closer to the beginning of an understanding, as we are in the case of the atmosphere, than to a comprehensive, powerful grasp of the fundamentals that always goes before the best engineering.

IF THE OUTLOOK for our abilities to manipulate the water supply on a grand scale is speculative and decidedly long range, the importance of effectively managing the waters as we find them on the earth's surface is redoubled. Research in this direction also is being pursued and has yielded valuable dividends.

The approaches to the efficient management of naturally occurring water supplies are many. All have been the subject of research investigations.

As illustrations, I describe work affecting the discovery, development, and management of ground water and that affecting the collection, regulation, and conservation of surface water. The problems of ground water development, in a general way, are that of discovery, because all ground water in greater or lesser degree lies concealed beneath the surface of the soil, sometimes at substantial depth; the construction of efficient wells and lifting devices to bring the water to the surface; and the management of the supply so as to produce sustained dependable yield.

Discovery and appraisal of the quantity, quality, and sustained-yield capacity of aquifers has been aided by the use of radioisotopes, electronic computers, geophysical equipment, and aerial photographs.

All those devices were developed primarily for other uses. Geophysical equipment, for example, like that depending on microseismic wave interpretation, has been used a number of years in the petroleum industry. More recently its applicability to the exploration for ground water has been exploited.

These techniques have made it possible to get a general bearing on the location of subsurface supplies far more cheaply than the older trial-and-error methods of sinking experimental wells.

Modern drilling techniques, again developed primarily for petroleum exploitation, permit the sinking of wells through all types of rock strata. Proved "well-logging" techniques can furnish information on rock type and the permeability, porosity, and salinity of water encountered from level to level in the well.

The use of harmless radioactive tracers, principally tritium, permits the collection of information on flow and storage underground with a degree of accuracy never before possible. This technique enables us to determine even the age of water newly tapped underground.

The processing of data with the aid of electronic computers can give a composite picture of the conditions in an aquifer or within the aquifers of a region, so that an effective and dependable sustained-yield plan for withdrawal can be constructed as never before.

Mechanical engineering has devised some new pumps, like the submersible pumps, which permit the lifting of water from depths at costs never before possible. Pump technology, of course, has a great variety of applications in modern industry.

This does not mean that research specifically undertaken for the purpose of understanding the nature and location of ground waters has not been extremely valuable. Indeed, the use of the new devices that have accelerated our acquisition of knowledge and capacity to develop ground water have been used against a base of hydrologic information, which gradually through the years has been acquired by public agencies, especially the Geological Survey.

The water resources agencies of a few of the States, like Illinois and California, also have been effective contributors to this hydrologic knowledge.

Perhaps the greatest need for research on future ground water development lies in much more hydrologic investigation. This would include more field observation of the actual conditions of underground storage and flow to supplement and test the theories of ground water movement that have been developed.

As man changes his environment, it becomes particularly important to understand the effect of the changes on the underground water on which he depends. There is, for example, now a sensitive modern laboratory technique of simulated ground water systems, an analog model, which is based on an analogy between hydraulic and electric fields.

Field studies to make use of the techniques we have but continued thought on hydrologic problems and further laboratory experiments, like those of H. E. Skibitzke and other men of the Geological Survey, may be expected to yield further dividends.

Hydrology has been a scientific stepchild until recently. Encouraging signs of support have appeared at last. Numbers of additional hydrologists need to be trained before the proper balance of attention in this subject will be achieved. The importance of a more complete understanding of ground water hydrology is underlined by the cheapness of storing water underground. Where adequate storage can be found, it can add substantially to the regulation and conservation of a local or regional water supply.

OUR CAPACITY to control or to regulate and conserve surface water also has attracted noteworthy research effort. Much of it has been associated with publicly recognized needs for developing the waters of the great river systems or controlling their propensities to damage or destroy while we build in their valleys.

Much has been learned about the art of managing a system of reservoirs on large streams, like the Tennessee or the Columbia, through the design studies of constructing and operating agencies like the Tennessee Valley Authority and the Corps of Engineers.

Surface water is much more complicated in development than ground water because of its multiple uses, including the generation of electric power, navigation, recreation, waste disposal, domestic and industrial use, and irrigation. Design for development therefore includes considerations of physical engineering and economic and political questions.

A rational development must seek the most efficient combination of uses, where multiple purposes are possible. Even if the uses are as few as three, the problem of design is not simple, particularly if an attempt must be made to take account of conditions that may arise in the future.

Regulation of natural water supplies is one of the longest lived of man's economic activities. Sections of the aqueducts built by the Romans almost 2,000 years ago are still in use. Most major facilities now should be considered in lifespans of at least 50 and possibly 100 years at least. Assessment of proper long-range, multiple-purpose development therefore demands sophisticated techniques, which can take care of a number of variables over time.

Not so many years ago, and to some extent even today, these problems had to be taken care of by "cut-and-try" and other ways of exercising individual professional engineering judgment. Research undertaken since 1954, however, applies a rigorous economic analysis to the problems of stream development as well as conventional engineering analysis and has pointed the way toward the future planning of surface water development.

This research, which probably was first explored in detail by R. N. McKean at the Rand Corp., views stream development as essentially a problem in systems analysis, subject to much more exact statistical analysis than heretofore had been used.

Further studies, using electronic computer calculation, were made at Harvard University, with the assistance of the Rockefeller Foundation. Resources for the Future, Inc., of Washington, D.C., has contributed some notable studies, which suggest economic criteria for evaluating alternative designs of multiple-purpose integrated surface water systems.

Thus, in a sense water system design has become a subject accessible to the techniques of operations research, the amazingly successful methods that mathematicians, physicists, and engineers developed for coping with some of the problems of wartime organization and logistics. The development of special methods to be applied to water development, however, may be considered to be only at its beginning.

Much more intensive research along these lines and the evolution of a true systems approach to water development may be expected. These techniques will have increased significance as the Nation and the continent realize the possibilities inherent in our great natural stream systems and in integrating a basin, like that of the Mississippi, or combining a number of basins, like those from northern Canada south into the dry Great Basin, for the best pattern of development.

IF WE MAY EXPECT our water development system to be more complex and if we must continue to depend for some years on taking water as it occurs naturally, the detailed understanding of surface water hydrology becomes no less important than that of ground water hydrology. For the most effective planning and development, a detailed knowledge of the geographical and temporal patterns of precipitation and runoff is necessary.

Even though the United States has one of the better networks in the world for measuring precipitation and runoff, it has been far from capable of supplying a full picture of these patterns.

A number of new tools, which extend our capacity for observing and understanding the occurrence of water in the natural environment of the earth, have been made since 1950.

The use of special radar equipment has enabled the measurement of storm precipitation patterns with a speed and geographical coverage heretofore financially impossible. Radar measurements are applicable even in the most difficult mountainous terrain.

Significant advances also have been made in equipment for measuring stream stages and other aspects of runoff. The basic principle of the improvements is the mechanizing of the entire operation, with instruments like the digital recorder. The invention of some devices, like the bubble gage, however, have reduced the capital investment required for obtaining records, as well as increased their sensitivity. New techniques of measuring the velocity of flowing water, for example, are being studied, with view toward detailed velocity measurements from the electromagnetic effect of flowing water.

Another device, employing the Doppler effect, may be especially valuable in measuring very slow velocities.

The techniques of modern statistics also have been applied to the problems of measuring streamflow with some success. With their aid, "synthetic hydrology" can be constructed. It gives a better picture of runoff or flow patterns and probabilities over a period of years than otherwise would be available and solves partly our inability to forecast long-term variations.

Studies of comparative hydrology also have commenced to help us see what generalizations apply to streams of a given type or types the world over. All these techniques will assist in providing a more complete understanding of the availability of water in its variations from locality to locality and year to year.

The problems of adequate measurement are becoming more complex, even as methods for treating them are improved. As more and more purposes must be served by surface water supplies, hydrologic observation must yield data specific for each of these purposes. Furthermore, development of streams usually causes changes in stream characteristics.

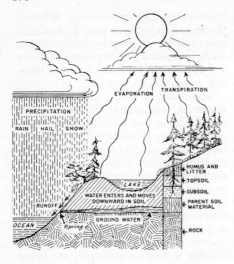

Design of networks for collecting data in the field therefore is difficult and cannot yet be considered completely in the United States. Despite the strides that automation and the application of mathematical analysis have made possible, a great deal of further research and data collection in hydrology must be undertaken before the surface waters of the United States will be understood as well as they should be for the most economical and useful development.

THE EVENTUAL practical reason for hydrologic study is the regulation of streams so as to store water from times of precipitation surpluses (by day, season, or year) for availability during periods of lesser receipts. Another way of expressing this is to describe it as the prevention of the wastage of runoff into the sea when there exists beneficial uses for the water on land. Regulation in this sense is a form of conservation.

There are still other approaches to conservation, which take account of the fact that water may be "wasted" through evaporation into the atmosphere or may be transpired into the air through economically unusable vegetation.

Thus, for a number of years, re-search and experiment have been directed toward elimination of the salt cedars which may be found near water courses or reservoirs in the Southwest. These almost valueless trees transpire an amazing amount of moisture. Their elimination would save substantial quantities of water for beneficial use. The only problem, therefore, has been the development of economical methods of eradication, assuring that the water released from transpiration was indeed cheaply produced water.

Eradication programs have proceeded in parts of the Southwest following earlier experiments, but repetition of cutting appears necessary, and operations still are expensive. Thomas Maddock, of the Geological Survey, has observed, "It is simpler to keep water away from salt cedars than to keep salt cedars away from the water."

From the lessons learned in the observation on salt cedars, it was only a step to question the effects of transpiration from other types of unneeded vegetation and from some economically useful vegetation in localities where water production has high priority. Experiments, in fact, have been conducted for many years on different types of vegetational management by the Forest Service at Coweeta, N.C., and elsewhere, by the Soil Conservation Service on many watersheds of different sizes throughout the country, and the Tennessee Valley Authority on its Parker Branch and several other watershed projects. These experiments and observations have given much information on the responses of runoff to different ways of managing vegetational cover.

In more recent years, experiments in the arid West—where the augmenting of runoff is most valuable—have been of increasing interest. The oldest of the experiments of the Forest Service concerned tree spacing in upper watersheds to increase snow cover and the water yield therefrom during the melting season. Experiment and observation has been extended to the plant cover in dry watersheds of relatively sparse vegetational cover. Several Federal agencies, including Department of Agriculture agencies and the Geological Survey, are cooperating with the State of Arizona on a longer term, more careful experiment on vegetational management for increasing water yields.

It is now generally conceded that the application of proper management, based on scientific observations, can improve water quality and reduce sediment production from some watersheds. It also may affect water supply by dampening the extreme ranges of flow. No general formula seems to be applicable everywhere, however. Each watershed is likely to be a special situation. We know that thinning dense coniferous stands on northern slopes will allow more snow to accumulate in areas of heavy snowfall, with subsequent increases in streamflow. We also know that on soils of adequate depth the replacement of deep-rooted vegetation by shallow-rooted plants will increase streamflow, if there is enough precipitation to infiltrate the soil. Further experimentation has been started to see if still other principles of management can be detected.

AN INTERESTING VARIANT on vegetational management has been experimented with and proposed for pilot use by the Esso Research & Engineering Co. of Linden, N.J. This company proposes to pave all or parts of small watersheds with a specially developed asphalt compound, nearly eliminating infiltration in the paved areas and substantially reducing evaporation because of the rapidity of flow to storage reservoirs. There is promise water may be produced, or conserved, quite cheaply by this method where esthetic considerations or other uses for vegetation would permit such a watershed treatment.

Other experiments using the same principle have been conducted by the United States Water Conservation Laboratory at Tempe, Ariz. These experiments made use of chemicals to stabilize and waterproof soil surfaces for the purpose of increasing runoff. Such treatment appears to be especially applicable to the conserving of runoff in small areas to improve stock water supplies.

SUBSTANTIAL AMOUNTS of water are lost into the atmosphere from all standing or flowing water surfaces. Lake Mead, in Arizona, for example, is estimated to lose through evaporation each year more water than the individual storage capacity of most reservoirs in the United States. Evaporation in the 17 Western States from open water surfaces may be somewhere between 6 million and 10 million acre-feet a year. Some estimates have placed it even higher.

Experiments with the reduction of evaporation losses from surfaces therefore have been an attractive target for applied research. Nearly all such research has centered on two alcohols, hexadecanol and octadecanol, which can form monomolecular films on the surface of water. They at least partly meet the requirements of such a film from physical and biological points of view. These requirements are exacting, for the film must be able to retard the movement of water vapor from the water surface, but it must not restrict the free movement of oxygen, carbon dioxide, and other gases through the water surface. It must be nontoxic to life. It must resist the action of wind, dust, or physical disturbance by boats. It must be able to restore itself after a disturbance. The evaporation-suppressing capacities of hexadecanol were known in England as early as 1925, but research in this country was not started until 1943, when Drs. Langmuir and Schaefer became interested in the problem.

Since that time, a number of field experiments on the reduction of evaporation through the use of these compounds have been conducted in the United States and in Australia.

Field results generally have been good on small bodies of water. Lake

Hefner, a reservoir near Oklahoma City, showed a reduction of 9 percent in evaporation through the maintenance of a hexadecanol film. Other tests in California, Arizona, and elsewhere indicate possible reductions of 10 to 30 percent. The use of these films for larger reservoirs has not yet been as successful, however, and it has not been possible to maintain the films under high windspeeds, particularly with shelving reservoir shorelines.

The results thus far indicate no possible danger from toxicity, but a number of problems of application and maintenance must be solved if these techniques become economically feasible on large surfaces. Until they are, they cannot be expected to contribute, in the West or elsewhere, any substantial amount to the conservation of the water that now disappears into the atmosphere by evaporation from open water surfaces.

At this time, the use of underground reservoirs appears to be much more practical than dependence upon the monomolecular films.

ANOTHER ENTICING avenue for conservation of water is the reduction of transpiration by crop plants.

For many years plant physiologists have suspected that most plants transpire much more water into the atmosphere than is necessary for their physiological functions and growth and maturation. In theory it should be possible to use chemicals to control the opening and closing of stomata, or otherwise influence plant respiration in a manner that would reduce transpiration and at the same time leave growth unaffected.

Should successful methods be devised, the water savings (and therefore the potential effectiveness of water used both as soil moisture and applied irrigation water) could support a much greater crop production. Comparatively little research has been directed toward this end, however, partly because plant physiology itself is still imperfectly understood, and the

process of photosynthesis is still not fully explained.

Two points are clear from this illustration: First, the close connection between fundamental research and the horizon open for applied results; and, second, the close connection between measures which control water demand and the amounts of water available as supply. If water is saved from crop growth, while production remains the same, more water is available for other uses or other areas.

ANY CAREFUL review of research on the water supply in the United States must conclude that the substantial expenditures of money and effort in these directions we have made could be profitably extended or expanded. The scientific horizon is such that the outlines can be seen of a potentiality having very high promise.

We can be reasonably certain that if the technology of the Nation continues to be as vigorous and comprehensive as it now is, the benefits that will be forthcoming as the years go on can be applied effectively and profitably to improvement in the water supply. This is precisely what has happened in the past, and a significant proportion of the advances which have been made toward improved water supply have resulted from these windfalls from other fields.

Conscious public effort to support and promote both fundamental and applied research related to water in all of its aspects, however, can undoubtedly hasten the day when the results from research become economically meaningful. The Nation probably could go on increasing the relatively tiny share of its gross national product that goes into fields related to water supply for a long time before it reached the point of diminishing returns.

I have described some of the needs in my statements about the different aspects of the water supply. There are others.

They include such subjects as the measurement of the dynamics of water at all the microscopic sites as it moves in the soil-water-plant system; the physics of evaporation from soil surfaces; the physics of infiltration and the mechanics of liquid and gaseous flow in and from the soil profile; the study of chemicals that can beneficially alter infiltration, control transpiration, and improve use of moisture; the differential rates of evaporation by different species of plants, or by intraspecific races; the relations of aquifers and streamflow; the influence of the use of agricultural machinery on infiltration; the study of erosion mechanisms and the "sedimentation continuum"; the most efficient overall design of irrigation systems; the physical and chemical factors affecting water quality; and analytical devices for tracing the hydrologic and other effects of alternative patterns of water use within localities and stream basins.

IN SUM, if there is any lesson to be learned from the history of research in this and in many other problems of physical and biological science, it is that the most practical things of tomorrow have a habit of developing from the obscure, "impractical," and esoteric of today.

When I was a graduate student in Harvard University in the late thirties, a serious public seminar was given on "The Usefulness of Useless Research." The day probably long since has passed when such a public justification of research is necessary. Indeed, in some fields, as in public health, the problem instead has been that of finding competent research workers to make use of the funds which are publicly pressed in their direction.

At the same time, there are other fields in which expanded support and effort appear to be eminently capable of producing a long-term social profit. The fields that concern an understanding of the water supply appear to be among them.

EDWARD A. ACKERMAN *is Executive Officer, Carnegie Institution of Washington,*

a foundation that operates research laboratories in the physical and biological sciences. Previously he was Director, Water Resources Program, Resources for the Future, Inc.; Assistant General Manager, Tennessee Valley Authority; Chief, Resources and Civil Works Branch, Bureau of the Budget; and professor of geography, the University of Chicago. Dr. Ackerman also has been consultant to a number of Federal and State Government agencies concerned with the development of water resources.

For further reading:

Barron, E. G., "New Instruments of the Surface Water Branch, U.S. Geological Survey." *Proceedings, Western Snow Conference,* 28th Annual Meeting, Santa Fe, N. Mex., 1960.

Ferris, John G., and Sayre, A. Nelson, "The Quantitative Approach to Ground-Water Investigations." *Economic Geology,* 50th Anniversary Volume, 1955.

Garstka, Walter U., "Reservoir Evaporation and Its Reduction." *Proceedings, Western Snow Conference,* 28th Annual Meeting, Santa Fe, N. Mex., 1960.

Hicks, Tyler Gregory, *Pump Selection and Application,* First Edition. McGraw-Hill Book Co., Inc., New York, 1957.

Jones, P. H., and Skibitzke, H. E., "Subsurface Geophysical Methods in Ground-Water Hydrology." *Advances in Geophysics,* Vol. 3, The Academic Press, Inc., New York, 1956.

Krutilla, John V., *Sequence and Timing in River Basin Development.* Resources for the Future, Inc., Washington, D.C., 1960.

Langbein, Walter B., and Hoyt, William G., *Water Facts for the Nation's Future.* The Ronald Press Co., New York, 1959.

Large-Scale Ground-Water Development. United Nations Water Resources Centre, New York, 1960.

Maass, Arthur, and others, *Design of Water-Resource Systems.* Harvard University Press, Cambridge, 1962.

National Academy of Sciences-National Research Council, *Desalination Research and the Water Problem.* Publication 941, Washington, D.C., 1962.

Skibitzke, H. E., "Electronic Computers as an Aid to the Analysis of Hydrologic Problems." *International Association of Scientific Hydrology—General Assembly of Helsinki,* Publication 52, 1960.

Smith, D. B., "Ground Water Tracing." *The South African Mining & Engineering Journal,* (Oct. 6, 1961).

Todd, David K., *Ground Water Hydrology.* John Wiley & Sons, Inc., New York, 1959.

U.S. Department of the Interior, *Water-Loss Investigations: Lake Hefner 1958 Evaporation Reduction Investigations.* Bureau of Reclamation, Denver, 1958.

J. DEAN JANSMA AND DALE O. ANDERSON

WATER IS ALWAYS
A CRITICAL FACTOR

A CARDINAL precept in archeological exploration is that communities were built where there was an ample supply of good water. The axiom is relevant also in planning for the development of a modern community. The importance of water to human existence is obvious. The same degree of importance, however, can be attached to food, oxygen, and other necessities. Thus the question: Why does water require special attention in community development?

One item is the amount of water we use. The average American citizen uses about 1,500 tons of fresh water each year but only 18 tons of all other materials necessary for his existence.

Another consideration is that water usually is considered a common property under the law. A farmer or businessman generally can plan the use of his land, labor, and capital as he desires, but the rights of other property owners must be considered in using water from rivers, streams, and underground aquifers.

The amount an individual property owner will invest in the development of water resources therefore is limited.

Before development will occur, the benefits must exceed costs for each property owner, or a system of assessing other beneficiaries must be devised. The "common-property" characteristic accentuates the social and legal (as well as the economic) aspects of the development.

Water is basically a flow resource rather than a stock resource.

A characteristic of a flow resource is that its supply is replenished periodically over time. For example, the water supply of an area is replenished by rain and snow at a fairly consistent rate.

The supply of a stock resource is limited and nonrenewable. For example, the amount of coal mined each year causes the total supply to diminish. The problems involved in allocating the supply of coal are somewhat simpler than that of water, because one needs to determine only the rate at which it will be used until the total supply is exhausted.

Another characteristic of water is

108

that a given quantity can be reused for several purposes: It can be used to generate hydroelectric power, then enter the public water supply, and finally be used for irrigation.

Such reuse may suggest that a given amount of water could be used indefinitely. The practical difficulty, though—aside from the problem of evaporation—is that the discharged water seldom has the same quality as when it was diverted. In most uses, some degree of pollution occurs that lowers its desirability to the subsequent user.

These characteristics of water indicate some reasons why water requires special attention in the development of a community.

We emphasize, however, that water is only one of a community's resources, and it should be developed within a whole-community framework. A well-developed water supply is of little value if it is not supported by the other resources needed in a dynamic community. In this chapter, we suggest a recipe—in which water is one of the primary ingredients—that may be used in planning a program to develop the resources of a community.

RESOURCES employed in an area are scarce relative to the demand for them.

Rules of proper allocation thus are necessary for placing the scarce resources into the best alternative employments.

Economic efficiency, the basic theory of allocation of resources in a competitive economy, suggests a method for making the allocation. Employing resources consistent with economic efficiency implies that resources are employed in such a manner that the community's output (and thus the net national product) is maximized. An allocation that provides for the greatest economic efficiency is defined as the correct allocation.

To illustrate the procedure, we consider a simple community (even simpler than the one in which Robinson Crusoe lived), in which water is the only scarce resource and can be used only for drinking or bathing.

The problem is to allocate the water between drinking and bathing in a way that makes the greatest contribution toward satisfying the wants of the members of the community. The allocation occurs when the value of an additional gallon of water for drinking is equal to the value of an additional gallon of water for bathing. When this condition exists and the entire amount of water is used, the water resources are allocated correctly and return the maximum satisfaction to the people.

Conversely, an incorrect allocation of water exists if the value of the additional unit of water is greater in one use than in the other. For example, if the value of the additional water used for drinking is greater than for bathing, the satisfaction from the use of water can be increased by reallocating more water for drinking—that is, the loss in satisfaction by using less water for bathing is more than compensated for by the gain in satisfaction from having additional drinking water.

The example illustrates a basic principle of economics—the principle of resource allocation. The same idea is involved when there are many resources that can be used in many alternative employments. This principle we use as the basis for analyzing the various possibilities the community faces when it develops water resources.

The problems of planners in community development are much more complex than those in our example. A plan for developing water resources must consider all possible uses of water, such as municipal, industrial, recreational, and others, as well as problems of flood control and pollution. All activities that are potential users (and polluters) of water must be analyzed carefully as to their overall effect on the community's well-being.

THE ECONOMIC criterion we suggest as a guide in planning a water project is known as the equimarginal-value-in-use principle, which can be broken down into value in use, marginal value in use, and equimarginal value in use.

Value in use refers to the maximum amount that a purchaser of water is willing to pay for a unit of water being used in a particular manner. For example, if a farmer is willing to pay 5 dollars an acre-inch for using water to produce alfalfa, the value of an acre-inch of water to the farm in the production of alfalfa is 5 dollars.

Marginal value in use refers to the increment added to total revenue by the employment of the last unit of water. If the total revenue from an acre of irrigated alfalfa increased from 50 dollars to 60 dollars by increasing the application of water from 19 to 20 acre-inches, the marginal value in use for this additional acre-inch of irrigation water applied to the alfalfa is 10 dollars.

Equimarginal value in use requires that the marginal value of all competing uses of water be equal—that is, the marginal value in use for industry is equal to marginal value in use for irrigation, which is equal to the marginal value in use for municipal water, and so forth.

Suppose there are two users of water in a community. One, a farmer, uses water for irrigation. The other, a manufacturing firm, uses large quantities of water for industrial cooling. Assume initially that each is using a given amount of water. The problem is to analyze the returns to water in the two uses and determine whether it is at the maximum potential or whether the community's output can be increased by reallocating water between them.

A comparison of returns to water of the two users may reveal that the marginal value in use to the manufacturer is 37 dollars and the marginal value in use to the farmer is only 8 dollars. Water in the two uses then is not being used at its maximum potential. The farmer is willing to pay only 8 dollars for the last acre-foot of water he uses, while the manufacturer would be willing to pay 37 dollars for an additional acre-foot. Evidently both users of water, as well as the community, can be made better off in an economic-efficiency sense by transferring water.

For example, suppose the farmer sells an acre-foot of water to the manufacturing firm for 10 dollars. The sale increases the manufacturer's net income by 27 dollars. The farmer's net income is raised by 2 dollars. The net income in the community is increased by 29 dollars. This transfer causes the marginal value of water to the farmer to increase, because his supply of water is decreased. Conversely, the manufacturer has more water at his disposal; thus the marginal value he places on water is lowered. After the initial transfer, the marginal value of water might be 15 dollars for the farmer and 30 dollars for the manufacturer. Both would still benefit from another transfer, but the gain would not be so large as it was for the first acre-foot.

This series of exchanges would continue (and be advantageous to both users) until the marginal value of water to the two businesses is equal.

OUR DISCUSSION so far assumes that a certain volume of water is available. The only problem is to allocate this supply among the community's potential users. This assumption probably will not be the situation in an area being planned for development. A likelier situation is that additional water could be made available by employing the necessary resources, at a cost, in a project to develop water resources. The question then is how large a project should be developed.

Our discussion of equimarginal value in use assumes a free exchange of water rights among all users and a market mechanism free to allocate water in a manner that equalizes the marginal value in use to all customers.

Now assume that the market price to all users has been established at 25 dollars an acre-foot for the existing available water. Assume also that the community can develop an additional water supply at a cost of 12 dollars an acre-foot. Since the value of an additional unit of water is 25 dollars but the cost of an additional unit is only 12 dollars, the community would be willing to develop this water project. From the viewpoint of economic efficiency, additional units of water should be developed as long as the value of an additional unit is greater than its cost.

This concept of equimarginal value in use provides a basic economic-efficiency model, which can be used as a guide for attaining an optimum level of development. Restated briefly, the principle requires that the cost of the last unit of water developed should be equal to the value of this additional water to the various users and that the marginal value of water to each user should be the same.

Strict adherence to the principle— although it expresses the ideal situation in terms of economic efficiency— usually is not possible at the practical level of resource development. Thus we shall consider several other factors that may force the planner to modify the general framework provided by the economic-efficiency model.

The distributional effects of a water project may be one reason for modifying our basic economic model. The efficiency criterion assumes, for example, that each dollar of net benefit from the project is of equal social value regardless of who receives it—that is, it assumes that a dollar of benefit to a millionaire is of the same value to the community as a dollar of benefit to the tenant farmer or the unskilled laborer. The progressive income tax, certain welfare programs, and such, however, suggest that society would not place an equal value on each dollar of benefits.

Strict reliance on the efficiency concept would require also that a project with only one beneficiary be chosen over a slightly less desirable project (measured in terms of net benefits), in which the benefits were diffused among all members of the community.

These distributional aspects often are highly important to a community, and they should be evaluated by the resource planner. The guidelines provided by economic theory, however, are less clear for this evaluation.

The basic problem is the lack of operational methods for measuring the satisfaction received (rather than net income received) by the various members of the community. Theoretical approaches have been suggested to deal with this situation, but they fail to provide an objective measurement. Thus some other method must be used to supplement the economic analysis.

We believe that a community's citizens, after being fully informed about the costs, benefits, and distributional effects of the alternatives available, are the best qualified to evaluate these distributional effects.

Institutional constraints also restrict the use of the criterion of economic efficiency as the only objective of resource development. These barriers, although subject to change, often possess rigidities for the planner.

A situation in which water rights cannot be transferred is an example of this type of constraint. For example, the efficiency criterion may indicate that water would be more profitable for industrial cooling than for irrigation. But if water rights are assigned to a particular parcel of irrigable land and would be void if not used on that land, the transfer of water to a more profitable use may not occur.

Other institutional constraints, whether imposed by law, or administrative policy, or interstate or international agreement, modify strict adherence to the objective of economic efficiency.

SECONDARY EFFECTS also should be considered. They arise mainly from two sources—the "stemming from" effects and the "induced by" effects.

The "stemming from" secondary effects accrue to the industries that supply goods and services. As a water resource project is developed in an area, the goods and services supplied to it will increase. The additional profits accruing to the various suppliers, which they would not have experienced without the project, is a secondary benefit of the project.

The "induced by" effects account for increases in profits of the industries that process, distribute, or consume the additional products of the project.

The intangible effects also restrict reliance on economic efficiency as the only guide for development.

Intangible effects in general are benefits or costs to society that cannot be measured in money, such as preservation of scenic or historic sites, strengthening of national security, improving public health, and so on. Once again, the decision on their importance should express the desires of the community. The Congress would be the appropriate agency for evaluating such effects if the project is built with funds from the National Treasury.

The criterion of economic efficiency, as modified by the factors we have considered, provides the basic framework in which the planner should work.

After becoming familiar with these economic tools, he is ready to tackle the important *what* and *when* problems of resource development.

WHAT COMES first? To answer the question, one must evaluate all phases of a community's present situation and its needs: Is the development of resources needed at all? Should the development consist of additional water, or should additional schools, streets, police protection, etc., be given a higher priority? What purposes should be included in each?

The alternatives in developing a project may range from a single-purpose recreation lake to a multiple-purpose project serving water supply, flood control, recreation, and power. Another question: Are the community's resources being used to the best advantage? Perhaps the needs that are to be met by developing additional resources can be achieved at a lower cost by reallocating present resources.

Assume, now, that a community has performed this soul-searching task and finds that resource development is the answer to its problem. The community then faces the question of which resources to develop.

We believe that the basic economic model we developed, modified to account for distributional effects, institutional restraints, and so on, would be an appropriate guide in deciding which types of projects should be developed and the purposes of each.

This model assumes, however, that all the benefits and costs take place within the community's boundaries, but that rarely happens. Financial assistance often is available from various public agencies and private groups. Similarly, all the beneficiaries may not be members of the community. The amount of financial assistance available and the distribution of the benefits also vary by the type and purpose of development.

From a strictly local viewpoint, a community would consider only the benefits and costs of individuals and organizations within its boundary. Thus, instead of attempting to realize the greatest benefit per dollar invested, the community's criterion may be to maximize the local benefits per dollar of local money invested. Which of these criteria to use will depend on whether the project is planned on the basis of a local community or a larger community, such as the State or the Nation.

In evaluating the *what* of resource development, the planner will encounter additional problems.

One relates to the relationship among various types of development. For example, a project that supplies additional water for a new industrial center may require additional sewage facilities to remove the industrial wastes. The new plants may also require additional roads, police protection, schools, and other public services.

Conversely, this relationship may permit the developed resources to be used for several purposes. The permanent pool of water stored in a flood-protection structure may provide a potential for recreational facilities at little extra cost.

The point we wish to stress is that development of resources does not take place in a vacuum. It is a dynamic force that affects many aspects of a community's economic life.

The relative abundance or shortage of the three primary resources—land, labor, and capital—varies considerably among communities. A good project in one community may be undesirable for another community. For example, a plan for a community with a high level of unemployment but a shortage of capital would probably be an undesirable plan for a community where the relative abundance of these resources was reversed.

THE SECOND step, the *when* of project development, is of equal importance.

The preliminary planning steps—an inventory of existing facilities, and the need for additional facilities—are now assumed to be complete. On the basis of the plan developed, a decision has been made to develop the community's water resources. It is now the responsibility of the planner to determine the order in which the phases of the project should be accomplished.

The basic economic model we propose is one criterion that could be used in ranking the various phases of the project in order of their importance. This approach would place the highest priority on the part of the project that has the highest return per dollar of resource investment. There are instances, however, when the criterion of economic efficiency must be modified to conform to the distributional and institutional restraints we discussed.

When planning the overall program, the planner should examine the resources available at any point in time and relate them to the size of the project the available resources will develop.

It often appears that projects are undertaken and construction is begun under the impression that the entire project will be completed. Thus, the order in which the various phases are developed is not considered. The re-

sult—a large project partly completed and of little benefit to the community. The appropriate alternative would be to limit the scope of the project. Then, as additional resources become available, other phases of the project could be developed.

In evaluating what particular phases of the project are most important, one must decide on the degree of development one phase of the project should reach before development of another phase is begun.

That leads to another important economic principle, which can be applied effectively to the employment of resources in a water development project. We refer to the opportunity-cost principle, which suggests that resources be employed in a particular use as long as the returns to the resource in that use is greater than its returns would be from any other use. When employment of resources in the first use reaches a point of intensity where returns in another use are greater than the first, employment of resources should be shifted to the second use.

The practical application of this principle will provide a guide to the optimum level of development, although it may be impractical to cease construction on one phase of the project at the precise level where its returns per dollar invested becomes less than the returns from another phase.

Another problem is the possibility of overbuilding a project. Overinvestment results in unused, wasted capacity and a relatively low rate of return on capital invested in that phase of the water project.

Investment in long-term water development projects indicates that a community places a higher value on returns at some future date than from the satisfaction received in the current use of these resources. That is, a community is willing to sacrifice the value of goods and services used in consumption for, say, a flood-prevention program, which may not provide benefits until some time in the future. Thus we are concerned with investments that provide income not only in one period, but as sequences over time.

Should the planner treat a dollar's income in a future period in the same manner as a dollar's income in the present period? If, for example, a dollar invested in flood protection provides 5 dollars this year, 7 dollars next year, and 4 dollars the following year, should these returns be added together and treated the same as a return of 16 dollars in the current year?

Problems like this introduce us to the concept of discounting future revenue. It permits one to discount revenue that will occur in the future back to the present time so they can be compared with an investment that returns benefits in the current year.

A general formula for discounting future income is the following:

$$PV = \frac{R}{(1+r)^t}$$

To compute the present value, *PV*, the future revenue, *R*, is divided by 1 plus the interest rate, *r*, raised to a power, *t*, which expresses the number of years when the income will occur.

For example, suppose we wish to know the present value of 100 dollars, which we will receive in 2 years, if the interest rate is 6 percent. Using the formula, we find:

$$PV = \frac{\$100}{(1+0.06)^2} = \frac{\$100}{(1.06)^2}$$

$$= \frac{\$100}{1.1236} = \$89$$

Thus, if the interest rate is 6 percent, the present value of 100 dollars received 2 years hence is 89 dollars. That is, 89 dollars presently invested at an interest rate of 6 percent will be worth 100 dollars in 2 years.

In order to reduce the arithmetic involved in making such calculations, tables in many appraisal and mathematics books show the present value of a dollar discounted at different interest rates and for alternative time periods. One need only multiply the present value indicated in the table by the number of dollars forthcoming in the future to complete the discounting process.

This principle can be used by a planner in deciding which of two alternative projects would yield greatest returns to the community's resources.

Let us suppose that the first alternative is to invest in one large flood-retarding structure with a capacity capable of providing adequate flood protection for 50 years. The cost of the project is 50 thousand dollars. The second alternative is to construct a smaller structure to provide protection for only 25 years. At the end of 25 years, a similar structure could be constructed to give the same protection for the remaining 25 years. The cost of each structure in the second alternative is 35 thousand dollars. The immediate conclusion is to invest in the first alternative, because it requires less total resources than the second. This conclusion may not be valid for determining the least-cost project. The comparison that should be made, from an economic point of view, is between the present investments in the two alternatives.

The present investment in the first alternative (the long-term project) is 50 thousand dollars. The present investment in the second alternative (two shorter term projects) is 35 thousand dollars, plus the present value of 35 thousand dollars discounted at 6 percent. Using the discounting procedure we outlined, we find that the present value (*PV*) of a return of 35 thousand dollars realized 25 years hence, discounted at a 6-percent rate of interest, is 8,155 dollars. That is, if the community presently invests 8,155 dollars at 6 percent, it will have available at the end of 25 years the 35 thousand dollars necessary to construct the second structure. Having determined the present value of 35 thousand dollars, we find the present investment in the second alternative is 35 thousand dollars, plus 8,155 dollars—a total of 43,155 dollars. Under such conditions, the second alternative is a less costly project to construct.

AN INTANGIBLE factor in a comparison of two or more projects is the flexibility each affords.

A flexible project is one that can be adjusted to meet the changing needs of the community. A short-term project is more flexible than a long-term project, as it is impossible to predict the future needs of the community.

A restriction that is not considered when comparing the present investment in the two alternatives is the physical feasibility of the alternatives. For example, the strategic site for a short-term structure may require that the second structure, 25 years later, be built in a less effective location or the cost of removing the first structure may be prohibitive. In that case, the alternative with the lower present investment may be impractical because of physical limitations.

Financing is a vital point. The simplest method would be to use public funds based on an ad valorem tax. It also would assess the indirect and the direct beneficiaries of the project. The disadvantage is that it tends to be an inequitable assessment unless the project benefits are widespread.

Assessing individual beneficiaries at a rate that will recover cost usually is considered a more equitable method. Several steps are involved. First the costs of a multiple-purpose project must be allocated to each project purpose. Then the beneficiaries must be defined. Finally, each of the beneficiaries is assigned a portion of the project costs. In practice, these calculations are necessarily only approximations, but they do represent a method that attempts to assign a larger share of the cost to the individuals who gain most.

Another way would be to assess on the basis of value of services received without regard to the cost of the project. Its advantage is that it requires no allocation of cost, but the difficulty (especially if the development is financed by private capital) is that the returns could be more or less than the cost of developing the project. The basis used for assessing within this framework usually is either the market value of service received (such as market value of power) or a computed value for services not normally available in the marketplace.

A third method is to allocate the cost on the basis of the beneficiary's ability to pay for the service.

ASSISTANCE from local, State, and Federal agencies is available and usually is necessary to apply successfully these economic concepts to the real problems of resource development.

Assistance on the technical problems of planning is available at the State and Federal levels. The Federal agencies include, among others, the Extension Service and Soil Conservation Service of the Department of Agriculture, the Public Health Service, the Bureau of Reclamation, and the Corps of Engineers.

The scientists at the State universities often can provide useful information on the technical problems encountered in planning and installing water projects. Others at the State level may include the State's department of agriculture, which often includes a water resources board, and the game and fish departments.

The lure of financial assistance should not affect the planner's dependence on basic economic principles, however. We believe a small, well-planned project is more desirable than a scheme that does not fit the needs and desires of the community.

J. DEAN JANSMA *is a graduate of Iowa State University. Since 1958 he has been employed by the Economic Research Service, Department of Agriculture, as an agricultural economist. His special field of interest is water resource development.*

DALE O. ANDERSON *joined the Department of Agriculture as an agricultural economist in the Economic Research Service. His special field is land and water economics. He is a graduate of North Dakota State University and in 1960–1961 was a graduate assistant in the Department of Agricultural Economics, Oklahoma State University.*

JAMES J. FLANNERY

WATER POLLUTION:
A PUBLIC CONCERN

WATER pollution became a major public concern in the United States in the late 19th century, when typhoid epidemics of great virulence appeared in various cities. The then new science of bacteriology identified many of them as caused by contaminated water supplies. Public outcry against pollution was great. Health officers met the challenge in two ways.

The first was to concede certain streams for waste disposal and to reserve other, protected streams for municipal supplies. This is the method followed by New York City and other communities fortunate enough to own or control adequate watersheds. It is satisfactory as long as the location of a community permits—that is, until waste from other cities or its own increasing demands for water call for more strenuous methods.

The other method was filtration and disinfection of water. Sanitary engineers perfected techniques that were effective and reasonable in cost. They permitted cities to have safe and reasonably palatable water even from such heavily polluted sources as the Missouri, the Mississippi, and the Ohio Rivers.

In a sense, the success of the two methods has had an adverse effect on the control of pollution in rivers and streams: It removed, at least for a time, one of the most pressing reasons for public action—to protect health.

Even in the 19th century, however, certain groups realized that water pollution was an economic and social evil for other than reasons of health. Sometimes their protests brought correction of a particularly unpleasant situation, but usually they failed. Pollution increased along river banks and shores throughout the United States; the uses of land near polluted waters were debased, as residences disappeared, industrial activities moved in, or the land was abandoned.

Particularly noticeable was the loss of recreational waters. Sportsmen complained that fish were among the more conspicuous victims of unchecked pollution. "Next in importance to public health," one sportsmen's group told Congress in 1900, "the preservation of the 'finney denizens' of these waters

116

demands the attention of your honorable body."

Public protests brought about some response in State legislatures, but not in the Congress. Some of the State laws prohibited the discharge of specifically defined wastes so as to protect fish. Usually the prohibitions referred to solid wastes, particularly sawdust.

Other State laws sought to protect municipal water supplies by prohibiting the discharge of any wastes into specifically named waterways that municipalities used as sources of water.

Nevertheless, the chief hope for correction until rather recent years lay in lawsuits under common law. Common law, as an aspect of riparian rights, requires that water shall not be diminished in quantity or quality by one user to the detriment of other users.

Legal redress under common or statutory law was often an unequal contest between a large manufacturing corporation and an individual farmer or other landowner. When complainants won their cases, awards were seldom large enough for satisfaction. Cease-and-desist orders rarely were issued. Sometimes the courts weighed what they conceived to be the contributions of the manufacturer to the community against the apparently lesser contributions of the complainant. A doctrine referred to as "reasonable use" developed from this rationale to the detriment of some legitimate users.

These weak legal restraints and a general public apathy during the early years of this century compounded the problem, while three factors were operating to increase the pollution load. They were a growing population, growing urbanization, and a growing and changing industry.

As big a difficulty as any was the lack of public knowledge as to the nature of pollution. It persists to some extent to this day.

THE EXTENT of pollution in a given body of water can be measured in part by the amount of organic wastes in the water (which in turn is measured by the water's biochemical oxygen demand). The amount of such organic wastes in all United States waters increased six times in the first six decades of this century.

Most organic wastes can be destroyed by biochemical action, either naturally in a free-flowing stream or in an artificially created environment in a municipal or industrial waste treatment plant.

Some pollutants cannot be removed or similarly degraded. Among them are minerals and acids from mining and industrial activities.

Still other pollutants are heat, radioactive substances, silt, and the synthetic organic chemicals, which have become prominent since the Second World War. They include such substances as pesticides, detergents, and petrochemical wastes. They are highly resistant to breakdown and are not removed by any of the ordinary methods of water treatment.

This range of materials and substances suggests this definition of water pollution: The presence in water of any substance that impairs any of its legitimate uses. The legitimate uses include water for public water supplies, recreation, agriculture and industry, the preservation of fish and wildlife, and esthetic purposes.

Another legitimate but paradoxical use of water is for waste disposal into various bodies of water, both surface and underground. This use arises from the need to dispose of water after its purpose has been fulfilled. Disposal also serves to maintain the volume or flow of water for other purposes.

Therefore the apparently legitimate use for waste disposal constitutes a contradiction to the common law and desirable practice, and consequently becomes, in a sense, illegitimate. The problem is one of adjustment, so that the conflict between disposal and the other purposes is controlled or eliminated.

Adjustment is essential because the increasing demand will soon far exceed the comparatively constant supply of water. Only by the reuse of water will the supply meet the increases in demand.

Reuse cannot occur if the water is degraded by pollution. Investment in pollution control therefore is of the utmost significance in coping with the national water situation.

The process of adjustment in pollution control has become known as management of water quality. The body of law, administrative organization, and procedures that compose the management process evolved in the past generation to its present state, supported by similar developments in science and technology.

The evolution of the management process can be traced to the realization that effective control of other aspects of the problem was not provided, despite diligent efforts toward identification and control of hazards to health.

Conservation and fish and game commissions—usually understaffed—were given jurisdictions over some aspects that did not pertain to health. This disjointed approach did not produce concerted action and was confined to a procedure of counterattack.

Then came full-time administrative agencies and general statutes to control pollution in several States. They permitted surveillance, study, corrective action, and a unified attack, because the agencies were controlled by committees composed of representatives of State agencies whose work was related to water. The staffs usually were established in the sanitary engineering division of the State health agency.

Despite these legal and administrative improvements and the assistance of the Public Health Service for particular studies, such as at the southern end of Lake Michigan and the Ohio River, however, progress remained slow, and antipollution forces demanded positive Federal action.

After about 20 years of consideration of various aspects of the pollution problem, the Congress passed the Oil Pollution Control Act of 1924. The act

established certain controls over the discharge of oil from ships in coastal waters. The administration of the act was placed with the Corps of Engineers.

THE CONGRESS in 1948 provided for general control of water pollution by passing the Water Pollution Control Act, to be administered by the Public Health Service.

The act recognized the primary responsibility of the States and provided for enforcement authority, technical assistance, comprehensive planning, and financial loans to municipalities for their construction of treatment plants. After a 3-year extension in 1953 of its original 5-year trial period, the act was made permanent in 1956.

During the first 5 years of the act, the Federal program provided financial assistance to more than 2,700 cities for the construction of sewage treatment plants, cleaned up more than 4 thousand miles of streams through Federal enforcement action, and laid the groundwork for a continuing research effort.

Despite these considerable gains, it was evident that the 1956 authority was not strong enough to cope with the problem. The President recognized this situation and in a message in 1961 urged the Congress to take note.

The Congress responded by amending the act in five important ways: By increasing Federal financial support for the construction of municipal waste treatment facilities; broadening and strengthening the Federal enforcement powers; emphasizing research, with particular attention to regional variations; increasing Federal support of State and interstate pollution control programs; and providing for water storage in Federal reservoirs for pollution control purposes.

The Federal pollution control program now has strong statutory support, both in legal powers and financial authorization. The attack on the problem proceeds on the four fronts of enforcement, financial assistance, research, and studies of river basins.

Enforcement is concerned with persistent situations that have not yielded to the conventional approach of education and persuasion. Correction often is obtained after an initial conference in the enforcement procedure.

Indeed, in only one instance, involving the pollution of the Missouri River at St. Joseph, Mo., had the enforcement procedure reached the Federal courts by the end of 1962. In that instance, further court action was deferred because a favorable referendum on a bond issue to build a sewage treatment plant was voted in April 1962. In other words, the process of enforcement, itself, produces corrective results short of the ultimate court test.

Several other cases involving interstate waters, such as the Androscoggin River in New Hampshire and Maine and the Holston in Virginia and Tennessee, were in the conference stage in 1962. Two intrastate cases, involving Puget Sound in Washington and the Detroit River in Michigan, were instituted at the request of the States.

Financial assistance is provided for State and interstate pollution control agencies to develop their programs as well as for municipalities to build sewage treatment plants.

Research expenditures on pollution control during the 1950's averaged less than 4 million dollars annually, including sums for research in universities and industry and by State and Federal Governments. The new Federal legislation authorized 5 million dollars a year, up to a total of 25 million dollars.

The objectives include maximum removal of pollutants from municipal sewage, improved techniques for determining effects of pollution on the uses of water, and the evaluation of reservoir functions for control of pollution in streams.

Research is conducted at the Public Health Service Sanitary Engineering Center in Cincinnati and on a contract and grant basis with universities and other institutions and technicians.

Seven new regional laboratories were provided for in the 1961 law to give scientists and engineers an opportunity to study regional problems, such as acid mine drainage in the Ohio River Basin. The sites of six of the laboratories were announced by February 1963—Corvallis, Oreg., to serve the Northwest; College, Alaska, near Fairbanks; Ada, Okla., to serve the Southwest; Athens, Ga., to serve the Southeast; Ann Arbor, Mich., to serve the Midwest, and the Boston area to serve the East. In addition, laboratories will be established at Kingston, R. I., for research on salt water and at Duluth, Minn., for research on fresh water.

The comprehensive basin studies are designed to develop programs of pollution control with State cooperation, based on the changing water needs of the next 50 years. These programs will establish the nature of the present and future needs for water and the measures necessary to meet them.

Comprehensive studies of the Great Lakes, the Columbia River Basin, the Ohio Basin, the Colorado Basin, Susquehanna-Chesapeake Bay, and the Delaware River were underway in 1962. Plans were made to begin studies in New England and the Southeast in 1963. The aim of the studies is to assure that control of pollution is based on foresight to avoid problems and the correction of past errors.

Despite the favorable prospects for control indicated by the strong status of legislation, finances, and activity, much remains to be done. Continuing surveillance is therefore necessary.

A nationwide backlog of 5,290 municipal sewage treatment needs existed in 1962. The number manifests the prevalence of pollution.

Another indication is the drainage of acid from abandoned coal mines in Ohio, Pennsylvania, and West Virginia, which seriously impairs the water quality of many miles of the Ohio River and its tributaries.

More than 400 notifications of pollution-caused fish kills were reported to the Public Health Service by State conservation and fish and game agencies in 1962—another indication of serious pollution and an obvious contradiction to the water needs of an expanding population and industry.

The pollution problems of the future will be particularly acute in the large metropolitan areas. Investment requirements in waste collection and treatment will be high because of the construction of trunk sewers, which collect and transmit sewage from large areas to central treatment and disposal points. For instance, an investment of more than 35 million dollars for a 25-mile trunk sewer is required in the Washington metropolitan area during the early sixties to assure that development associated with the Dulles Airport does not impair the water supply of the Capital.

A major problem associated with trunk sewers is the equitable distribution of their cost among the communities that may be involved. The timing of construction and financing and the creation of the necessary administrative organizations in areas undergoing rural-urban change present critical questions of justice, efficiency, and of management. Often interim technical and administrative arrangements must be utilized.

Land use and other forms of development can be controlled through the timing and location of sewage systems. The relationships of various land and water functions must be recognized to achieve coherent and workable results. Regional master plans for sewerage systems therefore must be developed in conjunction with other phases of community and regional planning. In this sense, the urban water service, especially in its supply and waste disposal functions, has become a key to the form and management of metropolitan areas.

The impact of the metropolitan and other urban centers, however, is not solely in land use or through sewerlines. The recreational demand on water areas is conspicuous among the other effects. Swimming areas and marinas for boats produce special problems of waste and disposal. The sanitary hazards they present threaten all uses of water. An effective and economical method of waste treatment for small boats is needed. An intensive study of all sanitary aspects of this problem was begun in 1962.

Drainage from agricultural, urban, and undeveloped land also presents problems. Siltation, street refuse, and, in some areas, salts and other minerals that reach the streams impair the quality of water. Technology, organizational arrangements, and managerial skills in planning and coordination are necessary to cope with such conditions.

Little cognizance has been so far accorded the extent to which the management of water functions in urban areas and their impact on transition zones may be used to control or shape development for definite objectives in the use of land and water. Pollution control programs are an integral and essential part of regional and river basin planning. Pollution that occurs in the urban areas affects long stretches of the streams and all water uses well beyond the urban boundaries. What is needed is a comprehensive attack.

JAMES J. FLANNERY *is Chief Economist, Division of Water Supply and Pollution Control, United States Public Health Service.*

For further reading:
Kneese, Allen V., *Water Pollution—Economic Aspects and Needs.* Resources for the Future, Inc., Washington, D.C., 1962.

U.S. Congress, Senate Select Committee on National Water Resources, *Future Water Requirements for Municipal Use.* Committee Print No. 7, Washington, D.C., 1960.

——— *Water Quality Management.* Committee Print No. 24, Washington, D.C., 1960.

——— *Water Requirements for Pollution Abatement.* Committee Print No. 29, Washington, D.C., 1960.

U.S. Department of Health, Education, and Welfare, *Clean Water—A Challenge to the Nation, Highlights and Recommendations of the National Conference on Water Pollution.* December 1960.

C. STAFFORD BRANDT

AIR IS FOR
MORE THAN BREATHING

THE fact that air is essential to life is as old as knowledge. The fact that polluted air can cause discomfort is probably just as old. As soon as primitive man moved his fire into his cave, he certainly became aware of air pollution in the form of smoke. He also probably soon learned to reduce the smoke in the cave by careful placement and stoking. He then decided to accept some smoke in return for the warmth and convenience of the fire nearby.

We have been weighing pollution against convenience ever since. Now we are beginning to realize that more than convenience is involved and that the air around us is not a limitless sea into which we can continue to pour waste without serious consequences.

Our health and our well-being are threatened.

We are also using more and more air and dumping more and more waste into it. Just as some people show surprise that we need water for things other than washing and drinking, some find it surprising that air is used for more than breathing.

You and I, if we are average, take less than 20 cubic feet of air an hour into our lungs. A cow may use 200 cubic feet an hour. A modern power station may use 100 million cubic feet an hour to burn the coal or oil it uses. Your home oil burner or gas furnace requires about 6 thousand cubic feet an hour. An average acre of corn will require all of the carbon dioxide from more than one-half billion cubic feet of air. These are a few of our uses of air.

I do not wish to belabor the point, but I do want to stress how much air we all require in our daily living. The average automobile, which uses a little more than 1 thousand cubic feet of air per gallon of gasoline burned, is a familiar example. This is not a large figure until you apply it to the estimated 60 billion gallons of gasoline used in 1963. To put it another way, the carbon dioxide in the exhaust from the average car for a year is enough to grow more than an acre of corn. There are about 75 million cars and about 80 million acres of corn.

I use carbon dioxide only as an example of how much air we are using and what we are doing to it. It is not

121

673–282°—63——10

usually considered an air pollutant but an essential constituent of the air. Yet some writers, including a former president of the American Association for the Advancement of Science, Dr. C. D. Leake, have expressed concern over our increasing use of fossil fuels (coal, oil, and natural gas).

The carbon dioxide content of the air is increasing. Since this material is important in the heat balance of the earth, an increase is of concern.

If the increase goes too far, the polar ice could melt and our coastlines could be flooded. With the change of climate that would occur, the farmer in Iowa would no longer worry about corn borers unless the corn borer adapts itself and becomes a pest on bananas or similar crops. That is a long way off; we have more immediate problems of air pollution.

To MANY, air pollution means smoke.

Smoke has been an important air pollutant in the past and still is an important aspect of pollution.

As long ago as the 13th century, smoke in London became so unpleasant that regulations were imposed on the use of coal. The efforts of St. Louis, Pittsburgh, and other communities to control their smoke problems are well known.

There is, of course, more to air pollution than just smoke, and many definitions try to describe air pollution. Usually the basic process is defined as the introduction of materials into the air as a result of man's activity— meaning that natural processes such as volcanoes should be ruled out of our definitions. This can become rather trivial if we try to distinguish between smoke from a forest fire started by lightning or by a cigarette. The smoke will have the same effect. As generally used, pollution usually implies the possibility of control.

"Effect" is the keyword in all definitions of air pollution.

If in the fall I burn some leaves along the street, is that air pollution? Certainly material is going into the air as a result of man's activity. Many people find the smell of burning leaves and the sight of the smoke lying in a low line down the street rather pleasant sensations. But if the smoke interferes with the visibility of a driver on the street, it is a hazard to life and property. If the smoke dirties the wash hanging on the line down the street, it has interfered with the reasonable use of property.

The simple act of introducing material into the air is not air pollution. If the materials produce or contribute to an adverse effect on the health and well-being of man or interfere with his normal and reasonable activities or use of property, it is air pollution.

Defining the effect, evaluating the degree, and relating the effect to an air pollutant become more complicated as our patterns of living become more complex.

The old smoke problem of St. Louis, Pittsburgh, and many other cities seems rather simple in retrospect and in comparison to our current problems. It was just a problem of dirt and grime from smoke, which, while inconvenient, could be tolerated. After all, factories put out smoke but mean jobs, and smoky air with pay is preferable to clean air without pay.

There is a point where the inconvenience becomes intolerable. In any of these communities, however, it was not a matter of pointing to one chimney and saying, "This has to be cleaned up." Thousands of chimneys were putting out smoke, including the chimneys of households. Control would cost everyone. The cost had to be balanced against the desirability, or value, of cleaner air.

Air pollution problems from single sources had been faced and solved before. The classic example of the smelter in the Copper Hill district of Tennessee is a case in point. In the smelting of the copper ore, sulfur was removed and vented to the atmosphere as a gas, sulfur dioxide, which above certain concentrations is toxic to plants. When the sulfur dioxide from the smelter affected the crops, the farmers entered claims for damages.

Here, cause, or source, and effect were related fairly readily, and there was some basis for evaluation in terms of costs. The result was modernization of the smelter so as to recover the sulfur dioxide. The smelter has realized considerable monetary return from the byproduct of the sulfur recovery, sulfuric acid.

St. Louis had no such simple evaluation. It had its major sources of sulfur dioxide and smoke. It also had thousands of minor sources, since burning coal, especially high-sulfur coals, results in considerable sulfur dioxide. There was damage to the vegetation of the area from the gas, but that was only part of the problem. What value do you put on sunlight or having a white shirt stay white all day? The evaluations were made, and St. Louis initiated effective regulations to control smoke.

These two cases, St. Louis and the smelter in Tennessee, were not unique or highly original in their approach; other smelters and other cities have controlled smoke and sulfur dioxide. London had regulations on the use of coal more than 500 years before St. Louis was settled.

I cite these cases as representative of types of pollution and effects of evaluation. Because of their timing and the successes achieved in control, they do represent significant steps in the recognition of air pollution as a problem in this country.

THE AGENTS—pollutants—that cause effects can be considered in two broad categories, the particulates and gases, based on their physical state.

The gaseous pollutants, such as carbon monoxide, sulfur dioxide, and the various oxides of nitrogen, exist as simple molecular entities and behave like the air itself. They do not settle out.

The particulate pollutants are finely divided solids or liquid droplets. The larger fractions of particulates will set-

tle out. The finer particulates can be buoyed up by the slightest air movement or even by the movement of the gas molecules, so that essentially they never settle out. We frequently give the name "aerosol" to these very fine particles. The distinction is somewhat arbitrary, but usually is applied to those particles or droplets with diameters less than 20 microns (less than 0.0008 inch). You can readily demonstrate the size effect on behavior of particulates by tossing a handful of dry soil into the air. Some particles fall back immediately, and some drift off as though they would never settle out.

This classification may seem academic, since I have implied that the effect is of prime importance. The make of the car that runs into you is really of only passing interest. In this instance, however, we are interested in the size, since size affects the transport of the pollutant from the source to the point of effect, the type of effect, and the control of the pollutant.

The large particulate will fall back close to the source, depending on the wind. The effect is often on the source in the form of dirt. Finer particles will travel farther. The aerosol size diffuses into the air like a gas finally becoming diluted. These fine materials are the dirt and grime that seep into buildings, soil clothes, reduce visibility, and possibly affect our health. The problem of their transport from the source to the point of effect becomes a problem for the meteorologist.

The meteorologist can give us a fair idea of where the material—particulate as well as gaseous—from a single source will go. He can define the most adverse meteorological conditions and state with fair assurance, "Under these conditions the concentration at this point will not exceed this value." If he has proper meteorological data for the specific area, he can often give us some fair estimates of the frequency of concentrations above a certain value.

When we consider an extensive urban area with thousands of individual sources, the problem becomes highly complex. Much of the problem arises from a lack of knowledge on atmospheric diffusion and dispersion. We have a good deal of basic theory. We are short on ability to apply it to practical problems in a metropolitan area. Much of this problem in application arises from an inability to describe the complex of sources adequately.

The United States Weather Bureau maintains a research group in the Division of Air Pollution of the Public Health Service in Cincinnati. This group, along with several other groups and individuals, is making considerable progress, practical and theoretical, in this whole problem of what happens to pollutants in the air on their trip from source to receptor. The Cincinnati group also has been making progress on forecasting the large-scale meteorological conditions that may worsen local pollution.

THE GENERAL EFFECTS of air pollution can be considered in rather broad categories: General nuisance, effects on plants and animals, and effects on man's health.

Nuisance is perhaps an inadequate term for dust, dirt, grime, corrosion, odor, and reduced visibility. Certainly some of these nuisance effects of air pollution exceed simple annoyance. Many of them can be considered as part of the impact of our physical environment on our sense of well-being, if not directly on our health.

The commonest effect of particulate air pollutants is the nuisance from soiling and altered visibility. One of the major problems St. Louis set out to correct was that of the dirt and grime from the gray-black pall that on occasion could block out the noon sun. This type of nuisance from particulates is still a major problem in any highly developed urban area. It is not only the heavy industries that put out particulates. That average car as well as the power station, the large steel plant, and the backyard incinerator all contribute to the particulate load and to the nuisance problem of dirt, dust, and grime.

Another aspect of nuisance is the problem of corrosion. Some of the gaseous materials put out in combustion and some other processes are acidic in nature. The sulfur and nitrogen oxides and carbon dioxide are examples. They can form corrosive acids when they react with water. Some of the particulates in the presence of moisture hydrolyze, or react, to give acidic or basic reactions. Only such materials in the air may cause accelerated weathering and corrosion of all exposed materials, which, with dust and grime, add to the cost of upkeep and maintenance of property.

The matter of visibility is a subtle one. A heavy pall of smoke over an area is easily recognized as a serious nuisance. We are likely to accept much of the less dramatic reductions in visibility as a direct consequence of the weather. Overcast skies and hazes are common, natural phenomena. Yet in many, if not most, of our large cities the natural phenomena are augmented, extended, and duplicated by manmade covers of aerosols. Under unfavorable conditions, the problem can interfere with transportation and related activities. These reductions in visibility may also have a psychological effect—again the matter of our well-being.

The problem of odors is definitely in this psychological sphere. The variation in our individual responses to odors is amazing. What may be highly objectionable to your neighbor may be hardly detectable to you. We rapidly become used to some odors. The sensation we get at one concentration may be entirely different at a higher or lower concentration. Add these wide variations in response to the fantastically low concentration that can give an odor response—a few parts in a billion parts of air are not uncommon threshold concentrations—and you realize why it is difficult to evaluate, measure, and control.

It is perhaps fortunate that the usual effects of air pollution on plants is not so dramatic as from the smelter at Ducktown, Tenn. Here a "little desert" still remains after close to 50 years as a reminder of what sulfur dioxide can do to vegetation. While we are no longer killing all the vegetation of an area on quite such a grand scale, sulfur dioxide injury to vegetation is still common in many parts of the country.

Various air pollutants cause lesions on the leaves of many plants. Sulfur dioxide, fluorides, and ethylene are the commonest of the materials. While the symptoms of injury are characteristic, they are by no means specific.

Insects, diseases, droughts, and the like can cause similar symptoms.

Another group of agents cause considerable injury to plants. This is a big air pollution problem—smog. Smog, a term coined in England from "smoke" and "fog," describes the air pollution situation of London. Smog is basically a smoke problem of heavy particulate and sulfur dioxide loadings complicated and made worse by fog. We have adopted the term and applied it to a type of problem that is not smoke or fog. Some people associate the term in this country with Los Angeles.

Heavy particulate or high sulfur dioxide was never a really serious problem in Los Angeles. Rather rigid controls have reduced these loadings, yet the smog remains.

Actually, the materials that result in the undesirable effects of smog would by themselves not be considered serious air pollutants.

Hydrocarbons resulting from handling fuel and from unburned fuel from auto exhaust, boilers, and so on are generally gaseous. In high enough concentrations, they could cause undesirable effects, including odor problems, but under normal conditions of most areas, the effect would not be great.

Nitrogen oxides result from combustion processes. They can contribute under certain conditions to the corrosion and the material deterioration I noted, yet in the usual concentrations found in most areas would be of only minor concern by themselves.

Put these two materials together under a meteorological condition that restricts diffusion or large-scale dilution but permits exposure to sunlight, and the result is a smog of the Los Angeles variety.

We now generally refer to these air pollution conditions as photochemical smogs to distinguish the condition from the smoke-fog type. The term also recognizes that the condition results from reactions between pollutants (innocuous or not) induced by light.

We do not know all the details of these reactions. We do know that aerosols are formed. We know ozone is produced during the reactions. Under some conditions, ozone levels will increase; under other conditions, it is transitory, reacting almost immediately with other materials.

We know that under some conditions organic nitrogen compounds are formed. One of these compounds, peroxyacetyl nitrate (PAN), is an eye irritant and causes injury to vegetation. We believe that PAN is just one member of a class of compounds of similar nature and effect that can be produced in photochemical smogs.

The effect of smog on vegetation has caused rather severe economic losses to vegetable crops in the Los Angeles area. These effects have also given us means of identifying the presence of smog. Reduced visibility and eye irritation are subjective observations difficult to evaluate.

The lesions on plant leaves characteristic of photochemical smog offer a type of proof of the existence of smog conditions not obtainable by other means. It is evidence from plants that leads us to some far-reaching conclusions regarding the potential impact of photochemical smog on our future development.

Los Angeles no longer has, if it ever had, a monopoly on photochemical smog. The characteristic symptoms on plants have been found in almost every metropolitan area of this country.

The degree and extent in many areas is not severe but is recognizable. However, the entire coastal area from roughly Washington, D.C., to Boston has come to rival southern California for extent, severity, and economic loss to agriculture because of photochemical smog. The occasional appearance of smog symptoms on vegetation of other sections is a reason for serious concern.

The effects of air pollution on animals has been mainly of concern from two toxicants, arsenic and fluoride.

Arsenic problems have arisen as a result of smelter operations. Arsenic is a common trace element of many sulfide ores. In the process of heating to drive off the sulfur, arsenic is volatilized. This condenses again and settles out on the vegetation. Where conditions for driving off enough arsenic and for settling out on limited areas were favorable, cattle grazing the vegetation could be poisoned.

Once the problem was recognized, arsenic recovery was a fairly simple process, and this problem is now of only minor concern.

The fluoride problem has been serious in many sections. Gaseous fluorides cause definite patterns of injury to

plants. Injury is roughly related to the amount of fluoride absorbed. Yet many of our forage plants can tolerate relatively high levels of fluoride without any apparent injury. In the animal, fluoride is essential to normal development of bone and teeth. As with many things, however, where a little is good, too much can be disastrous. So it is with fluorides. Thus our concern is as much for the animal as the plant in many of the areas with elevated atmospheric fluorides.

Fluorides therefore have been one of the most thoroughly studied air pollutants, and we have learned a lot. We know that for chronic fluorosis in the animal we need be concerned only with the total daily dietary fluoride intake. We know that probably we need be concerned only with the average daily intake over a period of several weeks. Thus, with the cow a few days on a high-fluoride pasture or a portion of its diet from high-fluoride hay will cause no trouble, provided fairly well known times and levels are not exceeded.

Fluorosis in humans is known—but not from community air pollution.

A few sections have waters with enough fluoride to cause characteristic markings on teeth. It would be extremely unlikely because of our dietary habits for us to exceed the safe fluoride intake from air-contaminated vegetables. The hazard to man or animals by inhalation in the range of fluoride levels experienced in the open atmosphere (a few parts per billion) is essentially nil.

In the case of the plant, the gross leaf symptoms of fluoride injury have been adequately described. Because such symptoms are always associated with elevated fluoride content of the leaf, confirmation by direct analysis is possible. Despite a great deal of work, we can still not give a definitive answer to what fluoride levels below those required to produce the characteristic leaf lesions do to a plant. You can find data suggestive of a range from no effect to rather dramatic upsets in plant processes.

The effect of air pollution on human health is not nearly so clear-cut as with plants. We do not develop visible characteristic lesions, and air pollution is rarely, if ever, listed as a cause of death on a death certificate.

Yet you will read reports indicating that 20 persons died in Donora, Pa., in October 1948, and that 4 thousand died in London in December 1952, as a result of air pollution. True, these tragic figures represent rather special conditions—meteorological conditions that allowed the pollutants to build up to higher than usual levels.

In few of these cases was air pollution listed as the cause of death. And for the majority we would probably not be able to give specific names. These deaths are statistics, but nonetheless real. They represent excess deaths due to "natural" causes over and above what would normally be expected, occurring during periods of excessive air pollution. There are other known instances of such periods of excess death, which correlate with high levels of pollution. More cases may be found as existing records are reworked.

In addition to these acute episodes, in which excess deaths correlate with rather short-time exposure, evidence of chronic or long-term exposure effects is being found. Chronic bronchitis, emphysema, lung cancer, and other respiratory diseases seem to correlate with air pollution levels. Such evidence does not offer firm conclusive proof of cause and effect. Yet no other factor than air pollution offers quite as good a correlation. Work with experimental animals is giving strong support to the conclusions from these correlations. As a result, we can no longer ignore these effects on health.

I have not mentioned two pollutants that seriously affect our health.

One of them, pollens, frequently is not directly the result of man's activity, but nevertheless is usually considered an air pollutant. Their effect needs no documentation, as anyone who suffers from "hay fever" or related pollen-induced diseases can tell you.

Radioactivity is the other pollutant. We recognize definite health hazards from it. In the case of military use of nuclear energy, health hazards must be weighed against other hazards. We can only work and pray for the day such weighing will not be necessary.

Nonmilitary uses of nuclear power are growing and will continue to grow. The known air pollution hazards from radioactivity are one of the factors in any considered use of this power. It is inconceivable that these known hazards will not continue to dictate the limits of use and the extent of controls needed for safe use of nuclear energy systems.

THE CONTROL of air pollution is a complex of social and economic and engineering problems.

Many of these problems are implicit in the answers we give to three questions: How clean must the air be? How clean do we want it? How much are we willing to pay for it?

Obviously, there is a simple answer to the first question: As clean as necessary to assure no effects on our health!

Neither of the other questions applies up to this point. There is, however, another question that must be answered: What or how much is safe? That is the difficult question.

We can prepare a long list of materials with definite concentrations that are unsafe. But just because something is not in a definite "unsafe" category does not mean it is safe. It is inherent in the nature of things that we can never prove a material safe—that it has no detrimental effect under all possible conditions. We may, after repeated failures to demonstrate an effect, accept the premise of no effect. Yet we must always remember this is a conditional acceptance.

Modern chemistry had long accepted the premise that a group of elements, the noble gases, such as neon and xenon, were unreactive and did not form compounds. This premise was based on failure of experiments to prove the existence of compounds involving these elements. All lectures covering these noble gases beginning in the fall of 1962 had to be revised to note a fall from unique status. During the summer some compounds of xenon were prepared with embarrassing ease. But before you throw out all our premises based on lack of evidence to the contrary, remember that the tomato for a long time was "known" to be poisonous.

The Human Health Section of the Seminar on Community Air Quality Standards, conducted at the University of Michigan in 1962, discussed this problem of evidence of health effects and the basis for possible standards of air quality. In brief, the conclusion of the scientists was that they were unable at that time to establish standards of air quality in relation to human health. They did agree that some standards could be set in specific areas where certain known irritants appeared to be a threat to health.

Since, even by turning the clock back, we cannot eliminate all air pollution, highly restrictive controls on all sources, based on nonspecific and fragmentary evidence of health effects or on fear, are not warranted. To this extent the caution of the scientists in

the seminar is warranted and in its way encouraging. This does not mean there are no health effects or that control of air pollution is not needed to protect our health.

If clear-cut evidence of an effect can be demonstrated, the course is obvious—eliminate the pollutant. But if the effect is not obvious and can be related only to general pollution, we need to exercise some caution in demanding highly restrictive controls just for the sake of action. Yet we must not ignore repeated evidence suggesting effects while waiting patiently for the final definitive study to prove the effect. Caution is commendable; apathy or procrastination is foolish.

It would be foolhardy not to pursue vigorously research on the possible effects of air pollutants and the air pollution complex upon our health and well-being. We must see where we are going. You would not, I hope, drive that average car on a dark, rainy night without headlights. In this field of air conservation, research is our headlights. To delay action on reasonable evidence that suggests an effect on our health while we wait for conclusive proof is also foolhardy. Procrastination could be disastrous.

The answer to the second question, "How clean do we want the air?" is also rather obvious: As clean as necessary to assure no interference with the use of property. Our comfort, our welfare, our living standard, and a host of other social and economic aspects of our lives involved here, are, for simplicity, lumped with property. Property, unlike our health, however, has a market value. The question, "How much are we willing to pay?" therefore comes in. Now the engineering aspects of the complex become involved. Some of the aspects are rather straightforward.

That powerplant we used as an example could put out into the air about 25 tons of particulate matter an hour and 20 tons of sulfur dioxide an hour. If you asked the engineer to reduce that particulate output by about

80 percent or to about 2 tons an hour, he would do that fairly easily. If you asked him to reduce the output to less than a ton an hour, he could do it, but would want to be sure you realized how much it would cost. It may be possible to go farther in some instances, but the cost would be much greater.

If you asked the engineer if he could reduce the sulfur dioxide by 90 percent, his first reaction would be an emphatic "No!" If he could be assured of plenty of water and no water-disposal problems and if you would accept a sizable increase in cost of power produced, the engineer could probably make the reduction.

In general, some degree of control of particulate emissions from industrial processes is available and is rather widely used.

Only in very specialized cases is the collection approaching 100 percent. Coarse particulate can be collected rather easily with high efficiency. The finer the material, the more difficult it is to collect with high efficiency and the higher is the cost. Modification of the process itself sometimes has given a high degree of control.

At present, there is a limit to which we can control many industrial particulate sources at permissible costs. The limit is partly a matter of engineering skill and ingenuity. There are also installations that do not fully use the controls that are available. That is inexcusable.

The control of gaseous material from industrial processes generally is not nearly so readily available or efficient as for particulates. Where the concentration in the gas stream is high, various scrubbing and reaction systems may work. Recovery of sulfur dioxide is feasible in the high-concentration airstream from a smelter, but is difficult in the low concentration in the flue gas of a steamplant.

By improved design over the past few decades, we have markedly reduced the gaseous and particulate organic matter emissions from our large energy producers. Because these materials represented incompletely used fuel, there was an economic incentive for such improvement.

A similar incentive applies to the smaller sources of energy, such as household heating and the automobile, but other considerations of initial cost and performance also enter into the problem. In almost all instances, a balance among the considerations is reached before complete combustion. Yet if we are to control photochemical smogs, the emission of organic compounds will have to be controlled from all sources. If combustion cannot be further improved, other means of control will have to be used.

Take the automobile. In many areas it represents a major source of organic materials vented to the atmosphere. A modern automobile properly tuned and maintained represents a fairly efficient combustion device at a steady cruising speed. In order to get the needed flexibility in performance, a certain degree of inefficient combustion must be accepted. That means that the output of organic compounds from an auto is greatest where the traffic is greatest, thus compounding the problem.

Until the engineers are able to solve the problem by engine design, the control of automobile emissions must rely on a secondary control system. Devices to reduce the material vented from the crankcase—blowby—are now available. Progress has been made on exhaust control devices, and some should be commercially available soon.

The other major ingredient of the photochemical smog stew, nitrogen oxides, cannot at present be satisfactorily controlled from most energy producers. While hydrocarbon control holds considerable promise for photochemical smog control, we will be seriously remiss if we do not continue to work on possible controls for nitrogen oxides.

The whole question of control of industrial, public, and private individual sources requires continued and

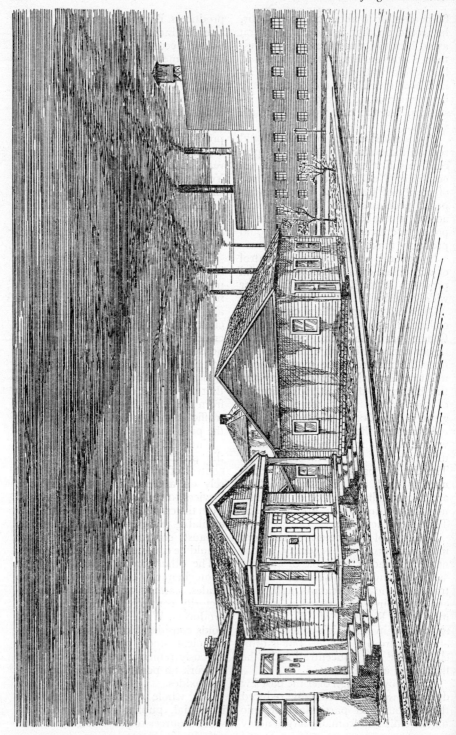

expanded effort. Only a few years ago we thought we had air pollution solved through smoke control and control of the major sulfur dioxide emitters. Now we realize more control is needed. Then, too, few anticipated the large urbanization that many areas have undergone. We must, in fairness to the future, expect even greater change and make every effort to gain control of our growing problems of air pollution.

Zoning may be considered as a way to control air pollution. Through planning and regulations, it is possible to obtain physical isolation of major sources of pollution from residential, recreational, and other such places where pollution would severely interfere with use of property. Yet since airborne pollutants do not recognize zoning or political boundaries, such control has limitations.

Zoning or other locational restrictions on sources must recognize the meteorological conditions that apply if effective control is to be obtained by them—we count on dilution and dispersion in the atmosphere to reduce the concentration of the pollutant to a level that will not produce an effect on the receptor. The other control methods I have outlined were based upon collection at the source. Isolation by zoning is helpful in reducing effects from the residual emissions not collected by other techniques.

THE LEGAL and regulatory aspects of air pollution are as involved as the effects.

The first documented law on air pollution was by royal proclamation in 1306, but the basic legal premises are as old as the laws of property.

The legal basis for control of air pollution hinges on a balance between two prime interests—the free use of property by the owner and the right of the individual to be free from harm to himself or his property from the acts of others.

We must in our present society use the air as a sewer to dispose of wastes.

Yet we must do so in such a way that we do not interfere with the health or function of our society.

The histories of water use and water pollution, of public roads, transportation and access, of public health, and of a host of other areas of social and public interest contain conflicts of interest and use similar to those in air pollution. There are similar elements in all the approaches toward "solution" or "adjustment."

THERE IS no single, simple formula. When people have recognized the problem, evaluated the cost, and decided what they wanted, the legal and administrative mechanisms to accomplish the job have usually been found.

Many communities have made great progress in cleaning up the dust-smoke-grime complex of nuisances. Political boundaries—village, city, county, and State lines—have caused problems.

These are not insurmountable, just difficult.

Communities have found ways to cooperate on water supplies, sewage disposal, police and fire protection, and air pollution control whenever the residents saw the need to cooperate: The old Copper Hill Smelter problem involved a State boundary; the Trail Smelter problem involved an international boundary; the San Francisco Bay area has an air pollution control district involving six counties.

Most of the general legal and administrative approaches are known and have been tried. The details will vary greatly. The program must be tailored to fit the needs of the area. Again, the problem is not insurmountable, just difficult.

We do not know enough about air pollution and air pollutants to detail all the effects they have on health, on animals, on plants, or on property.

We do know enough about some of the effects to say, "This should not be permitted." We do not know enough about controls to eliminate pollution. We do know enough to reduce many pollutants. We must learn more, but we must also use what knowledge we have.

If St. Louis or Pittsburgh or any other community had waited until dust and dirt and grime could be eliminated completely, they would still be waiting. If they relax and do not take advantage of technological advances in control, their gains will disappear.

If the farmers of northern Georgia had not pleaded their case as a group, Copper Hill might still be blanketed with sulfur dioxide. (Probably not, with sulfuric acid now such a valuable byproduct, but, for the sake of argument, it could be.) Had these farmers insisted on complete, total control, Tennessee would have lost a large industry. If the industry now did not recognize its responsibility to the entire area, the occasional, accidental fumigation under adverse conditions could become frequent and then continual.

Air pollution is the result of *our* activities, not just *their* activity, and *we*, not *they*, must accept responsibility.

All of us need the air to dispose of some wastes. All of us need the air for our lives. All of us must be sure we do not use the air as a sewer unnecessarily.

The air around us is a vital, natural resource that we must preserve.

C. STAFFORD BRANDT, *chemist in the Soil and Water Conservation Research Division, Agricultural Research Service, was assigned by cooperative agreement to the Division of Air Pollution, Public Health Service, in 1956 for liaison on air pollution as it affects agriculture. He is stationed at the Robert A. Taft Sanitary Engineering Center, Cincinnati, Ohio, where he serves within the Public Health Service organization as Chief of the Agricultural Section, Laboratory of Medical and Biological Sciences, Division of Air Pollution, Public Health Service.*

For further reading:
Air Pollution, A. C. Stern, editor. Academic Press, New York, 1962 (two volumes).
Air Pollution Handbook, P. L. Magill, F. R. Holden, and C. Ackley, editors. McGraw-Hill Book Co., Inc., New York, 1956.

Brandt, C. Stafford, "Special Jubilee Symposium: Air Pollution With Relation to Agronomic Crops." *Agronomy Journal,* Vol. 50 (1958), pp. 544–568.
Greathouse, G. A., and Wessel, C. J., *Deterioration of Materials—Causes and Preventive Techniques.* Reinhold Publishing Corp., New York, 1954.
Greenburg, L., and Jacobs, M. B., "Corrosion Aspects of Air Pollution." *American Paint Journal,* Vol. 39 (July 1955), pp. 64–78.
Heimann, H., Emik, L. O., Prindle, R. A., and Fisher, W. M., "Progress in Medical Research on Air Pollution." *Public Health Reports,* Vol. 73 (1958), pp. 1055–1069.
"How To Control Gaseous Emissions To Abate Air Pollution." *Heating, Piping & Air Conditioning,* Vol. 31 (December 1959), pp. 113–126.
"How To Control Particulate Emissions To Abate Air Pollution." *Heating, Piping & Air Conditioning,* Vol. 31 (June 1959), pp. 138–152.
"Industrial Gas Cleaning." *British Chemical Engineering,* Vol. 5 (August 1960), pp. 542–550.
Kane, J. M., "Operation, Application, and Effectiveness of Dust Collection Equipment." *Heating & Ventilating,* Vol. 49, Reference Section, August 1952.
Kennedy, H. W., "Fifty Years of Air Pollution Law." *Journal of the Air Pollution Control Association,* Vol. 7 (August 1957), pp. 125–141.
Middleton, J. T., "Photochemical Air Pollution Damage to Plants." *Annual Review of Plant Physiology,* Vol. 12 (1961), pp. 431–448.
Nelson, N., "Some Toxicologic Aspects of Atmospheric Pollution." *American Journal of Public Health,* Vol. 45 (1955), pp. 1289–1301.
Niemeyer, L. E., "Forecasting Air Pollution Potential." *Monthly Weather Review,* Vol. 88 (1960), p. 88.
"Pollution Control." *Chemical Engineering,* Vol. 58 (May 1951), pp. 132–159.
Prindle, R. A., "Air Pollution as a Public Health Hazard." *A.M.A. Archives of Environmental Health,* Vol. 4 (1962), pp. 401–407.
Proceedings, National Conference on Air Pollution. Public Health Service Publication No. 654, 1959, pp. 187–233.
Rogers, S. M., "A Review and Appraisal of Air Pollution Legislation in the United States." *Journal of the Air Pollution Control Association,* Vol. 4 (February 1958), pp. 308–315.
Rogers, S. M., and Edelman, S., *A Digest of State Air Pollution Laws.* Public Health Service Publication No. 711, revised 1960 with 1961 supplement.
Tetzlaff, F., Rogers, S. M., and Edelman, S., "Guiding Principles for State Air Pollution Legislation." *American Journal of Public Health,* Vol. 51 (February 1961), pp. 182–189.
World Health Organization, *Air Pollution.* WHO Monograph No. 46, Geneva, 1961.

FARMING

THE net effect of our rapid growth of farm productivity has been to modify the place of agriculture in the economy and to set the stage for further changes. The effect of urban expansion on agriculture is seen in matters of taxes, markets, ownership, and part-time farming. We are keenly aware of farming and farmers on the economic margins, and the agonizing reappraisal of the farming structure and farm programs. In the words of one economist, "I foresee a national economy in which the urban-industrial sector is the dominant generator of economic change, but in which agriculture continues to make an important contribution through further gains in production efficiency. Agriculture can share most effectively from the gains in the national economy if national growth can be achieved without price inflation." Occasionally we hear that the tradition of the family farm is no longer relevant to the realities of American agriculture: "The family farm has adjusted to many stresses, but when we focus attention on some of its characteristics we may overlook the significance of other important trends."

VERNON W. RUTTAN

AGRICULTURE
IN THE NATIONAL ECONOMY

OUR rapid growth of agricultural productivity has strengthened the favorable terms on which we and the world have had access to agricultural raw materials and has made available an increasing share of the national labor force for nonagricultural employment. In turn, the expanding industrial and urban economy has exerted a strong force on agriculture through the markets for agricultural products, the new technologies embodied in the products of the farm supply industry, an expansion of employment opportunities for workers released from agriculture, and on rural life through a rise in standards of consumption.

The net effect has been to modify the place of agriculture in the national economy and to set the stage for further modifications.

The position of agriculture in the economy has undergone three shifts since 1870.

Between then and 1900, an annual increase in gross inputs of 2 percent a year combined with an increase in productivity of 1.1 percent a year to produce an annual increase in farm output of 3.2 percent. Only a minor increase occurred in the price of agricultural raw materials relative to the wholesale price index, although the additional inputs in the form of land, labor, and capital equipment were substantial.

The rise in output was fast enough to permit sizable exports of farm products to meet the Nation's need for foreign exchange. Agricultural products accounted for 77 percent of the value of American exports in 1870 and still accounted for 65 percent in 1900. A modest rise in farm employment and a rapid rise in nonfarm employment occurred.

The relative contribution of agriculture to national economic growth was less dramatic between 1900 and 1925.

A slow rate of growth in inputs of resources and a failure to achieve measurable increases in output per unit of total input in agriculture reduced the rate of growth of farm output to an average of less than 1 percent a year.

This lag in expansion of production and a continuation of rising domestic

135

and export demand for farm products brought the longest sustained increase in agricultural prices relative to the general price level since 1870. The lag reflected the changing importance of land and the other resources, brought about by the closing of the land frontier. New lands no longer were readily available, and laborsaving technological changes of 1850–1900 had to be supplemented with land-saving technological changes. Rising food prices made clear to many people the meaning of lagging productivity growth in agriculture during the first quarter of this century. Public concern was manifest in increased emphasis on resource development and conservation, and in increased allocation of public funds for research and education designed to increase the rate of productivity.

Agriculture again resumed its historic role during the 1920's as a major contributor to our national economic growth. The replacement of horses and mules by tractors and the release of land formerly used to produce feed for horses and mules for the production of food and fiber proceeded rapidly even during the Great Depression. By the beginning of the Second World War, agriculture was in a position to release a substantial flow of labor to the nonfarm sector and to achieve rapid increases in farm output.

The rate of productivity growth has continued to accelerate. Between 1950 and 1961, farm employment declined by more than one-third, while total inputs used in agricultural production remained unchanged and farm output expanded at 2 percent a year—the highest rate since the turn of the century—despite efforts to control the rate of increase in farm output.

During the 1950's, close to 40 percent of the growth in the nonagricultural labor force was accounted for by shifts of labor out of agriculture and declining farm product prices exerted an important restraining force on the rising retail price index.

The effect of urban and industrial development on American agriculture also has changed sharply in a century.

As the agricultural frontier was pushed across the country, the growth of the farm production provided an impetus for the growth of local nonagricultural employment in transportation, processing, and commerce.

Differences in rates of growth in output among areas and regions made for local and regional differences in nonfarm growth.

As the accumulation of capital and the growth of population have continued, however, the influence of local and regional variations in resource endowments has become more difficult to distinguish. Research at Vanderbilt University by William H. Nicholls and Anthony M. Tang indicates that in the Southern Piedmont and the Tennessee Valley the impact of "original" differences in resource endowments on differences in agricultural productivity and income among counties had largely disappeared by the turn of the century.

By 1950 there was ample evidence that the level of local industrial and urban development exerts a significant positive impact on the level of income achieved by farm families in most regions. The major exceptions to this generalization are in the West, where the resource base continues to represent an important factor in the location of economic activity.

The economic interactions between the farm and nonfarm parts of the local economy that give rise to these changing relationships have occurred primarily through three sets of market relationships: The product market—the markets for the products produced by agriculture; the input market—the market for the manufactured inputs and capital used in agricultural production; and the labor market—through which labor is allocated between the agricultural and nonagricultural parts of the economy and among firms.

The product market has been regarded as the dominant channel through which the impact of national fluctuations in nonfarm income and local variations in nonfarm demand have been channeled into the agricultural sector. The declining response of consumption of food and fiber to increases in nonfarm income and the development of farm commodity programs, however, have dampened the commodity market effects of economic fluctuations in the nonfarm sector. The regional specialization in production stimulated by technological and organizational changes in processing, transportation, and distribution have reduced the impact of local urban-industrial development on the demand for locally produced farm products. Milk remains a major exception.

The markets for manufactured goods and capital equipment have become increasingly important in transmitting the effect of changes in the nonfarm economy to agriculture. Much of the new technology utilized by agriculture is incorporated in the form of new capital equipment or more efficient fertilizer, insecticides, and other items that raise operating expenses, for which in 1870 the charges amounted to less than 3 percent of the value of farm production. By 1900 nonfarm inputs still amounted to only 7 percent, but by 1960 they accounted for approximately 27 percent of the value of farm output.

The rising importance of purchased inputs makes net farm income increasingly sensitive to variations in input prices relative to product prices. Rising input prices during the 1950's, combined with declining or stable product prices, meant a rapid transfer of the gains in farm productivity to the nonfarm sector.

The labor market has increasingly become the primary channel through which local and regional variations in nonfarm developments are transmitted to agriculture in most regions. It has been possible to realize the full potentials for rapid growth in agricultural productivity and income per farmworker only when local or regional economic growth has been rapid enough to absorb both the new entrants from the farm sector and the farmworkers released from productive employment in agriculture by advancing technology into the local nonfarm labor force.

By and large, interregional migration, in the absence of growth of local industrial and urban employment, has not been sufficient to narrow income differentials between agricultural and nonagricultural employment in localities or among the regions. Failure to achieve rapid growth in employment opportunities in the local nonfarm economy therefore has resulted in failure to achieve the adjustment necessary to bring about higher levels of productivity and income of the farmworker.

THE CHANGES of the past several decades have set the stage for the development of several additional changes in the relationship between the agricultural and nonagricultural parts of the economy.

First of all, it is clear that agriculture in the future is likely to make an even smaller contribution to foreign exchange earnings than at present.

Rising agricultural productivity in Europe and the emerging structure of world trade will make it difficult for

ANNUAL AVERAGE RATES OF CHANGE IN TOTAL OUTPUT, INPUTS, AND TOTAL PRODUCTIVITY IN AMERICAN AGRICULTURE, 1870–1961

	Percentage per year			
	1870–1900	*1900–25*	*1925–50*	*1950–61*
Farm output............................	3.2	0.9	1.5	2.0
Total inputs............................	2.0	1.0	.4	.0
Total productivity.......................	1.1	—.0	1.2	2.0

Source: *Changes in Farm Production and Efficiency, A Summary Report, 1962*, U.S. Department of Agriculture, Statistical Bulletin No. 233, Washington, September 1962.

673–282°—63——11

agriculture to maintain the position it has occupied as a source of approximately 20 percent of the foreign trade earnings.

Furthermore, agriculture will not provide an important source of growth in the nonfarm labor force, even if farm employment continues to decline relatively rapidly. The decline of farm employment and the rising rate of new entrants to the nonfarm labor force as a result of the high nonfarm birth rates of the 1940's and 1950's has reduced farm employment to less than 8 percent of the labor force.

Within the next decade, farm employment will fall below the number of unemployed workers in the United States economy even during periods of prosperity. (Two earlier benchmarks in agriculture's changing role in the national labor force were 1880, when the nonagricultural employment first exceeded agricultural employment, and 1929, when employment in manufacturing alone exceeded agricultural employment.)

A continuation of the rapid technological change of the past decade can permit agriculture to retain its role as a source of restraint on the American consumer's cost of living if appropriate farm price and income policies are developed.

Lower prices for farm products will not be able to exert as significant an impact on the consumer price index in the future as in the past, however. Food items were given a weight of 28.1 percent and apparel a weight of 8.8 percent in the consumer price index in 1961. Since the farmer receives less than 40 percent of the consumer's food dollar and an even smaller share of the consumer's clothing dollar, the farm component of the cost-of-living index was only 12 percent in 1963. I expect it to decline further.

A continuation of technological change also can permit agriculture to make a contribution to the national economic growth by releasing land for nonagricultural uses during the next several decades. We expect that extensive acreages will be released for urban development, transportation, forestry, and recreational uses at little real sacrifice in output.

Changes in the nonfarm economy will continue to influence the farm sector strongly through the labor market and the market for purchased inputs. Rapid and continuous nonfarm economic growth nationally and locally will remain a necessary condition for agricultural prosperity.

The farmworkers released from productive agricultural employment and the new entrants to the labor force from rural areas can find productive nonfarm employment most readily when employment opportunities are expanding rapidly. Annual net migration from farms since the war has typically been above 5 percent of farm population at the beginning of the year during periods of high-level economic activity. During each recession since the war, net migration has fallen to below 3 percent of the farm population.

The gains to agriculture from rapid economic growth in the nonfarm sector will be greatest if this growth is achieved without inflation in the general price level. The impact of moderate inflation has been transmitted to agriculture primarily through the market for manufactured inputs. Rising input prices and declining or stable prices of products have reduced farmers' gains from productivity increases in agriculture below the level that could have been achieved with stable input prices.

In summary, then, I foresee a national economy in which the urban-industrial sector is the dominant generator of economic change, but in which agriculture continues to make an important contribution through further gains in production efficiency.

Vernon W. Ruttan *is professor of agricultural economics at Purdue University. He served in 1962 as a member of the staff of the President's Council of Economic Advisers.*

ARLEY D. WALDO

FARMING ON THE URBAN FRINGE

CITIES have grown outward into the countryside throughout our history. The displacement of agriculture has long been a feature of urban industrial development in some sections—for example, the northeastern seaboard. Now, however, the effect of urban expansion on agriculture is regarded with a much greater degree of urgency because its nature has changed and because it has become a national phenomenon.

Urbanization takes a variety of forms. It used to be confined chiefly to a gradual expansion of cities, whose outward growth was limited by the prevailing means of transportation. Improved transportation has altered the pattern to include rapid urbanization of land along arterial highways, encirclement of agricultural land, and an uneven diffusion of the urban uses over the countryside.

Rural-urban fringe areas are characterized by a shift of rural land to urban uses. The economic force of city growth on farming is more important, however, than the actual loss of farmland. One sign of it is a rise in land values and real estate tax levels, so that farmers find it difficult to expand their operations through the purchase of additional land.

The growth of the nonfarm population in formerly rural sections leads to a demand for more public facilities and services, like new schools, roads, and water and sewer mains. The sequel is higher tax rates on property, higher land values, and a greater tax burden.

Real estate taxes on farm property are higher near cities than in predominantly rural areas.

McGehee H. Spears, of the Department of Agriculture, indicated that farm real estate taxes per acre in metropolitan counties were twice as high as taxes on farms in counties next to metropolitan counties and five times the level of taxes in rural counties in 1960. Part of the higher real estate tax burden on farms in the rural-urban fringe is due to the higher value of farm real estate. The average value of farms in metropolitan counties was nearly 300 dollars an acre and in nonmetropolitan counties slightly more than 100 dollars in 1959.

139

The higher property taxloads mean higher fixed costs for the farm operation. Tax increases have led sometimes to more intensive use of the land remaining in agriculture, but they have also been partly responsible for forcing land out of agriculture before it is actually needed for urban development. The amount of land forced out of agriculture often exceeds the amount moving into nonagricultural uses. It is not uncommon therefore to find temporary increases in the amount of idle land near expanding urban centers.

Although urban encroachment has proceeded rapidly, farmlands still account for most of our land resources.

The surface land area of the United States (including 369 million acres in Alaska and Hawaii) totals approximately 2.3 billion acres. Hugh H. Wooten, Karl Gertel, and William C. Pendleton, of the Department of Agriculture, have indicated that 75 percent of the total land area of the 48 contiguous States was used for crops, pasture, and range in 1959.

Special-use areas—including urban and built-up areas; parks and other extensive facilities; and farmsteads and farm roads and lanes—accounted for 139 million acres in 1959. Some lands in nonagricultural uses are excluded from this classification. Not counted among special-use areas are rural lands used for industrial and commercial sites, mining areas, quarry sites, power-line rights-of-way, cemeteries, and golf courses. In addition, special-use areas exclude the area occupied by villages and towns with populations of less than a thousand and by nonfarm residences located in rural areas.

The amount of land used for nonagricultural purposes is small compared with our total land resources. Land in nonfarm uses and wasteland comprise only about 10 percent of the total land area of the Nation.

The amount of land in special uses has increased at a substantial rate in the past decade. Messrs. Wooten, Gertel, and Pendleton estimated that rural land was diverted to nonagri-

cultural uses at the rate of about 2 million acres a year between 1950 and 1960. Approximately one-half of the rural land taken for nonagricultural uses over this period went into residential, commercial, industrial, and transportation uses. The remaining land was diverted to use for parks, wildlife refuges, national defense areas, and other extensive, nonagricultural uses.

How much additional land will go into nonagricultural uses in the future? Prof. Raleigh Barlowe, of Michigan State University, has suggested that approximately 205 million acres of nonagricultural land will be needed for a national population of 225 million, and 226 million acres for 300 million. These projections are equal to about 11 percent and 12 percent, respectively, of the total land area of the conterminous States.

The diversion of rural land to nonagricultural uses undoubtedly will continue as our urban population grows and standards of living rise.

But, as Dr. Barlowe and others have contended, the shift of agricultural lands to nonagricultural uses will have only a modest influence on total land use patterns in the United States over the next half century.

The loss of farmland to nonagricultural uses has created some concern about our ability to provide adequate supplies of agricultural products for future generations. Because of the relatively small effect of urban expansion on the overall supply of agricultural land and continued technological advances in American agriculture, it is unlikely that underproduction will be a problem in the near future. The present status of our productive capacity is reflected by a decline in the total land in farms, notwithstanding a sizable amount of tillable land that was not under cultivation in 1963.

A shortage of agricultural land over the next 50 years is not probable. Marion Clawson, R. Burnell Held, and Charles H. Stoddard, in their study of the future land requirements of the United States for Resources for the

Future, Inc. (published in *Land for the Future* by The Johns Hopkins Press, Baltimore, in 1960), concluded that a shortage of agricultural land is unlikely for the period up to the year 2000. Rather, they have suggested that a continued excess supply of cropland is likelier in the next few decades.

More important is the influence of urban industrial development on the rural communities near expanding metropolitan centers.

We all have seen how fertile farmland is being taken for residences, commercial and industrial purposes, and roadways. But only a part of the land going into nonagricultural uses each year comes from land that was used for crops or livestock. Of the land diverted from rural uses between 1950 and 1960, 40 percent was from cropland and grassland pasture, 40 percent from forest, and 20 percent from idle land.

Estimates of the amount of farmland moving into urban uses tend to understate, however, the effect of urban expansion on land use patterns.

Often there is a tendency toward less intensive use of some of the land that remains in agriculture. Moreover, urban dispersal often leads to an increase in the acreage of idle land. Considered over a longer period of time, changes in land use in the rural-urban fringe are likely to involve a shift from agricultural use to nonuse and a subsequent shift of idle land and forest land into urban uses. Part of the forest land and idle land going into nonagricultural uses was used at one time for farming.

In a study of landholdings in 1960 in the northern part of New Castle County, Del., William M. Crosswhite, of the University of Delaware, and Gerald F. Vaughn, of the Department of Agriculture, classified ownership units of 10 or more acres lying outside subdivisions and incorporated municipalities. They found that agricultural ownership units contained 48 percent of the land area included in the survey. Commercial farms, though, accounted

for only 61 percent of the land in agricultural property classes. The remaining 39 percent was in residential farms, farms in the process of being transferred to nonagricultural use, and farms on which more than one-half of the cropland had been placed in the Federal Conservation Reserve Program.

Ownership units being used primarily for purposes other than farming contained 35 percent of the total acreage of cropland and uncropped tillable land in the area. Nearly half of this land was in units used chiefly as rural residences and country estates. Much of the tillable land was not being farmed. Idle tillable land accounted for 14 percent of the total land area, and cropland represented only 38 percent.

THE PROXIMITY of urban markets has been important in the development of agriculture in the vicinity of metropolitan centers.

More than a century ago, J. H. von Thünen, a German economist, studied the impact of location on the pattern of agricultural land use. He developed a theoretical model based on distance to market and commodity characteristics as the major determinants of land use patterns around an isolated central city. Other factors—such as soil, climate, topography, and transportation facilities—were assumed to be uniform throughout the area.

Von Thünen concluded, on the basis of his simple model, that the intensity of land use would diminish as distance to the central market increased. Nearby areas would be devoted to the production of bulky and perishable commodities. The more distant areas would be used for raising products that were more easily transported and for grazing.

Economic models explaining the location of agricultural production have been modified subsequently to account for variations in some of the factors that Von Thünen assumed to be constant. These models recognize the importance of distance to market and transportation costs as well as differences in other factors in affecting the location of agricultural production. Specialized areas of farming have developed within the United States as a result of spatial, natural, and institutional factors. Economists have explained the tendency toward regional specialization by what is called the "principle of comparative advantage."

Comparative advantage refers to the relative profitability of producing various commodities in different geographic areas, given the existing differences in location with respect to markets, transportation costs, natural conditions, and other factors. The principle of comparative advantage is simply a concept that indicates that farmers in a particular section will tend to emphasize the production of commodities that give them the highest net returns.

Regional specialization in agriculture cannot be attributed entirely to differences in either natural or spatial factors. Some areas may have advantages with respect to various institutional factors, such as public subsidies and tax concessions, zoning ordinances, and legal regulation of production and marketing areas. Such factors affect production costs within regions and the cost of moving commodities between various regions.

Farms near cities have realized certain locational advantages. The influence of population growth on agriculture in the rural-urban fringe is reflected by changes in land use patterns. But it is difficult to ascertain the relative importance of nearness to urban markets because of the trend toward regional specialization in American agriculture. Part of the difference between farms in metropolitan counties and those in other counties is due to the fact that metropolitan centers and urban growth are concentrated in certain regions.

Donald J. Bogue has attempted to measure changes in the amount of land used for urban purposes within standard metropolitan statistical areas between 1929 and 1955.

His findings, presented in *Metropolitan Growth and the Conversion of Land to Nonagricultural Uses* (Studies in Population Distribution, No. 11, Scripps Foundation, 1956), indicated that the land area in agricultural uses actually increased in 60 of 147 areas. The amount of increase in agricultural land in these areas exceeded the loss of agricultural land to other uses in the remaining 87 areas over the 20-year period. An increased demand for agricultural commodities because of growth of population in the metropolitan counties may have been partly responsible for the overall increase in agricultural lands.

Approximately 13 percent of all farms in the United States in 1959 were located within standard metropolitan statistical areas, which (with minor exceptions) include counties that have a central city of at least 50 thousand inhabitants and adjacent counties that are essentially metropolitan in nature and economically and socially integrated with the county of the central city. Farms in the 211 standard metropolitan statistical areas in the conterminous States in 1959 contained 9 percent of all land in farms and represented 23 percent of the aggregate value of farm real estate.

Commercial farms near cities have tended to emphasize the production of perishable products for direct human consumption. Agriculture on the rural-urban fringe has differed therefore from farming in other areas because of the disproportionately large number of farms that concentrate on the production of certain kinds of bulky and perishable products, such as milk for fluid consumption, fresh fruits and vegetables, poultry and eggs, and nursery products.

Distance to market at one time was a major factor in the competitive position of farms producing bulky and perishable commodities. New technologies in processing, handling, and storage of those products and the development of modern transportation have lessened the competitive advantage of farms near cities. Many farms on the rural-urban fringe are still oriented, however, to local markets. And the local production of various perishable and specialty products is found on the periphery of most cities.

Comparison of commercial farms classified by major source of income indicates that 4 of the 11 major types of farms identified in the 1959 Census of Agriculture accounted for a disproportionately large number of farms in metropolitan counties. Only 12 percent of all commercial farms in the United States in 1959 were located in those counties. But metropolitan counties contained 44 percent of all vegetable farms, 36 percent of all fruit-and-nut farms, 22 percent of all poultry farms, and 17 percent of all dairy farms. Less important than in nonmetropolitan counties were livestock farms and ranches, general farms, and the various types of field-crop farms.

CERTAIN REGIONS have become noted as dairy areas because they are responsible for a significant part of our dairy production and because dairy products account for a major part of their agricultural production. The major concentrations of dairy farms are in the Northeast, the Lake States, and the Pacific Coast States. Dairy farming, however, is carried on in every part of the United States, and milk markets have developed around urban centers as a direct result of growth of the urban population.

The production of milk for fluid consumption is an enterprise on a large number of farms on the rural-urban fringes. Dairy farms accounted for 26 percent of all commercial farms in metropolitan counties in 1959. Producing milk for fresh use was restricted in earlier years to farms close to consuming centers because of the perishability of the product and the relatively high cost of transportation. The zone in which fresh milk is produced has widened over time as a result of improvements in transportation and marketing facilities. Nonetheless, farms specializing in the production of fresh milk have continued to be important in areas around urban centers. The locational advantages of dairy farms with nearby urban markets can be attributed partly to lower transportation costs and partly to the regulation of milk marketing areas.

Dairy farms in the United States range in size from small enterprises, sometimes associated with a system of diversified farming, to the large and highly specialized operations. They are characterized, in terms of the value of agricultural production, by a small proportion of very large farms and a small proportion of very small farms as compared with other types of commercial farms.

Farms producing fresh milk tend to be larger than dairy farms producing milk for manufacturing uses. This is partly a result of the sanitary requirements of the production of milk for fluid consumption, which make small-scale units relatively uneconomical.

There has been a significant trend toward larger dairy operations. The number of farms with milk cows declined by 39 percent between 1954 and 1960, but this drop was confined mostly to farms with relatively small herds. The number of farms with 50 or more cows actually increased by 41 percent.

Los Angeles County, Calif., is an example of a county that is highly urbanized and important from the standpoint of agricultural production. Most of the 6 million residents were classified as urban in 1960. Rural nonfarm and rural farm residents accounted for only 1.1 percent and 0.1 percent, respectively, of the county's total population. There were, however, 4,811 farms in the county in 1959. Around 479 thousand acres were included in farms—about 18 percent of the total land area of the county.

Although urban land pressures have resulted in the loss of farmland to urban uses, Los Angeles County is the center of the highly specialized dairy area of southern California.

It ranked first among all counties in the United States in 1954 and 1959 in volume of whole milk sold and in value of dairy products sold. The total value of dairy products sold in 1959 was 55 million dollars—about 1.4 percent of the total value of all dairy sales in the Nation.

Dairy farms in Los Angeles County are among the largest and most specialized in the United States. The value of dairy production per farm on 418 farms reporting sales of dairy products in 1959 averaged 132 thousand dollars. Most dairy farms in the county have adopted the practice of drylot dairy farming. Nearly all feed and replacement stock are purchased, and the farms are typically small in terms of acreage.

High land values are chiefly responsible for the intensive land use practices followed by dairy producers in Los Angeles County. Urban encroachment upon agricultural land has been an important factor leading to high land values and corresponding increases in real estate taxes. In addition, dairy farms have had to compete with high-value vegetable and fruit crops for the land remaining in agriculture. As a result, most of the forage fed on dairy farms in the county is produced in other counties of the State where the competition for land is less severe.

Dairy farms in Los Angeles County are not typical operations. They are much larger in terms of gross sales and more specialized than most dairy farms found in other metropolitan counties.

Dairy farms on the periphery of other urban centers exhibit similar but less extreme characteristics, however. Dairy producers on the rural-urban fringe tend to make intensive use of land as a consequence of increasing urban land pressures. This has led in some instances to the adoption of land-saving, drylot dairy farming and the purchase of most of the feed required for the herd. In other areas, where land pressures have not been so great, at least part of the feed requirement is raised on the farm.

An important characteristic of dairy farms is their relatively high labor requirement. Many dairy farms depend almost exclusively on family labor, but labor from outside the family is required on the larger farms. The major labor requirement on drylot dairy farms is for the milking operation. Labor is required for both milking and the production of feed on other farms.

A study of 30 large dairy farms in Massachusetts in 1960, by Deane Lee, of the University of Massachusetts, indicated that hired labor represented more than two-thirds of the total labor force required by the farms. The average labor force on the 30 farms, each of which had dairy herds of 100 or more cows, was 6 man-equivalents. These farms had an average of 197 owned tillable acres, and 25 farms rented some additional cropland.

Another characteristic of dairy farms should be noted. A large share of the financial investment on dairy farms is in capital items other than land.

Dairy producers cannot easily shift from milk production to other agricultural enterprises because of their large investment in the herd and in specialized buildings and equipment. Moreover, increases in the size of the operation usually involve substantial increases in nonland investment. Rising land values around urban centers offer to some farmers a chance of large capital gains. But farmers forced to sell farms because of urban land pressures also may suffer capital losses on that part of their investment which is in nonland items. Dairy producers are particularly liable to those capital losses because of their large nonland investment.

POULTRY FARMS accounted for 8 percent of all commercial farms in metropolitan counties in 1959.

Farms specializing in poultry production are generally most numerous in the Northeastern States. Areas with a high concentration of poultry farms are in Massachusetts, Connecticut, Rhode Island, Pennsylvania, and the Delaware-Maryland-Virginia peninsula.

Significant changes have occurred with respect to poultry enterprises. Small flocks of chickens traditionally have been a sideline. Small enterprises, however, are becoming less common.

Vegetable farms and fruit-and-nut farms accounted for a total of 11 percent of all commercial farms in metropolitan counties in 1959. Prominent among areas in which vegetable production is highly concentrated are such diverse areas as Long Island, Florida, the lower Rio Grande Valley in Texas, southwestern Arizona, and the area near San Francisco Bay.

The production of fruit and vegetables for local markets is important on the fringe of a number of metropolitan areas. But large quantities of fruit and vegetables are produced at considerable distances from large centers.

Thus farming on the rural-urban fringe is a complex mixture of farms ranging from small, part-time operations to large, highly specialized units. Because they tend to concentrate on the production of perishable products for direct human consumption, farms near urban markets tend to differ in some respects from farms in other areas.

The advantage of proximity to urban markets has tended, however, to decline with the development of our modern transportation system and technical advances in the processing, handling, and storage of agricultural commodities. Meanwhile, urban land pressures have increased.

ARLEY D. WALDO *is assistant professor of agricultural economics in the University of Connecticut. He has master's and doctor's degrees from Michigan State University, where he was a research associate before he assumed his present position in 1962.*

Agricultural Employment

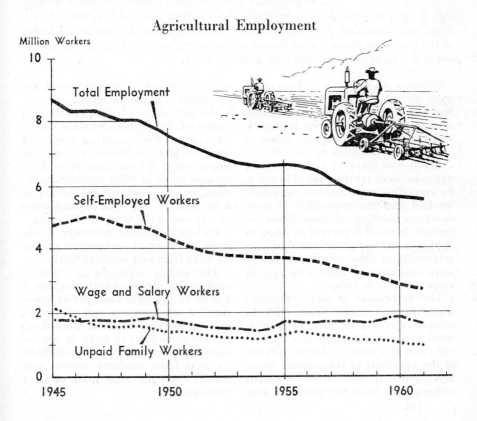

WILLIAM M. CROSSWHITE

PART-TIME FARMING;
PART-TIME JOBS

NONFARM income of farm families has grown steadily and in 1963 accounted for more than a third of their disposable income. At the same time, changing work patterns have been reshaping the traditional image of the part-time farmer from that of an amateur farmer to that of an underemployed farm operator who does nonfarm work.

Off-farm work is done by farm operators in all economic farm classes. Some are commercial farmers who seek seasonal employment when farmwork is slack. Some have regular nonfarm employment and farm on the side.

About 5 of every 11 farm operators did some work off their farms in 1963. By extending the trends of the fifties, we find that the proportion of farm operators working off their farms increased from 38.8 percent in 1949 to approximately 47 percent in 1963; the percentage of those who had nonfarm work 100 days or more was 23.3 in 1949 and 32.5 in 1959.

The percentage of farm operators whose family income from off-farm sources exceeded the value of agricultural products they sold was 29.8 in 1954 and 37.2 in 1963. Twelve percent of the operators of commercial farms had more income from nonfarm sources than from the products they sold, compared to 89 percent of the operators of part-time farms.

We have not yet faced up to the real extent of the shifts of workers out of agriculture. Only 1 of 12 employed males in the United States was in farming in 1963. A large number of these farmers work in other major occupations, but do some farming and are in a position to shift quickly and completely out of the farm classification.

Part-time farming generally is defined as the use of the operator's labor for both farm and nonfarm work.

The census definition is: "Farms with a value of sales of farm products of $50 to $2,499 were classified as 'part-time' if the operator was under 65 years of age and he either worked off the farm 100 days or more or the income he and members of his household received from nonfarm sources was greater than the total value of farm products sold."

146

The 1959 Census of Agriculture classified 885,785 farms as part-time farms; they were 24 percent of all our farms.

The South Atlantic States had the highest proportion, 31.1 percent of part-time farms. The West North Central States had the lowest, 11.4 percent. West Virginia had the highest rate among the States, 48.8 percent. Nebraska had the lowest, 5.2 percent.

Part-time farms generally are small. More than half of the farms operated by part-time farmers have fewer than 50 acres. One in seven has fewer than 10 acres. Three-fourths of the total number of part-time farms had fewer than 100 acres. Only 1.1 percent of all part-time farms were larger than 500 acres.

Family income of part-time farm families reported in the 1959 census averaged 4,890 dollars. Income from the sale of farm products, after expenses, averaged 176 dollars per farm and made up only 3.5 percent of family income. Income from off-farm sources added 4,459 dollars to family income. Nonmoney income from food produced and eaten on the farm and house rental made up the remaining 431 dollars.

Small part-time farms are common in all sections. The incidence of part-time farms is high near industrial areas and in the South. Part-time farms with large acreage are commoner in the mountain region and in Texas and California.

Harvested cropland was reported by 73.4 percent of the part-time farm operators. Farms reporting harvested cropland had an average of 18 acres of crops. More than two-thirds had fewer than 19 acres of harvested cropland. Only 5 percent had 50 acres or more of harvested cropland. More than 60 percent of the land used for harvested crops was in corn and hay.

Cattle were kept on almost 70 percent of the part-time farms, milk cows on 41 percent, hogs on 46 percent, and chickens on 53 percent. The sale of cattle and calves accounted for more than one-fourth of all the farm products sold. The sale of cattle, calves, hogs, pigs, and dairy products accounted for nearly one-half of the value of all farm products sold.

The use of land is much the same on part-time farms and full-time farms. A four-county study in Ohio by H. R. Moore and W. A. Wayt, of Ohio State University, indicated that the full-time farmer may operate a larger number of acres, but the percentage of lands in various crops was much the same on both part-time and commercial farms. It seems therefore that the kind of land resources—and not whether the farming is part time or full time—determines the utilization of land.

Most part-time farmers develop enterprises that fit their vicinity. The part-time farmer tends to conform to the dominant type of farming around him. For example, in a study in the cotton-producing Clay-Hills area of Mississippi, Herbert Hoover and John C. Crecink, of the Department of Agriculture, classified 7 in 10 of the part-time farms as cotton farms and 1 in 10 as cash-grain farms. Only 1 in 20 could be classified as a livestock farm.

PART-TIME farmers work in many types of industrial, commercial, and service occupations, depending primarily on the jobs available in their communities.

James R. Martin and John H. Southern, of the Department of Agriculture, in a study of northeast Texas, learned that farming was the major occupation of 44 percent of the part-time farmers. Sixteen percent worked in construction and manufacturing, including carpentry, painting, electrification, and a steel plant. Eleven percent were employed as operators of bulldozers, garage mechanics, and laborers in oil and gas fields. Seven percent worked in stores. Six percent were in professional occupations. Eight percent were retired. The remaining 8 percent were in other occupations, which included domestic and custodial workers and housekeepers.

Part-time farm operators included in the 1959 Census of Agriculture ranged in age from 25 to 64. Part-time farm operators 45 to 54 years old included 33 percent of all part-time farm operators. Twenty-five percent ranged in age from 55 to 64, 25 percent from 35 to 44, and 13 percent from 25 to 34 years of age. Only 2 percent were under 25. By definition, operators over 65 years of age are classified as part-retirement and are not included as part-time farm operators in the census of agriculture.

THE DECISION to become a part-time farmer is determined by many economic, social, and personal motives.

The need to supplement family income is the reason most frequently given by farm families who have decided to farm part time and engage in nonfarm work. The influence of a farm background, however, is often cited by the city dweller who has purchased a farm and moved back to the country.

Others say they became part-time farmers because they liked farming, wanted a hobby, wished to give their children a farming experience, wanted to get away from city living, sought security and retirement, or looked on it as a step to full-time farming.

In a study of part-time farming in the rural-urban fringe of Philadelphia in 1961, I found the types of nonfarm employment of part-time farmers clustering around three groups—professionals, the craftsmen, and operatives. The professional occupations were primarily in engineering and research near Chester, Pa., and Wilmington, Del. Occupations of 22 percent of the sample of 146 part-time farm operators were classified as professional; 27 percent, craftsmen; 23 percent, operatives; 15 percent, retail and clerical; 8 percent, service; and 5 percent, farm labor.

I GIVE two examples of the differences in circumstances and background of persons in part-time farming.

Mr. Jones considers himself to be an amateur farmer. The family is pleased with his decision in 1960 to buy the 45-acre farm on which they are now living. It provides a place to forget the problems and noise of the shop where Mr. Jones has worked as a machine operator since 1950.

The family keeps a cow and 35 laying hens to provide milk and eggs for family use. Feed produced on 19 acres of corn and 5 acres of alfalfa is used in feeding the cow and chickens, and any remaining feed is sold. They have a garden and an acre of potatoes.

Farm products used in the home in 1962 had a value of 1,010 dollars. Four sons and a daughter, 4 to 17 years old, consumed a lot of vegetables, and did much of the work in the garden and with the chickens.

Both Mr. and Mrs. Jones are employed off the farm and receive a combined income of 8,978 dollars. Farm sales average only 250 dollars, and so nonfarm income must be used to pay the additional farm expenses, which average 950 dollars a year.

Mr. and Mrs. Jones feel that part-time farming is a wonderful way to spend the family's spare time. The farm provides much of the food for the family and an opportunity for the children to learn the responsibilities of caring for the animals.

Mr. Smith is 50 years old. The farm had been his livelihood until he left to work for the Government in 1933. The family moved back to the farm in 1946 and farmed full time until 1959. He was working on an assembly line in 1963 while farming 30 acres of his own and renting 75 acres more.

Mr. Smith thinks that work off the farm was necessary in order for the family to achieve a desirable level of living. Earnings from the farm were not providing an adequate income for the family, which includes a 25-year-old son, who began working off the farm in 1960.

Vegetable crop production provided the major source of farm income. The cropping program consists of 10 acres of corn, 13 acres of tomatoes, 25 acres of asparagus, and 6 acres of melons. There is a minimum of conflict between farm-nonfarm labor requirements, since Mr. Smith works on the second shift from 4 p.m. until 12:30 a.m. His retired father living nearby works about 100 hours each year on the farm. Obtaining sufficient help during the harvest season has been a common problem on vegetable farms in the area and also a major problem for Mr. Smith.

The farm is being maintained in a condition that makes it possible to earn additional income for the family. Although Mr. Smith does not expect to return to full-time farming in the near future, the farm will provide security and income if the nonfarm job should end. He believes that if the farm is profitable while he is working off the farm, it will be ready to use if he should become unemployed.

THE ADVANTAGES and disadvantages of a part-time farming enterprise depend largely on the circumstances under which the operator enters part-time farming. The primary advantage of part-time farming for operators on low-producing, low-income farms is that fuller use is made of labor. Many small farms have underemployed labor resources that can be shifted into non-farm employment to provide additional income.

Hobbyists and many of those moving into part-time farming from urban communities are primarily seeking the benefits of rural life. Country living, special livestock and crop enterprises, and training for children are important intangibles they seek. Additional family income may be relatively unimportant to the hobbyist. Nonfarm income may even be required to support the farm operation.

Results of a study of rural development problems and prospects in 1960 in Fayette, Raleigh, and Summers Counties in West Virginia by W. H. Metzler and W. W. Amentrout, of the University of West Virginia, indicate there is a hard core of farm people who wish to stay in the area and combine small-scale farming with a nonfarm job. Expanded agricultural activity, training of young adults in nonfarm skills, and greater efforts toward industrial expansion were the recommended lines for rural development. Local industrial expansion was found to be desirable in the three counties because most of the people hold a strong attachment to the area and have interest and experience in industry and other nonfarm employment as well as in agriculture.

The small size of many part-time farms is a major disadvantage and severely limits income earned from the farm enterprise. Small farms can mean high costs of production and high costs of marketing. Production costs tend to be high because technological gains through mechanization cannot be realized on small farms, and good management practices often are neglected.

Lack of farming experience is another major disadvantage for some. Technology and farming methods have been changing so fast that even the operators with farming experience find it difficult to keep up to date. Time must be allocated to gaining new information and planning the farm operation. The part-time farmer must spend much of his mental effort on his nonfarm job, and farm planning may suffer in the competition among family and nonfarm work activities for his time.

Underemployed farm labor has long been an important farm problem. Theodore Schultz, of the University of Chicago, has encouraged full employment with many jobs in the rest of the economy as a first step in correcting the excessive supply of labor in farming.

Industrial development, harnessed to modern technology, has broadened the economic interdependence of rural and urban people during the fifties and early sixties. Advances in agricultural technology, coupled with relatively full employment outside agriculture, have enabled many farmers to leave the farm. For some of those remaining on farms the movement of industrial plants into rural communities has created new off-farm jobs close to home.

Part-time farming may help solve the problem of underemployment in agriculture. The growth in industry, trade, and services has coincided with such developments as improvements of roads and the almost universal ownership of automobiles. Farm people therefore can commute to jobs in towns and continue to live on farms.

Technological forces in our highly competitive commercial agriculture will continue to press for greater efficiency. Many farmers whose small resources of land, equipment, capital, and income can hardly meet that competition and therefore welcome the chance to supplement their income by off-farm work.

Unlike an expansion of the farm operation to a level that will provide a satisfactory income, the move into part-time farming may not involve an undue financial burden. Nonfarm employment provides an opportunity for full employment of labor. In addition, the rental value of the home, farm-produced food, and the appreciation of land value frequently provide returns at a rate comparable to returns that may be obtained if the investment funds in land, buildings, and equipment were invested elsewhere.

The effects of rural industrialization influence most segments of a community. In a summary of five studies of the effects of locating industrial plants in several communities in Louisiana, Iowa, Utah, and Mississippi, T. Maitland and R. E. Friend, of the Department of Agriculture, found that about 3 out of 10 of the plant workers lived on farms. It could reasonably be expected that with Federal, State, and local agencies giving increased attention to the problems associated with underemployed farm labor, rural industrialization will foster participation in part-time farming.

Changes in agriculture indicate that part-time farmers will continue to be an important segment of the farm population. Mechanization, larger farms, and increased capital requirements are shaping farming along the lines of a highly specialized occupation. As fewer farms are required to provide food and fiber, many operators will be forced to seek nonfarm employment. Many will prefer to live on the farm and work in local industries rather than move to cities.

There is little agreement as to the extent to which part-time farming is becoming an accepted permanent arrangement. Many think that part-time farming is an intermediate stage in the transition of the family from full-time farming to either full-time nonfarm work or retirement. Less frequently, part-time farming is a way of getting started in full-time farming. With 45 percent of all farmers working off their farms and with part-time farms constituting 30 percent of all farms in 1963, I believe there is some basis for recognizing part-time farming as an acceptable adjustment to changing conditions in agriculture.

I found in my study of part-time farming near Philadelphia that 10 years was the usual length of time in part-time farming for the sample of 146 part-time farm operators. Twelve percent had been in part-time farming 20 years or more. Only 5 percent had less than 2 years of experience in part-time farming. Besides being a transitional phase to leaving farming, therefore, it seems that part-time farming may be a semipermanent arrangement for an important part of our farm population. For many farm operators, however, part-time farming will continue to provide a temporary stage in the process of adjusting to changing economic conditions and will be apparent particularly in the rural-urban fringe of cities and in submarginal agricultural areas.

There are a number of implications of the increasing role that part-time farming is assuming in agriculture. For some time in the future, I expect that part-time farming will provide a means of facilitating the movement of farm operators out of agriculture; enable many families to supplement family income from farm earnings; bring about a decreasing dependence on farming as a source of family income; control a large portion of total farm resources; and foster a continued response to differentials in labor productivity and wages between the agricultural and nonagricultural sectors of the economy.

A good first step in planning a farm operation is to set family goals. Good organization and operation of any farm are closely related to what the family is hoping to gain from the farming operation and activity.

It is important to remember that the nonfarm job will obligate a certain portion of one's time. The hours remaining for farmwork may not be compatible with many livestock and crop enterprises, and care must be taken to minimize the conflict between farm and nonfarm labor requirements.

Family and hired labor are part of the potential farm labor supply. Because the family may be directly involved in the farm operation, it is necessary to consider the preferences of all members of the family. One may want to organize the farm so that it does not interfere seriously with other interests of the family.

WILLIAM M. CROSSWHITE *joined the faculty of the University of Delaware as assistant professor of agricultural economics in 1960. In 1962 he completed a four-county study of part-time farming in the tristate area of Pennsylvania, New Jersey, and Delaware.*

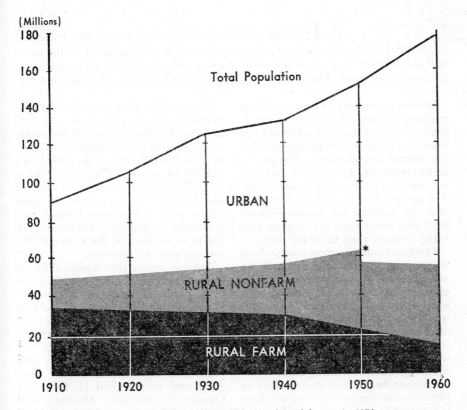

*Difference due to new urban and rural definition adopted for use in 1950 census. Data from Bureau of the Census and Economic Research Service.

WARREN R. BAILEY AND E. L. BAUM

FARMING ON THE
ECONOMIC MARGINS

I N ANY discussion of land and people and the effect of national change and growth on them, we need to be mindful of the acres and the farmers that according to some standards are failures or near-failures in agriculture, even though we can offer no perfect solution to their situation.

We imply no odious or smug comparisons when we use the term "marginal" for land that has relatively low value for farming and returns little to the farmer for his efforts. Nor do we lack in humanity when we say the farmers are the have-nots of agriculture. The point is that the land is a resource and the farmers are people—people who may need help or, indeed, may want no more than to be left alone.

Marginal land is not necessarily land whose crop yields are the lowest per acre. Because gross return or total revenue is related directly to yields, it may seem obvious that low-yielding land is marginal. But the key is net revenue after expenses are met. If the low-yielding land also has low acreable expenses, net revenue may be greater than on somewhat higher yielding land.

Another key is not the amount of net acreable return—as long as there is a net—but the farmer's total annual income.

For example, suppose 50 acres of type A land yields a net return of 20 dollars an acre; the farmer's yearly income is 1 thousand dollars. Suppose 100 acres of type B land yields a net of only 15 dollars an acre—and 1,500 dollars a year. This is the situation of some of our low-yielding (per acre) dryland wheat areas in Montana, Kansas, and Colorado, for example. Yet some think the drier sections of the Great Plains are marginal for farming.

Another section that is generally considered marginal for farming is the cut-over parts of northern Minnesota, Wisconsin, and Michigan, where thin forest-type soils, a short growing season, and small-size farms mean relatively low annual returns from farming.

Still other areas of relatively low yields and farm income include marginal and submarginal lands in the Ozarks—in Arkansas, Missouri, and southern Illinois—and the southern and northern Appalachian region. These

152

areas came to public notice when they were designated as redevelopment areas eligible to receive technical and financial assistance under the Area Redevelopment Act of 1961. The farms are characterized by large amounts of idle land, low productivity, infertile and eroded land, small-scale units, insufficient capital to bring about desirable farm adjustments, low levels of management, and low volume of marketable products.

These farmers do not have adequate productive resources. They generally do not have the education and off-farm employment opportunities or receive as many benefits from Federal and State educational and farm programs as the more successful farmers. Generally, they are inefficient producers and may farm good or poor land. Operators of small farms may not necessarily be inefficient and low-income farmers, but they usually are.

Because marginal farmers lack adequate capital, land resources, and possibly education to enable them to use the latest technical knowledge and innovations, the adjustments that successful farmers usually make appear to be impossible to them. The technological revolution in agriculture has bypassed the have-not farm people and actually may have left them relatively worse off.

Their ability to eke out a return from farming to support their families depends largely on cost-price relationships, which have been unfavorable since about 1950.

Furthermore, many of the farmers on substandard farms are of an age that may limit their productivity and their willingness to take risks and adopt new practices. Some of these older men lack adequate physical strength for farmwork; their children may have left to work elsewhere. These have-not farms therefore do not receive a sufficient labor input for their best economic production. Farm operators more than 45 years old may find it hard to enter nonfarm employment, because industry prefers younger peo-

ple and also because uncertainties and obstacles are associated with migration to cities.

Let us examine four kinds of marginal farming localities as a lesson in agricultural history and maybe as a warning.

FARMING has been marginal in the Lake States cutover area. Once heavily timbered with straight-stemmed fir and pine trees, the northern third of Minnesota, Wisconsin, and Michigan long since was cutover.

A big influx of population came between 1870 and 1900, when the harvesting and processing of timber was at its height. The first farming was associated closely with the logging camps and mill towns. The chief farm product was hay for the draft animals used in logging. Fresh produce was grown for local use. When the trees had been cut, the loggers moved to the Oregon forests. The cash-hay farmers were stranded.

The fertility of the relatively thin forest soils was depleted after a few years. The shorter growing season dictated the crops that could be grown. Hay and pasture consequently became the important uses of the farmland, and some dairy farming was started on a small—but relatively efficient— scale. The cows are of good quality. They are well cared for and are good producers. The cutover dairy farm must be efficiently operated if it is to prosper, as most of the grain fed the cows is imported, chiefly from the Corn Belt, 100 miles or more to the south. Soils and climate are not well suited to growing corn, and the limited acreage must be reserved for hay and pasture.

An example of farming in the cutover is Bayfield County, in Wisconsin, where 60 percent of the farms were classified in the 1959 Census of Agriculture as commercial farms and 40 percent as part-time or part-residential farms. The 538 commercial farms averaged 236 acres, and the value of land and buildings averaged 9,820 dollars. For comparison, Corn Belt farms, as represented by Webster County, Iowa, had about the same total acreage of land, but had land and buildings valued about eight times higher than the cutover farm.

The average Bayfield County farm had 8 acres of corn, harvested as silage, and 12 acres of oats—about one-eighth as many acres of grain and soybeans as the Corn Belt farm. The average cutover farm used the largest portion of its land, 60 acres, for hay to provide the forage for its 15 milk cows. It sold 5,320 dollars' worth of farm products. Its total expenses for purchased livestock feed, fertilizer, seeds, tractor fuel and oil, machine hire, and hired labor averaged 1,240 dollars, leaving a net return of 4,080 dollars to cover overhead expenses and any return to the operator for his labor and his investment in the farm. Net return, thus defined, was less than half that of the Corn Belt farm. At best, the average commercial farm in the cutover provides a modest living for its family. Forty-three percent of the operators of commercial farms worked off their farms for wages in 1959. One-fourth of them worked off their farms 100 days or more.

One farm in three in Bayfield County was a part-time farm in 1959. (A part-time farmer is defined as one who sells farm products in total value of 50 to 2,499 dollars, is less than 65 years old, and worked at least 100 days off the farm or received more income from nonfarm sources than the value of farm products sold.)

A MARGINAL farming area in the eastern Ozarks of Missouri has a rugged terrain, droughty soils that are low in plant nutrients, and much land not suited to farming. Only 6 percent of the area is cultivated. About two-thirds is woodland. Alluvial soils in the narrow valleys are the principal production resource of farming.

Early settlers were attracted by the hunting, fishing, the trees for homebuilding, and the streams. After about 1870, the population grew rapidly because of employment in railroad building and in the harvest of timber. Most people made their living from fishing, hunting, trapping, mining, logging, construction, and other nonfarm activities. When the railroad building and lumbering ceased, and the mines gave out, economic activity began to decline in the early 1900's.

From the beginning, a little farming had been practiced along the valleys. After the decline in construction, logging, and mining, many families were left stranded. Many who owned land turned to farming, often on subsistence units. In more recent years, many farmers and part-time farmers have found employment in construction, woodworking, cutting railroad ties, and related industries.

Farming in the eastern Ozarks of Missouri can be illustrated by data for the average commercial farm in Douglas County, in Missouri. Slightly more than half the farms classify as commercial farms, and a third of these had gross farm incomes of less than 2,500 dollars. The average commercial farm had 274 acres of land, but its lack of productivity is indicated by the low average farm value of about 10,150 dollars, as compared to nearly 80 thousand dollars for farms in Webster County, Iowa.

The Ozark commercial farm harvested crops on only 40 of its 274 acres. It had 5 acres in grain crops. The remaining 35 acres were mostly in hay crops. The chief source of income was a herd of 30 cattle, including 11 milk cows. The value of all products sold averaged about 4,460 dollars in 1959, about one-third as large as the sales on the Corn Belt farm. Out-of-pocket production expenses averaged about 2,600 dollars, leaving a net average return of 1,860 dollars to cover overhead expenses and a return to the operator for his labor and investment. Net return was about one-fifth as large as on the Corn Belt farm and about half as large as on the commercial farm in the cutover.

A third of the 934 commercial farm operators in Douglas County worked off their farms for wages in 1959. Almost half of them worked off their farms 100 days or more. There were 540 part-time farms whose operators worked off their farms for wages. These commercial and part-time farm operators held jobs in the commerce, trade, light industries, and services of the community.

In the Ozarks, many of the people with nonfarm jobs choose to continue living on the farms, which may have been in the family for generations.

One-seventh of the farms in Douglas County are part-retirement farms, which are much like the part-time farms, except that the operators are 65 years of age or more, and they do not work off the farm.

A MARGINAL farming area in northeastern Tennessee lies in the Great Valley between the Cumberland Mountains on the northwest and the Unakas on the southeast. The soils include fertile, alluvial limestone loams in the valleys and infertile stony ridges and knobs. Hills and streams limit the sizes of fields and farms. Only small machinery can be used efficiently.

Settlement began in the area late in the 18th century. Early settlers relied heavily on hunting and fishing, which they supplemented with small patches of corn and other crops for their living. The woods provided logs for their cabins, and the streams their water.

Improved transportation beginning about 1830 provided access to markets in the East and South. An agricultural economy was developed around the production of corn, whisky, tobacco, and livestock. By the end of the Civil War, the hilly soils had become depleted, and many farmers began migrating from the area in search of better land. The opening up of fertile prairies to the west and farm mechanization combined to reduce grain prices and forced the hill country of northeast Tennessee out of grain production into livestock farming.

Farming in the area is illustrated by data for Campbell County, Tenn. Only a third of the farms can be classified as commercial farms. Only one farm in eight sold more than 2,500 dollars' worth of products in 1959. Two-thirds of the farms were part-time or part-retirement farms. The farms averaged about 100 acres, less than one-half the acres in Corn Belt farms.

Despite its small size, the farm in east Tennessee uses less than one-fifth of its acres for harvested crops. Five of the 18 harvested acres are in grain. Such small acreages can support only the simplest and least expensive machines and the smallest of tractors. Much farmwork is done by mules. The grain is custom harvested. The chief source of cash income is tobacco, which often is grown on less than an acre. Some farmers have small herds of cattle. The total value of products sold in 1962 averaged about 3,100 dollars, only a fourth as large as the sales of the Corn Belt farm. Net returns above cash production expenses averaged 1,875 dollars on the commercial farms.

More than 40 percent of the operators of commercial farms worked off their farms for wages in 1959. There were also 455 operators of part-time farms; in all, 496 operators depended heavily on nonfarm income for their living.

Farming in northeastern Tennessee is marginal because hills handicap mechanization, poor soils and climate limit the potential for high-return cash crops, and small acreages long held as family properties seriously limit expansion and total output per farm.

THE HIGH PLAINS of the Southwest are considered marginal for farming by some people. It has a subhumid climate and a highly variable annual rainfall. Droughts and crop failures are frequent. Wind erosion was so severe during the thirties that many despaired of it as a farming area. After the Second World War, grain farming returned to the area, with some evidence of success.

The High Plains lie along the front of the Rocky Mountains, where Kansas, Oklahoma, and Texas meet Colorado and New Mexico. Much of the area is more than 4 thousand feet above sea level. Most of it was in cultivation by 1930. A remnant of native sod remained in eastern Colorado until after the Second World War, when some 600 thousand acres were plowed up in Kiowa County alone.

The earlier settlement generally was by small farmers, who were too poorly equipped and financed and who operated on too small a scale to survive the economic depression and the drought of the thirties. Many went bankrupt. Many moved west to seek a new start, leaving the Dust Bowl behind them.

Since 1940, the High Plains have been resettled by larger commercial farmers, who have modern, high-speed machinery that performs operations at the critical time. Today's farmers are using the latest scientific methods of dryland farming. Many are financially successful despite their comparatively low average yields of wheat and grain sorghum and despite an occasional year of crop failure.

Data from the 1959 Census of Agriculture show that in Kiowa County, about 9 in 10 farms are commercial farms—those whose value of products sold exceeded 2,500 dollars. A high percentage of commercial farms is not the earmark of a marginal farming area, as was noted in other areas. The average commercial farm in Kiowa County in 1959 was large in acreage. The value of land and buildings was equal to farm values in Webster County, Iowa. The value of products sold and net returns were a half larger than for the Iowa farms.

Some persons contend the High Plains is a marginal farming area because farm income varies greatly from year to year. This contention seems to be refuted by the economic situation of farms, which experienced drought in 1946–1961.

Good crops of wheat in 1946–1952 (except 1950) helped farmers get through the poor years of 1953–1957.

Wheat farmers survived the severe drought of the midfifties in various ways. One was the time-honored way of saving income from the good years to cover the expenses of living during succeeding poor crop years. Farmers in dryland areas, perhaps more than in other areas, have learned this from necessity. All people must learn to husband their wages between paychecks. In Great Plains wheat farming, the "paychecks" come less frequently. In the good years farm income may be two or three times the average, as it was on Kiowa County farms in 1947, 1948, 1951, and 1959–1961.

Another way that Kiowa County farmers and others survived the drought of the 1950's was to work for wages. Some took the idle combine harvester to another area where the crops were not hurt by drought and there earned wages by custom harvesting wheat for other farmers.

Some farmers in the drought area had a few cattle, which they maintained on the sparse native range and on forage sorghum raised whenever there was an occasional shower.

Still other grain farmers had slowly accumulated small herds of cattle during the good crop years (grass was good, too). When the poor years came and the grass was gone, they converted the accumulated herd into cash for use in the poor-crop, no-grass years. This is a special way in which livestock can lend stability to grain farming in the Plains. The livestock are built up during the good years, to be cashed when the drought comes and there is no longer any grass for the cattle. Finally, some grain farmers, as well as cattle ranchers, survived the drought of the midfifties by means of emergency feed programs subsidized by the Government.

Many of the farm families in the High Plains live in nearby towns, where they can enjoy city services and conveniences. About one-third of the commercial farmers in Kiowa County reported they did not live on their farms (1959 Census of Agriculture). Many country schools have been replaced by consolidated school systems in county seat towns. Wheat farmers now have no reason for living on the land itself because they no longer have workstock or other livestock on the farm requiring close attention. This pattern of living is tending to reduce the costs of community services for schools and roads.

There are lands in the High Plains that are marginal for farming, but they are not so extensive as once was believed. If they were extensive, their effect would be more noticeable in the wheat crop reports of eastern Colorado counties.

WHAT, IF ANYTHING, should be done about marginal farms? Several somewhat traditional suggestions come to mind.

One is to direct and train rural farm youths for nonfarm employment opportunities and to expand and strengthen educational programs so as to equip retrainable adults with the knowledge and skills necessary to compete in the nonfarm job market.

Another is to encourage shifts of land from agriculture into new uses. Recreation uses are mentioned now and then—but those are risky, competitive enterprises that require skills that marginal farmers may not have or may not be able to acquire.

Another way that has been suggested would be for the Government to buy the land outright and develop it for recreation, forestry, or game production. This way would be expensive and probably unnecessary except for a few special sites. The purchases would exclude existing rural homes in accordance with some public zoning plans.

Still another way would be for the Government to lease the cropland on marginal farms. The State and Federal Government would develop the land for forests or recreation. Leasing would be less costly than outright purchase.

The lease could expire on the farmer's retirement.

Some operators of marginal farms may do well to seek technical counseling to determine the potentials of their present farm organization and potentials for expanding their own managerial abilities. Even though low levels of capital have perpetuated and made more difficult the problems of low income, public credit and technical assistance programs have been made available to farm operators who can adjust their farms to become profitable operations.

Those who lack a potential for their farm resources could be retrained for nonfarm job opportunities if they have the health and age qualifications. If nonfarm jobs are available within commuting distance of the farm, various schemes for renting out the land and buildings may be considered, so as to yield a satisfactory return on the capital already invested in the farm. An acceptable leasing provision should provide for soil and water conservation practices. Maintenance of a desirable level of productivity will make the particular land desirable for future consolidation at a favorable price. Those who cannot remain in the area may consider a farm rental scheme if a favorable sale price is not available at the time of the move.

Many farmers on marginal, low-income farms are advanced in age or have physical handicaps. They are in no position to retrain for nonfarm jobs or move from their present farms. They are boxed in for the rest of their lives, unless members of their immediate families are in a position to bail them out of their difficult situation. The only practical alternative is to secure technical help so as to manage their resources for the attainment of sustained economic security.

WARREN R. BAILEY *and* E. L. BAUM *are agricultural economists in the Farm Production Economics Division and the Resource Development Economics Division, respectively, of Economic Research Service.*

FREDERICK D. STOCKER

THE TAXATION
OF FARMLAND

Iт HAD been a nice, pleasant day for Sam Agricola up to the time he turned his truck into his lane. As he stopped at the mailbox he felt again a relief at getting out of the rush-hour traffic. It seemed each year more suburbanites' cars were clogging the highway past his farm. Even widening the road to four lanes had not helped for long.

The first letter Sam glanced at had the return address of the county treasurer's office. It contained his tax bill for the year.

The real jolt came later, back at the house, when he opened the bill to find that it was about 20 percent higher than last year's. And last year's bill had been much higher than the one of the year before.

Sam took another look at his bill. Most of the tax was on real estate—his 120 acres and dairy buildings. Taxes levied on land and buildings totaled almost 1,500 dollars, or 12.50 dollars an acre. He could remember that 12 years earlier, when he had taken over the farm from his father, real estate taxes had been only 350 dollars. He had thought that was high.

His first reaction was anger, and he determined to go to the county treasurer's office first thing in the morning and protest. But as he thought it over

he realized that would do no good. The real culprit was the assessor, who more than a year ago had increased the assessment on Sam's farm for the third time in 12 years.

Sam had protested then. He had pointed out that the net income from his dairy herd was scarcely larger than it had been 10 years ago, even though he was now milking half again as many cows. Milk prices had not gone up in that period, but expenses had. It was all he could do to keep going, he had told the assessor, without higher taxes. An increase in assessment might put him out of business.

The assessor had replied that his job was simply to value all taxable property at what it would bring on the market.

Not that the job was simple. Sam knew, and the assessor had admitted, that values are hard to estimate in an active land market on the fringe of a

158

growing city. But the assessor was sure that, in the case of this farm, he had evidence of its "full and true" market value.

He knew that a farm less than a mile away had been sold at 500 dollars an acre for a shopping center. He knew that Sam's neighbor had sold his highway frontage at a price of more than 2 thousand dollars an acre. The owner of the farm across the road, a wealthy investor from New York, had given the tenant notice that he planned to turn the property over to a development corporation. Most significant, the assessor knew that Sam had shortly before turned down an offer of 1 thousand dollars an acre from a local developer; Sam could only speculate how the assessor had made that discovery.

All these facts convinced the assessor that Sam's farm was worth a lot more than the few hundred dollars an acre it might be worth as a dairy farm.

The law gave him no alternative but to assess the farm at its market value, which he judged to be 1 thousand dollars an acre. At a 40-percent assessment level (which the assessor was able to show was the level at which he set assessments), that meant an assessment of 400 dollars an acre. Sam had to admit that the assessor was right.

But the increase in Sam's real estate tax was not entirely a result of increased assessment on his place. As he examined the bill more closely, he saw that tax rates also had gone up. This year's rate (actually the sum of county, township, and school district rates) was 31.25 mills, or 3.125 cents per dollar of assessed valuation. The year before, the rate had been 28 mills. It seemed that rates, like assessed values, were going up all the time.

At this point Sam's thoughts turned back to a series of events in the past year. He remembered having attended a public hearing before the county board, at which spokesmen for various groups had expressed their views on the proposed budget and the tax in-crease it implied. The biggest increases in the budget were for county roads and welfare. With the rapid increase in population throughout the county, there was no questioning the need for more roads. Strong support also was voiced for improved maintenance of the existing road system.

Population growth also seemed to be the major cause for the increase in welfare expenditures, and residents of the newer developed parts of the county spoke in favor of broader and more costly welfare programs.

The farm organizations had been the only ones to argue for scaling down the budget and holding the tax line. At one time, their view would have carried weight with the county board. This time, it did not seem to have much influence. Sam recalled thinking to himself, in light of the persuasive arguments on the need for higher public expenditure, how weak the arguments against a tax rise sounded. The board voted the increased budget.

As a member of the school board, Sam had knowledge of the reasons for raising school taxes. New residential developments had doubled the number of schoolchildren in the district in 2 years. The six-room elementary school, erected only 10 years earlier on the site of the old one-room schoolhouse, was not big enough. A four-room addition had been necessary, and money had been borrowed to build it. New equipment and four additional teachers had been necessary. On top of this had come a State-mandated increase in teachers' salaries. Sam himself had voted for the increase in school taxes.

That night Sam Agricola did some hard thinking. The next morning he got busy and called other farmers whose judgment he respected to talk over a plan he had for holding down taxes on their farmland. The plan, as Sam outlined it, made sense to the others, and they agreed to help him put it over.

So it happened that several weeks later, at the next meeting of the county farm organization, Sam took the floor to present his proposal for a statewide law that would require assessors in valuing land used in agriculture to take account only of factors relevant to the agricultural use of the land. The assessor would be instructed, in effect, to ignore any potential for nonagricultural use as long as the land continued to be farmed.

His argument was worked out carefully. It is not fair, he said, to tax the owner of farmland as though it were a subdivision. To do so results in a tax that bears no relation to the income the owner can obtain or to his "ability to pay." Nor does the owner of farmland receive additional benefits from public services that would justify his higher tax.

Moreover, he argued, there is no sense in valuing all farmland in the fringe area as though it were about to be subdivided, simply because it could be subdivided. In all probability, the pace of urban growth will be such that much of the land may not be developed for years, and some of it, never. Finally, Sam pointed out that such a law would benefit the entire community by keeping farmland in active use and forestalling abandonment of farms.

He reported that in studying up on the matter, he had found that Maryland, New Jersey, Florida, and California all had enacted laws of this kind. Legal difficulties had been encountered, but he expressed his confidence that these could be overcome.

Sam's arguments fell on fertile ground. Everyone shared his concern and his sense of frustration over steadily rising taxes. When the discussion was over, Sam found himself appointed head of a committee to develop such a proposal and take it to their representative in the State legislature, with the request that he introduce and sponsor the bill in the forthcoming session of the legislature.

Sam's committee did its work well. They got in touch with farm leaders throughout the State to explain the proposal and enlist their support. In some places they were told that the problem was not an immediate problem to farmers, as assessors were already tacitly ignoring nonagricultural values in assessing land that continued to be farmed. When the committee pointed out that this system had no legal sanction and might be terminated any time, however, the farmers there agreed to support the proposed change in the law.

SOON AFTER the legislature convened the following January, the representative from Sam's district introduced the so-called "preferential assessment" bill. The committee on taxation in due course announced public hearings.

Sam himself made the opening presentation at the hearing. He set forth the same arguments he had presented before his farm organization, being careful to add that the problem pertained not only to his county but occurred or could occur throughout the State wherever urban expansion was pressing into hitherto undeveloped countryside.

He referred the committee to a report of the Department of Agriculture, in which Peter House reviewed the experience of Maryland with just such a law as he was proposing. According to this study, preferential assessment had held farmland assessments in the Baltimore-Washington area to an average level about one-third lower than they would have been if assessments had been tied to market values. Nor was the loss in tax base excessive—the greatest loss was estimated at between 1 and 2 percent. Despite some legal and procedural difficulties, the law seemed to have worked well over a period of 5 years.

Sam felt that his presentation was effective and well received. The committee members questioned him politely and appeared to incline favorably to the proposal.

The next witness was a member of the State tax commission. He opposed the bill. Such a law, he asserted, would unfairly create a favored class of taxpayers. It would represent a departure from the time-honored principle of ad valorem taxation—that all property should be taxed according to its market value. It would play into the hands of speculators and investors, he argued, who would be permitted to hold property indefinitely at low taxes as long as they put up at least a pretense of farming.

Finally, he argued, it would be difficult to administer, for how would an assessor judge "agricultural value" in a market where all farmland is, to some degree, a speculative investment? And how, in the absence of some legal definition or criterion, would the assessor know what constitutes land "used in farming"? Citing the Department's report, he noted that Maryland had had much difficulty in defining "agricultural use" and "agricultural value."

Sam could tell by the questions that followed and the answers given by the tax commissioner that the members of the committee were having some second thoughts about his proposal. What had appeared to be such a sound, sensible proposal evidently contained a few pitfalls.

In answering a question about the economic effects of high property taxes, the commissioner cited statistics to show that in the aggregate there was no shortage of agricultural productive capacity and that the farms affected by these high taxes were only a small part of the total agriculture picture. As for the individual farmers, his attitude was that they could sell out at any time, pocket their capital gain, and go farther out in the country to do their farming.

Sam restrained himself from jumping to his feet. He wanted to point out that it is no easy matter to buy a good farm nowadays. More than that, he wanted to protest against the suggestion that a farmer can readily and easily pull up stakes and move to a new community. Farmers, perhaps more than most urban dwellers, put down deep roots. In Sam's own case, his farm had been in the family for generations. He had been born and reared there.

Sam was well known and respected throughout the community, as shown by his election to the school board. Despite the changes that had taken place in his community in the past few years, he had a deep personal interest in its affairs. His friends all lived there. He certainly was not about to move over to the next county and buy a dairy farm there.

SAM'S HOPES received another setback from the next witness, a young attorney on the attorney general's staff. He concentrated his criticism on the legal problems in such a proposal, problems which Sam had been aware of but had not really understood. In the first place, he charged, it is not clear what public purpose would be served. Citing the Maryland experience, where the law as originally enacted was found unconstitutional for this reason, he predicted that the proposal as introduced would not stand up in the courts. Passage of a constitutional amendment eventually had been necessary to give effect to this policy in Maryland.

More significant, in his opinion, was its apparent inconsistency with the "uniformity" clause of the State constitution, which requires that "all property shall be taxed uniformly in accordance with its full and true value." Similar provisions had been cited by the Maryland courts, in overruling the original preferential assessment law in 1958, and it had been the cause of adverse court rulings in New Jersey and Florida. Without specific constitutional authorization, he concluded, preferential assessment of farmland would not be valid.

At this point it looked as though Sam's proposal was dead. One more witness was to be heard. A representative of several statewide conservation organizations breathed some life back into the bill. Granting the difficulties that the two preceding witnesses had pointed out, he argued nevertheless that so much was at stake that some means should be found to preserve and protect the countryside against the inroads of urban expansion. If tax reduction would help to keep the land open and unspoiled, the public stake in it was clear. The benefit of tax abatement would go not just to a few farmers but to millions of city dwellers who love and appreciate the open country.

He argued eloquently and persuasively. When he concluded, Sam felt perhaps he had won the committee over. But the tax commissioner and the attorney had raised doubts in the minds of the committee members— and in Sam's own mind—that were not easily dispelled. It was clear that the bill was not going to receive quick approval by the committee.

The chairman recessed the hearings at that point, and the real work of legislation began. A group immediately gathered in a corner of the room—Sam, the tax commissioner, the young man from the attorney general's office, the conservationist, several State legislators who were interested in the bill, and several other representatives of various State agencies.

As the young attorney began talking, it quickly became apparent that he had been assigned to carry the ball for the State administration.

Speaking especially to Sam and the representative from the conservation organizations, he acknowledged that their proposal had wide public support. If it received approval from the committee, it could probably pass the legislature. He told them that in reviewing the experience of other States, he had found that legislative support for similar proposals had been overwhelming. In fact, he thought there might be enough votes, as there had been in other States, to override a veto by the Governor.

But, turning to Sam, he asked him to consider whether this proposal was really a good thing for farmers. Experience in Maryland had shown that without some kind of safeguards, preferential assessment opens a door to speculators and investors, who stand to gain far more from such a law than does the average farmer. Abuses of this kind can easily give farmers a black eye. A few flagrant instances of big taxsavings to nonfarmers could well kill the whole program, leaving the farmer with nothing.

As Sam considered this point, the speaker turned to the man from the conservation organizations with a similar question. Was the preferential assessment of farmland really an effective way to preserve open spaces? Was it really an effective protection against urban sprawl? He acknowledged that conservation groups throughout the State, as in other States, had strongly favored preferential assessment on this ground, and that the slogan "Preserve Our Countryside" had proved highly effective in enlisting support of suburban and city dwellers for lower assessment for farmland. But he doubted that simple tax abatement would help achieve this goal.

To support this argument, an economist from the State tax commission interjected that, according to accepted economic doctrine, it is high prices, rather than high taxes, that cause land to be shifted from a lower to a higher use.

Sam took exception to this point. If a man's sole source of income is his farm, he argued, taxes of 10, 15, or 20 dollars an acre may well be more than he can pay out of current income. What can a man do except sell out?

The economist's reply was that, assuming accurate assessment, taxes of this magnitude on farmland can mean only one thing—that the land has become enormously valuable for other uses. As the owner of a small fortune in real estate, one would think the farmer would have little trouble borrowing the relatively small amounts needed to meet the annual tax bill.

FORESTALLING THE objection Sam started to raise, the economist quickly went on to admit that few lenders are willing to advance a farmer money on the security of something as risky as the potential development value of his land. Perhaps the problem that high taxes force farmers out of business can best be regarded as a credit problem rather than a tax problem.

Obviously concerned that the discussion was straying from the subject, the attorney resumed. Going back to his point that tax abatement through preferential assessment would be ineffective in preserving open spaces, he pointed out that the bill before the committee required no assurance from the landowner that the land would in fact be kept in agriculture any longer than it might be to his advantage to do so. He could, at any time, sell out to a developer and pocket his entire capital gain, subject only to the Federal tax on capital gains. He would owe the community nothing in exchange for the tax reduction. What is more, he would not even be under any compulsion, if he did develop his land, to see to it that the development pattern conforms to any overall community plan.

Besides failing to give protection against urban sprawl and loss of open space, the bill offered the same tax protection to all farmland, including that which ought to be opened up for development in the interest of the community. Cities must have room to grow. The important job is to see that they grow in the right direction and do not spill over the countryside.

The attorney paused for a moment to let the force of his argument sink in. He could see that Sam Agricola, the man from the conservation organizations, and the others in the small group had followed his reasoning and understood his objections. But they were wondering what he was leading up to.

In a more confidential tone he continued. The Governor, he told them, was opposed to this bill. If the measure were enacted in its present form, he would probably feel obliged to veto it. But because he was sympathetic to its central purpose, the Governor was very anxious to avoid this necessity. He much preferred modifying the proposal to remove some of the objection-able features while retaining the basic features.

The attorney thought there was a way this could be done. He reminded his listeners that the Governor had long held a reputation as one interested in conservation. He had, in fact, proposed a broad program for conserving and developing the State's natural resources, including farmland, forests, watersheds, recreational lands, and scenic resources. The program had broad support. The farm organizations and the conservation organizations were among the groups that were behind it.

His suggestion was that tax abatement for farmland be tied into the Governor's overall conservation program. In this context, the emphasis would be not so much on reducing the farmer's taxes as on promoting a pattern of land use that would be to the advantage of both the farmers and nonfarmers. The tax provisions also would apply not just to farmland but to all land in which there is a public interest in its use or continued openness.

Most important, it would not appear as just another "tax grab." In exchange for lower taxes, the property owner would give certain assurances or accept certain limitations on the use of his land. There would, for example, be zoning restrictions limiting the development opportunities. In some cases, the right to develop property for residential, commercial, or similar purposes would be removed altogether.

Sam felt skeptical. He did not take to the idea of accepting limitations on the use of his land, and he doubted if many other farmers would. Still, if such limitations were the price of some protection from the tax collector, and if they were really necessary to stop uncontrolled urban growth, he was willing to listen. Besides, he noted that the conservationists were reacting favorably to the idea.

The attorney proceeded to outline the proposal he had in mind. The Governor's conservation and development program authorized and encouraged the establishment of local planning boards, with power to draw up master plans covering rural as well as urban territory.

These boards were to be given authority to designate certain areas as permanent open space reserves. Farming would be permitted in these areas, but development would not. Local governments would be authorized to purchase property or rights in property in the designated areas, with the assistance of Federal grants under title VII of the Housing Act of 1961 (75 Stat. 149).

IT WAS THE Governor's hope that farmers and other owners of land in the designated open space areas would choose to donate or sell the "development rights" in their property to the local government—in other words, to give a "conservation easement." This would effectively guarantee that land would not be used in development. In exchange there would be an express requirement in the law that assessment of such land for tax purposes should recognize the fact that certain of the property rights had been given up. The assessor would make his valuation on the basis of the rights that remained.

In addition to these "permanent" reserves, there would be established, by vote of the local planning boards, other areas in which urban development might be expected to occur some years in the future. The aim here would be to preserve the integrity of the area against scattered or haphazard development that might destroy its future value for development. Development would be discouraged by a combination of zoning regulations and controls over sewer and water lines and road construction and access.

The Governor visualized a definite role for property taxation in supporting and implementing local plans for such areas. Undeveloped land in these areas would continue to be assessed as required by the constitution, on the basis of market value. The controls on

land use would help hold down speculative values, and hence taxes. But as prospects for development became more evident, or as restrictions were relaxed, property values and assessments would normally be expected to rise.

The proposal was that farmers and other landowners be given the option of deferring a portion of their taxes. They would continue to pay currently that part of the tax bill that represented the "agricultural value" of the land, but could choose to defer that part attributable to its potential for later development.

The deferred taxes would be carried forward as a lien against the property. When eventually the property is sold for development, the accumulated taxes would become due and payable.

The benefit to the owner would lie in the protection he received from increased tax pressure while he keeps his land undeveloped. The benefit to the community would be the increased likelihood that land will continue to be used productively and cared for, right up to the time it is ready for development. In addition, tax revenues would not be lost outright, but would be recouped eventually, and at a time when local government costs for sewers, streets, and other facilities are likely to be greatest.

IN A SENSE, he went on, the local government is extending the farmer credit to pay his taxes, taking a lien on the property as security. At this point, one listener interjected that if the deferred taxes are really a sort of loan, the landowner ought really to be charged interest on taxpayments he has postponed. The attorney replied that mathematical equivalence would indeed require an interest charge on deferred taxes, but that, in the Governor's view, foregoing the interest seemed only right in view of the benefit the community stood to receive. Besides, it would involve an unnecessary administrative complexity.

Someone else asked about the tax

treatment of farmland that is not included in either a permanent open-space reserve or one of the other "temporary" reserves. The reply was that such land would continue to be taxed, as under present law, on the basis of full market value. If the land is not encompassed by one or the other of the reserves, it is available for development. Urban growth would thereby be channeled into these areas. And property owners would be free to use their land or dispose of it as they see fit.

As the discussion continued, several other questions arose.

Wouldn't the proposal be difficult to administer, as the assessor, who has difficulty enough making a single value estimate, would now be asked to make two?

Wouldn't the assessors' organization be likely to oppose the idea?

Might not this device actually bring on higher assessments, by causing assessors to look for nonfarm values where none might in fact exist?

And might not the lower cost of holding land make it even more difficult for developers to obtain land close in to the city, thereby leading to even more scatteration?

As Sam drove home that evening he reflected on the events of the day. He had failed in his original objective, to gain committee approval for preferential assessment of farmland. But he had come to realize that the variant proposed by the representatives of the attorney general's office had merit.

It was more defensible as a tax measure, because it provided a deferral of taxes rather than outright abatement. It would be less susceptible to misuse by speculators and investors, and yet would give the farmers the protection from higher taxes which was their major concern. Moreover, as part of a general land use plan, it would contribute to a pattern of development that could, if properly designed, bring great benefit not only to farmers but to the community at large.

Sam was convinced the plan was good. At least it would be worth trying. The job that lay before him now was to convince other farm leaders in his State and perhaps in other States that the alternative, which involved more restrictions on their freedom of action than the original proposal, nevertheless deserved their support. This might be a tough job, but he thought he could do it.

FREDERICK D. STOCKER *is an economist in the Agriculture Finance Branch, Economics Research Service.*

Level-of-Living Index of Farm Operators, 1959

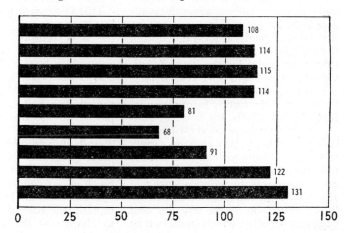

HOWARD L. HILL AND FRANK H. MAIER

THE FAMILY FARM
IN TRANSITION

As FARMING has become more closely related to urban occupations and life, the rural tradition of the family farm has been changing and is being challenged. The farm population has declined. Farm production has become specialized and mechanized. Most of the descriptive characteristics of the family farm system have changed. Occasionally it is suggested that the tradition of the family farm is no longer relevant to the realities of American agriculture in the sixties. What does it mean?

The ideal of the family farm had its roots in the colonial past, when land was abundant relative to labor. Early efforts to establish feudal systems of land tenure failed, because unsettled and unclaimed land was generally available to farmers of moderate means who depended on family labor. Thus, during the colonial period, settlers developed strong sympathy for the idea of individually owned and operated farms.

Thomas Jefferson's exposition of what we now call the family farm was nurtured in this soil. In his view, an agriculture of owner-operated farmers was desired as the means to a good society rather than being an end in itself. He held that the basis of enlightened self-government was the independence and self-reliance of the individual. Self-reliance rested on social equality and economic security, which could best be

achieved through a system of individually owned and operated family farms. Individual ownership of farms thus provided the foundation for civic virtue and for social and political stability.

This preference for the family farm in turn produced land policies during the next century that further reinforced the ideal, and, because agricultural lands were abundant, the Federal land policies during the 19th century gave it strong support. Although few Federal restrictions were placed on the transfer of lands once title was granted, the coincidence of abundant land and lenient land disposal programs assured wide distribution of ownership of farmland over much of our country.

Even during Jefferson's lifetime, though, the role of agriculture began to change as the percentage of the

166

total work force that was employed in agriculture began to decline—72 percent in 1820, 59 in 1860, 38 in 1900, 27 in 1920, 12 in 1950, and 6 in 1960.

However important the family farm is as a system of agriculture, the smallness of the farm sector means that the family farm cannot be relied upon as the only source of civic virtue and social and political stability.

Even before large-scale disposal of public lands ended, farm tenancy was increasing. As this trend progressed, the concept of the agricultural ladder emerged as an explanation for the existence of tenancy in a system that cherished the goal of owner-operatorship. A farm boy could climb up the agricultural ladder step by step—a worker on his parents' farm, a hired farmworker, renter of a farm, the owner of a mortgaged farm, and finally, owner of a debt-free farm.

Improving the operation of the agricultural ladder was seen as a way to preserve the system of owner-operated family farms. Such programs as publicly supported credit, research, and extension were also expected to assist family farmers.

Later, programs for conservation and for production control and price support that were developed gave further support to the idea of individually owned and operated farms. The right to participate in these programs, however, for the most part is not limited to family farms. Whether or not these programs tend to strengthen a family farm system of agriculture is not evident.

DISCUSSIONS of how to maintain and strengthen our system of family farms are no longer concentrated primarily on the issues of security of tenure and the rights of tenants and sharecroppers. Important changes in the tenure structure have taken place, and the inferior status sometimes associated with tenancy has changed.

The proportion of all farmers who are tenants (who operate only rented land) has declined, but the amount of land that is leased has been fairly stable—about one-third. In areas of commercial farming, with their increasing size of farms and higher farm income, the proportion of farmland under lease is high; land is commonly leased both by full tenants (who rent all the land they farm) and by part owners (who own some land and rent additional land). In most of the low-income farm sections, however, the proportion of full owners is relatively high.

For the country as a whole, the shift to fewer and larger farms has been accompanied by a rise in part ownership and increased use of such devices as vertical integration and land purchase contracts to gain control of the resources needed for larger operations. Farm operators seemingly have a basic interest in income levels and a secondary interest in tenure status.

Now the major concern is whether the trend toward the larger and more specialized farming operations is compatible with a family-farm system. As a goal or an ideal of farm organization, the family farm has changed little. But the actual conditions on what is commonly thought of as family farms have undergone continuous change, both in organization and in relation to other sectors of the economy.

Nevertheless, a study by Radoje Nikolitch, of the Economic Research Service of the Department of Agriculture, showed that in numbers of farms, the family farm overwhelmingly prevailed in 1949 and 1954 in all parts of the country and for most of the census types of commercial farms.

In that study, as in this paper, family farms were recognized as businesses in which operating families are risk-taking managers who do most of the work. The labor supply of the usual farm family is equivalent to 1.5 man-years.

Ninety-six percent of all farms and 94 percent of all commercial farms were classed as family farms in 1954. Moreover, these percentages seem to have increased slightly between 1949 and

Blue-Collar Workers Replace Farmers as Largest
Rural Occupational Group

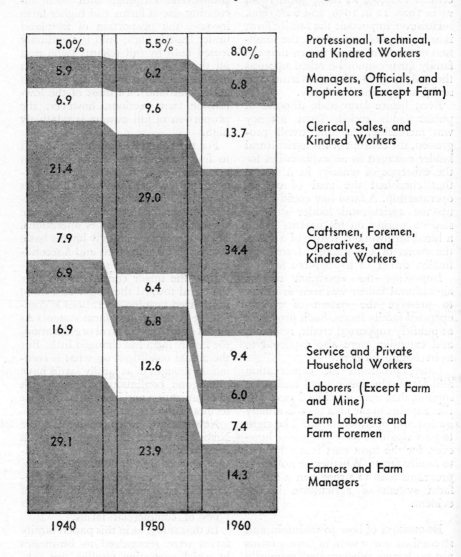

5.0%	5.5%	8.0%	Professional, Technical, and Kindred Workers
5.9	6.2	6.8	Managers, Officials, and Proprietors (Except Farm)
6.9	9.6	13.7	Clerical, Sales, and Kindred Workers
21.4	29.0	34.4	Craftsmen, Foremen, Operatives, and Kindred Workers
7.9			
6.9	6.4		
16.9	6.8	9.4	Service and Private Household Workers
	12.6	6.0	Laborers (Except Farm and Mine)
		7.4	Farm Laborers and Farm Foremen
29.1	23.9	14.3	Farmers and Farm Managers

1940   1950   1960

1954, even though the average size of all commercial farms increased from 276 to 310 acres.

THE 1959 CENSUS of Agriculture disclosed a situation not greatly different. In 1959, for the whole country, 5.6 percent of all census farms reported annual expenditures on hired labor in excess of 2,500 dollars a year. A hired wage expenditure of 2,500 dollars is roughly equivalent to 75 man-weeks of hired labor—slightly in excess of 1.5 man-years of hired labor.

The variation among regions, however, was considerable. In the Northeast, 11.1 percent of all census farms spent 2,500 dollars or more for hired labor in 1959; the Corn Belt, 3.2 percent; Lake States, 2.9; Northern Plains, 3.3; Appalachian, 2.5; Southeast, 5.0; Delta States, 4.6; Southern Plains, 8.0; Mountain, 12.7; Pacific, 19.6. The average in 48 States was 5.6 percent.

Census data on farm expenditures for hired labor also were analyzed for commercial farms by type of farm. The percentage of commercial vegetable producers who reported expenditures of 2,500 dollars or more for hired labor was 36.8; fruit and nut growers, 38.0; cotton, 12.0; tobacco, 2.1; cash grain, 4.9; miscellaneous, 28.1; other field crops, 25.4; poultry, 9.4; dairy, 7.9; livestock ranches, 16.6; other livestock, 5.4; general, 6.4. The figure for all commercial farms was 8.5 percent. Moreover, within each of the types of farm, regional variation was great.

ANOTHER WAY of looking at the position of the family farm is to look at the composition of the farm labor force between family workers and hired workers. This measure has the advantage of reflecting the tenure status of all the members of the farm labor force, whereas consideration of the proportion of family farms among all farms obscures the statistical weight of hired workers on the relatively few larger-than-family farms. For commercial farms for the country as a whole, Mr. Nikolitch found man-years of hired labor to have been 25.4 percent of all farm labor in 1954, having decreased from 27.8 percent in 1949. Not surprisingly, he also found that hired labor as a percentage of all labor varied considerably by type of commercial farm.

Regional variation also was great within each of the types of farm. For example, on vegetable farms in 1954, the relative importance of hired labor varied from 20 percent in the Northern Plains and 29 percent in the Delta States to about 80 percent in the Southeast and Pacific regions. On cash-grain farms in 1954, hired labor as a percentage of all farm labor ranged from 10 percent in the Lake States to 56 percent in the Delta States.

These data indicate that the ideal of the family farm as one relying primarily on family labor is more relevant and more easily attainable in some types of farming and regions than in others.

But what are the long-term trends in the family and hired worker composition of the farm labor force?

We obtained data from the Statistical Reporting Service of the Department of Agriculture on the annual average of monthly numbers of farm family workers and hired farmworkers by regions from 1929 to 1962. During the depressed years of the thirties, all regions experienced at least some drop in the relative importance of hired workers in the farm labor force, very likely because of an accumulation of family labor on farms as the rate of off-farm migration slowed.

DURING THE period of the Second World War, another drop in the proportion of hired workers in the farm labor force occurred in all regions except the Pacific States—probably a result of the retention of family workers on farms under Selective Service procedures, the general wartime scarcity of hired labor, and the limited mechanization of farm operations because of the planned wartime production of farm machinery.

In the period after 1945, however, several different patterns may be observed among the geographic regions. Only slight year-to-year changes and no trends have been evident in four regions—Middle Atlantic, East North Central, West North Central, and Mountain.

Moderate but fairly steady increases in the proportion of hired workers in the farm labor force after 1945 appear to be the pattern in the other five areas. Our data provide only inconclusive evidence of the relative position of the family farm in these areas.

In the Pacific region, an increase in hired labor probably resulted from increases in total production of specialty crops, which require much labor, and from farm enlargement. In this region, with by far the largest percentage of hired workers, the family farm has never dominated the farm scene as completely as in most other regions and could be declining further.

In New England, the increase in the hired-labor portion of the farm labor force has probably resulted in large part from a sharp drop in the number of smaller farms. This may actually represent little or no loss in the relative position of family farms.

In the South Atlantic, East South Central, and West South Central regions, the increasing proportion of hired workers is explained partly by sharp decreases in numbers of sharecropper units (whose family members are counted as family rather than hired workers) and reductions in numbers of low-production and subsistence farms. In all three of these regions, the decline in the number of small farms (including sharecropper units) was much sharper than for the Nation as a whole, so that between 1945 and 1962 the number of family workers fell by about one-half. Meanwhile, hired workers increased slightly in the South Atlantic region and decreased slightly in the other two regions. The resulting increasing proportion of hired labor in the farm work force, however, may not constitute an actual weakening of what our country desires as family farms, because sharecropper and other small, low-productive farms are usually not considered to be family farms.

LAND TENURE arrangements of farm operators take on particular importance in any appraisal of the family farm. The traditional tenure goal of full ownership has continued to hold a strong attraction for many farm people, yet it has been undergoing modification.

The percentage of all farm operators classed as full owners has been unchanged since 1950 at 57 percent—a higher proportion than any other period since 1900. At the same time, however, the proportion of land in full-owner farms declined from 53 percent of all land in farms in 1910 to 31 percent in 1959.

The proportion of full tenancy declined from a high point of 42 percent in 1930 to 20 percent in 1959, and the land area tenants operated decreased from 31 to 15 percent.

A significant tenure trend with reference to ownership of farms is the rise in part ownership—that is, farms made up of both owned and rented land. This tenure class since 1940 has increased steadily in relation to other tenure classes, comprising 23 percent of all farm operators in 1959. Part owners operated 45 percent of all land in farms.

Although a sharp drop in tenancy occurred after 1950, there was little decline in the total area leased. Two factors are responsible. Renting by part owners has increased. Part owners in 1963 operated 219 million acres under lease—more, in fact, than the 163 million acres rented by tenants. The other factor is the increase in average size of tenant farms. This has been due to the decline in the numbers of sharecropper farms, which are comparatively small, and of other small, tenant-operated farms.

Large declines in numbers of small- and medium-sized farms have occurred among tenant farms and among all categories of tenure. The number of farms from 10 to 500 acres declined by 1,467,000 between 1950 to 1959, while the number of farms with 500 acres or more rose by 33 thousand.

As one would expect, the dropout of farms was higher among smaller ones. Disappearance of farms of 260 to 499 acres accounted for less than 1 percent of the total decline. Seventy-two percent of the total decline consisted of farms of fewer than 100 acres. Exceptions to the overall pattern were the East North Central and West North Central States, where the heaviest dropout was in the 100- to 179-acre group, amounting to 36 and

44 percent, respectively, of the total decline in numbers of farms larger than 10 acres.

Rising land values permit comparatively few farmers to purchase enough land for large-scale operation. Many farmers with small acreages and excess machine capacity attempt to purchase more land and thereby contribute to upward pressure on land prices. Many other farmers choose to invest their limited capital in machinery or livestock and to rent some or all of their land. Thus only a fifth of all farms of 2 thousand acres or more are operated by full owners, while three-fifths are operated by part owners.

Farmers who prefer to rent (rather than purchase land) avoid paying high prices for land, but they probably pay higher rents. Their efforts to lease land have bid up effective rental rates. Moreover, higher rental returns also indirectly contribute to the upward pressure on prices of farmland because the higher rental returns make investment in farmland more attractive to farm and nonfarm people alike.

THE AMOUNT OF CAPITAL required for farming poses serious problems for many persons who wish to get established on farms of adequate size.

A 1962 report by the Economic Research Service, "Farm Costs and Returns, Commercial Farms by Type, Size, and Location," showed a large variation in total capital investments per farm. These investments range from 13 thousand dollars per farm on small tobacco farms of the North Carolina Coastal Plain—which had an annual net farm income of 2,500 dollars—to nearly 1 million dollars per farm for large cotton-general farms in the San Joaquin Valley of California, where net farm incomes amounted to nearly 80 thousand dollars annually.

Of 39 types of farms in 21 major farming areas reported in these studies, 25 had a total capital investment in 1961 of 50 thousand dollars or more, and 11 types exceeded 100 thousand dollars. Typical dairy farms had total

capital investments ranging from 30 thousand to 60 thousand dollars, and Corn Belt farms ranged from 50 thousand to 100 thousand dollars.

The lowest capital requirements were on farms in the Southeastern States that were representative of most cotton-, tobacco-, and peanut-producing farms in the region. But net farm incomes there were also low in relation to most typical farms in other areas.

The farm types selected for the annual costs and returns studies of the Economic Research Service are important, typical operating units in different farming areas, and in most instances they are the most common unit. They are representative of commercial farms. Thus their capital requirements and other organizational characteristics would be expected to differ from part-time or other farms, where the sale of farm products is not the major source of family income. Such part-time and residential farms are not family farms as the term is commonly understood.

All of the types of farms studied showed substantial increases since 1950 in their total capital requirements, reflecting increases in the amount and value of resources used. With few exceptions, the investment in land and buildings increased at a greater rate than total farm investment. Moreover, the investment in land and buildings makes up a sizable portion of the total capital investment, amounting to 80 percent or more on 18 of the typical commercial farms. Farms in these groups were primarily producers of cash crops, including cash grain, tobacco, and cotton farms, and ranged from small family units to highly capitalized, large-scale farms.

OVERALL, the asset position of commercial agriculture is good. At the beginning of 1962, the equities of farm operators and other owners of farm resources were nearly 87 percent of the value of farm assets. This ratio was 81 percent in 1940 and 91 percent in 1950. Capital assets of agriculture in 1962 were 207.3 billion dollars, compared to 131.6 billion dollars in 1950 and 52.9 billion dollars in 1940.

Increases in the sixties in the capital assets of agriculture resulted chiefly from rising prices of farmland. The increase in the level of capital assets and in prices of farmland has had an adverse effect on beginning farmers who are without substantial family assistance and on established farmers who need to enlarge if they are to meet minimum standards of farm income.

For farmers in these two kinds of situations particularly, means other than ownership must be used to some extent to gain control over resources needed to attain adequate levels of farm production.

In specific instances and on some types of farms, operators rely heavily on nonfarm sources to provide some of the farm resources. Livestock-share leases, farm partnerships, and producer-processor contracts are examples of this type of agreement. Each of these potentially provides that the person who supplies the farm operator with outside capital also participates actively in making some or all of the management decisions. Just how much the use of various arrangements to acquire more capital has diminished farmers' rights to make major management decisions is difficult to determine.

This matter has great significance, because the terms under which a farmer acquires land and capital resources determine whether he actually makes important management decisions, shares these decisions with someone else, or even largely turns them over to someone else. But even where farm management decisions rest mainly with farm operators, their decisions more and more must be coordinated with the operation of farm suppliers and processors, and adjusted to the requirements of government agricultural programs.

WE HAVE TRACED the development of the family farm tradition and described significant changes in agriculture that have transformed the organization of farms.

Still other changes, less apparent in their effect on farm organization, have direct meaning for the family farm tradition. Of particular importance are the declining need for land in crop production, reduction locally in land available for farming as a consequence of growth in urban and other nonfarm uses of land, and the increasing reliance of the farm people on nonfarm employment.

From 1950 to 1959, the acreage used for crop production in the United States declined from 377 million acres to 358 million, and the acreage harvested from 336 million acres to 317 million. The decline of about 6 percent in cropland harvested was more than offset by a 27-percent increase in the average productivity of harvested acres.

The increase in production per harvested acre has been attributed largely to increased use of fertilizer. Some of the increase is also due to concentration of production on better lands, as farmland is transferred to other uses such as to woodland and pasture. This is shown by the regional differences in the patterns of declining cropland and shifts of cropland to other uses.

Relatively large declines in the acreage of cropland harvested occurred from 1950 to 1959 in four regions— Southeast (23 percent), Appalachian (18 percent), Delta (16 percent), and Northeast (12 percent). The Northern Plains, Southern Plains, and Corn Belt all had a decrease of about 8 percent in crop acreage harvested. Slight increases occurred in the Mountain and Pacific regions.

The effect on farming opportunities of a continued drop in the use of land for crop production will depend on whether land taken out of production is suitable for farming and is actually needed for agricultural production. Attention was given to these points in a publication in 1962 of the Department of Agriculture, "Land and Water Resources, A Policy Guide."

According to projections it reported, the national need for harvested crop acreage by 1980 to supply domestic and export needs for food and fiber would be 291 million acres, or 26 million fewer acres than the acreage harvested in 1959. By 1962, the combined operation of the Feed Grain and Conservation Reserve programs were instrumental in reducing harvested crop acreage to 288 million acres— 3 million fewer acres than the projected needs by 1980.

Upon the completion of Conservation Reserve and Feed Grain contracts, a major problem relating to the family farm will be to find uses for this land that are compatible with production needs and also take account of the needs of farm families for adequate income. In the absence of continued payments for land diversion, it can be expected that the incentive to return land to crop production will be great, unless profitable alternative uses for diverted land are developed.

Urban and other nonfarm uses for land have had important effects on farming in many localities through a reduction in the acreage locally available for farming. The reduction is not great nationally, although the effects on individual farmers are sometimes serious and may necessitate relocation or continued operation with a reduced acreage. About 1 million acres a year were required for urban and industrial growth, highways, airports, and the like from 1950 to 1961. This land was classed as rural before its conversion to urban use, and some of it had not actually been in farm use. A problem that is more serious locally is the disruptive effect on farms of land speculation extending beyond the area of imminent urban expansion.

OFF-FARM EMPLOYMENT is an important source of income for many farm people. Thirty-four percent of all commercial farm operators reported some off-farm employment in 1959, compared to 27 percent in 1950. Off-farm employment of 100 days or more was reported by 15 percent of the commercial farm operators in 1959, compared to 9 percent in 1950.

A number of factors contributed to this trend. Urban and industrial expansion have multiplied the number of employment opportunities available to farm people. Decentralization of factories and businesses into rural areas and improvement in roads have made nonfarm job opportunities more accessible. A third consideration is the increased desire of farm people generally for higher incomes. Some farmers, with too little capital or credit to enlarge their farm, actively seek outside employment and make their farming a "moonlight" operation.

The combination of off-farm employment and farm operation is sometimes pointed to as being at variance with the family farm tradition, according to which a farm should be capable of providing adequately for a farm family and of utilizing fully its labor. More and more farms, however, have failed to meet one or both of these conditions, as the cash income needs for modern living standards continue to rise and as mechanization further reduces the time for farm operations.

REALISTICALLY, the alternatives to the combination of farming and off-farm employment may be much less desirable, from both an individual and community point of view. The alternatives, broadly speaking, are to continue as full-time farmers but to be underproductive, or to discontinue farming and seek full-time nonfarm employment.

To implement either alternative in a way that benefits the families concerned requires specific and sometimes difficult measures. For many such operators, a shift to full-time farming would involve the acquisition of additional land. Within limits, this could be done through the use of credit. But to try to achieve this on a large scale would seriously bid up prices of farmland.

Farm families who rely in part for their income on nonfarm work often are reluctant to seek full-time nonfarm work if it involves relocation to urban areas. Even those who would like to leave may lack the skills needed to get employment at a wage that would cover their relocation costs and exceed their present incomes, including the value of food produced for home consumption and housing.

ONE MEASURE that may ease the problem of some farm people in shifting to full-time nonfarm employment is the assistance provided by the Manpower Development and Training Act of 1962. Farmworkers with less than 1,200 dollars of annual net family income are eligible for assistance under the act, which provides financial assistance for training and relocation and allowances while training. The net income limit on eligibility, however, would eliminate from participation many farmers who still operate inadequate-sized farms and rely in part on off-farm employment for their income. Some young adults, however, may be able to qualify for training and allowances under the youth provisions of the act.

Probably the most serious challenge to the family farm ideal is the difficulty of entry into farming at a level that holds promise of economic progress for the farm family.

It spells a serious inequality of opportunity between young farm people who do and who do not inherit a substantial interest in a profitable and well-organized farm or otherwise benefit from family assistance. (It must be conceded, of course, that such inequalities of opportunity are not unknown in other economic activities.)

The difficulty of becoming a successful family farmer is made more serious by the fact that farm people, historically, have had high birth rates, so that each generation of farm children is more than sufficient to replace the preceding generation.

Furthermore, the actual numbers of opportunities for employment in agriculture have been declining steadily. The results are evident in nearly every rural community where pressure of economic and technological change in farming have brought about a sharp reduction in farm numbers and farming opportunities for rural youths.

Without doubt, migration from agriculture over the decades has benefited many of those who left and has exposed new opportunities outside agriculture to their descendants. Important benefits have accrued to agriculture also, for the decline in the farm population is one of the factors that underlie the great improvements in agricultural productivity.

THE FAMILY FARM has adjusted to many stresses, but when we focus attention on some of its characteristics we may overlook the significance of other important trends in the structure of agriculture.

The high capital needs and the more specialized management ability needed for modern commercial farming could lead in the direction that farms become quite dependent on outside financing, with farm operators divested of an ever larger share both of ownership of farm resources and of decisionmaking.

Furthermore, some types of farms may become sufficiently large and specialized that both their management and labor force are hired employees. Finally, farming opportunities more and more may come to be hereditary, so that farms are transferred within families from generation to generation.

Any of these developments could take a direction sharply contrary to the ideal of the family farm.

HOWARD L. HILL *joined the Department of Agriculture in 1957 and has been engaged in land tenure research in the Resource Development Economics Division of Economic Research Service. He was born in South Dakota and studied at South Dakota State College and the University of Wisconsin.*

FRANK H. MAIER *since 1954 has done research in land tenure and farm labor investigations in the Farm Production Economics Division of Economic Research Service. He studied at Valparaiso University and the University of Chicago.*

COMMUNITIES

A COMMUNITY is people who have common laws, interests, and hopes but not necessarily the same viewpoints, resources, or awareness of change and needs. A community may be a village, township, State, country. Whatever its size and wherever it is, the community has undergone great change, for good or ill, and faces problems of growth and adjustment or of declining population and inadequate services. The future of small towns, rural housing, health, and churches is not going to be enhanced by emotional conflict—"we must study their current utility, attempt to determine their future utility, and establish the alternatives." Communities that have faced squarely their problems, though, and have responsible leadership are on the road to progress. Signs of it are wider opportunities for work, industrial development through cooperatives, more capital for public facilities, and urban rehabilitation. The conclusion of one chapter has wide application: "It is more than just tearing down and putting up buildings; one must not lose sight of people and their homes and the way in which they want to live."

DWIGHT A. NESMITH

THE SMALL
RURAL TOWN

THE statement that the number of farms and farmers will continue to decline is no longer viewed as treasonous. People who tried to resist the modernization of agriculture by using emotional, quasi-religious programs for preserving the family farm have changed its definition to conform more closely with reality.

The corollary decline of the small rural town has not yet been accepted, however, and the same false, emotional arguments are being marshaled in its defense. Public utterances suggesting that the good life is not necessarily synonymous with the outhouse, the one-room schoolhouse, or the vacant stores and the empty houses of the small town may bring flurries of irate comments.

But the future of the rural towns is not going to be enhanced by emotional conflict. We must study their current utility, attempt to determine their future utility, and establish the alternatives or the means consistent with achieving a reality of this sort.

First, however, we should define what we mean by "small rural." For our purpose, the census division point of 2,500 population serves to define "small," and we may agree arbitrarily that a "rural" town is one that is not

in a standard metropolitan area or in a county adjacent to a standard metropolitan county—that is, a small town probably 50 miles from a major city and in an area that depends primarily on agriculture for its economic base.

When we restrict ourselves to such a definition, we realize that small rural towns are not a general, national phenomenon, but a regional attribute—a phenomenon of the Great Plains and Mountain States. East of the Mississippi River and west of the Rockies, there are only small pockets of land that are more than 50 miles from a city of 35 thousand.

Small towns that are on the fringes of large, growing cities face metropolitan problems of growth and adjustment, rather than the problems of declining populations and unused facilities.

We can make more valid generalities if we limit our discussion to small towns

177

in the Great Plains. These towns are similar. The agriculture carried on around them is of the same general nature. They face similar competition because of urbanization, specialization, and migration.

A glance at population figures for a number of the towns may lead one to believe they are holding their own. Many exhibit stable populations. Some even seem to be growing.

But figures on age distribution and population trends in the surrounding rural areas make it clear that the apparent growth is merely a temporary adjustment that foretells accelerated declines. The population pyramids become rectangular and (in some instances) inverted triangles, as the young people leave and the production of native stock slowly grinds to a halt. Graphs that indicate population change in rural areas in the Great Plains States by 5-year age groups since 1950 give proof of the loss of population in the productive age range.

Nor is the loss by the rural areas just a matter of numbers. It is a loss also of persons with higher educational attainment. In 1960, 8.9 percent of our urban population had 4 years or more of college, compared to 5.3 percent of the rural nonfarm population and 2.8 percent of the rural farm population. One-third of farm-reared youths are college bound; one-half of urban-reared youths are college bound.

The result of these losses in rural areas is a corresponding decline in the small rural community, which was established to serve people who are no longer there. And this decline of small towns must have a localized effect on the efficiency and livability of rural areas as services are withdrawn to the large cities.

THE AGRICULTURAL experiment stations at the University of Nebraska and at Kansas State University published findings in 1961 of similar studies in the rural areas of their respective States.

The study in Nebraska indicated a declining market radius for the small towns. The dominant towns increased their market radius. All other towns tended to decline in drawing power. A correlation exists between the size of the dominant town and the additional area it serves; the larger the town, the more significant the increase in market radius.

For example, a town that retained two-thirds of its former trade territory, while the population density in that trade territory was cut in half, ended up with one-third as many customers. Some small county-seat towns maintained the same market radius and maintained their city population but lost 20 to 40 percent of their market in terms of number of people.

The one town in the study that had more than 2,500 population expanded its regular market radius by 3 miles, and the town population grew by 750 persons. Even so, its total market population dropped 10 percent.

The function of the towns was to supply convenience goods and services, limited generally to such low-margin operations as grocery stores, filling stations, taverns, eating places, feedstores, and garages.

The study in Kansas supported these findings. It disclosed also that the more successful farmers, with increased disposable incomes, were more likely to shop away from their hometown. Thus the town merchants had a steadily declining number of potential customers; the remaining customers were less and less likely to be satisfied with the limited selection of the small town. Besides, people who are more likely to require urban services and have the higher incomes that let them afford the services are the ones most likely to leave the town.

When asked to indicate the adequacy of the facilities provided by small towns, most of the residents and rural customers described them as inadequate.

The researchers in Kansas and Nebraska suggested consolidation of public and private facilities, larger service areas, and combined governmental units—but the local resistance was intense.

In Nebraska, the number of rural schools dropped from 70 to 38 in 25 years, and the average enrollment of the schools dropped from 16 pupils to 10. Consolidations had not been affected fast enough even to maintain the substandard conditions of a quarter century earlier. In the meantime, the demands on the schools for sound preparation of their pupils had been multiplying.

STATE MEDICAL and mental health associations are becoming increasingly concerned about the difficulties of providing health services to people in rural sections where towns are too small to attract a young doctor or dentist. When the old doctor is lost through death or retirement, there is no one to replace him. Churches have the same problem. There are not enough qualified pastors to serve the small, scattered congregations.

One of the reasons put forth for retaining the small rural community is that it provides an inexpensive place for the elderly. The low taxes and relaxed atmosphere, it is said, make such towns havens for retired persons. A careful consideration of all factors, though, will indicate that this is not the most humanitarian solution.

It is true that property values are low and that taxes also may be low, but many necessary services are missing. A community of retired folk can operate without a new grade school or a new swimming pool, but it has special needs for nursing, medical, and sanitary facilities, good fire and police protection, churches, and the welfare agencies. These criticial services are among the first to be curtailed in a declining town.

If the town were to specialize in providing services for the aging, there would be, at best, a short-lived upturn of the population curve.

While a number of older rural people express a desire to stay in small towns, near their former homes, each year the number of rural people who retire becomes smaller, compared to the number retiring in urban areas. As young people continue to migrate to the cities, the number of future rural retired people will continue to fall.

It is doubtful that a lifelong city dweller would be content in most rural communities.

The conclusions of the two studies may be summed up by the final sentences in the Nebraska report:

"A 'struggle for survival' has been in progress for decades among the small town service centers. One constructive approach would appear to be widespread intercommunity planning; with attention to the appropriate role of the respective ranks of towns in a given area."

CURRENT TRENDS seem to indicate that the appropriate role for most of the very small towns is to pass slowly out of existence.

And that is where we encounter difficulty in intercommunity planning.

It is not a popular recommendation, but we do not do residents of small towns a favor by sheltering them from the knowledge which indicates their continued decline. Their best chance to get full value from their resources will come about if they are forewarned so that they may withdraw their resources for reinvestment or use them up. Only those who are adventuresome by nature should attempt to turn aside the trends and create a new future for their town.

We hear a great deal about the dramatic and drastic social changes faced by people who migrate to cities from the country. It may be, however, that the social and economic adjustments that will be required by those unable to compete successfully in the rural regions will be no less drastic and upsetting if they stay than if they go. It may be easier to accept changes brought about by a migration than to accept the decay of their old living patterns, especially if the migration to the city carries with it new economic advantages.

This idea was expressed by Glenn Johnson and Joel Smith in an Iowa State University symposium, *Problems and Policies of American Agriculture.* Here is a quotation from their conclusion:

"The 'folk' society is a non-existent constructed type and is a far cry from the contemporary social structure of rural America. The gap between rural and urban America has diminished to such an extent that the rural to urban migrant may experience no more adjustment difficulties than those encountered by any type of person in a new community. Rural migrants to cities, ultimately, are likely to gain at least as much material reward from their moves as they are likely to receive in their rural areas of residence. Rural migrants also gain psychic rewards in their newer places of urban residence. Those rural institutional facilities which disappear as a result of depopulation were usually inadequate as compared to their counterparts in more densely settled areas."

Much of the disagreement as to the merits of city and country living is brought about through comparisons of conditions in large metropolitan areas with those supposed to exist in the small towns.

If it were true that our only real alternatives were the slums or sprawling suburbs of a metropolis, on one hand, and a substandard farm or small, substandard rural town, on the other, the outlook would be bleak, indeed.

I would prefer to think that with proper direction of our efforts, we might create a third alternative by retaining and revitalizing small- to medium-size cities (between 5 thousand and 50 thousand population) spaced at sufficiently frequent intervals to allow the benefits of both city and open country living to be shared by urban and rural residents alike.

Unless we make some significant changes, the vast majority of our agricultural service communities will soon fall below useful minimums and will become so small that they cannot provide for the basic needs of people.

Gradually, since 1950, some communities have become aware of their plight. The solution, eagerly pursued by most of them, is to supplement or replace the agricultural economic base with another—manufacturing, service, tourism. Manufacturing has become the lodestar.

But in order to retain young people or to attract industry, a town must provide certain services. If its residents are to be able to afford such minimum services, certain minimum population must be there to share the cost.

To particularize, let us consider a county in the Great Plains that apparently is at a stable point with 275 farms, devoted primarily to livestock feeding and grain production. Ten years from now, if corporation farming were to become accepted, this number could be cut in half, and the number of farms would be fewer than 150.

The serious questions facing us, as I see it, are: How can 150 farmers provide an adequate high school? (A high school, according to Dr. James B. Conant, should have at least 400 pupils if it is to be economical and yet be able to provide the diversity of education that our modern society demands. Other authorities set an even higher minimum figure.)

How can these 150 farmers support adequate roads? Or even a semblance of rail or air passenger service? (They may temporarily muster enough political influence to prevent discontinuation of service, but that does not make the service good or economical.)

How can these 150 farmers hope to support churches of different faiths and denominations? (In order to have an adequate budget for a good building, a pastor's salary of at least 5 thousand dollars, a youth program, theological scholarships, and home and foreign missions, the church will need as many as 600 members. Since 60 percent of the total population are church members, it takes a population base of a thousand persons for a single, vital, adequate, self-supporting church.)

How can the 150 farmers hope to support hospitals or police and fire protection? (There is a direct correlation between the size of a town and its fire insurance rating. There is also an obvious correlation between the cost of fire insurance and the adequacy of fire protection.)

How can 150 farm families hope to support recreation, amusement, and entertainment facilities like motion picture theaters, swimming pools, playgrounds, golf courses, and fairgrounds?

How can they get electric service? (Rural electric companies are finding it necessary to compete for franchises in cities and towns now served by private utility companies as they come face to face with an immutable fact: You cannot provide electricity economically if it is necessary to maintain long transmission systems for a few scattered households and no industrial users.)

How can these few farmers support a local newspaper and a radio station?

How can they support a retail center with a reasonable variety of stores? (A large supermarket needs 2 thousand families to take full advantage of the facilities and to give the customers the maximum benefit of volume selling. If our 150 farmers are forced to drive to Kansas City or Denver or Wichita or Dallas for a loaf of bread, all the time they save by the use of labor-saving machinery will be squandered on trips to the store.)

And without these key facilities, how can these farmers hope to attract industry to supplement their economic base and to provide opportunities for future employment for their youth?

I think there is a great need to develop a concept of a minimum community that can provide the services required for a satisfying existence.

The metropolitan planners are concerned with the inefficiencies of bigness—the complex problems of too many people in too little space. I suggest that we address ourselves to the opposite end of the same problem, "How big must a small town be in order to be healthy and useful?"

As a part of the smalltown study in Kansas, the economists set out minimum markets in terms of numbers of customers that would be required to maintain a reasonable income for the proprietors. In the preceding paragraphs I cited a number of such standards from various sources. As a first approximation, a community of 5 thousand persons with a market radius of about 25 miles seems justified.

DR. CONANT's suggested minimum standard of one hundred pupils in a high school graduating class indicates that it would take a population base of 6,250 persons to support an adequate high school, because 1.6 percent of the United States population in 1960 was in the 17-year age group.

An estimate by Karl Fox, of Iowa State University, of 2 thousand families needed to support a large supermarket indicates a population base of 6,720 persons.

The Kansas economists determined the following population requirements for individually owned establishments to produce incomes of 7 thousand dollars a year or more for their owners: A grocery store, 1,340; a men's clothing store, 2,680; a hardware store, 6,720.

The American Library Association suggests that an expenditure of 2.25 dollars per capita is enough to provide "good" service. For a community of 5 thousand population, this would provide a budget of 11,250 dollars, which could be expected to pay a librarian, maintain a building, and provide money for new books and periodicals. Obviously, the community of 1 thousand would have to depend on volunteer help to maintain even a minimum library with the same per capita contribution.

A community of 5 thousand persons could support 5 churches of different denominations, each of 600 members.

The fire insurance classifications in Kansas also indicate that the population range of 5 thousand is the average required for good fire protection. The median fire insurance rating for cities of more than 30 thousand population is 4.0; for cities between 10 thousand and 29,999, 5.7; for the 5 thousand to 9,999 range, 6.4; for the 2,500 to 4,999 range, 6.8; for the 1 thousand to 2,499 range, 7.2; for towns between 500 and 999, 7.7; and for villages with fewer than 500 residents, 9.0.

While these approximate, minimum standards for adequate service should surely not be taken as the absolutely necessary and sufficient conditions for attempting to maintain a community, I believe that this kind of analysis on an area basis might give the rural town an insight into the cold reality of its chances for survival.

Obviously, a small town that is closer to large cities may be able to thrive as a dormitory town without providing some of the more expensive facilities, but, even so, such a town will be at a disadvantage as a trading center. If we send potential customers to a neighboring city for entertainment or for medical care because we cannot provide them at home, it will not be long before they will look also to that city for new cars, clothes, and appliances.

The residents of small towns must realize also that two towns of 2,500 population in a single county are not equivalent to one town of 5 thousand in terms of competition with the major cities in adjoining counties. When this divided emphasis exists, the people of the county must, for example, choose between two small, inadequate high schools and one large, efficient school. The former performs an injustice to the youngsters; the latter gives one of the two towns an advantage in the struggle. Many counties have elected to compromise by placing the new high school out in the country, halfway between the two towns. Now the children have a good school, but neither town has the advantage of the drawing power of the high school. While this may keep things on an even keel between the two small towns, it gives an additional edge to the larger city in an adjoining county.

At the risk of being repetitious, let me stress these points: The present pattern in the Great Plains is one of more small towns than the agriculture of the area can support. They are kept busy fighting among themselves for an ever-falling number of customers. They are so busy with their intramural battles that they cannot hope to compete successfully with the bigger towns nearby. The small town that finally emerges as victor may find that it has won a hollow victory, indeed, since the loss of resources and the waste of capital involved in maintaining an inefficient operation out of spite may have deprived the county of the assets and leadership necessary for growth. And so, although the small town won its battle, it may stand to lose the war, and the people of the county will have lost their area shopping center and cultural center and lost any hope of providing opportunities for their young people at home.

While it may be foolish to suggest that small towns which have been fighting one another for a hundred years should get together, combine resources, and make sacrifices for their mutual good, that seems to be the only way to revitalize the declining rural towns. They must develop some advantages—social, cultural, and economic— if they are to attract some of the outside capital investment that tends to flow toward the cities.

The other alternative, of course, is to lapse into suspended animation until the time that the metropolitan areas grow out to meet the small towns.

Because of their geographic location, this rescuing of small towns has already taken place in the megalopolis along the eastern seaboard.

Prof. Jean Gottmann, in a study for the Twentieth Century Fund, has described this populous region, in which urban and rural have merged, not without problems, but also with some marked mutual benefits. Here we find a thriving agriculture, often in direct competition for land with commercial and industrial uses. Here we find a high value of farm products per acre. In fact, if we select such items as value of farm products, value of farmland and buildings, dairy production, and horticultural production and plot them on a map, we find we have virtually reproduced the map of the United States showing the standard metropolitan statistical areas.

Of 100 leading agricultural counties, in terms of value of farm products, 42 were metropolitan counties in 1960. The 444 counties in standard metropolitan statistical areas and in potential metropolitan areas produced 23 percent of the value of farm products sold. The average value of products sold, per farm, in the 600 leading agricultural counties was 15,121 dollars in 1960. In the 146 metropolitan counties which were included in the top 600, the average value per farm was 16,995 dollars, but it will be a long time before the population concentrations in the Great Plains can hope to reach similar proportions. The population density in the United States is about 60 persons per square mile. It is 11 times greater in the eastern megalopolis, and only half that dense in the Great Plains.

But it is in the vicinity of these metropolitan areas that we might expect the most severe competition for land. As these larger cities continue to grow, some benefits may accrue to the more remote agricultural regions. As metropolitan land is priced out of the farm market, the rural areas may be able to absorb the increased transportation costs and compete successfully. This "decentralization" of agriculture, however, undoubtedly will follow a pattern somewhat like that of industrial decentralization—that is, the farm operations that are forced out of the metropolitan regions will be moved only just far enough to escape the excessive land and labor costs, while striving to keep transportation costs as low as possible.

While there has been a great deal of overemphasis of the possible future effects of the population explosion on the midwestern farming regions, the small rural towns may reap some limited benefits if risk taking and imagination reassert themselves in the Great Plains.

Thus far, the Great Plains States have found it difficult to break into the metropolitan markets for vegetables since the city farmers of the megalopolis have a big advantage with their nearby, compact market. But these same urban areas are also providing vegetables for the cities in the Great Plains. As the pressure of nonfarm uses takes these "urban" farms out of production, Great Plains farmers may be able to win away their own local markets, to which they have a transportation advantage. Intensification in the agriculture of small areas in the Great Plains would have benefits for some of its towns in that it would modify the rural depopulation.

Any attempt to encourage the acceleration of consolidation of towns and community facilities, in order to retain a combination of both rural and urban advantages, must overcome tremendous pressures created by the inertia of current trends in order to succeed.

Present indications point to an ever-increasing rate of urbanization, and yet the major opposition to any reasonable plan to deflect and modify these trends seems to arise from within those groups who profess the deepest interest in preserving rural Americana.

The basic changes in agriculture began to be evident right after the First World War, and the trends were established by the midtwenties. The depression of the early thirties deflected some of the indicators and disturbed the picture somewhat, but the real trends remained.

Still we have those who caution us against making hasty judgements, in the face of a history of 40 years of irreversible adjustments.

In an intensive study of the future

requirements for vocational training programs, the Kansas State Employment Service concluded that in the 1960–1970 decade only one farm-reared youth in seven would be able to remain on the farm. Nevertheless, those whose continued influence depends on retaining the rural-urban system contend that this is just city propaganda and refuse to admit that there is any drastic reduction of farm opportunity. We are told that two out of five workers are employed in agriculture. Obviously, to obtain such a statistic in the face of a preponderance of evidence to the contrary requires a broad definition of "agriculture."

THE 1940 YEARBOOK of Agriculture addressed itself to the problems of farmers in a changing world. Many of the authors showed deep insight in their prognostications. At one point a challenge was issued to develop a national policy aimed at increasing educational opportunities:

"Many of the children now being reared in rural areas will ultimately live elsewhere. They are not being equipped with the knowledge and skills they will need for effective adjustment, so that in many cases they press on the unskilled labor market and live under slum conditions."

This prediction has proved to be remarkably accurate, especially since it was written before our entrance into the Second World War, when the great migration of rural labor to metropolitan factories accelerated. And yet, later in the same publication, another author waxed eloquent over the return to subsubsistence farming, which occurred during the depression. He referred to it as "the rural renaissance . . . the return to the nourishing bosom of Mother Nature. . . ." The authors of such statements should consider carefully the long-range effect of the constant, hypnotic repetition of such myths. Many people come to believe them.

By the same token, those who are in possession of unpopular truths must realize that frequent repetition of these truths can speed their acceptance and bring about adjustment to change. More of our leaders, especially in education and politics, must have the courage and integrity to accept the short-term political disadvantages which may accrue to those who make honest statements of unpleasant facts in order to make possible the long-term gains to be obtained by an accurately informed population.

The necessary changes can be accomplished most painlessly through the use of the educational process. While it is highly idealistic to hope that those with a vested interest in the status quo will join with the proponents of change to spread the truth, it would be most desirable that the stand-patters remain silent in order that the harmful myths be laid to rest.

Some solution to this dilemma must be found.

The decline in numbers of people employed in farming is tending to eliminate the pure "agricultural service community."

The hard facts of mechanization and centralization in nonfarm industry eliminate the possibility that "industrial development" can save a significant number of rural communities.

A critical, realistic evaluation of the current condition of the social, cultural, and economic institutions in our small rural towns indicates that it is probably not in our best interest to save them all, anyway.

But there is a real danger that if we allow present trends to continue, we will lose more of our small cities and towns than is desirable from either an economic or a sociological standpoint.

DWIGHT A. NESMITH *joined the staff of the School of Engineering at Kansas State University, Manhattan, Kans., in 1948. As associate professor in the Division of Engineering and Industrial Services, he has been in charge of the Community Survey Program at Kansas State University since 1952 and has conducted surveys of community facilities all over Kansas.*

LOUIS D. MALOTKY

BETTER HOUSING
IN THE COUNTRY

HOUSING in the country historically has been in-ferior to housing in cities because of low income, competition between the farm business and the home for the receipts from sales, lack of credit, and the general absence of building and sanitary codes.

Rural housing has improved greatly in recent years, especially in places where families can earn an adequate income, because of such developments as the fading of the city limits as a sharp line between city and rural families, the availability of electricity, better financing, and the availability of information about house plans and improvements.

New homes financed by the Farmers Home Administration exemplify the kind of homes rural families of low and moderate incomes desire. Typically they are one-story, three-bedroom, brick homes with 1,200 square feet of living space. They may have central heat, a bath or a bath and a half, countertop stove, wall oven, and other features of some city homes. The average cost in 1962 was about 11 thousand dollars.

Better income prospects of many rural families and lenders' growing awareness of the opportunities for fi-nancing home improvements on farms and in rural communities will make it easier for rural families to continue to improve their housing.

A wealth of information on housing is in data assembled by the Bureau of the Census, which classifies housing as urban, rural nonfarm, and farm.

With minor exceptions, urban hous-ing includes homes in towns of 2,500 or more residents and the fringes of urban areas.

The farm dwellings are the occupied dwellings on farms.

The rural nonfarm group includes houses in the open country or in places of less than 2,500 that are not con-sidered urban and houses on farms that are unoccupied or rented for cash, if the rent does not include land for farming.

The farm, rural nonfarm, and urban groupings do not reflect necessarily the occupations of the residents.

The quality of farmhousing rose

185

between 1940 and 1960. Some of the reported improvement was the result of the abandonment of housing on marginally inadequate units, but this upgrading was largely the result of improvements made by the remaining farmers, who frequently supplemented farm income with nonfarm work.

The increased availability of electrical service has been an important factor. Only 31 percent of the farmhouses reported electricity in 1940. By 1950, the percentage was 77. By 1960, 97 percent of the farm homes had electricity. The installation of running water and central heating generally are associated with electrical service.

Only 18 percent of the farm homes had central heating in 1950; 36 percent had this convenience by 1960. Running water was available in 43 percent of the farm homes in 1950 and 75 percent in 1960.

Although the quality of both farm and nonfarm rural homes has improved, on the whole they are still less adequate, comfortable, and convenient than urban homes.

In 1960, 3.5 million of the 17.5 million homes in rural areas needed major repairs, and 1.5 million others were so dilapidated they endangered the health,

safety, and well-being of the occupants. Less than one-third of our population lives in rural areas, but more homes of these families are in a dilapidated condition than the 70 percent of the population living in urban areas. One out of every three homes in rural areas does not have complete bath facilities, and almost two out of three are without central heating.

The greatest increase in new homes during 1950–1960 was in the rural nonfarm group.

Movements of population prompted by the search for better income opportunities or for places to retire and the movement of urban families to a rural environment contributed to the increase in the nonfarm segment of our population. This migration of population has created a substantial demand for new and better rural housing in some States. The growing percentage of farm families who depend on off-farm employment to supplement farm income and the crisscrossing of commuters' paths also have influenced housing standards of rural families and helped provide the income needed to pay for home improvements.

The question of how to use net income best is acute particularly with

CONDITION OF URBAN AND RURAL HOUSING

Subject	Urban	Rural	
		Nonfarm[1]	Farm (occupied)
Number of Houses....................	40, 756, 817	13, 995, 159	3, 566, 321
Sound: [2]			
Number.....................	34, 799, 319	10, 064, 955	2, 486, 482
Percent of total..............	85. 4	71. 9	69. 7
Deteriorating: [3]			
Number.....................	4, 566, 699	2, 690, 802	818, 175
Percent of total..............	11. 2	19. 2	23. 0
Dilapidated: [4]			
Number.....................	1, 390, 799	1, 239, 402	261, 664
Percent of total..............	3. 4	8. 9	7. 3

[1] Includes unoccupied houses on farms and houses on farms rented for cash if rent does not include any land for farming.

[2] Sound housing: Has no defects or only slight defects which normally are corrected by regular maintenance.

[3] Deteriorating housing: Needs more repair than would be provided by regular maintenance. Such housing has one or more defects of an intermediate nature that must be corrected if the unit is to continue to provide safe and adequate shelter.

[4] Dilapidated housing: Does not provide safe and adequate shelter; and, in its present condition, endangers the health, safety, or well-being of the occupants.

Source: United States Census of Housing 1960.

families with moderate incomes who are endeavoring to expand the size of their farm business. Income-producing investments usually have first claim on a farmer's net income. In fact, for a beginning farm family to set aside a substantial portion of its net income for housing may even involve jeopardizing the farming business.

A study made by the agricultural experiment station of Auburn University in cooperation with the agricultural experiment stations of Colorado State University and the University of Missouri showed that many farm families placed the purchase of items such as television sets, boats, appliances, and automobiles ahead of housing improvements.

Young families in cities usually have the choice of starting in an apartment and later may move to a home in a location of their choice, but the opportunity to go house hunting does not exist on farms, and little choice is offered in most small rural country towns. Rural families have only a limited opportunity to shop for a house; they have to accept the facilities that are available close at hand.

New housing on farms has been largely the replacement of a home lost by a disaster or a home that had become so dilapidated that it no longer provided the family adequate shelter. The housing needs of families moving to rural communities, however, were met to a large extent by new housing. This explains why farm homes as a group are older than nonfarm homes. Only 12.2 percent of the occupied farm homes were built during 1950–1960, compared to 31 percent of the nonfarm rural homes. The comparable figure for urban homes was 27.7 percent.

Housing on farms and in nonfarm areas consists largely of one-unit structures. In 1960, 98.9 percent of the occupied farm homes and 95.5 percent of the nonfarm homes were one-unit structures; in rural areas the percentage was 96.2. In cities, on the other hand, only 67.8 percent were single-family structures.

Much has been done by banks, savings and loan associations, insurance companies, and other lenders active in the housing credit field. Nationally, the flow of investment capital to homes has been stimulated by the operations of the Housing and Home Finance Agency and the Veterans' Administration, but those Federal programs have been most effective in urban areas.

The Auburn University research showed that Government agencies and programs designed to aid the flow of funds for home mortgages appeared to have little effect in providing more mortgage funds at favorable terms to rural residents. The major sources of home financing available to rural residents in the areas studied in the Cotton Belt are conventional loans with relatively low loans-to-value ratios or short repayment periods.

The rural housing loan program of the Farmers Home Administration was designed particularly to meet the housing credit needs of families of lower and moderate incomes who are unable to obtain the credit they need from other sources. The loans bear 4 percent interest and payments may be extended up to 33 years.

Rural housing loans of the Farmers Home Administration were available only to farmowners until 1961. Since then they also have been available to families who own building sites in the open country or a small country town of not more than 2,500 population.

Action also has been taken by the Housing and Home Finance Agency to extend its services into the more remote areas. The agency has modified its housing standards to adapt them more readily to rural conditions. It also endeavors to place both Federal Housing Administration and Veterans' Administration insured loans in remote areas through its Voluntary Home Mortgage Credit Program. Under this program, families who are eligible for insured loans under the Federal Housing Administration or the Veterans' Administration, but are unable to obtain housing credit from a local source, may be able to locate a lender through the program.

These actions by the Federal Government are one recognition of the importance of adequate credit at reasonable terms as a means of improving the quantity and quality of housing and extending reasonable equality of opportunity to families on farms and in country towns to obtain credit for housing.

Two groups in rural communities have special needs—the migrant farmworkers and older persons.

Migrant agricultural laborers as a group are the poorest housed of our rural population. The nearly half million domestic laborers and almost as many foreign nationals who follow the crops frequently live under deplorable conditions. Many of the migrant workers, especially the citizen group, travel as families. They seek immediate employment, but many also are looking for a place to settle.

The Federal Government during the late thirties and early forties constructed and operated migratory farm labor camps, which later were turned over to private organizations or public authorities. Some of them still serve the needs of migrants.

A new approach to providing and encouraging better housing for migrant families was enacted by the Congress in 1961 when title V of the Housing Act of 1949 was amended to provide for insured loans to owners of farms and qualified organizations to finance the construction of housing and related facilities for domestic farm labor.

More than 6 million persons in rural communities in 1963 were 62 years old or older. They were the fastest growing segment of the population. Those who live in small towns may not need to move when they retire, but the farm families when they retire need to leave the homes in which they spent their productive years. This usually means moving to town and sometimes starting and adjusting to a new way of life. For economic reasons, some have remained on the farms; others have moved to small towns; and a few have gone to cities.

When they move to a small town, they frequently have to buy a home because satisfactory rental housing is not available. To buy a home, they usually have to use their savings, because credit ordinarily is not available to them. The Congress has given increased attention to their special problems. The Senior Citizens Housing Act of 1962 authorizes loans to persons who are at least 62 years old to buy an existing home or to buy a building site and construct a home. Loans also are authorized to finance the construction and improvement of rental housing for senior citizens in rural areas.

To sum up: The quality of housing in rural areas will continue to improve. Better communications and transportation and the ready availability of community services, such as roads, electricity, and schools, will continue to influence the housing goals.

The rate at which home improvements will take place will depend to a large degree on the extent to which increased income opportunities become available to farmers, ranchers, and other rural families. The families who have adequate financial means will be able to keep pace with the ever-increasing levels of housing comfort and convenience.

A continuing challenge, however, will be how rural families at the lower levels of income will be able to obtain at least minimum adequate housing. A realization of their hopes for better housing is related closely to an effective rural renewal program that will provide them additional income.

Louis D. Malotky *is Director, Rural Housing Loan Division, Farmers Home Administration. He joined the staff of the Department of Agriculture in 1941, and since then has been working in various phases of farm real estate credit. He has been associated with the rural housing loan program of the Farmers Home Administration since the program started in 1949.*

HELEN L. JOHNSTON

HEALTH TRENDS
IN RURAL AMERICA

HUNDREDS of small, new, modern hospitals everywhere in rural America attest the changes in conditions and attitudes that affect the health of individuals and communities. The changes may have both positive and negative effects. They include the hospitals themselves, the readiness of rural people to use them, a modification of the rural living and working environment, and changes in the rural population itself.

Rural outmigration, for example, has relieved overpopulation and stabilized the economic level of some communities. It has also left behind a disproportionate share of the young and the old—the age groups with the greatest relative need for health care. It has made the support of needed health services increasingly difficult in some small communities. The overall rural economy has improved, but one-third of the Nation's rural families still have incomes of less than 2 thousand dollars.

The urbanizing and broadening influences of radio, newspapers, telephones, highways, and automobiles, moreover, touch even the most remote farm family and tend to reduce old rural-urban differences in health needs, attitudes, and behavior. Visiting and shopping in nearby towns and cities have become a part of daily living, rather than a rare occurrence, and the visits to town often become the occasion for seeking medical or dental care as well.

Especially among farm residents of metropolitan counties, the rural-urban contacts have increased through off-the-farm employment. Off-the-farm work helps to stabilize farm income and makes possible improved nutrition, clothing, and shelter; greater use of medical, dental, and hospital care; and more enrollment in health insurance plans, often in connection with industrial employment.

Offsetting those advantages to some degree, however, are the lack of anyone at home to care for sick or injured family members when the homemaker is employed elsewhere, less close supervision of the health of school and preschool children, less time devoted to the preparation of nutritious meals,

189

and more eating away from home. Cafes and restaurants in small towns, moreover, are less likely than those in urban centers to be well equipped, have well-trained workers, and be supervised by agencies to protect the public health.

Where suburban sprawl has encroached on farm communities with little forethought or planning, the haphazard use of land for farming and nonfarm purposes may lead to health and safety risks for farm and nonfarm residents alike. Farm families may have substantial sums invested in their own water supplies and septic tanks; they may resist taxation for public improvements even after increased density of population threatens contamination of their own wells.

Both farm and nonfarm residents may also be subject to the risks involved in the drift of poisonous sprays from aerial spraying equipment, the use of crowded highways for slow-moving farm equipment, and other hazards arising from rapidly increasing population in a previously rural community.

Machines have greatly eased the burden of farmwork. They also have made the character of work hazards more and more like those of industry, but with far fewer controls. Safety devices may be lacking or misused. Overfatigue may result from long hours of work during peak seasons. Mechanized equipment may be used by young people or temporary workers who lack adequate supervision.

Expanded farm operations made possible by the use of machines have created new needs in some communities for short-term workers from outside the county or even outside the State. Such measures as the provision of field toilets, safe drinking water, handwashing facilities, and a safe means of preserving food for field lunches become increasingly important as larger numbers of fieldworkers are employed. Adequate temporary housing for workers and families from outside the area is also important.

BYPASSED BY ECONOMIC and social change, some rural people continue to live at a depressed level. They may live in the midst of relative prosperity, but are themselves handicapped by farm units that are too small to provide an adequate family living; by age, which may force them into retirement without adequate resources to support a satisfactory level of living, including adequate health care; or by other economic, or social, or maybe physical disabilities.

Other communities have become stranded where farmland has been depleted or forests and mines have been exhausted. The people live in dilapidated homes with few conveniences. They have little access to health or other community services.

Some of these handicapped rural people, with incomes far below a taxable level, take refuge in city slums. Some become migrant farmworkers. Some deteriorate in a steadily more hopeless setting. The greatest concentration of the deteriorating rural communities is in the Southeastern and Southwestern States. Others are scattered throughout the country.

Rural people of the Great Plains, on the other hand, share in general rural economic and social improvements. Nevertheless, they suffer a growing handicap in their efforts to maintain adequate community health services as the population of the Great Plains counties continues to decrease. Speed and ease of transportation compensate to some degree by enabling the average family to reach physicians and hospitals even at distances of 50 miles or more. For the less mobile aged or chronically ill, especially those who live alone, distance may be an insurmountable barrier to obtaining needed health care. Moreover, the typical lack of arrangements to meet unexpected health emergencies affects all families of the Great Plains region.

INFANT MORTALITY is among the indexes of the health status of a population. During most of the years since

1928, infants born to urban families had the best chance of survival. Rural people have now regained a slight advantage over urban people, according to 1959 infant mortality rates (infant deaths under a year per thousand live births).

Comparisons of infant mortality according to residence, however, show that babies born outside metropolitan counties had a poorer chance to survive in 1959 than babies born to residents of metropolitan counties. Small places of 2,500 to 10 thousand in nonmetropolitan counties had the highest infant mortality rates. The rural nonwhite infant mortality rate in nonmetropolitan counties was nearly twice the national average.

Regional differences also appear in infant mortality rates. Although the situation in the South has improved greatly since 1928, mortality rates for both rural and urban infants in the South have continued to average higher than those for any other region.

Most deaths of infants 1 to 11 months old are considered preventable. The Children's Bureau reported for 1959 that infants of that age have the best survival chances if they belong to white families living in metropolitan counties. The mortality rate for all infants aged 1 to 11 months *declined* by 21 percent during the decade to 1960. During the same period, the mortality rate for nonwhite rural infants living outside metropolitan counties *increased* by 5 percent.

DATA on injuries in accidents during work and on chronically disabling conditions provided by the National Health Survey of the Public Health Service offer other clues to rural-urban differences in health status. Fifty-six per thousand persons in farm sections and 46 per thousand city persons were hurt in work accidents each year in 1960 and 1961.

For all ages, the percentage of rural persons who have some degree of activity-limitation due to chronic conditions exceeds that of urban people.

Because many farm operators are over 50 years old, it is significant that 24 percent of the rural farm people 45 to 64 years old were limited in their activity by some type of chronic condition, compared with 20 percent for rural nonfarm and 16 percent for urban residents.

More than half of the rural farm people over 65 reported some degree of activity-limitation from a chronic condition, compared with less than 40 percent of the urban and 46 percent of the rural nonfarm people of that age.

Among the chronic conditions reported oftener among rural farm than among nonfarm and urban residents were hernia, heart conditions, high blood pressure, as well as arthritis and rheumatism.

The number of days spent in bed as a result of disability was about the same among urban and rural residents. But after age 65 rural nonfarm and rural farm people reported an average of 17 days spent in bed during a year, compared with 16 days reported for urban persons.

Regional differences appear in the number of days of bed disability. For all rural farm people in the South, regardless of age, an average of 9 days of bed disability was reported—the highest for any residence group. Rural residents of both the West and the North Central States, on the other hand, reported lower rates of bed disability than other population groups by residence in their respective regions.

Only a few clues exist to the relative health disability among especially disadvantaged rural groups. In 102 low-income rural counties designated by the Department of Agriculture as pilot counties for the Rural Areas Development program during the fifties, infant mortality averaged 31 deaths under a year per thousand live births, compared with 27 for the Nation as a whole. The pilot counties were concentrated in the Southeastern States.

A study of the California Vocational Rehabilitation Service in 1955–1958 assessed the seriousness of disability among seasonal farmworkers in that State. About one of five adults had a physical handicap that affected earning capacity.

RURAL HEALTH facilities have improved measurably since the Second World War.

The Hill-Burton Hospital Survey and Construction Act of 1946 had provisions to equalize the distribution of modern hospitals so that all people, regardless of where they lived, may have ready access to general hospital care.

Up to 1962, two-thirds of the beds in general hospitals built with Hill-Burton aid were in small towns and cities. Nine hundred new hospitals—nearly one-third of the total built with Federal aid—were in communities of less than 2,500. About one-fifth were in communities of 2,500 to 50 thousand.

Besides the general hospitals, about half of the public health centers built with Hill-Burton aid are located in small communities. Small communities have been able also to qualify for assistance in the construction or improvement of nursing homes and diagnostic and treatment centers.

A study by the Public Health Service suggested that income level, rather than rurality, is a governing factor in the location of health facilities. Metropolitan and nonmetropolitan counties of comparable per capita income had comparable numbers of beds in general hospitals and nursing homes in relation to their population.

CONTINUING REGIONAL disparities appear when data on the distribution of physicians, dentists, and nurses per 100 thousand of population are examined by year and by region.

Throughout 1921–1960, the South's supply of physicians, dentists, and nurses was at a lower level than that of any other geographic region.

Metropolitan counties in 1940 had 153 physicians per 100 thousand residents, compared with 90 per 100

thousand in bordering counties and 79 in all other counties. Twenty years later—in mid-1959—the physician-population ratios for each group of counties had *decreased*. Highly urbanized counties continued to have about twice as many physicians per 100 thousand people as isolated counties. Specifically, in mid-1959, metropolitan counties had 146 physicians per 100 thousand persons; bordering counties, 77; and isolated counties, 75.

ESTABLISHING functional relationships between health personnel and facilities in small communities and those in urban centers is viewed by many health experts as a way to maintain quality of rural health care.

They cite as some of the advantages the opportunity for physicians to maintain the contacts that contribute to professional growth; easier referrals without loss of patients; and provision of a wide range of diagnostic and treatment services for rural residents without costly duplication of facilities.

The number of formalized relationships between health facilities in small and large population centers is still negligible, although one of the initial objectives of the Hill-Burton program was to facilitate such relationships.

Less formal and extensive relationships, on the other hand, have increased. They involve such arrangements as the new establishment of preceptorships by medical schools, which assign graduate students to physicians in smaller centers, and periodic institutes given by teaching hospitals or other institutions for practitioners from the area.

A report in 1962 of an experiment in Michigan in establishing relationships among small and large health centers suggested that the difficulty of implementing regionalization in the health field has corollaries in library, school, and other fields. Small institutions desire autonomy and self-sufficiency. They fear being swallowed up by larger institutions if they establish working relationships with them.

Group practice, in which several physicians representing different specialized interests work together, also is viewed as a means of improving and stabilizing rural health services. It helps "put the patient together," in that a single group of individuals takes responsibility for his medical care in much the same way as the old-fashioned country doctor took responsibility for total health care of his patients.

Formalized group practice has grown in number of units and in number of physicians associated with group practice organizations since 1940. The Public Health Service reported a threefold increase between 1946 and 1959. Of the 1,200 groups in 1959, more than one-third were in isolated counties.

In addition to these formalized groups, which usually share facilities, equipment, and income, informal referral arrangements apparently have increased between the physicians of small and large communities.

SERVICES FOR rural groups having special needs because of age, health condition, or income status are minimal in most small communities.

Homemaker and home nursing services are least well developed in the small community and the sparsely settled farming areas, despite growing needs because of the increasing employment of homemakers away from the farm home.

Physiotherapy services can greatly relieve the suffering of some chronically ill and aging persons; they seldom are found outside of major urban centers.

School health services, if they exist at all, are usually inadequate.

Health services especially geared to meet the needs of a temporary influx of farmworkers and their families seldom exist. Psychiatric service for the mentally ill is almost entirely lacking, and so is counseling for families of former mental patients on their return to the community.

The continuing rural shortages of health personnel to some extent are ac-centuated by increasing demands for some types of health service. The use by rural people of hospitals for maternity care has risen sharply. Only 45 percent of rural mothers in 1940 were hospitalized at childbirth, compared with more than 90 percent in 1959. Urban births in hospitals have increased also but at a less rapid rate; 97 percent now take place in hospitals.

Overall rates of utilization of hospitals by rural people, on the other hand, remain little changed since about 1930. The Committee on the Costs of Medical Care reported at that time that 4.6 percent of the residents of small towns and rural sections had some hospital experience in an average year, compared with 7.1 percent of large city residents. In 1957–1958, the National Health Survey reported, 5 percent of open-country residents were hospitalized, compared with 10 percent of the residents of cities of 100 thousand or more. The average length of stay for rural farm and nonfarm residents was 7 to 8 days, compared with 9 for urban residents.

The use of physicians' and dentists' services by rural people has increased, but continuing disparities exist between rural and urban levels of use.

Rural farm people averaged 3.8 visits annually to physicians, compared with 4.9 for rural nonfarm and 5.3 for urban residents in 1957–1959. People of the rural South reported the fewest visits, although the South had the greatest proportion of rural farm people with limitation of activity resulting from chronic conditions.

Rural people are also less likely to use dental care. When they do, more likely it is for extractions rather than for fillings or other remedial services. One-fourth of the rural farm people reported never having visited a dentist, compared with 20 percent of the rural nonfarm and 16 percent of urban people.

GEOGRAPHIC PROXIMITY makes less difference than in the past in the distances people go for health care.

Residents of a county in the Great Plains region—Kit Carson County in Colorado—used more than 200 different physicians in 1958. Seven physicians practiced in the county at the time. Most of the out-of-county physicians consulted were specialists, nearly one-half of whom practiced in Denver, more than 150 miles from Burlington, the county seat.

Studies in Mississippi, Connecticut, and New York counties indicated that the proximity of a doctor or hospital does not determine where people will purchase medical or hospital care. The increasing mobility of the population makes the majority of rural people far less dependent than in the past on nearby resources, except for emergency cases.

MEDICAL FOLKWAYS, including the use of old home remedies and folk practitioners, still compete with more sophisticated methods of treatment, especially among the low-income rural minorities.

The use of midwifery, for example, has almost disappeared among rural families in general. Nonwhite rural families, however, continue to use midwives, especially in some of the more isolated rural communities of the South.

Health neglect also is common among low-income rural groups. Physicians in California, who studied the reasons for failure to use prenatal care, even when it was offered through free clinics, found that major obstacles included inadequate understanding, dissatisfaction with the services made available to indigent persons, or failure to qualify for indigent care because family income was too high—even though marginal—or because residence requirements could not be met.

For the migratory farm family, lack of residence status is likely to bar the use of community services offered to others of similar income, even in the place they call home.

Not only purchasing power but also perceptions of health needs and appropriate means of care affect rural families' demand for the community health services. Differences among rural people in their awareness of need and proper care are associated with differences in education and level of participation in community affairs, as well as differences in occupation and income.

Rural family health expenditures in 1955 averaged about 63 dollars a person—more than double those in 1941, in terms of dollars of constant purchasing power. They were about 80 percent of the health expenditures of urban families in 1955, compared with less than half the urban expenditures in 1941. In both years, the variations in expenditures may in part be accounted for by differences in levels of charges between rural and urban areas. As data as to utilization show, however, there are also real differences between the two population groups in use of care.

The medical expenditures of farm people in families with incomes of less than 2 thousand dollars averaged 55 dollars per person and represented about 9 percent of their total outlay for family living in 1955, compared with about 5 percent in the general population for the year. For farm people with incomes between 2 thousand and 5 thousand dollars, medical expenditures averaged between 60 and 65 dollars. Expenditures rose rapidly in groups that had incomes of more than 5 thousand dollars.

The expenditures of nonwhite families tended to be lower and to represent a smaller percentage of total family outlay than among white families. This may, in part, reflect nonwhite families' lack of access to services, especially in the South.

Prepayment coverage has expanded among people in the half-dozen most rural States faster than for the United States as a whole in recent years. The National Health Survey's report on insurance coverage for rural farm, rural nonfarm, and urban people, however, shows that rural farm people continue to have less insurance coverage than other groups. They differ also in type of coverage and in the proportion of hospital bills paid by insurance.

According to the National Health Survey, one-half of rural farm residents had no insurance. About one-third of rural nonfarm and fewer than one-third of urban residents had no insurance. A smaller proportion of persons in all residence categories had surgical insurance, compared with hospital insurance; a still smaller proportion had other medical coverage.

For each type, the proportion of rural farm people having the specified coverage was smaller than the proportion of urban or rural nonfarm. Urban people were most likely to have a Blue Cross or Blue Shield type of coverage. The insurance held by rural farm people was likely to fall in the category, "other."

The proportion of the hospital bill of discharged patients paid for by insurance averaged 70 percent for urban and rural nonfarm people. For rural farm people, it averaged 55 percent. The proportion of persons discharged from hospitals with more than three-fourths of the bill paid by insurance averaged 50 percent for urban and rural nonfarm patients. For rural farm patients, it averaged 39 percent.

The rural aged—and especially those from farms—must rely on their own financial resources to pay for needed health care oftener than the urban residents.

The possible influence of method of payment on utilization of service is implied in another Social Security Administration report of the early fifties.

The rural farm population past 65 averaged 86 days of hospital care per 100 persons in comparison with 184—more than twice as many—for urban persons. When the insured population only was considered, however, insured farm groups had high hospital admission rates accompanied by average stays only moderately less than other population groups. Their resulting

average of 208 days of hospital care per 100 persons was greater than the national average.

How much farther the possibilities of rural enrollment can be stretched may be questioned under existing circumstances. National Health Survey reports show a rapid increase in the percentage of persons enrolled with increase in income. To urge individuals or families to join prepayment organizations when their income averages 2 thousand dollars or less, as is true of one-third of the Nation's rural families, would seem likely to be costly, unproductive, and questionable from the point of view of the needs of the people. The individual insurance they would be likely to purchase would be the most costly and limited in benefits. It might provide for the economic catastrophe; it would be unlikely to encourage early detection and treatment of ailments before they reach the catastrophic stage.

On the other hand, when improvements in income are made by enlargement of the farm unit, off-farm work opportunities, or other means, rural people need to continue to work with voluntary health insurers to develop new community organization techniques and to gain acceptance of existing community organizations—other than employee groups—as a basis for group insurance coverage.

Insurance purchased on a group basis has the advantages of greater benefits at lower costs than individually purchased insurance.

In the future, as in the past, rural people will need to run fast to stay in place. The relative position of rural and urban residents in the availability and use of health facilities and services has remained about the same the past two or three decades.

Personal and community economic levels continue to be important keys to levels of health and health care. Geographic accessibility of service is of somewhat less importance than formerly to the majority of rural residents. It is still of crucial importance to some of those who are most needy— the aging, the chronically ill, migratory farm families, and the indigent rural resident.

In asking how rural areas might be brought up to the standards of urban communities, a question may be raised about urban standards. Even in the city setting where medical advances have been applied most fully, services still usually represent a hodgepodge, in the midst of which the consumer finds few guidelines to tap the services best fitted to his needs.

AMONG THE HOPEFUL factors are some legislative developments.

The Community Health Services and Facilities Act of 1961 opened the door for rural as well as urban experimentation in methods of providing health care to fit changing needs and circumstances. Emphasis is placed on services for the chronically ill and the aged.

Some examples of activities that may be undertaken under the program are demonstrations of nursing care of the sick at home, as a means of preventing or reducing disability; demonstration of specialized services, such as physiotherapy, supplied from a central source to patients at home or in nursing homes; and development and testing of methods of recruiting, training, and using homemakers, nurses' aides, and other subprofessional personnel in home-care programs.

Groups interested in this program can obtain information from their State health departments.

Financial support to help States and communities extend services to migrant workers and their families was authorized through the Public Health Service under 1962 legislation, which provides grants to pay part of the cost of family health service clinics and other projects to improve migrants' health services or conditions.

The objectives of the migrant health legislation are to provide a setting in which migrant farmworkers and families can realistically be expected and encouraged to take responsibility for meeting their own health needs. This will require the scheduling of services to prevent and treat illness at times and places accessible to migrants and without restrictions because they lack residence. It will also require upgrading their living and working environment to make such minimal facilities as toilets, drinking water, handwashing, and bathing and laundry facilities available in order that they can observe good personal health practices. Finally, it will require interarea coordination so that the present disparities in services and the methods whereby they are provided will be minimized.

The expanded Hill-Burton program of the Public Health Service continues to facilitate the efforts of rural people to provide facilities and services for general hospital care, nursing home care, public health, and some other types of services.

The Small Business Administration also assists rural hospitals, nursing homes, and local physicians and dentists who need loans for new or expanded facilities.

The banding together of two or more counties has succeeded in extending organized public health services to some rural counties. To accomplish the same general objective, contracts for service between the State health department and rural counties without local public health organization have proved successful in California.

Continuing shortages of health workers are neither a rural nor an urban problem, but a national problem. The Public Health Service reported that ratios of physicians to population have remained practically unchanged since 1940. With dentists, as with physicians, active practitioner-population ratios were lower in the early sixties than in the prewar period. The number of professional nurses has increased, but a serious shortage existed in 1963 in relation to demand. In hospitals alone, more than twice as many professional nurses were employed in 1956 as in 1943.

To maintain medical care of high quality for rural people will require continuing study and effort to organize services effectively, especially where depopulation, poverty, interarea farm migration, or other factors create special needs.

The growth of group practice units in rural areas gives promise for the future. A small town with several physicians practicing together may be less likely to become "doctorless" than the one-doctor community.

Moreover, nearly all group practice units have a built-in method of maintaining quality care, ranging from time off to attend meetings and postgraduate courses to participation on medical school faculties.

The continuing poverty of some people and of some communities is also neither a wholly rural nor a wholly urban problem. However, rural poverty may go unnoticed until a shift to urban residence brings it to light.

As one writer commented, "Neglected health conditions in the rural area fester into dependency in the cities, as city schools and other institutions identify problems that were unnoticed before."

A major objective for the improvement of both rural and urban health care is to plan, organize, and administer health services in a manner that will give the entire population maximum accessibility to service according to need.

To PROTECT and maintain the health of rural people, it is necessary to:

Continue to increase knowledge of the influence on health of the changing environment of rural people; for example, the effects of mechanization and the use of toxic substances in agriculture;

Continue "watchdog" observation of rural-urban differences in health status and utilization of health services, in relation to economic and social as well as geographic accessibility;

Continue investigation and development of methods to overcome the 'social costs" of distance in such areas of continuing depopulation as the Great Plains;

Continue research to determine the real roots of human health behavior, especially among the underprivileged groups whose need for health care may be especially great;

Continue application of research findings to processes of providing and financing service, methods of health education, and modification of the environment as necessary.

HELEN L. JOHNSTON *is in the Migrant Health Section, Division of Community Health Services, Public Health Service. Formerly she was employed by Farmer Cooperative Service, the Department of Agriculture and participated in the 1960 White House Conference on Children and Youth.*

For further reading:

Boggs, Stephen E., and others, *A Health Study in Kit Carson County, Colorado.* U.S. Public Health Service, 1962.

Homemaker Service in Public Welfare, North Carolina Experience. North Carolina Department of Public Welfare, 1961.

Loomis, Charles P., and Beegle, J. Allan, *Rural Sociology, The Strategy of Change.* Prentice-Hall, Inc., Englewood Cliffs, N.J., 1957.

McGibony, John R., and Johnston, Helen L., "Prospects for Rural Health Care." *Rural Sociology*, Vol. 19 (December 1954).

McNerney, Walter J., and Riedel, Donald C., *Regionalization and Rural Health Care.* University of Michigan, 1962.

Mott, Frederick D., and Roemer, Milton I., *Rural Health and Medical Care.* McGraw-Hill Book Co., Inc., New York, 1948.

Roemer, Milton I., "Rural Programs of Medical Care." *Annals American Academy of Political and Social Science* (No. 273, January 1951).

Rural Sociology, An Analysis of Contemporary Rural Life, Alvin L. Bertrand, editor. McGraw-Hill Book Co., Inc., New York, 1958.

Stewart, William H., and Pennell, Maryland Y., *Health Manpower Source Book*, Section 10. U.S. Public Health Service, 1960.

Tjalma, Richard, "Institute of Agricultural Medicine In Iowa." *Public Health Reports*, Vol. 73 (July 1958), pp. 615–618.

United States President's Commission on the Health Needs of the Nation, *Building America's Health*, Vol. 2. U.S. Government Printing Office, Washington, D.C., 1953.

JOHN B. MITCHELL

THE CHURCH
IN TOWN AND COUNTRY

RURAL and smalltown churches are like the acres of cropland around them—some people say there are too many for present needs. The very bounty of those acres and the technology that fosters it have reduced the need for a church every few miles, plus five or six in each village.

Many churches were established decades ago to serve people who depended on horses for transportation. Churches, one-room schools, and a store at every crossroads served the needs of the people of a neighborhood. The same was true of the villages that sprang up every 5 or 10 miles.

Cars and hard roads released people from dependence on local stores and institutions and began a realinement of habits and loyalties.

Vacant store buildings attest the obsolescence of villages. The crossroads settlements of a generation ago are declining. The one-room school, the general store, the community institute, fraternal orders, and township halls are like the buffalo—not many are left.

Can the small church stem the tide of this institutional decline? It alone remains in large numbers in the open country, villages, and small towns.

Some signs of change are to be seen in a number of places.

Active membership has shown a slow downward trend. Many people on the church rolls have moved away but have not transferred their memberships.

A high percentage of the membership is concentrated in the older age groups. A decidedly smaller number of members are 25 to 50 years old.

Church offices have been held by the same persons 10 years or more.

Contributions have shown a steady decline in some localities.

The congregation is unable to keep a full-time pastor, and services have changed from every Sunday to twice a month.

The part-time "suitcase" minister does not live in the community. He has a full-time job during the week.

The church building has not had any major repairs or improvements for several years.

The decline of a church structure is symptomatic of the decline of the con-

198

gregation and its ability to be an effective institution. Can a congregation that is not vigorous enough to maintain its building exert much influence in the community?

The problems of small churches are acute in rural areas whose population is stable or declining. The proportion of elderly persons there is larger. The incomes of most persons past 65 generally are lower than those of younger adults. Problems are compounded by a smaller population base, a higher proportion of dependents to producers, and greater distances to cover in meeting church needs.

"Overchurching" may be a problem. One Ohio county with 11 thousand residents has 65 churches—a church for every 170 inhabitants. The situation is unrealistic when one considers the population and economic resources of most rural counties.

Every congregation in an overchurched locality needs to evaluate its situation and look into the future, while answering questions such as these: What do we hope to accomplish? Should we "sit tight" and hope for the best? Can we grow? Should we consolidate with another congregation of the same denomination? Should we merge with some congregation from another denomination? Should we help form a community church?

THINK OF THE TOWN and country churches in the changing, growing land where city and country meet, the fringe whose heterogeneous population has varied backgrounds, origins, values, interests, and occupations. The mobility of families adds yeast to this ferment of change. Such factors and others modify the importance of church doctrine and dogma in determining where people go to church.

The small church may find it increasingly difficult to provide the devotional and educational services expected by many residents in the suburban fringes.

It seems that new fringe and nonfarming rural residents are attracted by a larger facility and opportunities

for organized activities beyond the Sunday services.

Recent arrivals in a community are interested in developing a new web of relationships to replace the one they left behind. Adults are looking for organizations within the church that provide opportunities for religious education, social activities, and possibilities of holding an office. A small congregation may not have enough members to justify organizations for special-interest groups.

The rapidity and inevitability of change demands that persons concerned with the church in town and country take a critical look into the future. Every major change has implications for the community and its churches. No community has been standing still.

A key question is: What would be the most effective organization and use of resources in terms of congregations, ministers, programs, and facilities?

Four trends are evident: First, the number of full-time farmers will continue to decline; second, new residents in rural areas will not be farmers; third, the population in fringe areas adjoining metropolitan centers will increase rapidly; and fourth, the number of people in rural areas and small towns 70 or more miles from these centers will not change drastically.

Growth of population in most rural sections will be from nonfarming families moving out from cities and towns. These families will not have strong ties or long-established loyalties to rural institutions. They will be accustomed to making frequent trips into town, and some will maintain their membership in an urban church.

Church programs must be oriented to a mobile population and encompass a broad view. Tomorrow's population will be even more mobile than today's. It will be easier to travel greater distances from a home base. More families will have planes, helicars, flying platforms, or other means of air transportation.

THESE TRENDS and others indicate that tomorrow's church will need more facilities, more staff, and a larger congregation than the usual town and country church.

Every congregation needs to evaluate its condition and the situation in the community. A congregation that does not plan for the future and take action may fade.

Denominations must decide whether to maintain many churches with small memberships or reorganize. If a decision is made to reorganize, church leaders could establish minimum stand-

ards for an effective ministry—the size and type of facilities, educational programs, salary for a full-time minister, other staff people, and a parsonage.

Some of my conclusions may seem harsh to the Americans who were nurtured in small churches and in view of a general increase in church membership in the United States. I believe, though, that a thoughtful analysis will perform a useful service in this day of change.

The town and country church has served millions. With modifications, it can meet the challenge of change and render an effective ministry to additional millions.

JOHN B. MITCHELL *is associate professor and extension rural sociologist in the Department of Agricultural Economics and Rural Sociology, the Ohio State University. He holds two degrees from Louisiana State University and a doctorate from the University of Missouri. Dr. Mitchell was a member of the faculty of the University of Rhode Island from 1953 to 1958.*

For further reading:
   Bell, Wendell, "Familism and Suburbanization: One Test of the Social Choice Hypothesis." *Rural Sociology*, Vol. 21 (September–December 1956).
   Coughenour, Milton, and Hepple, Lawrence M., *The Church in Rural Missouri*, Part II. University of Missouri Agricultural Experiment Station, Research Bulletin 633B, September 1957.
   Eshleman, John Ross, *Motives for Church Participation in an Interstitial Rural Locale*. M.S. thesis, The Ohio State University, 1960.
   Gill, Charles Otis, and Pinchot, Gifford, *Six Thousand Country Churches*. The Macmillan Co., New York, 1919.
   Greene, Shirley E., *Ferment on the Fringe*. The Christian Education Press, Philadelphia, 1960.
   Olmstead, Clifton E., *History of Religion in the United States*. Prentice-Hall, Inc., Englewood Cliffs, N.J., 1960.
   "Religion in American Society." *Annals American Academy of Political and Social Science*, November 1960.
   Scaff, Alvin H., "The Effect of Commuting on Participation in Community Organization." *American Sociological Review*, Vol. 17 (April 1952).
   Yinger, J. Milton, *Religion, Society and the Individual*. The Macmillan Co., New York, 1957.

EVLON J. NIEDERFRANK

RESPONSIBILITIES OF COMMUNITY LEADERSHIP

LEADERS are interested in a problem, or they are not. They are the true leaders of the community, or they are not. They are hard put to it to find the answers to crucial problems, or they are able to cope with them satisfactorily. They are attuned to the concerns of the people and have their support, or they do not. They understand and want to serve the total community, or they tend to represent only special interests. They work positively toward decisions and progress, or they prolong delay.

Truly the solutions to community problems lie in the hands of leadership, but often the leaders are a part of the problem, too.

Differences among people are part of the problems of leadership of suburban fringes. Not all leaders see problems alike or believe in the same solutions. People in a growing community have differences in viewpoints, for often their farm, nonfarm rural, and urban backgrounds make for differences in attitudes and information on community subjects. They are not affected equally by a given problem and so do not favor the same solution. They have different working and living conditions and different kinds of jobs and professions. The farmers among them work at home. Some people work in a nearby town. Others commute long distances to work.

All of these differences among the people of a community that is becoming citified affect its leadership. They affect the number of people who are interested in assuming community leadership. They affect their abilities to be leaders and also their interest in civic affairs.

The older people and the still farm-oriented people want to keep things as they are and hold taxes down. The younger and city-oriented people want improvements in schools, roads, water systems, playgrounds, and, generally, "liberal" local officials who are not afraid to break with tradition.

Transiency or mobility, a common characteristic of the people in fringe communities, also affects leadership.

Census data indicate that at least 35 percent of metropolitan fringe families change residence after a few years,

201

sometimes three or four times during a working lifetime of 25 to 30 years in a locality. They go to new jobs or assignments elsewhere or move to another house in some other community that better fits their growing family needs. A typical pattern is an apartment first; then a small house; and then a larger, more modern house farther out, often in a neighborhood just carved out of the woods.

This mobility may produce a sense of impermanence among many suburbanites. Many who might be leaders among them hesitate therefore to run for local office or assume other community responsibilities. They reside in the community but are not truly of it for several years, if ever. They do not feel prepared to assume significant local leadership, and the more permanent residents do not think so, either.

But participation in citizens' associations that struggle with the problems of sidewalks, schools, and stoplights usually does bring to the surface a few able and community-minded newcomers who are thrust (or let it seem that they are thrust) into leadership to worry about public problems.

IT IS EASY to understand why problems of community adjustment and leadership exist in many places all over the United States. Most of them hinge on the changes and improvements in the resources and services people think they need. But underneath most of the community problems in urbanizing areas is the matter of the leadership itself—the numbers of leaders and their attitudes and abilities.

Several theses have been set forth on this point:

First, the farmers and other leaders of the rural communities are slow to realize or accept the urban growth taking place around them.

Second, the farmers and local rural leaders tend to be more conservative and hold back on various community changes and improvements, while the younger and more urban-oriented people want them.

Third, the primary decisionmaking body is local government, and rural people tend to retain their positions in local government for a long time after suburbanization takes place, because it takes time for the newcomers to become active in the governmental affairs and to get elected to offices. Instead, the local participation and leadership of newcomers generally is first found in the parents and teachers organizations, other civic organizations, and churches.

Fourth, the greatest conflict between the new suburban segments usually is over matters that the rural element think will lead to higher taxes. Usually the differences become focused on the school system, because it usually is the largest single tax expenditure, the property tax is the major source of local revenue, and school improvement usually is the greatest felt need of the newly expanding populations of urbanizing communities.

Fifth, the decisions about changes and adjustments are made too late, after the problem has become crucial, although a little more planning about the questions, aimed at guided development, could greatly reduce the problems and speed solutions to them.

Sixth, rural people tend to oppose rural zoning, land use planning, and other methods of guided development for fears of the restrictions they will place on their farming operations, incomes, building plans, and so on.

All these point up the need for educational efforts and communitywide involvement in new proposals.

Darrell Heasley, of The Pennsylvania State University, deduced from a study of a suburban township near Pittsburgh that the rural-experienced residents took stands that could be called more "individualistic or conservative" than the more urban-experienced resident. The rural residents held back from new devices to meet community problems. The persons with only rural experience were the most opposed to the zoning, new street lights, police protection, and curbs on speeding, and were least likely to favor enactment of regulations about them. When they did favor such improvements, they wanted the cost to be assigned not to the whole community but to the people who would benefit from the services.

On the other hand, the urban-experienced people in the township generally were most favorable to the idea of these community improvements and were most willing to have the cost spread over the community as a function of local government.

Mr. Heasley's findings also indicated that the longer the newcomers lived in the suburban community, the more they tended to become somewhat more conservative or like older residents.

Sheridan T. Maitland, of the Department of Agriculture, in a study of suburbanization in two Maryland counties near Washington, D.C., discovered a difference between farm and nonfarm people in their orientation to large cities, based on how often they went to the cities and whether they read metropolitan or rural newspapers and belonged to rural or urban organizations.

He also found some differences between farm and nonfarm residents as to their perceptions of what was happening in their counties and as to whether the new suburbanization would be having a bad or a good effect. The rural people seemed to be less aware of what was happening and were more likely to feel that such development would not have any adverse effect on the community. The people who were in higher levels of income and schooling, both rural and urban oriented, however, were much more aware of pending suburbanization and much more inclined to take a negative view of its probable effects.

Arthur Walrath, of the Department of Agriculture, has pointed out that the situation pertaining to schools and similar adjustments are aggravated by the timelag between the influx of population and the collection of taxes based on the value of new property for the improvements.

This emphasizes again the need for community leaders and local government officials to be alert to changes and to anticipate needs and plan for them, rather than let things reach a point of too little and too late.

Several other studies also conclude that there does not seem to be any deep-seated conflict or cleavage as such between rural people and urban-oriented newcomers, but rather that there is a range of feelings and opinions and knowledge, depending upon how a family or group is affected by a given issue at stake. There is a difference, yes, between the older, most rural resident, on one hand, and the younger, most urban-oriented newcomer, on the other. But between these extremes there is considerable mixture of common feelings and agreement relating to various community conditions. The conclusion is that the differences of opinion and action among people are more likely to arise on specific issues in relation to how they are affected by a given problem and how they will be affected by the proposed solution.

These points of difference, in turn, tend to be related to specific characteristics of the different families and population groups in the community— their age, length of residence, interest in children and youth, level of schooling, taxes, and other family economics. Decisions are made family by family, issue by issue, rather than on the basis of any alinement between rural and urban groups as such.

Thus, there is much basis for cooperation and progress on community adjustments, if the leadership is discerning and community minded and if there is promotion of common understanding. Lack of understanding about the facts of the issues seems to be a major factor in dealing with problems of community adjustment.

ANOTHER potentially retarding factor, however, is that farmers and rural people in the fringes tend to retain leadership for considerable time after urbanization begins to take place. This fact is pointed out by Charles Press, of Michigan State University, and Clarence J. Hein, of the Department of Agriculture, in a study of one rural township on the edge of Lansing.

They found that the full-time commercial farmers were still most active in the community affairs of the township, both in its leadership and in their trade relationships to local centers, rather than to Lansing.

Although the general level of knowledge of the full-time farmers about local government in general was low, they had a higher level of knowledge about township matters than did the suburbanite part-time farmers. The established full-time farmers also occupied the major township offices and seemed to have most to do with the affairs of local government, the community hall, and the party caucuses.

The more urban-oriented part-time farmers, on the other hand, were less familiar with township government and its affairs. Their participation was greatest in school affairs and in voting at general elections, an indication that they probably would have more effect upon leadership in later years.

Nearly all the people surveyed favored annexation of urbanized areas to nearby cities, but they were little aware that if this were done they might lose their opportunity to participate in key decisions that affect future problems of the township.

Although the full-time commercial farmers controlled the township government, they seemed to be the least likely to anticipate urbanization in the future and felt little need for giving attention to guiding development. Experiences in various areas that have become urbanized indicate that unless this attitude can be changed, uncontrolled development will increase the problems with which farmers must cope as urban areas surround farmland.

THE CONCLUSION was that farm people must realize that guided development will produce far more benefit than danger in the long run.

Local government—town, township, and county—is the point around which most major community problems revolve, and the inadequacy of local government also frequently causes or aggravates the problems all the more.

Thus, selection of local officials, including members of planning commissions, zoning boards, and other such organizations, is an important part of achieving timely and satisfactory community adjustments.

Especially noticeable is the lack of experience and training for dealing with guiding development by planning and zoning and with providing facilities and services to a growing population. I have found this in a number of States during fieldwork relating to community development and rural zoning. New zoning commissions and planning boards need and want educational assistance along this line; they are requesting it, and that is a good sign of their concern about the problems they face and their interest in wanting to do a good job as community leaders in such positions.

In many areas the problem also is aggravated by jurisdictional disputes, which may be centered around different forms of government and special districts, such as new consolidated school districts, municipal and regional planning commissions, maybe water and sewer districts, and transportation authorities. And in many instances the leadership problem usually centers around differences in authority and power of the various governmental bodies concerned and in the fact that some have more competent leadership than others. Thus, a challenge to the rural leaders of fringe areas is clear—they must be prepared and they must seek to express themselves through the organizations and governmental bodies that have influence.

The transition of fringe areas from rural to urban generally is accompanied by a governmental transition, which also presents a challenge to local leaders and citizens. The type of governmental organization adopted may affect the future of an entire metropolitan area for years to come.

Dr. Hein, in a bulletin, "The Stake of Rural People in Metropolitan Government," outlined five basic forms of government that may be suitable for urbanizing communities. They are: City-county consolidation, the urban county, multipurpose metropolitan special districts, federation of local bodies into some kind of a metropolitan council, and regional cooperation through the establishment of regional boards, authorities, and conferences.

SPECIALISTS in local government agree that any one of these five proposals would be an improvement over the existing system of government that exists in most metropolitan areas. Imperfect as they are, any of the types or some combination of them would be more responsive and responsible, would have a more adequate fiscal basis, and be more effective than the fragmented local governments that now exist in many metropolitan areas.

Dr. Hein concluded that the rural residents stand to gain from almost any change in governmental organization that will provide more adequate solutions to the governmental problems of metropolitan areas.

He emphasized that urbanization will continue in the United States for some time, spread farther and farther into the rural portions of existing metropolitan areas and around newer growing cities, and bring such problems as urban sprawl, traffic congestion, low-grade housing areas, spotty development, automobile graveyards, and ribbon communities up and down the highways—problems with which the traditional rural systems of government and many of our present urban governments cannot cope. Local governments, if they are to meet these metropolitan problems, must be modified, and local leadership must take it into their hands to do so.

Local residents will benefit most if they take an active part in bringing about the necessary adjustments in local government and in other community developments that are inevitable in expanding metropolitan areas. If they do not, such new developments likely will be directed from outside jurisdictions and authorities, and the rural people affected will lose both economically and socially.

SIGNS OF PROGRESS in meeting the problems abound.

Programs in community development, education in public affairs, leadership and organization methods, and citizenship have begun in the extension work of a number of States. Groups in counties here and there are discussing the functions and costs of local government, and changes in the forms of government have begun to emerge. Committees on rural areas resource development and area redevelopment are tackling problems of community adjustment. County and area development associations made up of local leaders and public and private agencies and organizations have sprung up here and there. Government agencies, university extension services, and "main street" organizations work together on economic and social development in many places.

More than 4 thousand small communities in the Southern States have organized overall community improvement clubs or associations and county councils of community improvement. Many of the groups are within the range of town expansion and urban sprawl. Thus they are beginning to study problems pertinent to this trend, which will help prepare local leaders for more effective work with new county zoning boards, metropolitan and regional planning commissions, and the like.

Established farm organizations, such as the Farm Bureau, Farmers Union, and Grange, have had an increase in membership within or near fringe areas, and new chapters have undertaken studies and planning relating to the problems of suburban community development. An example is a 2,800-

member Grange in Johnson County, Kans., in the fringe of Kansas City.

THE CHALLENGE is great.

What can agencies and organizations and community leaders themselves do to reduce conflicts between longtime residents and newcomers?

What can be done to help heterogeneous populations formulate a government structure better able to handle modern conditions?

What can be done to broaden the vision of urban and rural residents and leaders so they will see that town and country are more closely tied together than ever before?

Mervin Smith and John Mitchell, of Ohio State University, in a paper presented at a meeting of the American Country Life Association in 1962, pointed out that zoning is one development method in which citizens of town and country do not yet see sufficient mutual relationships. It was emphasized that they must also see mutual relationships in other methods and areas of living as well—education, public services, housing, and transportation.

The dynamic situation in terms of people and use of land increases the need for greater acceptance of the fact that change is inevitable. Wholehearted acceptance of this fact will help community leaders in their efforts to modify new conditions so that rural-urban change is oriented to progress rather than aimless drifting or chaos.

Nor is improvement merely a matter of selection by public agencies of "leaders" with whom to work. More important is for agencies to identify and accept the true leadership as defined by the people themselves, and then to help to develop them through training and guidance and assistance.

I offer some suggestions for strengthening leadership in growing communities:

Promote understanding among the groups and interests. Encourage organizations to discuss the developments that will have a great effect on families and communities next year and in the next decade.

Think of the total community and the total region. Concern with special interests and provincial civic pride must give way. Foster a cooperative attitude among governmental bodies and jurisdictions.

Develop and encourage participation in leadership training and adult education on public affairs. Get the facts, study their genesis, and plan what to do.

See to it that rural people are represented on planning commissions, zoning boards, and regional committees and councils.

Seek guidance from authorities who can help—experts in universities and State planning boards, for example.

Be mindful that the great challenge to leaders and citizens still lies ahead.

Learn from experiences so far. Be ready to give the leadership when it is needed for sound, long-range development.

EVLON J. NIEDERFRANK *is extension rural sociologist in the Federal Extension Service of the Department of Agriculture. He has engaged in extension and research work in various parts of the country and has written numerous articles and leaflets pertaining to leadership and community development.*

For further reading:
Hein, Clarence J., *The Stake of Rural People in Metropolitan Government.* U.S. Department of Agriculture, Miscellaneous Publication 869, 1961.
Kreitlow, Burton W., Aiton, E. W., and Torrence, Andrew P., *Leadership for Action in Rural Communities.* The Interstate Printers & Publishers, Inc., Danville, Ill., 1960.
Press, Charles, and Hein, Clarence J., *Farmers and Urban Expansion—A Study of a Michigan Township.* U.S. Department of Agriculture, Economic Research Service, ERS–59, 1962.
Price, Paul H., and Hillery, George A., Jr., *The Rural-Urban Fringe and Louisiana Agriculture—A Case Study of the Baton Rouge Area.* Louisiana State University, Agricultural Experiment Station, Bulletin 526, Baton Rouge, 1959.
Sanders, Irwin T., *Making Good Communities Better.* University of Kentucky Press, Lexington, 1953.

A. F. WILEDEN AND JOHN E. ROSS

COMMUNICATION:
A MATTER OF UNDERSTANDING

THERE is more "communication" in this one round world today than ever before. There are more channels for expression. The channels reach farther and are more complicated. They are crowded with many messages. With all this, man is learning, communicating, and changing at a new, rapid rate.

The very change in volume and tempo of communication creates a problem—perhaps the most serious problem of our time: Will the system of communication work efficiently and comprehensively enough to keep ahead of the rate of change? Will we achieve a common social understanding as quickly as we achieve technical communicative ability?

The technical competence is well advanced. In the United States about 98 percent of the people can read and write. We have mass media for communication unparalleled in history, which include 1,850 daily and 8,954 weekly newspapers. Television is in 46,900,000 of our residences, 90 percent of the total. Radio has 97 percent penetration of our residences. We publish about 12 thousand new books each year and 64,200 periodicals, which encompass almost every field of human interest and endeavor.

We have the time to read, look, and listen. Yet we often fail to communicate effectively with one another for at least three reasons.

The first has to do with the tempo of our life. Although we have more time to communicate, we feel compelled to achieve communication in short gasps. We rush from one situation to another. We read or listen in snatches. We often fail to achieve the full understanding of new, complicated facts and issues.

The second has to do with specialization. Our society is fractured economically and socially into relatively narrow-interest groups. Businessmen associate with other businessmen and read business journals. Farmers talk with other farmers and read farm publications. Laborers talk with other laborers and read labor periodicals. Some interplay is provided by organizations that cut across economic lines and by the system of mass circulation media.

207

For example, Republican farmers, Republican laborers, and Republican businessmen read Republican papers. Catholics of all these economic groups read Catholic papers. The largest single common denominator seems to be television. Nearly all of us watch it, yet we grasp only a small part of what it presents to us.

The third reason has to do with the nature of the problems that we must solve. The problems have become more complex. They demand a higher quality of performance from the communications system and from the people sending the messages. They also require a higher level of understanding from the people receiving the messages.

Underlying these three problems is the psychological principle that people tend to receive only what is acceptable to them. They tune out the information or concepts that do not fit their established value system. People tend to read and hear only what they want to read and hear of the array of information available to them. Farmers attend farm meetings, mostly sponsored by or supported by a farm group or by their farm organizations. Businessmen attend business meetings sponsored by their own business groups or organizations. Labor people attend labor meetings sponsored by their labor leaders. They are mentally and physically most comfortable that way.

Such selection is of concern to communicators, particularly since much of our analytical approach to the problem has been from the sending end. Not enough attention has been paid to critical analysis of how communication is received.

IN FEW FIELDS is the lack of effective communication more apparent than in rural-urban understanding and rural-urban relationships.

The farm movements, since they first began about a century ago, have been concerned with asserting the farmers' rights and alerting farmers in the expression of those rights. Leaders of the movements have given too little thought or attention to the concerns or rights of urban businessmen, urban laborers, and consumers. Their membership has stopped at the city limits. Similarly, the concerns of businessmen and, until recently, the concerns of organized labor also have stopped at the city limits, but at the other side of the limits.

This line of demarcation has been formalized through our prevailing systems of government—the town and county systems to meet the needs of farmers and the village and city systems to meet the needs of urban dwellers. Often State legislatures represent rural areas despite shifts in population. Persistent and heated are the clashes if the systems meet.

THE MEETING ground between farm and city is now in two areas.

One is in suburbia. It begins to appear that suburban and fringe areas are going to force at least some reconciliation of differences. The moving of businessmen and laborers to homes outside our cities and the increasing amount of part-time work of farmers in cities have placed different occupation groups side by side in the same basket. They have to do some things together.

Most immediate and maybe most obvious are the social groups that center on sociability and the welfare of children. Alongside the formal and informal social groups are the social institutions, particularly the schools and churches. The community school brings people of different economic and cultural backgrounds together in one educational enterprise, in which the parents may learn as much as the children.

Some church leaders recognize the suburban church to be as much a neighborhood church as a denominational church. If it is, it also, like schools and social groups, may be a force for understanding.

The second major meeting ground is in the marketplace. However indirect it may be, it has extremely personal aspects. On the farm end it has to do with the price a farmer receives. On the other, it has to do with the price the consumer pays and the quality and wholesomeness of the products he buys. In between are the processors and distributors, whose activities affect both ends.

Our point is that conflict will exist until both farmers and consumers arrive at an understanding of what comprises a just marketing system.

It is a task of communication to help develop this understanding. Until that is done, misunderstanding or lack of understanding probably will continue.

When that is done, the urban consumer will understand better the complexity of the problems, policies, and work that enable him to eat.

Alongside the complexity is a growing interdependence of the different segments of the economy. Not long ago most of the production and processing of farm products was on farms and in towns. Processing and distribution has been moving to larger centers and is giving employment to many city people, so that some 40 percent of our working force is engaged in farming and farm-related phases of our economy. This phase of interdependence needs to be appreciated by farm and nonfarm people.

Another phase is the production of food and fiber. Because American agriculture has become unprecedentedly productive, farmers may be at a disadvantage in the market. They are reminded continually that they are dependent on the consuming public for adequate returns for their labor. But consumers seem to forget that they in turn depend on farmers for the food they eat and much of their clothing.

The consumer is paying for more and more services as he makes his purchases in the marketplace. Packages, mixes, precooked food, and all such add to costs; convenience is not cheap. Retail costs of food to the urban family have gone up 11.5 percent since 1947, but the farmer's return for this food has gone down 14.5 percent. As a matter of fact, the farmer's return of the consumer's food dollar was only 38 cents in 1963. The rest went in getting the product from the farm to the housewife's kitchen.

The consuming public needs a greater awareness of this situation. This awareness is a matter of communication.

The process of communication itself needs attention, we think, because it is subject to all the cultural and psychological limitations that beset the rest of our society. Many of our media are urban centered. Many writers, editors, broadcasters, and actors are urban trained and urban oriented. Since their media are aimed at wide audiences and since the population has become largely urban, this is a logical and natural development.

Because mass communication wields tremendous power, its responsibility is to all people, the whole society. Power, responsibility, and understanding—these three.

TO THEM MAY be added a fourth pillar, the concept of intergroup and interagency communication and action that has such names as community development and area development. It is not a new idea, but the concerted effort in its behalf by all kinds of public and private groups and agencies is new. It is essentially a process of communication whose emphasis is on the receiver.

When the receiver receives an idea, considers it carefully, and attempts to apply it to the situation of which he is a part, communication is complete.

When rural people come to recognize and understand the situations of urban people and urban people come to recognize and understand the situations of rural people to the point where the ultimate decisions are in terms of the best interest of all, the goal of communication is achieved.

A. F. WILEDEN *is professor of rural sociology and* JOHN E. ROSS *is professor of agricultural journalism in the University of Wisconsin.*

LEE R. MARTIN

SOCIAL CAPITAL
AND LIVING STANDARDS

SOCIAL capital is used to produce services that increase living standards. Economic growth, whether homegrown or introduced from outside the community, depends on social capital. It is one of three forms of capital. What is generally called private capital, or private domestic investment, consists of residential and nonresidential construction, producers' durable equipment, and business inventories.

Human capital means the acquired qualities in human beings that are fostered by investments in education and training, health, and recreational and esthetic experiences.

The third form, social capital, includes social overhead capital, which is usually tangible and fixed in location and consists of the facilities and organizations used to produce public services. Streets and roads, sanitary and water systems, parks and recreational facilities, schools, libraries, hospitals, health services, museums, police and fire protection, and so on are forms of social overhead capital.

Another form of social capital is the total of all useful knowledge. Research and other innovating human actions create it in the form of new information. The transfer of new and old information into individual minds creates human capital, one of the things that determine the potential of rural communities for economic growth.

Intangible social capital includes the unofficial or volunteer organizations that are important in American society and often do much to help communities arrive at a workable consensus on issues of public policy, even though market and government agencies may have little interest in them.

Intangible social capital includes also the responsiveness of government to community needs and is a product of the efficiency of government agencies and of the effectiveness and sensitivity of legislative bodies and administrative groups.

Such factors determine whether the area takes a rational approach to economic and social development, and whether useful and consistent regulations can be developed for such devel-

210

opments as planning and zoning of land uses.

This responsiveness and effectiveness depends partly on the community's understanding and appreciation of two freedoms—freedom of political choice and freedom of economic choice. The understanding must include the cost of freedom and the benefits of freedom.

LET US NOW explore some of the applications of our definitions to the growth, primarily economic growth, of communities.

Knowledge is the beginning. Since 1940 the world has undergone an exciting growth in knowledge. Best known are the developments in the physical sciences. Less sensational but noteworthy are advances in the behavioral sciences and economics.

Several advances in economics have important implications for the problem of stimulating economic growth in places of low income.

First, the changes in demand that take place in an advanced society over a long period are becoming clearer. The proportions of employment and national income that originate in agriculture and mining have been declining for a long time. Manufacturing and construction are approaching a point beyond which their proportions of total employment appear likely to decline. Services, particularly those produced or financed by government, are growing as a proportion of employment. In 1963 nearly all major manufacturing industries have overcapacity, and a marked undercapacity exists for producing many kinds of government services. These demand relationships are important to communities that seek to increase employment. Their importance is magnified by popular attitudes toward government expenditures.

Another economic finding of importance to low-income sections describes the sources of economic growth and is based on research by several economists. One, Edward F. Denison, of the Brookings Institution, set out in his research to allocate, among its principal sources, the 1929–1957 growth in real national income per person employed:

Source	Percentage
Decrease in annual hours worked..	−33
Effect of shorter hours on quality of work.....................	21
Education.....................	42
Better utilization of women......	7
More capital per worker.........	9
Advances of knowledge..........	36
Economies of scale—growth in national and local markets.....	21
Other factors...................	−3
Total growth.............	100

Conventional economic wisdom usually assumes income growth per worker to be due to private capital per worker and natural resources. Dr. Denison presents evidence that education and technology accounted for most of the growth in real income during the past three decades, while additional private capital per worker accounted for no more than 10 percent. Technology comes largely from research and development. This research is not only of great importance for this country but has a particular relevance for low-income areas.

In another analysis, education, population, and regional variables accounted for more than 90 percent of the variation in State incomes per person. Not only are education and research financed largely by government; they utilize and create social and human capital.

SOCIAL CAPITAL influences the income level of a particular community in at least five ways.

First, social capital investments can increase the efficiency of existing industries or raise the potential efficiency that the prospective industries may achieve. Improved streets and roads, sanitary and water systems, training of workers, and police and fire protection may lower production costs per unit just as tax concessions or a rent-free building may.

Second, the services produced by

social capital have a role in the location of economic activity. While unskilled workers are in excess supply, highly educated and skilled workers are almost always in short supply. For economic activities that require high-quality human resources, communities without good schools, parks, museums, libraries, and other amenities will not be able to qualify, because other equally efficient sites have the amenities to attract professional, technical, and managerial personnel. Amenities include all the community's characteristics that make life comfortable, agreeable, and stimulating.

The importance of amenities as a screening device is magnified by chronic unemployment in the economy; chronic unemployment increases the number of communities that can meet all other requirements (than amenities) for a particular industry.

Third, investments in social capital add to community income, except in the unlikely instance of a low-income community in which all the revenue for the investment originated in that community.

The fourth way has to do with the fact that when research spawns a new product or process—as it often does—the first location considered for the new plant is near the research establishment. To the extent that social capital is specific to research and development or contributes to the location of a research establishment, the probability is increased that this will produce a new plant for the locality through research.

Finally, even when natural resources are the magnet for attracting additional employment (through recreation, for example), investments in particular natural resources are usually a prerequisite to development. Often private investment and additional employment opportunities are not likely to come about until public investments are made.

The foregoing concepts of social capital and their relations to economic growth are abstract. What are the actual ways by which rural localities can increase employment opportunities or otherwise increase welfare?

Three ways are to expand employment in the existing industries, such as agriculture, forestry, mining, and manufacturing; introduce new industries, such as manufacturing, service industries, and recreation; and induce workers employed elsewhere to reside in the community.

Expansion of existing employment may come about as a result of expanded demand or from technological developments that increase the efficiency of local industry. The developments may come from outside the area or be produced within it in a deliberate attempt to increase competitive advantage. Rural areas (and some suburban areas) are in the unfortunate position of having industries for which the need for workers is likely to decline or at least to grow more slowly than total employment. Among them are farming, mining, forestry, and manufacture of textiles, leather goods, and apparel.

Another possibility is to introduce new sources of employment. Growth activities are likely to be rigorous in their demands for human and social capital. Few rural areas can compete for demanding activities like research. The shortages of high-quality human capital and the importance of amenities are apparent in advertisements in metropolitan newspapers, in which many companies attempt to attract scientists and engineers and mention amenities of their plant location as inducements.

For industries less demanding in terms of human or natural resources, the executives who choose the new location have a wide range of choice; this range makes social capital critical. Competition from other qualified areas is so keen that social capital becomes a telling factor in the selection of a location for a new factory.

Counties that wish to grow in population and income by becoming residential communities for workers employed nearby also discover that social capital is important. Just as locators of undemanding economic activities have numerous communities from which to choose, so employed workers have many choices among communities within commuting distance of their employment. Here, too, the quality and quantity of social capital become important criteria for the decision-maker.

I do not mean to say that all householders seek the same advantages—those with children seek out good schools, and so on. Schools, parks, museums, hospitals, churches, civic activity, recreational programs, other organized leisure-time activities, libraries, medical specialists, careful landscaping, and a host of other amenities may become the basis for choosing where to live.

Particular communities may be eliminated from consideration by the lack of social capital, such as water supplies, sanitary services, surfaced roads and streets, convenient and economic shopping centers, mass transportation services, and so on. The wide range of choices available may transform any of these items into crucial factors.

I HAVE DISCUSSED the importance of social capital to rural localities that are trying to step up economic growth. How do rural areas stand, as far as the quantity and quality of social capital are concerned?

Most forms of social capital should be measured with relation to the number of persons served.

Rural population increased in every decade from 1790 to 1960, except from 1950 to 1960 (under the new definition of urban population, which added the urban fringe areas outside urban places and increased from 324 to 746 the number of unincorporated areas specially classified as urban).

Rural population grew faster than urban population only from 1810 to 1820 and 1930 to 1940. Rural farm population generally has been declining, at least since 1920, and the rural

nonfarm population has been growing faster than total population. Nearly 72 percent of 1960 rural farm population lived in the same house in 1955; the percentage for the rural nonfarm population was 49.

One may conclude that need for social capital is increasing in rural nonfarm areas, but the need for expansion would appear to be much less in rural farm areas, leaving aside the needs in both areas for improving quality or changing the form.

Precise data on the social capital in rural areas cannot be found, but indications are available, and they can be discussed.

The different forms of social capital can be grouped to facilitate discussion. Several are amenities; that is, they increase the quality of life for their users. Other amenities also provide the basis for a person's increased productive efficiency. The third category usually is oriented toward concentrations of urban population, even when they are in rural or suburban places. Thus:

Amenities only: Residential housing, churches, post offices, and hospitals and clinics. (Residential housing is an important item of private capital, but it is put here with social capital because housing in rural areas is similar in its characteristics and implications.)

Productivity-increasing amenities: Roads, schools, sanitary systems, water supplies, police, and fire protection.

Urban-oriented amenities: Parks and recreational facilities, museums, libraries, shopping centers, and airports.

Social capital that is only productivity increasing: Dams, public forests, canals, and research facilities.

Let us first examine urban-oriented amenities. Wherever they exist, their presence generally is due to the nearness of a city of at least 25 thousand population. By definition, rural and suburban areas containing these amenities are within commuting distance of the central city, and their employment and income situations are similar to the situations in nearby cities. Even when they are depressed, these areas usually have larger volumes of social capital of all sorts than smaller areas, and their development prospects are correspondingly better.

Accelerating economic growth in the larger cities is different from growth of towns or rural areas for two reasons: The number of feasible economic activities is much greater, and the costs per family for raising social capital to the minimum level are much less.

In order to become efficient sites for additional economic activities, many smaller places or rural communities will need outside assistance. Rural areas that are remote even from urban places with a population of 25 thousand or more are likely to have considerable difficulty in obtaining what we have called urban-oriented amenities. These items of social capital nevertheless are important for attracting any except marginal industries and equally important for attracting residents who are gainfully employed the year around.

On the average, the quality of residential housing in rural communities seems to be lower than in cities. Some houses are not well located for occupancy by gainfully employed workers. While the total rural population declined only 424,556 from 1950 to 1960, the 28 States that lost rural population lost 2,595,215, while the 22 gaining States gained 2,170,659 in rural population. If these individuals were in average rural households, then 28 States lost 727 thousand households and 22 States gained 608 thousand households. Unused residences in depressed rural communities are likely to be of low quality, although some might be made usable.

To develop economic activities that would return this residential housing to use would require adding other forms of social capital. For society, the decision may depend on the comparison of the cost of providing the social capital needed in this location to complement the residential housing as against the cost of providing residential housing in another location where other forms of social capital are in more nearly adequate supply.

Schools, churches, public buildings, and hospitals raise considerations similar to those for residential housing. School systems may be inadequate. A number of rural counties do not have a hospital or a clinic. A few have no doctor or dentist.

As to schools: Dedicated teachers and willing students make good schools, but dedication and willingness are hard to measure, and so we have to fall back on figures of size. It is true that smaller systems require greater numbers of employees per 100 pupils. A system with fewer than 50 pupils requires nearly twice as many full-time teachers per 100 pupils as one with more than 3 thousand pupils. The need for teachers and other employees per 100 pupils is much greater for schools with fewer than 1,200 pupils. Ninety-one percent of the public school systems in 1957 had fewer than 1,200 pupils; 58 percent had an enrollment of fewer than 50. Twenty percent of total enrollment was in systems with fewer than 1,200 pupils.

Enrollment per school seemed to be inversely related to the percentage of rural population. One could infer in 1957 that rural States needed to reorganize their schools—especially States in the west north-central region and individual States in other regions. Although also heavily rural, the South Atlantic States had completed much of the needed reorganization. Future reorganization is quite likely to make surplus a good deal of social capital in the form of school buildings in rural areas, especially in the rural areas that lost population between 1950 and 1960. Reorganizations already completed in the South Atlantic region and elsewhere have undoubtedly left many school buildings surplus.

SOCIAL CAPITAL in the form of amenities that also increase productivity should be discussed separately.

Rural roads may be adequate in number or mileage and have excess capacity relative to the traffic volume, but may be qualitatively inadequate for expansions in economic activity.

Public sanitary and water systems seldom are found in rural areas; the ones in private dwellings are surplus if the residence is surplus to the local needs. The police and fire protection usually are provided only on a county or State basis in rural areas. For nearly any kind of economic activity that is feasible for a low-income rural community, social capital for productivity-increasing amenities would be needed.

The social capital that increases productivity but has little effect on amenities is different. The location of dams and canals (and maybe of forests) is determined by natural resources. Its physical and economic environment—market position—makes an area suitable for dams, or canals, or forests. These forms of social capital are financed oftenest by a public agency, usually on behalf of the entire society.

Research facilities have their own locational requirements that involve large volumes of specific capital, except in the case of resource-based research, like a telescope on a mountaintop. Research facilities located with regard to natural resources are unlikely to lead to the development of complementary economic activities.

Social capital required for other types of research is most likely to be found near universities. Rural or suburban communities near universities would have great potential for developing research facilities, but requirements of social capital would still be demanding even for them.

As to the intangible social capital (exemplified by unofficial organizations), low-income rural communities often are not very well off. Apathy and inability to find bases for effective communitywide cooperation are typical. Some rural communities have much more capacity for being organized than others.

Responsiveness of government agencies to community needs sometimes is absent. Apathy and splintering of a community because of political differences are common. Competition for economic activities is so keen among communities of all types and sizes that shortcomings of this kind may be the straws to break the camel's back.

It is highly suggestive that the lowest per capita expenditures for social capital are in States with the largest proportions of rural population.

Considerable private capital may be available in rural areas for agriculture, forestry, mining, trade, transportation, communications, and services.

Because excess human resources in farming are more concentrated in distressed communities than evenly distributed in all farming areas and because of the excess production capacity in farming, it is almost certain that capital resources in farming are excess to needs, especially capital values embodied in farmland and forest land.

In many low-income areas, productive capacity in trade, transportation, and communications is excessive to existing levels of economic activity. The volume of business could be increased substantially without correspondingly large increases in facilities. Whether such existing facilities are satisfactory for large increases in production is doubtful. Because of declining production and technological change, the volume of capital in some lines of mining in rural areas is unquestionably excessive at current levels of demand.

An important prerequisite for economic growth—particularly for high-income employment — is human capital. Because all human beings embody some human capital, it is certain that—at present levels of economic activity—there is excess human capital in rural areas. Whether it is of high enough quality as it stands to be used for other types of employment is another question.

Rural areas lag badly behind urban areas in median years of schooling of the adult population, in percentage of the adult population with 4 years of high school or more, and in percentage with 4 years of college or more. Between 1950 and 1960, the differential favoring the urban population increased in median years of schooling, and in the percentage with 4 years of college or more. In 1960, the rural farm population was much below rural nonfarm and urban in all these measures: 2.3 years of schooling below urban, less than one-third as high a percentage with 4 years of college as urban, and only two-thirds as high a proportion with high school completion. These deficiencies may have to be made up, if rural youth and adults are to compete with urban workers.

A significant fact: For none of the age groups between 5 and 34 was the school attendance proportion for rural farm as high in 1960 as for urban, being barely one-half as large for 25–34—two-fifths as large for 20 and 21 and for 22–24. At current levels of investment in education, differences between the urban and rural areas in availability of the human capital are growing wider. Growing deficits of human capital, along with too little effective demand, may now be the greatest obstacles to economic growth in rural areas.

So, IN SUM, if we are to use social capital productively for today's needs, we may have to make considerable additional investment in social, human, and private capital.

For society, the relevant comparison is between the social costs of the additional social, human, and private capital that would be required for efficiency in the use of rural resources and the social costs of the additional social and private capital required in urban areas where human capital is not in short supply. It seems unlikely that developed areas will altruistically push new expansions in employment toward depressed rural communities.

In order to achieve a substantially higher rate of growth, low-income communities must be willing to make sacrifices. These may be in the form of willingness to accept lower returns to resources (particularly human resources) or to raise larger sums through conventional or voluntary taxation to support higher levels of social and human capital formation required.

With astuteness on the part of their political representatives, depressed rural areas might prevail upon the rest of society to assist them a great deal in these community-building activities.

Unfortunately for many rural residents, the traditional shrewdness of rural politicians is today being devoted much more to lowering public expenditures than to increasing them.

LEE R. MARTIN *is professor of agricultural economics in the University of Arkansas. He has a doctorate in economics from Harvard University. He was an adviser on agriculture to the Planning Board of the Government of Pakistan in 1954–1955. In 1962–1963, on leave from the University of Arkansas, he served with the New England Board of Higher Education as associate director of the board's study of agricultural colleges in New England.*

For further reading:
Abramowitz, Moses, "Resource and Output Trends in the U.S." *American Economic Review*, Vol. 46 (No. 2, May 1956), pp. 5–23.
Denison, Edward F., *The Sources of Economic Growth in the U.S. and the Alternatives Before Us*. Committee for Economic Development, Supplementary Paper No. 13, New York, January 1962.
Economics of Higher Education, Selma F. Mushkin, editor. U.S. Department of Health, Education, and Welfare, Office of Education, Washington, 1962.
Groves, Harold M., *Education and Economic Growth*. National Education Association, Washington, 1961.
Martin, Lee R., "Contributions Agricultural Marketing Research Might Make to Policy Formulation." *Journal of Farm Economics*, Vol. 44 (December 1962).
Schultz, Theodore W., "Education and Economic Growth," in Nelson B. Henry, editor, *Social Forces Influencing Education, 1961*. National Society for the Study of Education, Chicago, 1961.
——— "Reflections on Agricultural Production, Output and Supply." *Journal of Farm Economics*, Vol. 38 (August 1956).

ALMON T. MACE

ENCOURAGING INDUSTRY
IN THE COUNTRY

THE Department of Agriculture instituted in 1961 a broad-gage Rural Areas Development program to stimulate the economic forces that widen opportunities for work in rural sections.

The need was great. Some 74 million residents of the countryside, villages, and towns of rural America comprised about two-fifths of our population. More than one-half of them were poor. More than 4 million rural families had incomes of less than 2,500 dollars. There were 22 million youths younger than 20 years; a million or so are born each year in rural America, more than a fifth of them to poor families. Three-fourths of the 200 thousand families of hired farmworkers and 700 thousand nonfarm rural families and individuals who depend mostly on farm wagework had total incomes below accepted standards of adequacy. Most of the farm wageworkers were hired by some 50 thousand factory-type agricultural production units; fewer than 2 percent of all commercial farm operators had wage bills larger than 10 thousand dollars in 1959.

More than 7 million new or improved job opportunities were needed. Included among them were 4.5 million additional jobs for rural youths and women, who needed work; at least 250 thousand new jobs to overcome the seasonal unemployment among domestic farm wageworkers; nearly a million new jobs to overcome underemployment among low-income, rural, nonfarm families; and fuller employment for families on family farms whose income was too low.

No doubt many of these jobs could be found in cities, but we question whether so many unemployed and underemployed should be transplanted to cities.

That is the background of the Rural Areas Development program and a more intensive program to develop new job opportunities that was put into operation by the Department of Commerce, aided by six other departments of the Government, including the Department of Agriculture.

Some improvement in opportunities had occurred before the programs began. Industrialization had begun

217

several decades earlier in some places. Parts of the textile industry had moved from New England to Southeastern States. Some industries of smaller capital requirements had tended to relocate in the South or in rural localities elsewhere. Chambers of commerce vied for the attention of industrialists.

These efforts brought some payrolls, but the results fell short of the need. It became clear that a broader effort was required to foster the industrialization and commercialization that would provide the 7 million jobs.

It is no small task. It demands effective, imaginative efforts in communities to find an industry that fits their conditions, to determine the best means of financing to enlist technical assistance, and to bring the project to fruition.

Several alternatives may appear.

The industry may be one that produces for the national or world market from raw material shipped to the plant from a distance. If so, the industry may need an inducement, such as some dispensation in costs, a market or transportation advantage, or special facilities like libraries, schools, and hospitals that make the location attractive to management and staff.

A warning: Some industries have a habit of moving from place to place to court special advantages in taxes and cheap labor. A community that goes after such a firm has to realize that it may be participating in an action that will cause unemployment and financial difficulty in the neighborhood the industry is abandoning. A nationally encouraged program to stimulate growth in rural areas obviously must set safeguards against runaway industrialization.

Some communities can offer unique advantages in raw materials close at hand or an unusual market. A coastal town is a good place for a processor of seafood. A winter sports resort may appeal to a manufacturer of souvenirs. In these instances, community leaders will be alert to the possibilities and will present them effectively to a manufacturer who is looking for a new location.

Plants that use raw materials that are or can be produced in the vicinity—canneries and meatpackers, for example—have two advantages: They supply or increase the market for the local product and they work with products that the residents know how to grow and handle.

Wild rice is an example. Indian tribes in northern Minnesota go out to the swamps in pole-pushed boats, just as their fathers did. They harvest the wild rice by hand. Some of the tribes still roast the rice in iron kettles and trample out the grain. These primitive methods, however, meet only a small part of the demand. Among the efficient processing plants is one built by the Wild Rice Harvesters Association at Deerwood, Minn. It was financed by a loan from the Area Redevelopment Administration.

The processors of farm products can get advice and assistance about markets, demand, and supplies of raw materials from the Small Business Administration, the Department of Commerce, several agencies of the Department of Agriculture, the land-grant universities, county agents, and field employees of State departments of agriculture.

When ranchers in North Dakota formed a cooperative feedlot association in 1961, ARA financed supporting research by the agricultural experiment stations of Montana and North Dakota and the Farmer Cooperative Service of the Department of Agriculture. The purpose was to determine the potential of a larger enterprise that would include feedlots, chill-kill plants, and the distribution of a brand-name beef carcass to nearby and distant markets.

RURAL INDUSTRIALIZATION is one part of the Rural Areas Development program, whose aim is to encourage the full development of all resources on farms and in rural communities.

It is directed toward the development of efficient, economical family farms; the establishment of new industries or commercial institutions; the improvement of community facilities, such as water and sewage systems, improved roads, parks, libraries, and other facilities that can make a community more attractive economically and socially to industry; and the improvement of training programs so that rural people can compete better for jobs.

The Office of Rural Areas Development maintains a file of information about credit and technical assistance available for rural commercial enterprises from many sources, public and private. Employees of the Department and the Cooperative Extension Service in rural communities have access to the information and are encouraged to use it in helping business firms plan new enterprises.

A glass sand company in Indiana illustrates how the application of technology can provide new resources and how rural communities can develop the newly found resources for economic growth.

A geological survey indicated a huge supply of high grade silica sand in Harrison County, Indiana.

With the aid of the county rural areas development committee, a local businessman obtained nearly 775 thousand dollars to build a plant for mining the sand.

More than 100 thousand dollars of the money was raised locally. The Harrison County Rural Electric Membership Corporation obtained a Section 5 loan from the Department of Agriculture for almost 200 thousand dollars, which in turn was loaned to the new firm.

A loan from ARA supplied the remaining 400 thousand dollars to build the plant, which employs 33 people.

To make their assistance more effective than it would be if provided by each agency separately, the field people of the Department of Agriculture are banded together in what are termed

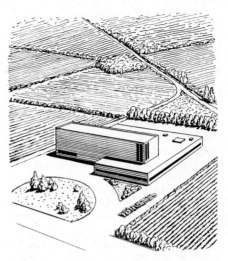

"Technical Action Panels."

The Rural Areas Development programs, including the establishment of new payrolls through new industrial and commercial enterprises, first appeared following the report of underemployment in agriculture prepared under the direction of Senator John J. Sparkman in 1951. The report revealed that because of lack of resources, millions of farm people were not using their income-producing abilities to full advantage and were thus underemployed. Better use of agricultural resources was part of the answer, but the study also revealed a need for new opportunities for work.

Thereupon the Department of Agriculture launched a pilot rural development program in 30 States in 1955. Selected counties in each of the States set up local committees, who worked with representatives of Federal agencies in the preparation of economic development programs. Because in many instances the programs called for the introduction of industry, new industry was sought and secured.

The pilot program was expanded in 1961 to cover the entire Nation. Within 9 months, more than half of the counties in the United States had organized development committees. Like the committees in the pilot counties, many of the new committees look to industrialization as one of the ways to encourage economic progress.

VARIOUS LEGISLATIVE measures were introduced in the fifties to provide Federal stimulus to industrial and commercial growth in economically lagging areas. A bill introduced by Senator Paul H. Douglas as Senate bill No. 1 was passed and signed early in President Kennedy's administration as Public Law 87–27. It is known as the Area Redevelopment Act.

The bill provided loans up to 65 percent of the cost of land and buildings for new industrial and commercial enterprises and loans or grants for building and developing public facilities that would lead to the establishment of new industrial and commercial enterprises.

The act also authorized funds for technical assistance leading to new employment opportunities and training of unemployed or underemployed people in order to assist them to qualify for available job opportunities.

The act provided for two general types of areas to receive assistance: Labor market areas of substantial and persistent unemployment, and predominately rural areas where low income, the size of public assistance payments, the amount of outmigration, and depressed farm conditions gave evidence of major underemployment.

Responsibility for the administration of the program in the latter was delegated to the Department of Agriculture insofar as stimulation to participate in the program and broad appraisal of the applications were concerned.

In addition to the major labor market areas and Indian reservations that were eligible to receive assistance, nearly 800 rural counties were designated. Most are in the Southeastern States, but in order to spread the benefits of the act over a wide area, a few counties have been made eligible in almost every State. Actually, income levels in some 900 other counties would justify eligibility, but since the authorization of funds of the act is limited, the decision was made to concentrate the program in a relatively small number of severely affected counties rather than to spread the funds over a broader area.

The legislation provided that application for loans or grants cannot be made until a written Overall Economic Development Program has been received and approved. Eligible counties immediately went to work with the local rural areas development committees to prepare written programs, and within a year more than three-fourths of the counties had submitted their proposals for economic development. The proposals usually give a brief economic profile of the county, set forth the major economic problems, and serve as a base for a continuing effort to generate economic growth through local planning and action.

More than 250 rural applications for industrial and commercial loans or for community facilities had been received under the program by September 1, 1962. Fund requirements for the projects were averaging about 400 thousand dollars, and the average estimated new employment per project was 200. Nearly 4 thousand industrial, commercial, or community facility projects had been started or planned in 1963.

THE VIGOROUS efforts in rural areas development that began in 1961 have drawn upon the experiences of communities across the Nation in overcoming economic and physical resource problems.

A case in point is Culpeper, Va.

Farms in Culpeper County were becoming larger, and many farm people had to have some other income. Many small businessmen could no longer look to the farm population for the bulk of their trade. Merchants, cooperative leaders, and officials of the town started a rural development program.

One of their first steps was the successful completion of a small watershed project, financed partly by the Department of Agriculture, with the technical aid of the Soil Conservation Service. Dams were built, conservation plans were developed, and more than half the farms were drained.

Townspeople and farms alike benefited. The town got a pure and much larger water supply. The danger of flooding to homeowners and businessmen was greatly reduced. Townfolk have places to fish, boat, and camp. Three major industries have been attracted to the area.

Another example is Watauga County, N.C. The average per capita income of its people in 1950 was 1,063 dollars, compared to 2,121 dollars in the State. In 1956, citizens met and voted to take advantage of the pilot rural development program set up by the Cooperative Extension Service at that time. They named a committee to analyze the needs of the county, make an inventory of resources, set goals, and decide on ways to reach the goals.

Problems were broken down into manageable segments, and subcommittees were named to deal with each.

Watauga needed more industry that would offer seasonal, part-time, and full employment. A business and industrial committee compiled information on natural and human resources, created a development corporation to sell stock and buy sites and erect buildings, and approached prospective industrialists. An underwear factory accepted the proposal. It employed 100 persons at first. It was enlarged twice, and in 1963 employed 250 Watauga residents.

Other improvements and plans followed. A movement was started to make the county, which has a pleasant climate and scenery, a resort center. A new golf course was financed by the sale of stock. The situation of farmers was improved as a result of efforts of the Watauga Agriculture Committee to encourage them to grow poultry and small fruits and vegetables, which are suitable to the terrain.

A program of vocational guidance was started for young people in school. New homes have been built. A homemaking committee has encouraged better nutrition, better sanitation in homes, and inoculations against diseases. Needy families have received surplus food. An educational program led to the qualification of 125 older farm people for old age and survivors insurance payments.

A third example: Rural areas development helped Gassville, Ark., get a water supply ample for the needs of the town and possibly three new industries.

In Baxter County, where Gassville is located, and in the neighboring county of Marion, local leaders raised some 535 thousand dollars to build a factory. After this display of initiative, the Department of Agriculture and the Department of Commerce helped make the project successful.

ALMON T. MACE *is Director, Office of Rural Areas Development.*

For further reading:
Anderson, A. H., and Miller, C. J., *The Changing Role of the Small Town in Farm Areas.* Nebraska Agricultural Experiment Station, Bulletin 419, Lincoln, 1953.
Area Development—An Interdisciplinary Approach to Research. Kansas Agricultural Experiment Station, Bulletin 440, Manhattan, 1961.
Dakin, Ralph E., *Planning, Services, and Facilities in Kansas Communities.* Kansas State University Press, Manhattan, 1960.

KERMIT OVERBY

ELECTRICITY
IN RURAL REDEVELOPMENT

As MIGHT be expected by the cooperative nature of redevelopment, rural-oriented cooperatives are in the forefront of the struggle to create new job opportunities and better living conditions in rural counties. One group in particular, rural electric cooperatives, is exerting extensive leadership in redevelopment. These cooperatives, the only corporate entities serving in all or parts of 80 percent of the Nation's counties, feel they have a primary obligation of helping their millions of members, who make up a large part of the rural population.

Rural electrics look upon redevelopment as an extension of the type of activity they have been carrying on since the midthirties. They recognize that the program of the Rural Electrification Administration has set a pattern that can be applied to area improvement—the use by people of tools made available through their government to help themselves.

Through their national and state-wide organizations, they have supported all major rural development legislation. Co-op directors and managers have taken the lead in community campaigns to attract new enterprises. Rural electric systems have contributed considerable financial assistance and have made available personnel and office facilities to local rural areas development groups.

While they have accomplished much toward ending drudgery on the farm, enriching rural life, and making it possible for rural residents to enjoy modern conveniences, they recognize that they must accelerate their efforts to reverse economic degeneration in some rural sections.

In fact and in practice, rural cooperative electrification has been a rural development program. It has generated thousands of new jobs. Cooperative power has made it possible for thousands of industries to locate in rural America. In 1961, for instance, nearly a thousand borrowers of the Rural Electrification Administration connected an estimated 12 thousand new business firms to their lines.

The story can best be told by a few examples of redevelopment in which

222

electric systems have been prominent.

In the Red River Valley of North Dakota, Nodak Rural Electric Cooperative at Grand Forks has been promoting rural development since 1940. Among the more than 9 thousand consumer-members it serves are more than 440 commercial enterprises, of which 110 are classified as large industrial accounts. Its 5,600 miles of line stretch 120 miles from the Red River on the east to Devil's Lake on the west and 150 miles southward from the Canadian border.

It and leading civic organizations joined in supporting a drive to expand homegrown industries and attract new ones.

The manager and 4 other members of the 25-member committee set up an industrial foundation in 1958. This organization raises funds, which are used to help provide facilities for new industries. One of its achievements was to bring a 5-million-bushel grain storage terminal to the area. The availability of ample and reasonably priced electric power through Nodak was an important factor in attracting the terminal.

The foundation and the Industrial Development Committee of the Grand Forks Chamber of Commerce help about 30 businesses a year with site selections, advice, information concerning facilities, and a number of other matters.

Nodak in 1948 hooked up its first new rural industry, a factory that makes flour from locally grown potatoes. The plant has processed as much as 48 million pounds of potatoes in a year.

Another large local industry that developed on Nodak's lines is a firm that manufactures chemical fertilizer, insecticides, and herbicides.

Employees and directors of Nodak have been active in affairs of several groups, including chambers of commerce, industrial development organizations, and school boards. Nodak is one of the sponsors of the Greater North Dakota Association, which an-nually sponsors an inventors' congress, one result of which is the formation of a number of new companies to manufacture some of the inventions.

A FEW MONTHS after the Area Redevelopment Administration was established in 1961, nationwide attention was focused on the pioneering efforts of rural electrics in community development. ARA announced that its first loan would go to the small community of Gassville, Ark., in an area where an electric cooperative had sparked the redevelopment.

The North Arkansas Electric Cooperative had been at work for some years to translate into realities the hopes and plans of the small communities in its service area.

The loan and grant of 160 thousand dollars approved by ARA made it possible for Gassville to construct a water system necessary to develop a new industry. This initial project of the new agency is an example of how local initiative and financing can be combined with the resources of the Government to combat problems of unemployment and low income.

Before asking for ARA assistance, the citizens of the two counties surrounding Gassville raised 535 thousand dollars through local bond issues to finance the site and building for the new factory. With their local credit extended to the limit, the counties then turned to ARA to help construct the community water system, the last item needed to complete the project.

The new industry has planned for expansion that will mean the employment of more than a thousand workers. Its sizable weekly payroll has created a new demand for goods and services.

The North Arkansas Electric Cooperative helped with the project from the beginning. It assisted in carrying out a labor survey and contributed funds to a retraining program for workers. It furnishes low-cost, dependable power to the factory.

The new factory is one of several redevelopment achievements in which the cooperative's leadership had a part. Others include a milk processing plant, which employs 100 workers; a shoe-last factory, which employs 80 people; and a silica plant. Smaller enterprises include a slaughterhouse, a tire recapping plant, and a sales barn.

The rural electric manager has been a leader in the industrial development corporation of Salem, Ark., the headquarters town of the cooperative. Other employees and directors serve on development councils in the area. Several other cooperatives in Arkansas have promoted redevelopment. Their efforts are backed up by their statewide association and State government.

The Edgecombe-Martin County Electric Membership Corp. of Tarboro, N.C., started the development of rural sections in 1957, when its manager made a study of the effect of new industry on the community.

With the support of his board of directors, the manager set about to explain to the members of the various civic clubs the possibilities for creating new and better opportunities for residents. He pointed out that Tarboro had missed getting an industry merely because it did not have a development organization. The mayor and the town council became interested and appropriated 7,500 dollars a year for 3 years to launch a development program.

Business and professional people agreed to support the development plan and to match the funds approved by the town council. The Tarboro citizens then enlisted the aid of the county government, which promised to appropriate 10 thousand dollars a year for 3 years.

The next step was the formation of an industrial development board, of which the cooperative manager was made president. The board hired a full-time professional development expert. He stressed the community's three big selling points—water, electric power, and an ample supply of trainable workers. He succeeded in getting three industries to locate at Tarboro.

One, which makes plastic toys, employs 350 workers. The second, a manufacturer of synthetic pile fabric, has about 150 workers. The third, a folding paper box company, set up a branch in Tarboro.

The industrial development board also has done much to encourage existing industry to enlarge. For instance, one company, organized in 1943 with 3 workers, employed 750 in 1963. It made a capital investment of 750 thousand dollars for expansion in 1960.

Tarboro has made progress as well in modernizing public facilities. The town raised 1.5 million dollars for a hospital; 700 thousand dollars for a sewage disposal plant; and 1.5 million dollars for new schools.

The effects of redevelopment have been widespread in the entire county. New families have moved in, offsetting to some extent the loss of farmworkers. The industries are giving employment to many members of farm families. The new payrolls have bolstered the local economy and have done much to restore confidence in the future.

Another example is the Gateway Industrial Park, near Columbia City, Ind. The 160-acre development site is the outgrowth of a study an electric cooperative conducted to determine the need for more off-the-farm jobs.

The board of directors of the Whitley County Rural Electric Membership Corp. agreed in January 1959, to purchase the tract for 48 thousand dollars. Excellent highways and a railroad are near the tract. An automatic sewage system was installed, and roads sufficient to bear truck traffic were built.

By January 1, 1961, the cooperative had constructed a 100-thousand-dollar warehouse on the site. The Farm Bureau had built a 20-thousand-dollar office, and the Whitley Building Co. had erected a factory building costing 175 thousand dollars for an industrial corporation.

The reason the cooperative invested so much in the industrial park was that it was the only organization with the finances and experience to provide the facility. Moreover, about 60 percent of its members rely on nonfarm jobs for a major part of their incomes. Local civic groups gave the rural electric support in making the project a reality.

TEN RURAL ELECTRIC cooperatives in northern Mississippi banded together in 1951 with 13 municipal power suppliers to form the North Mississippi Industrial Development Association. Their objective was to upgrade the economy. The efforts of the association were responsible for creating 43 thousand new jobs up to 1963.

The organization does not pirate a plant from another part of the country. Instead, it deals with two major types of prospects: First, a plant owner who already operates one factory and wants to open a branch to obtain raw materials more easily and to enlarge his potential market; and, second, a local industry or food processing plant that needs larger facilities.

A serious decline in population and the absence of industrial development in the 28 counties served by members of North Mississippi Industrial Development Association made the association a necessity. Northern Mississippi counties lost nearly 100 thousand residents between 1940 and 1950. The drop in income that followed was felt in nearly all lines of local business and government.

The rural economy of northern Mississippi is based on small landholdings, most of which provide only a subsistence income and fail to offer any assurance of satisfactory employment for future generations. The principal sources of income are cotton, fresh vegetables, cattle, and dairy farming. Suppliers of power hope to balance agriculture with industry.

In other sections of the State, distributors of electric power have been working with other utilities, railroads, and the Mississippi State Agriculture and Industry Board to encourage industries to locate in their areas.

The organizers of the association

recognized that it would have to be financed adequately if it were to survive. They agreed on a minimum budget of 25 thousand dollars and the employment of a capable executive manager and staff.

Each member organization makes an annual contribution of no more than 5 thousand dollars a year. The annual budget was 50 thousand dollars in 1962—double what it was 10 years earlier, and the staff included an executive manager, a director of development, a director of research, an office manager, and a secretary.

The staff carries on a program of creating new jobs and new payrolls for the communities. Its members have visited every major metropolitan and industrial area in the East and Midwest at least once, some of them several times. The association's leadership has brought about the formation of 21 cooperating industrial committees in 21 communities in northern Mississippi, 9 county development foundations, and 8 chambers of commerce.

The association works with State organizations, among them the State Agriculture Industry Board, which includes rural electric cooperative managers on its board of directors, and the Balance Agriculture With Industry program of Mississippi, which enables local governments to own factories and to lease them to manufacturing enterprises and to finance part of the cost of the buildings by bond issues.

The steady success of the program has breathed new life in north Mississippi's economy and has brightened prospects for the future of rural communities and their residents.

IN NORTH CENTRAL Kentucky, Harrison County Rural Electric Cooperative serves an eight-county area between the bluegrass country on the west and the Cumberland mountains on the east. The area had been losing ground economically for many years. Industries shut down or moved away. Young people went elsewhere to find work.

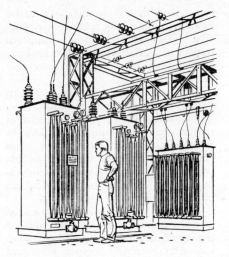

Led by the statewide development association, citizens formed committees to try to improve conditions in the Cynthiana area. Harrison County Rural Electric made its facilities available to these action committees. Its manager, employees, and directors joined the committees, purchased bonds, and otherwise backed the drive.

The change that has taken place is an inspiring example of what people can do when they are determined to solve their problems. Old buildings sport modern faces. Many new buildings have been erected. Young people can find employment in new industries that have come into the area.

A metal fabricating plant located near Cynthiana in 1960. Among its 600 employees are many farmers who work at the factory part time.

Other industries have come to the community—a mill, which makes men's underwear and employs 100 persons; a tobacco auction warehouse, which employs 50 farmers during a 3-month season; a factory that manufactures wood and metal screws and employs 40 persons; and a manufacturer of tools, dyes, valves, and hacksaw blades, whose payroll was expected to be 300 when it reached full production. An existing industry,

a sausage plant, enlarged and remodeled its plant to handle increased production.

The north central Kentucky development groups also have begun to exploit the recreational potential of the area. Of two lakes in Nicholas County, one has become a site of a 4–H camp, which more than 2 thousand young people enjoy each summer. Plans have been made for 300 homesites along the shores of the larger lake and a 30-unit, all-electric motel, boat dock, and bathing beach.

As a project of its own, the Harrison County cooperative bought a farm on the outskirts of Cynthiana. It built a picnic shelter with an all-electric kitchen, a baseball diamond, and other recreational facilities, which are available to civic, educational, and church organizations in summer.

As the illustrations indicate, rural electric cooperatives offer a sizable potential for assisting in community redevelopment. But they represent only one of many sources of assistance available to help rural America.

Heading the list of Government agencies that provide programs geared to rural development needs are the United States Department of Agriculture and the Area Redevelopment Administration, an agency of the Department of Commerce.

The agencies of the Department of Agriculture are coordinating their nationwide program under the title of Rural Areas Development.

The ARA program differs from the RAD program in that it provides assistance only to rural counties that are designated as eligible under the Area Redevelopment Act passed in 1961. More than 1,132 counties had been designated by 1963. The program of the Department of Agriculture is being carried on in all rural counties.

RAD works through an organizational structure that includes State and local development committees, which are representative of a wide range of community interests. Assistance, technical and financial, of the Department of Agriculture is channeled through these committees through technical action panels established in rural counties and headed by the county supervisor of the Farmers Home Administration. The membership of the technical panels consists of personnel of the various Department agencies working in the county and representatives of other Government units.

The local RAD committee provides the initiative for mapping long-range development plans, and the technical action panel supplies the advice and services of Government agencies and other organizations in the area. Coordinating the work of these two groups in the States are two similar groups, one composed of residents and the other of Government staff people.

In addition to the aid that the Department and Government agencies provide to local planning-action groups, they also contribute important redevelopment support through their ongoing programs.

Several agencies of the Department—Farmers Home Administration, Rural Electrification Administration, Federal Extension Service, Agricultural Stabilization and Conservation Service, Economic Research Service, Farmer Cooperative Service, Soil Conservation Service, Forest Service, Agricultural Marketing Service, and Agricultural Research Service—have responsibilities in the work of rural areas development.

Several State governments furnish resources to stimulate rural development. In Pennsylvania, Arkansas, New Hampshire, and Maine, for example, publicly owned or supported industrial authorities lend financial help to community development organizations for such things as factory construction. Privately financed State development corporations, in operation in many States, make similar loans.

Some States have been carrying on active redevelopment programs with excellent results. State-sponsored organizations provide a large variety of aids to help local communities improve their economy. North Carolina, Kentucky, and Arkansas are leading examples of far-reaching and effective State development efforts.

BESIDES THE NUMEROUS Federal and State programs, much assistance is available from private organizations and businesses including rural electric and other cooperatives, chambers of commerce, public utilities, women's clubs, civic clubs, church groups, labor unions, and community development groups.

Though vast resources, both governmental and private, are available to help rebuild rural America, the factor that will determine whether the resources can be used to achieve the purposes for which they are intended is local initiative.

Transforming this initiative into action and progress is the primary task of rural redevelopment. It cannot be superimposed by government. Instead, rural citizens must supply the spark and momentum to turn the opportunities into realities. To do this, each community needs an organizational vehicle. None is more ideally suited than cooperatives.

Both from a philosophical and practical standpoint, cooperatives are well fitted to redevelopment needs. They are grassroots organizations established to help local people. Moreover, through home-owned and home-controlled cooperatives, rural people are more apt to achieve the permanent type of development that they desire and to avoid being victimized by opportunists. Cooperatives also supply the essential elements of local pride, self-dependence, and self-confidence that are necessary to encourage people to solve their own problems.

KERMIT OVERBY *is director of the Legislation and Research Department, National Rural Electric Cooperative Association, Washington, D.C. Formerly he was Director of the Information Division, Rural Electrification Administration.*

MARTIN A. ABRAHAMSEN

COOPERATIVES—
A FORCE FOR STRONGER TIES

COOPERATION is an idea firmly rooted in American tradition. Our pioneer forefathers joined together in barn raisings, husking bees, threshing rings, and in building roads as they carved their farms out of the Nation's wilderness and prairies.

With the increase in specialization and commercialization that come to characterize American agriculture, cooperative business enterprise becomes an increasingly important tool for farm people. They turned to their cooperatives in growing numbers to market their produce. They also looked to these organizations to obtain the various production supplies and business services that modern farm operations required. With the subsequent decline in farm numbers and the growth of suburban communities, the benefits of cooperatives have come to be recognized as extending to rural and urban citizens alike.

Findings of Farmer Cooperative Service show that in the past decade the number of marketing, purchasing, and related service cooperatives decreased from 10,064 to 9,163; memberships increased from 7.1 to 7.2 million; and the net volume of business increased from 8.1 to 12.4 billion dollars.

It is recognized quite generally that farmer-owned marketing associations strengthen the bargaining power of producers and increase their income. They go much farther. These cooperatives make high-quality farm products available for the urban consumers—a fact often not recognized by many segments of society.

Most urban people, for example, are not aware that farmer cooperatives provide them with such well-known foods as Sunkist oranges, Land O'Lakes butter and cheese, Diamond walnuts, Ocean Spray cranberries, Rockingham meats, and Norbest turkeys—to mention only a few of the many products farmer-owned business organizations handle.

Another contribution of marketing cooperatives that benefits both producer and consumer alike is the way in which they reduce market risks. Through pooling practices, these associations help stabilize prices, increase

228

distribution efficiency, reduce market costs, and help assure a constant flow of products the year around.

Farmers also have found from actual experience that their own production supply cooperatives are important to them in carrying out their farm operations. These cooperatives assure them of quality feed, seed, fertilizer, petroleum products, and related production supply items needed to carry out their day-to-day farm operations. Through their cooperatives they obtain these products in just the right way and under the conditions best suited to their needs. Perhaps most important, however, is the fact that the money saved by using cooperatives to provide these off-the-farm production supply departments accrues directly to the farmers themselves.

Important as some of these services are to farm people, it is not always recognized that the contributions these cooperatives make to meeting the needs of urban people can be very substantial. For instance, many of these associations provide heating fuels, a wide range of appliances, and many garden items for suburbanites as well as farmers.

Both marketing and farm supply cooperatives, through their emphasis on sound business practices, increased competition, and the pioneering of new techniques in processing farm products as well as in assuring high analysis of feed and fertilizer, are making important contributions that redound to the benefit of consumers—rural and urban alike.

The contributions of these cooperatives in building rural communities can be very important. The competition they provide stimulates other businesses—the individual proprietor or the investor-oriented business—to do a better job in serving their communities.

IN MANY instances the cooperative marketing and processing plant or the cooperative supply business is the largest business in town. This means greater employment opportunities and

further serves to support the manufacturing, wholesale and retail, financial, service, and other business firms that go to make up urban communities.

Moreover, savings realized by their marketing and farm supply cooperatives enable farm people to pump an additional one-quarter of a billion dollars annually into the economy of rural communities. This helps to keep the cash registers on Main Street ringing and, in many instances, is a stabilizing influence in maintaining a healthy rural economy.

The benefits of farm cooperatives do not stop with selling farm products or providing supplies. A growing number of services are required to effectively perform the business operations of today's farmers. Some 11 thousand service cooperatives serve rural people and in so doing many of them also benefit urban communities. Among the more important of these cooperative services are:

Meeting Credit Needs: A cooperative credit system has been established that provides both long- and short-term credit for farmers. It also makes funds available to cooperative organizations through banks for cooperatives. And city people have a lot of faith in the financial integrity of these cooperatives. For through the cooperative Farm Credit System, farmers have built a financial institution that brings city capital into rural areas. The 13 banks for cooperatives sell consolidated debentures to the investing public—primarily urban financial institutions—to provide funds that are in turn loaned to cooperatives.

In some areas, rural credit needs are supplemented further by credit unions, which, in themselves, are a cooperative credit agency. Credit unions are gaining increased recognition and are used by both rural and urban people.

Providing Fire Insurance: Some 1,600 mutual fire insurance cooperatives provide low-cost protection for more than half of the farm properties in the United States. Many urban people in rural communities also avail themselves of the services of these cooperatives.

Water for Irrigation Purposes: Thousands of irrigation companies, particularly in the West, operate on a cooperative basis and add to the productivity of millions of acres of land. They provide the basis for the development and maintenance of many supporting businesses in these communities.

Electricity and Telephone Services: Some 1,200 electrical and telephone cooperatives meet the increasingly important needs of rural and urban families. In some instances they provide the impetus necessary to establish and maintain industries in the areas they serve.

RECENT DEVELOPMENTS also suggest many new fields of cooperative endeavor that may come to the forefront. For instance, forestry cooperatives help the farmer realize the potential of his farm woodlot. Also, grazing, farm machinery, and housing (for senior citizens) cooperatives are some of the developments that are of interest to rural people.

Likewise, to the extent that recreation and fishing cooperatives may develop, the various services they provide will be in response to demands of both rural and urban people. Moreover, as more urban people move to suburbs, the interest in and need for the services cooperatives provide is likely to increase.

COOPERATIVES of all kinds make important contributions by serving as an educational tool in helping members develop leadership qualities vital in building rural and urban communities. Records of Farmer Cooperative Service indicate that between 10 to 15 percent of the membership of cooperatives are or have been directors or officials of these organizations. In this capacity, they not only have gained a better understanding of how the business economy of the Nation functions but also they have become better community citizens.

For example, the merging of school districts and other local governmental units calls for a high order of political and community statesmanship. Cooperative leaders in many areas are in the forefront in such efforts as well as in the support of laws desired by all types of business.

Cooperatives thus benefit rural and urban people alike. Their contributions to better farm practices and greater efficiency of the marketing system mean increased income for farmers, better quality food for consumers, and higher quality products for industrial use.

Increased farm income resulting from successful cooperative business activities assures a higher standard of living for members of these businesses, jobs for local people, and increased income for the owners of the business firms on Main Street.

Finally, the contributions that cooperatives make to the development of community leaders do not stop at the farm fence but become interwoven in the economic and business life of rural villages and towns.

MARTIN A. ABRAHAMSEN *is Deputy Administrrator, Farmer Cooperative Sevice*

ROBERT E. NIPP

CAPITAL
AND THE COMMUNITY

A COMMUNITY without capital is like a carpenter without tools. Work and progress are impossible. Capital to Henry Ford meant the difference between having an idea and selling 56 million cars. Capital to most of us is the standard of living we can provide our families—a shack or a house, good clothes or poor clothes, adequate food or subsistence diet. Capital to a community is the difference between development and stagnation.

Capital moves to places where it is invested wisely and used profitably. The communities that show the scars of depression once had capital churning in their economic bloodstreams, but they were caught off guard by 20th-century growth and change and are proof of what happens when dollars stop moving, the economy stops growing, and capital becomes unavailable.

Alert trade areas recognize the value of capital in financing new technology, business, and industry. Because local leadership knows how to convert capital into progress, their entire economy is on solid footing, keyed to the proper combination of productive enterprises, community facilities, and a civic responsibility.

The rural community today is in the middle of a changing economic environment. Its main industry, agriculture, has made wholehearted use of capital in revolutionizing its operations. Efficiency on farms is the order of the day, and production continues to increase.

Greater inputs of capital have boosted output per man-hour and reduced total labor requirements. The total amount spent annually for current farm operating expenses and capital items used in the farm business, excluding land, was 3 billion dollars in 1910–1914. This rose to 5.1 billion dollars by 1930, 5.6 billion dollars by 1940, and 18.7 billion dollars by 1950. It climbed to 23.8 billion dollars in 1961, an overall increase of nearly 700 percent in 50 years.

Farmers have used this capital to substitute machinery for labor and to substitute improved farming practices for land. Although the productive assets (farm real estate excluding dwellings, livestock, machinery, feed, and working capital) of this giant industry are worth more than 162.5 billion dollars, the need for capital in farming and associated industries and businesses will continue to grow as new technology comes into being, changes are made in farm organization and management, machines do the work of hands and feet, even closer ties develop between actual farming and off-farm supply, processing, and marketing.

Savings must precede capital investment, but it does not follow that the investor must have been the saver also. This is where the use of credit enters. Pressures of growth and change will force more and more members in the community to turn to lending institutions for part of the capital they use. Stable sources of adequate credit will be necessary.

Borrowed capital usually is obtained in the form of cash from a credit source, such as a bank, insurance company, finance company, credit cooperative, or a Government agency.

Farmers' and other businessmen's attitudes are becoming more favorable toward the use of credit in their operations. Years ago, businesses, particularly farming, were more self-sufficing and less commercialized. Credit was used to cover operating deficits and family emergencies. Then, too, bankruptcies and foreclosures on unfulfilled loan commitments often brought about fear of debt, which was handed down from father to son. Many felt that debt was something to be avoided at almost any cost, a trap that was easy to fall into and hard to get out of. Credit today is used more to boost production and increase sales, and suspicions and fears of using credit are being overcome by education and investment planning.

Agriculture owed 27.4 billion dollars on total assets of 207.5 billion dollars in early 1962. The borrowed capital, small in relation to assets, was necessary, even though farmers save a larger proportion of their income than any other occupational group.

Much of the farmer's savings are

"forced" by the nature of his business. For example, many farmers have farm mortgages or chattel mortgages, payments of which are amortized and usually made on a semiannual or annual basis. Also earnings from the sale of livestock or crops seldom are available for nonproductive purposes, but instead must be reinvested in the farm business.

Although the farm business constantly demands more and more money, the farmers' attitudes also favor the practice of putting all available funds into their productive plant.

A study published by Iowa State University indicated that farmers 25 to 55 years old favored plowing 49 to 56 percent of their farm income back into the farm business. They recognized that adequate capital is vital to success and that aside from borrowing, reinvesting savings and income was about the only other way to secure this resource. In fact, a farmer's savings invested in his business tends to expand his borrowing capacity.

Credit in rural trade areas is less expensive and scarce than it used to be. Interest rates on short-term loans generally were 6 to 7 percent in 1963. Rates on long-term mortgage loans were about 5.5 or 6 percent. The rates were low compared with rates in some other countries, where 100 percent and more is not uncommon and debt is passed from generation to generation.

Capital is invested competitively and moves freely back and forth across the country without regard to State or county lines.

Businesses in cities generally have been able to pay more for the use of capital. From the lender's standpoint, loans in cities are less risky, capital turnover is faster, and more opportunities prevail if the loan goes sour for liquidating the business and recovering the money invested. Cities therefore usually have had the greatest access to capital.

Rural communities, handicapped because of more limited ways in which to use capital and difficulties in obtaining profitable enough returns on investments, often are unable to secure this resource in adequate amounts.

THE BUYING habits of rural people are changing. They spend more of their money in cities and less in their own communities. Advertising, good roads, and automobiles make it easier to shop in the larger places for a wider selection of things and lower prices. Small community businesses suffer when they fail to meet the competition.

No easy way is in sight to shore up the supply of capital in the rural locality where low returns from investments in agriculture and changing buying habits cut down the flow of money.

One step in that direction is a local program of rural areas development, sponsored by several Federal agencies, including the Department of Agriculture. By joining hands and working together, members of a trade area can attract new industry, shift farming programs, if necessary, and install modern community facilities and so develop an environment that will attract capital investments and provide rapid turnover of capital.

This push for progress must come from within the communities. Working in their favor are the higher operating and overhead expenses in cities. The possibility of lower-cost labor, lower taxes, cheaper land and power, and modern roads encourage the decentralization of industry. The smaller community has good reason therefore to take the initiative in attracting new business that may strengthen its capital structure.

One business that moved from a city to a rural community found that its unit production costs today were no higher than before, despite a general rise of costs over the years. Some residents, who operated small farms and needed additional income, were hired and soon demonstrated their skill and industry. A 10-acre site was purchased for 10 thousand dollars,

much less than the cost of a new site in a city. The firm's taxes were about 58 percent of what they were at the old plant, and insurance costs dropped 17 percent.

Federal technical and financial aid to communities has been increasing, but hardly enough to help some rural communities whose economy needs a complete overhaul. Cities faced with problems of underemployment and a paucity of resources can turn for help to Federal urban renewal programs. The answer for the rural community is a rural renewal program, where local community action is sparked with Federal funds and technical aid. The successful use of Government credit and technical aid to agriculture provides strong evidence that a similar program may provide the help needed to pull the community out of its doldrums.

Such a rural renewal program would have to have strong local powers and adequate borrowing authority to reshape the community. The citizens would be encouraged to band together in public bodies and in cooperation with Federal and State agencies obtain low-interest, long-term loans to carry out plans for more jobs and business activity. By making the community more attractive to new industry and business, the program would offer an opportunity to increase efficiency by moving employment to people rather than by moving people to employment.

Legislation in 1962 authorized some pilot rural renewal projects in a few severely disadvantaged communities, but no Federal funds had been provided for the program in 1962.

The Congress developed the renewal program partly on the basis of the success of the credit program to farmers carried out by the Farmers Home Administration of the Department of Agriculture. Out of the 4.6 billion dollars that the Farmers Home Administration had lent through June 30, 1962, 2.9 billion dollars had been repaid and 436 million dollars in interest had been collected. Only 0.7 percent of the total loans had been written off as uncollectible.

SPECIAL Federal loan and grant programs have been developed over the years for rural areas.

The Federal Farm Loan Act was enacted in 1916. It did not provide direct loans but laid the groundwork whereby farmers could build a credit system of their own.

Out of it evolved what is known as a cooperative Farm Credit System.

Established in 1933, the Farm Credit Administration, an independent agency of the Federal Government, supervises this system, which provides three types of credit services through banks and associations largely owned and operated by borrower-members: Federal land banks and associations; Federal intermediate credit banks and production credit associations; and banks for cooperatives. The first two services lend to farmers and ranchers for general purposes. The third lends money to farmer cooperatives for operating capital; financing facilities (land, buildings, and the equipment needed to operate the cooperative); and commodities (inventories).

The amounts of the loans and the repayment periods vary. The interest rate is 4.5 to 7 percent. As of July 1, 1962, the three services had lent 57 billion dollars. The Farm Credit System in 1962 had repaid the Federal Government most of the money originally borrowed to get it started.

Through 13 banks for cooperatives, farmer cooperatives have built a vehicle to funnel city capital into rural communities. Their funds are obtained by selling securities to the public. The entire cooperative Farm Credit System, of which the 13 banks are a part, obtains about 4 billion dollars a year in this manner and makes it available to farmers and their cooperatives throughout the country.

SUCCESSFUL COOPERATIVES stem initially from an existing need and a desire locally to fill this need, including the willingness to invest in it: If farmers provide a base of reasonable equity, banks for cooperatives can extend loans.

An example is the Plains Cooperative Oil Mill at Lubbock, Tex. It was organized in 1936 by 35 operators of cotton gins on an initial investment of about 125 thousand dollars. It later built additional facilities that cost 3 million dollars. It had a daily capacity of 1,200 tons in 1962 and provided seed storage of 230 thousand tons.

During the fiscal year ended June 30, 1962, the co-op sold cottonseed and cottonseed products for 24 million dollars; spent 980 thousand dollars in wages and salaries; and paid out 417 thousand dollars in repairs and supplies, 258 thousand for electric power, 80 thousand for taxes, 66 thousand for fuel, 30 thousand for advertising and donations, 225 thousand for interest, and 125 thousand for insurance. It returned dividends of 1.467 million dollars to the member gins.

Another type of cooperative, the rural credit union, provides a source of rural credit by mobilizing or pooling financial resources of the community. They are owned, controlled, and used only by members. About 800 rural communities had credit unions in 1962. The amount of business they did ranged from 50 thousand dollars to 3 million dollars.

ANOTHER SOURCE of credit for rural communities is the direct Government loan programs, which started during the First World War when seed and feed loans were first made. They became firmly established during the depression of the thirties when the Resettlement Administration was created to rehabilitate destitute farm families by making them loans and grants and giving them guidance in managing their affairs.

Because of farm price supports and other efforts, farm income began picking up in the late thirties. At the time of the outbreak of war, the need for emergency financing by the Government agency diminished, but technological changes in agriculture brought a need for heavy investments, which multiplied the problems of beginning farmers and other farmers with limited capital. Capital was in greater and greater demand, and the Congress in 1946 enacted a bill that created the Farmers Home Administration and transferred to it the loan services of the abolished Farm Security Administration and the Emergency Crop and Feed Loan Division of the Farm Credit Administration. Since then, authorizations have been broadened to meet emergencies, to serve better the needs of modern farming, and to stabilize and improve rural economic conditions.

The credit services of the Farmers Home Administration supplement but do not compete with those of other lenders. Help with farm and financial management accompanies each loan.

LEGISLATION that has broadened and modernized Government agricultural credit services include the Bankhead-Jones Farm Tenant Act of 1937; the Water Facilities Act of 1937; the Farmers Home Administration Act of 1946; the Housing Act of 1949, further broadened and improved by amendments in 1961 and 1962; the Emergency Credit Act of 1949; the Watershed Protection and Flood Prevention Act of 1954; and the Consolidated Farmers Home Administration Act of 1961, further broadened by amendments contained in the Food and Agriculture Act of 1962.

The Farmers Home Administration is charged with administering a line of credit services to farmers and to rural residents and local community groups as well. It makes low-interest loans amortized over long periods to buy, develop, and operate farms and to provide housing and water systems on farms and in rural communities up to 2,500 population. The Food and Agriculture Act of 1962 authorized the agency to make loans to farmers to develop recreational enterprises as a supplemental source of income and to nonprofit community groups for shifting farmland to other uses, including recreation.

THE COMMUNITY of Litchfield, Ill., had floods and drainage problems during wet seasons and too little water to carry the area (including a small city) through drought periods. The Farmers Home Administration approved a watershed loan for 1.769 million dollars to help finance construction of a multiple-purpose reservoir for flood prevention and municipal water storage and two related flood-retarding reservoirs. The reservoir for municipal water can store 23 thousand acre-feet. Nearly 35 thousand acres drain into it. Water backs up 4 miles above the dam and forms a lake whose 25-mile shoreline offers opportunities for recreation. The loan, to be repaid over 40 years, bears 2.632 percent interest on the unpaid principal. Loans of this type can be made up to 5 million dollars.

A rural community in Kentucky was getting much of its water from ponds, springs, and branches, some of which often were muddy or stagnant. Sporadic outbreaks of illness, including hepatitis and typhoid, were attributed to the water, and because of it operators of dairy farms were threatened with losing their Grade A milk markets.

Members of the community banded together and obtained a loan of 119 thousand dollars from the Farmers Home Administration. The funds financed a water system consisting of 8 miles of water main, a chlorinator station, watermeters, and a storage tank of 100 thousand gallons. Water is purchased from a nearby city. More than 100 farm and rural families, schools, and several businesses now have all the good water they need.

The loan is to be repaid over 40 years and bears 4 percent interest. Loans of this type may be made in amounts up to 500 thousand dollars when funds appropriated by the Congress are used, and 1 million dollars when funds are provided by private lenders and insured by the Farmers Home Administration.

Eleven tenant families who farmed on a large estate in Texas faced a loss of their leases and possible eviction in 1962 because the estate was to be sold. The families received loans totaling 430 thousand dollars and purchased the 5 thousand acres of land. Additional credit was used to finance land development, improve buildings, and buy good livestock. Businesses in the community benefited because the families were kept in the area as customers. These loans bear 5 percent interest. Loans for land development and purchase may be made up to 60 thousand dollars for periods up to 40 years. Loans for livestock, machinery, and farm operating expenses may be made up to 35 thousand dollars for periods up to 7 years.

COMMUNITIES traditionally have obtained much of their capital for public facilities and other developments through bond issues and taxes.

Bond issues require approval by the voters, however, and even after a favorable referendum it may be hard to sell the bonds because of the community's weak economic base.

Increasing taxes presents difficulties, too. About 87 percent of the local tax collections come from levies on property. Since there has been quite a rise in taxes, including those on property, there is growing concern in many communities over how much higher they can go with their tax rates before they stifle enterprise and investment, the very thing they are trying to avoid in their efforts to attract new industry.

Congressional action permits some Government agencies to extend a broad range of credit services to all rural communities. I cite examples of some other Government credit aids.

The Rural Electrification Administration, created in 1935, makes loans to qualified borrowers, with preference to nonprofit and cooperative associations and to public bodies. Funds may be used to finance electric and telephone service in rural areas. The loans may be made for any amount, bear 2 percent interest, and are repayable within 35 years. Where funds are not available from other sources at reasonable rates, Rural Electrification Administration also may make loans to electric cooperatives who in turn relend the funds to their consumer-members to finance electrical equipment, wiring, plumbing, and machinery. As of July 1, 1962, the agency had lent nearly 5.6 billion dollars.

A rural community in Tennessee was isolated from the outside world because of poor telephone service. It used Rural Electrification Administration loans of 512 thousand dollars to construct a telephone system that services 1,300 customers.

An electric cooperative in Wisconsin obtained an REA loan in 1936 to build a rural system to provide service to a thousand farm consumers. The farmers used the electricity primarily for lighting at first, but soon came to depend on it for many farm operations. The use of electricity and the number of people who wanted electricity from the cooperative increased steadily. The cooperative approached REA for a loan to build new facilities and to increase the capacity of the lines already in operation. In 1962, the cooperative had 2.7 million dollars in loans and served more than 3,500 consumers. Electricity has attracted three new industries to the area—two manufacturing concerns and a meat-packing plant, which created a number of jobs and stimulated the local economy.

Area Redevelopment Administration, an agency of the Department of Commerce, was established in 1961 to provide loans for industrial and commercial projects, loans and grants for public facilities, funds to an area to finance a review of their resources and means to solve their problems (technical assistance contracts), and retraining and subsistence programs.

The amount of a loan depends on

the purpose. The interest rate is 3.5 to 4 percent. The maximum repayment period is 25 to 40 years. As of April 15, 1963, Area Redevelopment Administration had made available 109.5 million dollars in grants, loans, and technical assistance contracts.

A rural community in Washington had persistent and substantial unemployment, particularly when its tourist and recreation centers closed in winter. Members of the community located a wood products corporation that would establish a new plywood plant in the area if 350 thousand dollars in financing could be arranged.

The Area Redevelopment Administration made a loan of 140 thousand dollars. It was scheduled to be repaid over 15 years at an annual interest rate of 4 percent. In addition to the Area Redevelopment Administration funds, a nonprofit local organization put in 35 thousand dollars, two local banks invested 40 thousand dollars, and the company itself furnished 135 thousand dollars in equity capital. The action created nearly 100 new jobs in the community.

A community in Illinois received a loan of 455 thousand dollars from the Area Redevelopment Administration to help an eastern manufacturer of industrial tapes expand into the Midwest. The loan stimulated additional local private and public investment of more than 2.6 million dollars—a token of the seed-money character of Federal credit assistance.

The one-time loan made possible an annual payroll of 4.3 million dollars, which is generating 266 thousand dollars each year in Federal income taxes, besides corporation taxes and local and State tax revenues. In addition, it means an annual saving of nearly 100 thousand dollars in welfare payments and an annual saving of 343 thousand dollars in unemployment compensation benefits.

The Small Business Administration, an independent Federal agency established in 1953, makes loans—some on a matching fund basis with private lenders—to individual small business firms when they are unable to obtain private financing on reasonable terms. Funds may be used for the construction, conversion, or expansion of business plants and for restoring homes or businesses hit by natural disaster or to restore businesses suffering economic injury from drought or excessive rainfall. Loans of up to 350 thousand dollars bear interest at 3 to 5.5 percent and are repaid over periods up to 25 years. As of July 1, 1962, Small Business Administration's share of loans made totaled more than 1.7 billion dollars.

A Missouri community was faced with the loss of an industry, a manufacturer of men's and boys' wear, because the manufacturer needed a larger and more modern building. As a start toward providing improved facilities for it, citizens raised 30 thousand dollars. This was supplemented with a loan of 95 thousand dollars made jointly by a local bank and the Small Business Administration, which provided 90 percent of the funds. The loan is to be repaid over 10 years, with a 5-percent interest charge on the unpaid principal. Funds were used to expand and modernize the factory, and the manufacturer remained in the town.

Because of changes in the State milk laws, a midwestern dairy had to build a new plant or go out of business. When it was unable to obtain financing from local banks, a development company was organized to help. More than 100 residents bought 51 thousand dollars in stock in the company, and 138 thousand dollars more were obtained by the company through a joint loan of the Small Business Administration and a bank. The 189 thousand dollars financed a modern plant. This saved some 50 jobs as well as the milk market for farmers in the area, who produced 10 to 20 million pounds of fluid milk a year.

Community Facilities Administration, of the Housing and Home Finance Agency, established in 1950, makes loans or advances to communities to build rental housing for the

elderly and to install public works, such as sewers, waterworks, public buildings, streets, sidewalks, street lights, and gas distribution systems; to colleges for student and faculty housing; to hospitals for housing for student nurses and interns; and to public agencies, such as municipalities, to plan public works. The size of the loans or advances, interest rates, and repayment periods vary. As of July 1, 1962, Community Facilities Administration had made loans of 2.5 billion dollars.

A town in North Carolina needed a sewer system to attract industry and to serve homes and businesses. Because it had no money to pay for drawing up the plans, the project could not be submitted to the voters. It applied to the Community Facilities Administration and received an interest-free advance for planning.

An engineer prepared the plans and estimated that the system would cost 200 thousand dollars. The voters approved the plan, but when the town inquired among investment firms, it discovered that because the community was small and had never borrowed before, it would have to pay a high interest rate and sell its bonds below par. The Community Facilities Ad-

ministration approved a loan after determining that the sewer system would earn enough to repay principal and interest and also cover maintenance and operation costs. The loan was scheduled for 40 years at 3.75 percent interest. The advance was repaid when construction began.

A community in a redevelopment area in Mississippi felt that it could get industry if it had a gas distribution system. Local residents also wanted the improvement for their homes and businesses. It had tried to borrow money from private sources but was unable to obtain the 153 thousand dollars needed. It received a 50-percent grant under the accelerated public works program from Community Facilities Administration. The assistance made it possible for the community to obtain the remaining amount from a private lender.

Public Health Service, an agency of the Department of Health, Education, and Welfare, established in 1798, makes grants under the Hill-Burton Act of 1946 to construct public and nonprofit hospitals and other medical facilities. On July 1, 1962, 1.7 billion dollars had been granted.

A small 50-bed hospital in a New England town had been declared unsuitable by the State department of health and faced the loss of its accredited status by a National Hospital Commission. It was the only medical facility in the community, which had been hard hit some years before by the loss of one of its two major industries. Extensive outside assistance was necessary if the hospital was to make the major alterations and additions to bring its physical plant up to acceptable standards. With a grant of 382 thousand dollars under the Hill-Burton program, plus local funds, the community replaced the existing obsolete hospital with a modern general hospital costing a million dollars.

A rural community in a sparsely populated mountainous area in New Mexico lacked medical facilities. Gross income averaged only 607 dollars per capita, and 19 percent of the people were receiving public welfare assistance. A Hill-Burton grant of 44.5 thousand dollars, combined with an equal amount from a religious group, enabled the community to construct a diagnostic and treatment center. It was staffed by a physician, licensed nurses, and laboratory technicians, and provides various services, including pediatric and maternity care, a well-baby clinic, and emergency and dental facilities. Cases requiring further treatment are sent to a hospital 43 miles away.

A South Dakota community of 6 thousand residents needed a nursing home for older people. The cost was more than 300 thousand dollars. Local organizations held bake sales, fairs, and other fund-raising projects. The Public Health Service provided an additional 150 thousand dollars through the Hill-Burton program, and the community's dream became a reality.

The only hospital facilities in a county in eastern Alabama were two clinics in private homes. The buildings held only 10 hospital beds. Residents petitioned the county board of revenue to create a hospital board, which determined that a hospital and new public health center were needed. County voters approved a tax of 4 mills. Income from this was combined with State funds and Federal money provided through Hill-Burton legislation. A 27-bed hospital was opened in 1957 and expanded in 1962. A modern public health center was opened in 1960, and a nursing home was constructed in 1961. The three buildings form a medical center on one plot. New private office facilities for doctors have been provided on adjoining property. The total cost of the installation was 981 thousand dollars. Approximately two-thirds of the financing were Hill-Burton funds.

BESIDES BRINGING needed capital into rural communities, Federal credit programs have brought many improvements and innovations to the credit industry.

Government leadership may be credited in some part for lengthening repayment periods, increasing loans in proportion to appraised value of security, equalizing interest rates across the Nation and reducing interest comparable to big city rates, amortizing loans with equal annual payments, deferred payments and prepayments to relate the ability of the borrower to the repayment schedule, establishing the borrower as an important criterion upon which to make the loan, regardless of its purpose, helping the borrower consider and plan for all his capital needs, and for serving as a successful testing ground for new types of credit, such as insured loans and loans to assist farmers and businessmen caught in emergency situations.

Whether capital is available to the rural community depends largely on the community itself. Capital generally is timid. Except when there is a chance of a large profit, as in exploration for oil, capital does not flow when risks are high. Capital does not travel to individuals or industries that have limited experience in handling borrowed funds, where managerial ability is low, and where labor and other resources are inadequate.

Because our Nation is going through such a rapid period of change, the rural community faces many problems of adjustment, and, in some cases, of survival. Larger and larger amounts of capital will be needed to help it successfully overcome these problems. A network of private and Government credit institutions must be maintained and strengthened so that a community may progress and keep its citizens independent and producing.

ROBERT E. NIPP *joined the Farmers Home Administration in 1957 as an information officer. Born and reared on a farm near Yankton, S. Dak., he is a graduate of Iowa State University. He taught vocational agriculture in Iowa before becoming a county supervisor of FHA in Iowa.*

WILLIAM L. SLAYTON

HOW TO CURE
A BLIGHT IN CITIES

SOUTHWEST Washington, which is a few steps from
the Capitol of the richest Nation in the world and three multimillion-dollar
congressional office buildings, had been allowed to become a slum of decaying
houses, dangerous alleys, dark and ominous streets, and a palpable hopelessness.
Several thousand human beings lived there, and uncounted rats and cockroaches.

Economic dry rot had put the blight
of decay on a large district at the very
heart of Boston, an area linked with
the brightest pages of American history. Yet history had passed by much
of Boston; its crooked, narrow downtown streets were unsuited to modern
traffic requirements. New investment
was going to other, more progressive
cities, and the city needed a comprehensive overhaul.

So, too, a squalid section near the
waterfront Embarcadero of otherwise
charming San Francisco; a part of
18th-century Philadelphia; a rundown
square not far from Yale University in
New Haven; and many more—several
hundred cities in need of rebuilding
and rehabilitation to make them fit
for people to live and work in.

They are being demolished, renewed,
and rebuilt. Our interest in them is in
their value as examples of what can
be done to renew and rehabilitate

240

blighted places in all parts of the
United States and in their bearing on
the movement of people to and from
and in our cities and counties.

The federally assisted program of
urban renewal was authorized by the
Housing Act of 1949, which provided
for a grant authorization of 500 million
dollars for slum clearance and urban
redevelopment. Later acts broadened
its scope and increased the total authorization to 4 billion dollars. Under
it, the Urban Renewal Administration
of the Housing and Home Finance
Agency makes grants to localities equal
to two-thirds (or sometimes three-
fourths) of the net cost of acquiring
slum property, clearing it of structures,
providing public facilities, and selling
the cleared land at its fair value for
new uses in accordance with a locally
developed renewal plan.

Urban renewal projects may provide also for the rehabilitation of

existing housing rather than its clearance. Funds then are used largely for public improvements and for advice and assistance to property owners. The cost of repairing and modernizing houses is borne by private owners, who obtain funds chiefly through liberal mortgages insured by the Federal Housing Administration under a special program.

URBAN RENEWAL rests on a belief that slums and blight are a social and economic debit to a community and that curing those conditions and making city land available for new uses are a justifiable basis for public investment and that public action is needed to make blighted areas, long neglected by private capital, once more attractive to investors. The net cost is a writedown that reflects the cost of clearing socially undesirable—but still economic—uses and is therefore a public responsibility. When the public absorbs the cost, the land sold at fair value for redevelopment should be competitive with undeveloped land in other parts of the community. Private enterprise lacks the power of eminent domain and therefore seldom is able to assemble land on the scale necessary to make an effective upgrading in its use.

The program at first concentrated on residential development almost entirely in order to carry out, in the words of the Declaration of National Housing Policy in the Housing Act of 1949, "the goal of a decent home and a suitable living environment for every American family."

The law specified that each project was to be predominantly residential in its existing use or its planned reuse under redevelopment. This limitation has been modified. A substantial fraction of the funds go into projects that are not predominantly residential in present use or reuse. Special provisions have been added for hospitals, universities, and industrial land projects in areas of surplus labor.

Urban renewal has been concerned more and more with the need to help make the city function effectively through a reorganization of land uses and the elimination of blight. It aims to strengthen the local economic base by providing sites for new industry, making possible the expansion of universities, hospitals, and cultural facilities that require more land, and improving housing.

Thus our cities are being rebuilt; problems of physical decay, economic obsolescence, and outmoded city structure at last are being coped with; the debris of earlier development is being removed; efforts are devoted to the prevention of future decay; the forces of change are being channeled to serve the objectives of the community.

People are the prime factor in all this. No project is approved until the Administrator of the Housing and Home Finance Agency certifies the acceptability of a plan for the relocation of the displaced families in decent, safe, and sanitary housing at rents and sales prices they can afford. Payments up to 200 dollars are made to displaced families and up to 25 thousand dollars for displaced businesses to cover moving costs and direct losses of property.

A TOTAL of 1,400 projects and other urban renewal activities were planned or underway in 1963 in 675 municipalities. They involved commitments for 3.3 billion dollars in Federal capital grants.

The work of acquiring land, relocating families, demolishing buildings, and selling the land is complex, and a typical project ordinarily requires 2 years or more for planning and 8 to 12 years for actual execution. Because Federal commitments are made before initiation of planning is started on most projects, the completion of all the projects under commitment in 1963 is not expected before the early 1970's. Furthermore, because the annual level of commitments has been sharply upward, 25 percent of the dollar volume of the program represents projects started in 1962. For example, the 1.4

billion dollars that we expected to commit during the fiscal years 1962 and 1963 may be compared with about 2 billion dollars committed for projects started between 1949 and 1961.

The rate of activity rose sharply after 1957. Some figures give cumulative measures of progress. At the end of fiscal 1957: Acres of land acquired, 665; price, 55.5 million dollars; families relocated, 8,753; dwelling units demolished, 14,703; land disposed of, 187 acres; price, 8.2 million dollars. Cumulative through 1962: Acres of land acquired, 14,977; price, 1,390.4 million dollars; families relocated, 150,306; dwelling units demolished, 196,162; land disposed of, 4,499 acres; price, 201.2 million dollars.

In absolute terms, the figures are substantial. They reveal one aspect of the extent of Government activities. The relocation of displaced families, for example, probably is at about the same annual rate as that for the Federal aid highway program, and I estimate that the two programs account for about two of every three families displaced by governmental action.

The movement of people because of urban renewal, however, is only a small proportion of the total movement of population. Today, approximately one of every five American families lives in a house different from the one it occupied last year. About 35 million Americans—12 million families—move each year. Displacement by urban renewal at the rate of 25 thousand families, about 75 thousand individuals, annually is a fraction of 1 percent of the total movement of population.

The figures are somewhat higher, but the story is not appreciably different if we consider only the major urban centers with which urban renewal has been primarily concerned. Cumulative family relocation in the 44 cities for which 10 million dollars or more in capital grant funds had been committed through 1962 for renewal totaled only 85,213, compared to a total population of 31,150,000 in the cities.

The importance of urban renewal,

then, is not in the size of its total thrust in comparison with the major forces of growth and mobility of population that affect our cities. Rather, urban renewal should be regarded as a strategic factor in shaping and directing the forces of change in terms of their influence at the margin. It cannot be expected to assume, for example, the position held by mortgages insured by the Federal Housing Administration or guaranteed by the Veterans' Administration or made by insured savings and loan associations in the provision of new housing, largely in suburban locations.

MOST OF the results we expect from urban renewal lie ahead.

During the coming decade it will begin to exert a significant force in the clearance of substandard housing, the relocation of families, the rehabilitation of existing housing, and the redevelopment of blighted areas.

Renewal should eliminate a large proportion of our urban housing that was reported in the 1960 Census of Housing to be dilapidated or without indoor plumbing. For example, 660 clearance projects, which involve 1.6 billion dollars in Federal capital grants, included 322,640 dwelling units, of which 257,221 were substandard. The total for all projects under commitment in 1962 (including projects in planning) would be about 400 thousand units—a significant fraction of the 4.2 million substandard units cities reported in the 1960 Census of Housing. Before 1970, the rate of clearance will probably be 60 thousand to 80 thousand units annually.

Analyses by the Urban Renewal Administration staff of renewal programs in 44 cities, which had an aggregate population of 31,150,000 and 10,676,470 dwellings, disclosed 222,256 substandard dwelling units in the renewal projects in 1962. The estimated number of substandard units cleared in renewal projects before the census reporting date was 67,555; 154,500 programed units remained. The total of all substandard housing units in these cities in the 1960 census was 1,139,400, and the percentage of 1960 inventory of substandard dwelling units included in urban renewal projects was 13.6.

I consider it likely that the continued initiation of new projects in the 44 cities and the rehabilitation activities and the demolition of housing by other Government programs should result in the elimination before 1980 of nearly all of the housing in those cities that has been classified as substandard.

This does affect the ebb and flow of people in the city. It will improve the condition of nearly all the worst housed—the impoverished, the minorities, and the newcomers. It will remove, I hope forever, the worst of the tenements and the jerry-built shack towns that are not fit to live in.

The relocation of families, perhaps the most delicate and critical operation in the urban renewal process, is closely related to the demolition of their substandard housing. This is a parallel action that follows the same general pattern, but some additional observations are needed.

The number of families displaced is about 20 percent smaller than the number of units demolished in clearance projects because of vacancies, which usually are higher in substandard housing than elsewhere.

Most of the families in project areas have been relocated in standard housing—17 percent in public housing and 62 percent in standard private housing.

Only 7 percent are known to have moved to substandard housing after standard housing had been offered to them. The whereabouts of an additional 7 percent is unknown. Another 7 percent relocated out of the city, where inspection of the new dwelling was not possible.

Relocation has tended to be concentrated in areas close to the project.

Success in relocation was possible largely because of three factors: The relatively high level of vacancies in most cities provided good opportunities for relocation; public housing has been available (with some important exceptions) for families unable to afford standard private housing; and the Federal Housing Administration since 1954 has provided special liberal terms for sales and rental housing for displaced families.

Future relocations are hard to estimate, but an annual rate of 65 thousand to 75 thousand families by 1970 is possible. However, a trend toward the redevelopment of nonresidential areas and the increasing application of rehabilitation rather than clearance of blighted housing will cause fewer dislocations and may mean the annual relocation of 50 thousand families.

On December 31, 1962, 225 projects were in planning or in execution, which involved the conservation and rehabilitation of 25 or more dwelling units in each project. These projects had a total of 148 thousand dwelling units. Rehabilitation had been completed for only about 25 thousand units, however. In the 44 cities covered by a special Urban Renewal Administration staff analysis, projects actually underway (excluding those still in planning) included 58,345 dwelling units scheduled for conservation; this represents approximately 5.1 percent of the substandard housing inventory in these cities and is in addition to the substandard units to be demolished.

The techniques for conservation and reconditioning of entire neighborhoods are still being developed. A fully effective approach could accelerate substantially the current slow rate of progress. An annual rate of 50 thousand or more dwelling units a year is not beyond accomplishment.

REHABILITATION offers stability to neighborhoods buffeted by our rapidly moving and expanding population and, hence, a potential and desirable decline in the ebb and flow of population. It is also an effort to protect our national investment in housing.

The benefits of the rehabilitation approach were evident in the few projects approaching completion in 1963.

The clearance of a produce market

in the Society Hill section of Philadelphia made possible the construction of new housing and the rehabilitation of 18th- and 19th-century houses for a magnificent new residential area between Independence Hall and the Delaware River. Rehabilitation brought major investments by homeowners, and the favorable effects were felt almost at once in nearby sections.

Wooster Square, a blighted middle-class residential area in New Haven, has been rehabilitated. The threat to the stability of the community was removed, and the longer terms and lower interest rates on Federal Housing Administration mortgages often made possible lower monthly housing costs, despite the increase in debt necessary to cover modernization costs.

Outstanding in the urban renewal program is the redevelopment of the blighted areas. By restoring their attractiveness to investors and introducing appropriate new uses, renewal can affect their pattern of land use.

Approximately one-half of the land available for redevelopment is to be used for residential purposes. In 679 projects, well advanced in 1963, planned reuses, in acres, were: Residential, including related public and semipublic uses, 12,187; commercial, 4,054; industrial, 5,622; and public and semipublic, 2,874.

Mixed uses predominate. Only 68 projects are exclusively residential; 214 are exclusively nonresidential. The total investment—Federal, local, and private—in these projects may total five times the Federal capital grant of 1.6 billion dollars.

In residential projects, the Federal Housing Administration in 1962 had issued commitments for the insurance of mortgages on approximately 36,106 dwelling units in 158 projects. The commitments accounted for most of the private housing then built or underway on urban renewal sites. It excluded a few projects financed through conventional mortgages or direct investment. Since the land was sold at its fair market value, the housing sells or rents at levels competitive with private housing constructed on open land or on sites otherwise available to private enterprise without governmental assistance. Moreover, since the commitments of Federal Housing Administration are typically issued in stages, this accounts for only a part of the housing being built on land now available for disposition and excludes entirely projects that had not yet reached the stage where such land is available.

THE UPGRADING of land use is expected to have a major effect on the placement of real estate investment capital in a city. A few examples:

In Southwest Washington, three projects cover 562 acres, on which used to be some of the worst housing in Washington—or any city. Construction began in 1958 on 5,400 private units at various rents and sales prices, a shopping center, a major group of Government offices, restaurants, and a theater. Nine hundred units of low-rent public housing on an adjacent site also have been completed. The total private investment was expected to be more than 400 million dollars. Washingtonians have watched its development with keen interest. The area shows increasing promise of becoming a fashionable area because of its nearness to Capitol Hill, the Potomac River, and the Mall.

An extremely rundown area near the waterfront Embarcadero in San Francisco was cleared for the construction of a high-quality residential project of unusual beauty of design. The total investment on this relatively small site may exceed 100 million dollars.

The Michael Reese and Lake Meadows projects in the south side of Chicago have been blocked out of almost complete slum. Good new rental housing has been constructed and made available to Negroes who have had the finances and desire to purchase good housing but who, because of restrictions, have been unable to obtain it. An outgrowth is a striking example of integrated housing. The occupancy of one project is approximately 25 percent white and 75 percent Negro, and of the other, 75 percent white and 25 percent Negro. These ratios have remained relatively stable.

Comparatively little public housing has been constructed on urban renewal sites, although tendencies to do so have grown. A number of projects have been approved for the construction of middle-income housing in renewal areas with a new subsidized interest rate, authorized by the Housing Act of 1961.

It is worth mentioning, in addition, that a number of the projects include buildings to be sold as cooperative housing so as to extend advantages of homeownership to persons living in in-town residential neighborhoods of high density.

Nonresidential redevelopment has attained importance in the renewal program and, as I noted, represents approximately half the planned land use in a number of projects, which very likely can have great influence on the form of a city because commercial, industrial, and institutional facilities tend to attract complementary and related activities.

A RENEWAL project typically can deal with only a segment of the downtown problem, because sizable sections ordinarily are not so far gone as to meet the standards for urban renewal projects. A number of such undertakings have been started.

In the middle of Boston, the rehabilitation of an extremely deteriorated commercial and residential area was undertaken for a major center of Federal, State, and city office buildings. It will strengthen an important and historic area in the heart of the city that had received almost no new investment for decades.

Work started in 1961 on a complex of office buildings and commercial facilities in the Charles Center project near the center of Baltimore. Its basic purpose was to help revive a sagging district. Even before its first building

was finished, construction began on another office building across the street.

A new commercial area in New Haven, Conn., fronts directly on the Green. This project, including a hotel and department store, is integrated with the construction of a central city arterial road with direct access to a large parking garage from ramps. It thus introduces advanced principles of transportation planning through unique arrangements for goods handling and a complete separation of pedestrian and vehicular traffic.

In Hartford, Conn., downtown areas had deteriorated and seemed to be getting worse. A large department store had closed. Smaller businesses had failed. An insurance company had moved to the suburbs, and another was planning to do so. Through three related urban renewal projects, a 15-acre blighted area in the center of Hartford was cleared, and work began on major new structures, among them a new home for a major insurance company, two combined bank and office buildings, a hotel, and a broadcasting station. All the facilities have underground parking space under a plaza that forms the core of the area. The 15 acres were assessed at 2 million dollars; one estimate placed the value of the new development at more than 40 million dollars. Other major new investments were planned in the revitalized core.

URBAN RENEWAL projects have furthered cultural facilities of all kinds.

Lincoln Center for the Performing Arts in New York is one. Its site was a dreary place of poor houses and down-at-the-mouth shops. Plans for it include a new hall for the New York Philharmonic Symphony Orchestra, a new Metropolitan Opera House, a repertory theater, a new home for the Juilliard School of Music, and related facilities. This project has a place in a grand strategy to attract people and capital to the neglected west side of Manhattan. Urban renewal activities, ranging from the New York Coliseum to the south to new housing on Morningside

Heights near Columbia University, are aimed at the upgrading of the deteriorated sections of a large area. Housing is being constructed or rehabilitated for all income groups.

In Pittsburgh's Lower Hill, a sports arena with a movable steel roof was built on a site convenient to the downtown district. Near it is a substantial volume of new housing.

Most of the efforts to provide places for cultural institutions have been on a lesser scale than the projects I have mentioned, but the growing list of projects in which sites have been provided for museums, theaters, and music halls is impressive. They will encourage people to live in the area and attract visitors to the central city.

The urban renewal statute contains special incentives and inducements to provide land for the expansion of universities and hospitals, which have grown more important in the employment base of the city. In some residential projects such as those in Hyde Park in Chicago and Morningside Heights in New York, urban renewal also has helped to stabilize university neighborhoods and provide the housing badly needed by teachers and students.

University City in West Philadelphia will provide land needed by Drexel Institute and the University of Pennsylvania for their building programs. It is expected that the current project will do much to improve the entire neighborhood. It is the first part of long-range plans of the institutions for expansion and is linked with the development of an urban research park to strengthen the economic base of the area and the city.

In the Harrison-Halsted project in Chicago, a site in the vicinity of historic Hull House has been provided for a new campus for the Chicago branch of the University of Illinois.

In the Medical Center project in Birmingham, Ala., a large site has been provided for new hospital and medical facilities in a major medical center.

The Baltimore facility of the University of Maryland, which houses the university's medical school, is in one of the older sections. The area once had rundown commercial establishments and tenements and was hardly the place for an educational institution. The environment blocked plans for expansion to take care of a rising enrollment and research and educational programs. Two renewal projects made a dramatic change in the environment, and 12 acres of land were provided for new facilities.

Industrial parks of various sizes are being constructed on cleared land in some renewal projects. Examples are the West River project in Providence, R.I., the industrial sections of the great Eastwick project in Philadelphia, and the Western and Harrison projects in Chicago.

MORE THAN 80 cities were preparing community renewal programs in 1963 and were outlining long-term, comprehensive, and citywide plans for community improvement.

Their approach emphasizes the interrelationships between urban renewal and Government activities and takes into account a series of problems that are related to urban renewal but not a part of it. For example, in developing measures for the elimination of all substandard housing in a city, one must deal concretely with the problems of the families who live in the slums. It is not simply a matter of rehousing them. It is a matter also of integrating them into the mainstreams of the community. The city, in this context, must be concerned with jobs and education for jobs, social and welfare services, and the effects of discrimination in jobs and housing opportunities.

It is more than just tearing down and putting up buildings; one must not lose sight of people and their homes and habits and the way in which they want to live.

WILLIAM L. SLAYTON *is Commissioner, Urban Renewal Administration, Housing and Home Finance Agency.*

GOVERNMENT

ON the basic principles of democracy, the right to vote, freedom of expression, and civic responsibility, all Americans agree. On the size of a governing unit—local, county, State, regional—its obligations, its efficiency, and its ability to serve its constituents, though, citizens (among them the writers of these chapters) may disagree and may have differing ideas about what should be done. The symptoms of the stresses and strains of urbanization on local governments, visible everywhere, give evidence of the fundamental difficulties before us. How best to organize the areas in which public services are performed, how to insure that all interested citizens and groups have a voice in decisions affecting their lives, and how to get the money to pay for the necessary services are basic problems. Is consolidation the answer? One writer says: "Wholesale assumption by the Federal Government of functions of metropolitan areas is now recommended by few, if any, thoughtful people, but it will surely come to pass if the only alternative is chaos, disintegration, and bickering at the local level."

CLARENCE J. HEIN

PROBLEMS OF
LOCAL GOVERNMENT

THE symptoms of the stresses and strains of urbanization on local governments, visible everywhere, give evidence of fundamental difficulties before us. A basic one is that of fitting an activity into the area in which it can best be carried out. It is like trying to work several jigsaw puzzles one on top of another. Each activity of local government usually has a different geographic area in which it can best be carried out.

For example, the locality that can best be protected by a fire department and its crews and equipment is not the same as the territory that can best be serviced by a sewage system, and it would be best to have a third set of boundaries in which to administer a building code.

Adjustments can be made so as to fit the activities together. Another fire station can be built. More equipment can be bought in order to service the entire community, or additional sewers and treatment plants can be built to cover the area serviced by the fire department. But it may be better from the standpoint of diseconomies of scale to operate the two systems independently of each other.

Local governments have a special difficulty with this problem, because each government has jurisdiction over a definite territory and normally can-

not undertake any activities outside its boundaries. Often the limits do not have much relationship to the best areas in which to undertake the activities of local government.

It is not a matter of changing the boundaries of the local unit to conform with the area in which an activity can best be undertaken. Because there are many activities and the best boundaries for one are not necessarily identical with the best territory for any of the others, no exclusive boundary can be set that would be best for all activities.

The problem is complicated in many localities because of the great number of small units of government. Some of them seem more concerned with maintaining their independent status, and therefore their boundaries, than with providing a better area for the activities they undertake. Special groups may play one unit of government off

249

against another. Almost every urbanized area, for example, has experienced attempts to get a sizable acreage annexed by a small unit of government with less stringent planning and zoning laws than those of adjacent townships or cities.

Eliminating some of the small units would undoubtedly make the problem easier to deal with. But it would remain, and it exists in localities with only a few units of local government.

A SECOND basic problem is that the existing governmental organization does not provide a means by which the issues resulting from urbanization can be identified and understood, the different possible courses of action can be discussed by all the people affected by the issue, and decisions can be made by a majority.

Again, this is not simply a matter of putting the entire area under a single unit of government. The problem exists even within a single city. It is partly a result of the fact that our systems of representation and our laws were designed to handle the conditions of an earlier era and have not been adjusted to meet the challenges of urbanization today.

In most communities, any one local government or social group or economic organization may act in such a way as to cause harmful effects for some individual. The person affected usually is not aware of the action until it is too late. He frequently has no way of collecting compensation for the damages done. Often the harmful effects are due to a number of different actions, and it is impossible to identify any individual as the one at fault. This does not help the person who has suffered inconvenience or loss.

A familiar example is the costliness and inconvenience of urban sprawl. Many are involved—developers, builders, homeowners, speculators, local officials, and farmers. Because of uncoordinated development in a period, their actions may cause many problems for the future residents. Poor

drainage floods basements and farmland, overloaded water and sewage systems threaten health, inadequate roads cause unnecessary wear on vehicles and delays in transportation, and schools are overcrowded.

Many people have been blamed for such a situation. But the underlying problem is that the existing governmental organization is not set up to make areawide decisions about dealing with the harmful effects of urban expansion.

A THIRD basic problem is that our local governments do not yet have enough funds to do a decent job of all the things that people expect them to do. In part this is a natural outgrowth of the shift in our economy toward more service occupations and businesses. As consumers, we require more services and we spend an increasing portion of our income on them. Many of these services are of a kind that government is expected to supply.

Elementary and secondary education is the service that most frequently receives notice because it is the largest single item in most local government budgets, but many other services are also being increased and are equally costly. Protective services such as fire and police take an increasing amount of funds as urbanization increases. The trend toward more professional fulltime departments and toward shorter hours of work causes higher service costs. Other protective services, such as those done by the health department to insure pure water and food and the control of air pollution, are increasing also. Trained technicians are needed for them, and the services are costly.

Services needed from local government take a larger proportion of the community's income than formerly. The combination of the shift toward more service activities in the economy and toward putting more of these activities in the public sector requires larger expenditures by local units.

These basic problems—how best to organize the areas in which public services are performed, how to provide each interested party with a voice in critical decisions affecting his life, and how to get the money to pay for the necessary governmental services—are interrelated in most communities.

THE PRESSURE of urbanization has brought about many an attempt to change the organization and powers of local government to deal more effectively with the three problems.

Seven of the more important methods I explore briefly; more details about some are given in other chapters.

The earliest tool of governments to cope with the emergence of urban centers in rural areas was incorporation of a city.

Incorporation separated people who wanted urban services from those who did not, and rural taxpayers felt that they did not contribute directly to the streets and sidewalks and water systems of the city. But as the effects of urbanization have become more widespread, incorporation of new urban areas to separate people from their neighbors has been questioned as a means of dealing with the problems of urbanization. Some States now restrict the incorporation of small municipalities in the rural-urban fringes of larger metropolitan areas.

Incorporated places traditionally have been granted more authority and can undertake more activities than can the rural unincorporated localities. Many of the problems associated with urbanization can be dealt with by existing units of government, rural and urban, only if they receive additional powers.

When the residents of an area adjoining a municipality have wanted to get urban services, they have usually asked the municipality to annex their property. Sometimes their request has been granted. Frequently the city residents felt that the costs of providing the services would be greater than the amount paid in taxes by the area that wished to be annexed, and the annexation would increase the taxes of the

residents of the older parts of the city.

This is in part an example of the basic problem I mentioned of how best to organize the areas in which governmental services are performed, and the allied question of who should pay the costs caused by increasing the area in which activities are undertaken.

In practice, many cities have annexed where the immediate revenues were greater than the immediate costs. The fringes that were rejected for annexation were left without services or were forced to incorporate separately and provide their own services, frequently at high costs and with less satisfactory services, because the incorporated area was too small to be economically efficient.

Thus our traditional devices for organizing local government to provide urban services, incorporation and annexation, have in practice often failed to solve satisfactorily the problems accompanying urbanization. Nevertheless annexation has been one useful device under certain circumstances.

Frequently, when the need for a particular service was acute, communities resorted to what might be called a limited kind of municipality, the special district or authority. Sometimes the district has been set under the jurisdiction of an existing unit of government—for example, a drainage district governed by the county board but covering only one small area.

At other times the district has been made an independent unit of government, as in the case of a water and sewer district governed by a commission elected directly by the residents of the district. As additional services are required, more and more special districts may be set up, with differing boundaries and governing bodies.

The result often is too many units of government for the citizen to keep an eye on and a lack of coordination between the various local government services in the community. Many experts regard the growth of one-function independent special districts and authorities as the most undesirable feature of the current development of local government agencies.

These single-function units to some extent provide a solution for our first basic problem—they do sometimes fit the governmental service into the area in which it can most economically be provided.

Serious questions have been raised, however, about the disadvantages as compared with the benefits of the way in which many special districts are operated, so there is doubt that they solve even this problem. There is no question but that special districts complicate rather than solve the underlying problems of an adequate decisionmaking framework for local governments and of supplying adequate funds.

Theoretically, a multifunctional special district could be set up which would provide some coordination of several functions. It would be similar to a large incorporated city, but would undertake far fewer activities. Also, it would have the same disadvantages as other special districts and cities. No multifunctional special districts have been put into successful operation thus far. The municipality of Metropolitan Seattle is a special district for sewage disposal and control of water pollution, which some authorities consider to be different functions.

A THIRD WAY of changing local government to deal with urbanization is the consolidation of local units. It can take the form of uniting similar units, such as school districts, or different entities, such as a city and a county.

Consolidation has occurred in many places, but it is difficult to accomplish because of local loyalties to existing units of government.

A fourth way is by internal reorganization of the local unit. Examples are the introduction of the city manager system or the elected county executive system of government. These are usually accompanied by other internal changes, such as setting up a merit system for local government personnel

and a centralized purchasing system.

Many of these internal changes make local government more efficient, more effective, and sometimes more responsive to its citizens. They may also make it easier to see the basic problems and to take action to deal with them. Of themselves, however, these internal changes do not solve the underlying problems, although they help as much as anything else now being tried.

A fifth method is to shift an activity from one local government to another. For example, the building and maintenance of roads may be done by the county instead of the township. Or the job may be shifted away from local government entirely, and the major roads may be provided by the State.

In general, shifting responsibility to the State may provide a partial solution for the underlying financial problem and also make possible more efficient areas in which to provide the service. But many people have serious doubts about whether this kind of change provides an adequate opportunity for interested local citizens to participate in making decisions on such matters as the location and construction of a new freeway.

A sixth way is cooperation among existing local units of government. An example is a regional council or coordinating committee, composed of representatives of the local governments. Unlike the previous changes, cooperation is voluntary and continues only as long as the participating units are willing. One unwilling unit thus can prevent any fully coordinated action. On the other hand, any action undertaken will be likely to have the full support of most participating units.

Many European cities are equipped to deal with the problems of urbanization in a seventh way. Basically, these cities have more money and more powers over the way in which private property may be used than do cities in the United States. For example, many European cities are permitted to buy and own comparatively large amounts of real estate. They can buy up the rural land surrounding the city and can impose conditions on how the land shall be used before they sell it to a developer. In this way, they can prevent many problems, such as those that arise in the rural-urban fringes around cities in the United States.

At the same time, this governmental control tends to restrict the choices of the individual citizen, who might prefer single-family detached houses instead of row houses and apartment buildings, which the city officials may regard as more efficient and economical.

In addition, not much is known about the effects of this kind of control on the economic development of an urban area, especially where entry into industrial and commercial activity may be limited by the controls.

Many Americans still feel that the advantages of a free market economy offset the diseconomies and disadvantages that are noticeable in our rural-urban fringes. But as urbanization continues, controls over real estate are being extended in the Nation.

THESE SEVEN examples indicate that many remedies have been used. The dislocations caused by urbanization are still evident, however, even in places where one or more of these governmental reorganizations have been put into effect. The basic problems remain and may be getting worse—an indication that changes in local government alone may not deal with the underlying difficulties.

At the same time, reorganization of local government may be combined with other actions to make headway against the basic problems.

Because some of them have statewide and nationwide aspects, the States and the National Government have a significant role in dealing with the impact of urbanization. For example, the State and local revenue structures are so interrelated that no solution to the underlying fiscal problem is likely without State action.

Other adjustments may also be necessary. The pressures of urbanization on government stem from basic social and economic changes. The flow of population from rural to urban areas and from central cities to the rural-urban fringes is a response to the forces and in turn creates further changes. The migration of industry from central cities to suburban areas is another example of the response of our economy to urbanization.

These dynamic changes cause stresses and strains in our social, economic, and governmental institutions. Traditional economic and social controls tend to become less effective in preventing undesirable actions. As private controls become less effective, it becomes necessary to introduce governmental restraints.

For example, as the undesirable results of the early postwar mass subdivision of land became apparent, the movement for more stringent land use controls gained momentum. Now most local governments no longer permit the building of blocks and blocks of identical houses on 40-foot lots.

Governmental action to deal with undesirable effects of urbanization will increase as long as problems continue to pile up. Yet governmental action alone probably will not produce the desired results. Changes in social and economic institutions will be needed to supplement changes in governmental organization and functions.

But first the people of an area must decide what it is they want the area to become. Unless decisions of this kind can be made, urbanization will continue to produce undesirable results. All levels of government, together with many economic interests and social groups, will need to take part in this decisionmaking process.

CLARENCE J. HEIN *is doing research on rural government in the Agricultural Finance Branch, Economic Research Service. He has taught at West Virginia University and at the University of Kansas, where he also served as assistant director of the Governmental Research Center. Dr. Hein holds degrees from the University of Minnesota.*

DANIEL R. GRANT

THE CONSOLIDATION OF
LOCAL GOVERNMENTS

FOR much of the 20th century, students of local government have been writing about the "chaotic jumble" of counties, townships, towns, cities, school districts, and other special districts, with their inadequate tax bases, arbitrary boundary lines, overlapping jurisdictions, and conflicting responsibilities. Many writings and endless speeches have bemoaned that our local governments are too many and too small to cope with the demands that urban, industrialized, modern America places on them.

One of the time-honored recommendations to offer some relief for the pressures on local government has been large-scale consolidation of governmental units. Yet the trends in the total number of units of local government in the United States reveal that consolidation (except of school districts) is making almost no headway and actually is operating in reverse in special districts and municipalities.

The census of governments in 1962 reported 3,043 counties, 17,997 municipalities, 17,144 townships and towns, 34,678 school districts, and 18,323 special districts, a total of 91,236 units of local government. The number of local governments in 1942 was 155,116, but the difference between the 1962 and 1942 totals is more than accounted for by the consolidation of school districts.

The number of municipalities increased by more than 1,750 during that time, and the number of special district governments swelled by more than 10 thousand.

The case against so many units of government and for consolidations is simple.

It is that the political map does not reflect modern economic, technological, and social realities and that the units are far too small to finance and administer effective programs.

There was an excuse for such a structure in rural, 19th-century America: Trade was local. Wealth was mainly in real estate or other types of tangible property. Horse-and-buggy transportation dictated the distance from the county seat to the county boundary line. Functions were few and simple enough for laymen to discharge.

254

But these conditions have changed. Trade is regional and interstate. Wealth is in far less visible things, such as corporate securities. Taxpaying ability ignores local boundary lines. The population is highly mobile. The functions of local government are multiple and complex.

Not only have political scientists argued the cause of consolidating local governments. With few exceptions, specialists in the fields of governmental service—health, welfare, education, highways, water supply, sewage disposal, traffic engineering, mass transportation, and others—call for much larger areas of jurisdiction as a requirement for meeting a minimum standard of performance and economy in their particular function.

Many health authorities, for example, estimate a minimum population requirement of 50 thousand to sustain an adequate public health program. Only 310 municipalities and fewer than 600 of the counties were of sufficient size in 1960 to operate adequate public health programs, according to that standard.

Similarly, authorities in school administration and tax administration have cited the inadequacies of small units of government. Even in judicial administration, which some may consider to be less affected by economic and social change, authorities have been urging that the elected township justices of the peace be supplanted by trial justices for the whole county.

The case against the present number and size of units of local government in the United States does not go unchallenged, of course.

Some persons argue that small units permit citizens to have a high degree of personal knowledge of public officials and personal watchfulness over their actions. An extension of this argument is that larger units of government lead to impersonal government—to large and irresponsible administrative bureaucracies in hierarchical form.

Yet, if strictly impartial enforcement of the law is what is wanted (a government of laws and not of men), rather than ties of friendship, personal favoritism, and bias, the development of professionalism and an impersonal attitude among public servants becomes essential. Professionalism, in turn, is not encouraged by small-scale operations or by bondage to the courthouse gang.

Rational argument for consolidating local governments into units of adequate size is one thing. The record of the actual consolidations is something quite different.

Despite all the arguments for merging counties that fall below minimum standards of population, area, and tax resource, only two instances of county consolidation are recorded in recent history. James County, Tenn., voted in 1919 to join with neighboring Hamilton County (Chattanooga). Campbell and Milton Counties in Georgia were consolidated with Fulton County (Atlanta) in 1932. Even these two were somewhat exceptional in that they were in metropolitan areas and did not illustrate the potentialities of consolidation for rural administration.

FAILURE of the county consolidation movement, if it may in fact be called a movement, is a result of many factors, but it may be attributed primarily to intense local loyalties and a variety of vested interests in the status quo.

County residents, especially in the Southern States, have strong attachments to their county name, which has come to be as much a part of the family tree as the names of ancestors who lived in the same region. County officeholders have been opposed fairly consistently to consolidation and the probable loss of jobs that would result. County-seat merchants and businessmen fight to preserve their county-seat status and the trade that it brings. Newspapers are hardly enthusiastic at the prospect of losing lucrative county printing. And frequently there is the opposition of richer counties that fear that consolidation with poorer counties would increase their tax burden to help raise the service standards in the other counties.

In short, the forces against county mergers have been more than a match for the rationally strong but politically weak arguments for larger units of local government.

The record of township consolidations has been no more fruitful than in the case of counties, but in many States the townships seem to be on the way out, either through the informal process of withering away or by the more formal process of deorganization, as provided by State legislation.

Some States provide by general law for deorganization of particular townships that fall below a minimum total assessed valuation of property or have a high record of tax delinquency. Their functions are turned over to county authorities in the event of a deorganization.

The Oklahoma Legislature virtually eliminated townships by indirection by withdrawing their right to levy taxes for township purposes. Iowa townships were excluded from the 1952 tabulations of the Bureau of the Census because county governments "have absorbed substantially all the former township functions."

Yet township officers in some States continue to be influential in State legislative maneuvering, and—especially in the case of urban townships in the fringe of metropolitan areas—the township remains firmly ensconced in the structure of local government.

THE PUSH for city-county consolidation in the United States is a much older movement and can claim a few more actual adoptions than the county consolidation movement.

With the exception of Virginia, where cities of 10 thousand or more are separated from the county, all cases of city-county consolidation have taken place in metropolitan areas and have been looked upon as one of several alternative approaches to metropolitan governmental problems.

City-county separation and city-county consolidation are similar in that both result in a single unit of government, which performs both city and county functions. The difference lies in the disposition made of the rural area surrounding the core city. In the case of separation, the rural area is not included as a part of the new city-county, and remains as a rump county or may be simply added to neighboring counties.

Four outstanding examples of city-county separation are Baltimore, separated from its county in 1851; San Francisco, in 1856; St. Louis, in 1875; and Denver, in 1903. Close to 30 Virginia cities are separated from their counties, and city officers carry out county functions.

City-county consolidation constitutes a slightly different method of accomplishing substantially the same result as city-county separation.

Under city-county consolidation, the city limits are extended to coincide with the county boundaries, and the two governments are consolidated, leaving no remnant county.

Philadelphia in 1854, New York in 1898, Honolulu in 1907, Baton Rouge in 1947, and Nashville in 1962 adopted forms of a consolidated city-county government in varying degrees.

Some of the earlier consolidations, as well as separations, were followed by long court battles over the legal status of the merged government, and the outcome was often disappointing to supporters of consolidation.

In almost all instances of city-county consolidation or separation, the urban population has expanded beyond the city-county's boundaries, and the result has been a more difficult problem of boundary alteration than under normal annexation procedures. In Virginia, however, the city-county separation procedure has been coupled with a plan for court-approved extension of the city limits as the population spreads outside the city.

The Nashville plan of city-county consolidation, adopted by city and county voters in 1962, is of interest be-

cause of its unique approach to governing the suburban and rural fringe areas of the county. While creating a single metropolitan government with a single mayor and council on a countywide basis, the plan established an expandable urban services district, designed to grow with the urbanized area. Architects of the plan contend that it incorporates the benefits of unified area-wide government without the inflexibilities of previous city-county consolidations relating to the problem of governing both the developing suburban fringe and the more stable rural areas. All persons are in the general services district and receive and pay for all areawide services of the metropolitan government. The Nashville plan may offer hope to many medium and small metropolitan areas that are entirely within single counties.

Two city-county mergers in the Norfolk-Portsmouth area in Virginia provide somewhat unusual examples of the reunion of a county with a city that had previously separated from it under the Virginia separation system. Princess Anne County in January 1962 voted to become a part of the city of Virginia Beach. In February of the same year, Norfolk County voted to merge with the city of South Norfolk. The two mergers had the effect of blocking any further annexation by the city of Norfolk by eliminating all unincorporated areas contiguous to Norfolk. The combined area of Norfolk County and the city of South Norfolk totals 344 square miles and is known as Chesapeake.

THE CONSOLIDATION of one or more cities with another city is probably not quite so rare as county consolidation or city-county consolidation, but this type of merger is insignificant in the total picture of 18 thousand municipalities. Every year or so, one may read of the merger of municipalities, but they are usually small, and the situation is sufficiently unique that it bears little relevance to any coordinated movement for city consolidation.

For example, two small towns in Virginia, Tazewell and North Tazewell, voted in June 1962 to merge into a single municipality. The merger was an outgrowth of the need for a sewage treatment plant to prevent pollution of the Clinch River.

Four cities in Oregon—North Bend, Coos Bay, Empire, and Eastside—failed in 1962 to approve a merger proposal because 1 of the 4 (North Bend) voted against the plan by a margin of 16 votes. The total vote in all 4 was 5,141 in favor and 2,116 against.

Two cities in Michigan, Muskegon (46,485) and Muskegon Heights (19,552), voted on a merger proposal in late 1961, but it received a favorable vote only in the larger city and was rejected by the smaller city, a fairly common pattern for such referendums.

ONE BRIGHT SPOT in the consolidation movement, in terms of the overall picture, is the long-term success of the movement to combine school districts.

The clearest measure of the results of the movement is in the steady decline in the number of school districts, from more than 127 thousand in 1932 to approximately 110 thousand in 1942, about 69 thousand in 1952, and fewer than 35 thousand in 1962.

The reduction in number of school districts has been accompanied by an even more striking reduction in the number of one-room schools—from 143 thousand such schools in 1932 to fewer than 20 thousand in 1961.

What explains the success of the movement for the consolidation of school districts?

The answer is not in any single factor but in a combination of several supporting forces and circumstances.

At the outset, the aims and arguments for consolidation were fairly clear and simple: Securing a better school plant, better teachers, and a better course of study. The method was simply to carry the pupil to a more efficient school rather than trying to carry the school to the pupil. The inability of the small school district to provide adequate library facilities, attract well-trained teachers, offer special instruction, or even to support a high school was documented time after time by well-publicized studies.

Research and rational arguments have been only one part of the movement, however. Reorganizations of school districts usually have taken place only after well-organized, statewide publicity campaigns have combined the efforts of professional educators and State departments of education, working through facilitating legislation and varieties of financial inducements. It has been common practice to offer State aid for transportation, State funds to local schools that maintain a minimum school program, assistance for new buildings, and, not infrequently, State-aid formulas for penalizing small school districts that do not consolidate.

Consolidation has not come easily. It is the reflection of a long, hard struggle by sincere, dedicated persons who appreciated its importance. Their efforts were furthered by such external factors as the improvement of roads and buses so that schoolchildren can be transported more easily.

Although in some instances, such as in Florida and West Virginia, consolidation was mandatory under State legislation that set up county units for school responsibility, more voluntary arrangements have been used in most States. A commoner practice has been to grant county boards of education or special committees the authority to redistrict, with or without a vote of the people.

WHY HAS THERE been no corresponding record of steady reduction in the number of governmental units for counties, cities, special districts, and townships? Several factors are involved in any attempt to explain this failure.

The proponents of consolidation of school districts may have been better organized and more numerous than supporters of other governmental consolidations. State departments of education and teachers colleges provided important rallying points and staying power for advocates of consolidation.

Important financial incentives frequently have been available to encourage consolidations of schools, but seldom have they been available for other consolidations.

It is possible that the school reform movement has siphoned off much of the potential support for local government reform generally. The strong tradition of separating school government from the rest of government has made it difficult to tie together various groups interested in improving local government. Thus school reformers, public health reformers, police reformers, parks reformers, and county or city reformers (to name a few) have tended to go their separate ways. School reformers have had sufficient numbers, ability, and influence to go it alone, but many others have not.

Much of the pressure for county consolidation seems to have relaxed after the Federal health and welfare programs were expanded in the thirties. An exception to this generalization may be the problem of fractionalized governmental units in the expanding metropolitan areas, where the heat is still on, and seems to be rising in intensity. Whether the answer to metropolitan problems will come through consolidations at the local level, or through State and Federal intervention to deal with the more pressing metropolitan problems is a question that was in the balance in 1963.

The prospects for future consolidations continue to look good for school districts and bleak for all other units of local government. Unless State governments and the Federal Government, through its many programs that affect local units of government, take action to promote consolidations in much the same way as consolidations of school districts have been promoted, future consolidations will be minimal.

What will be the result of failure to reduce the number of local units of government?

If we concede that many of them are too small to perform reasonably competently many of the basic, modern functions and consolidations are not forthcoming; an alternative is to move the functions to a higher level of government that will meet such demands as society places upon it.

DANIEL R. GRANT *is serving as professor of political science in Vanderbilt University, Nashville, Tenn. He was visiting professor of municipal government and planning at Thammasat University, Bangkok, Thailand, in 1958–1959. He served as consultant in the preparation of the Plan of Metropolitan Government for Nashville and Davidson County, and is consultant for the United States Advisory Commission on Intergovernmental Relations.*

Urban and Rural Population: 1790 to 1960

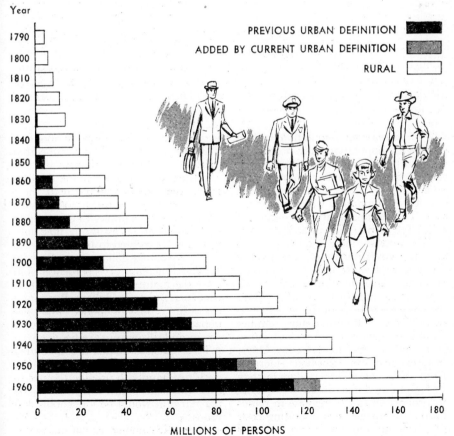

MILLIONS OF PERSONS

HARVEY SHAPIRO

THE FINANCES
OF LOCAL GOVERNMENTS

SERIOUS financial problems have been created for the local governments of the rapidly growing areas around cities. The problems stem from the need of the burgeoning communities to expand their existing services to accommodate the new residents. The increase in governmental activities in turn probably will require an expansion in the number of employees and facilities—in schools, for example.

The increase in population and in density of population may necessitate also an upgrading of existing governmental functions and the provision of some services that were not needed when the community was sparsely settled. This expansion and improvement will have to be made in a short time.

To meet these increased responsibilities, the governments of the growing communities must obtain additional revenues. An indication of how much is given in a study by the Southern California Research Council, which estimated that 730 thousand more families would be living in Los Angeles County in 1970 than were there in 1957. Operating expenses were expected to increase from about 900 million dollars in 1957 to 1.3 billion dollars in 1970—roughly in proportion to the increase in population. The per capita operating costs of education and police and fire serv-

260

ices were expected to rise by about 15 percent. These estimates assume that existing costs will not change.

Estimates also were made of how much these costs would rise if there were increases in salary of varying amounts. For example, the per capita cost of education, assuming no salary increase, is expected to be 70 dollars in 1970, against 62 dollars in 1956–1957. A salary increase of 1 percent would raise the figure to 86 dollars; a 2-percent increase, to 94 dollars. Per capita operating costs of police and fire departments were expected to increase by 40 and 48 percent, respectively.

The council estimated that an outlay of 13,290 dollars would be needed for each new family to provide the necessary physical plant. More than 90 percent of it would be for schools and roads.

The choice among the various methods of raising the revenues is of concern to present and future residents of growing communities: How are the rising costs (taxes) to be distributed among the taxpayers at the present time and to what extent are the costs to be shared with future residents, who will benefit also? The total cost of government also will be affected.

If the additional sums are not raised, such undesirable conditions as overcrowded schools, poor instruction, and crowded roads will worsen.

THE PROBLEM of obtaining adequate revenues comes first.

"Adequate revenues" means different things to different persons, but broadly defined it is a sum large enough to enable the local unit to provide an adequate level of services. It is rarely possible, however, to spend a sum on any particular function that would be large enough to satisfy everyone. A government that is inclined to do so would have to neglect other responsibilities or raise additional revenues.

Thus, to quote a study by C. E. Ridley and H. A. Simon for the International City Managers' Association:

"Adequacy is entirely a relative matter: There is no such thing as an adequate administrative service, for higher levels of service can always be provided if more funds are available. Likewise, there is no such thing as inadequate service, for inadequacy, too, is entirely relative to the standard the community wants and is willing to pay for."

The term "adequate revenues," therefore, I define as a sum that is large enough at least to maintain current service levels as the community's population expands.

The limitations imposed on local powers to raise revenue are likely to be an obstacle. It arises partly out of the enabling legislation that pertains to local governments, which are a creation of the State government. Whatever powers they possess—including their ability to raise revenues—derive

from the States. Taxing powers of local governments generally have been confined to levies on property. This one tax in 1960 provided 15.8 billion dollars, or about 87 percent of local tax collections.

The starting point in an inquiry into the adequacy of local revenues therefore is to examine the productivity of the property tax. Some insight into this problem can be gained by reviewing local governmental finances in aggregate since 1902. This 60-year interval was one of rapid growth of population and a period of considerable urbanization in the United States.

The total local government general revenue in 1902 equaled 854 million dollars. About 624 million dollars—or 73 percent of the total—were supplied by property taxes. Both total general revenues and property tax collections exhibited an uptrend between 1902 and 1962. The ratio of property tax revenues to total local general revenues, however, declined during the period. The proportion fell to 60 percent in 1940, declined farther by 1950 to 50 percent, and in 1961 stood at 49 percent.

Thus, on a nationwide basis, property tax revenues have not increased so rapidly as total local revenues. If additional sources of revenue, notably State funds, had not been made available during this period, the local units would have been confronted with the necessity of choosing from among several courses of action: Services would have been curtailed, property taxes would have been increased substantially, or some combination of both measures would have been needed. The failure of local property tax revenues to rise as rapidly as total local general revenues suggests that this source of revenue generally could not keep up with the growing local government revenue requirements during the 60 years.

The governmental structure in the standard metropolitan statistical areas (SMSA)—counties that include a city or twin cities of at least 50 thousand inhabitants—also bears importantly on whether revenues from property taxes will be adequate in many communities.

The 1957 Census of Governments found 15,658 governments in 174 metropolitan areas, or about 90 per metropolitan area. The division of the SMSA into numerous independent governments also results in a division of total taxable resources and a distribution of these resources among the various units. Studies in different metropolitan areas have demonstrated that the distribution of taxable property values varied widely among the different governments.

A problem arises because the service needs of any community are not determined necessarily by its wealth, while the ability of the local government to finance these needs is directly related to the opulence of its citizens. A poorer community may actually require a higher level of services than a richer one. Its buildings may be older and rundown and cannot be maintained; they may therefore be a fire hazard. The poorer town then actually would require better fire protection.

Thus the adequacy or inadequacy of the property tax in any unit will depend on several variables, including taxable property values, the number of residents, and the amount of government services they expect.

Another factor is the number of people to be serviced by any one government. Within the SMSA's, populations vary greatly in size. Some central cities have more than a million people. Some municipalities have fewer than a thousand inhabitants. The 1957 Census of Governments indicated that 36 percent of the municipalities had fewer than a thousand inhabitants; 82 percent had fewer than 10 thousand. Fewer than 7 percent had more than 50 thousand.

A study by Prof. Henry Schmandt, of the University of Wisconsin-Milwaukee, provides information about developments in the rural-urban fringe.

In the fifties, 1,076 new municipalities were created in the United States; slightly more than half were within SMSA's. The new cities and villages generally had relatively few inhabitants; about 80 percent had fewer than 5 thousand, and about half had fewer than 1 thousand residents. Only 4 percent had populations exceeding 25 thousand.

Two facts thus are evident: There are many small governments beyond the borders of the central city but within the boundaries of the metropolitan county; the newly created governments also are generally small.

It is hard to say anything definite about the relationships between size of population and per capita cost of government, because there is no generally accepted measure of service levels. For example, if City A (which has a smaller population) spends more per capita for any one service than City B, the difference may be attributable to economies of scale. But it may indicate also that City A is purchasing a higher quality of service.

Certain generalizations can be made nevertheless. The administration of a government, no matter how small, involves certain overhead costs, which are relatively fixed. The smaller the number of people sharing the expense therefor, the greater will be the per capita cost.

The quality of service demanded is an important determinant of the cost of government and the adequacy of existing revenues. Profs. Walter Isard and Robert E. Coughlin, in a study conducted at the Section of Urban and Regional Studies of the Massachusetts Institute of Technology, stated that, "variations in municipal costs arise . . . to a lesser extent from differences in density and the pattern of development" than they do from "differences in the level of municipal services provided."

In the small governments, population is related to the costs of improving local services. A large enough population will enable the government to operate on a level that will permit a separation of functions.

The benefits deriving from specialization were noted almost 200 years ago, when Adam Smith, the Scottish economist who wrote *Wealth of Nations*, said, "The greatest improvement in the productive powers of labour, and the greater part of the skill, dexterity and judgment with which it is anywhere directed, or applied, seem to have been the effects of the division of labour."

The problem of determining the minimum size of population for particular services has never been resolved precisely, partly because service needs of separate communities differ because of such factors as weather and geography.

Some evidence, however, is available regarding education, which must be provided everywhere. Expenditures for schools are the single largest item in budgets of local governments. The Committee for Economic Development expressed doubt as to whether a unified school system with fewer than 2 thousand students could provide a complete program, and estimated that advantages would continue to accrue until the school had 25 thousand pupils.

The 1957 Census of Governments indicated that about 43 percent of the public school systems in metropolitan areas had fewer than 300 pupils and that 66 percent had fewer than 2 thousand. Those figures and the demands of parents for improved schools give an indication as to why costs of government are so high and why the local sources of revenue are strained severely in many suburbs.

The existence of numerous local units in an SMSA may also dampen the productivity of the tax structure in the entire area. Many units, recognizing the need for additional revenues, may attempt to cope with this problem by persuading industry to relocate and settle in their area, the object being an increase in the units' tax base, coupled with the hope that expenditures will not grow so fast.

There is little evidence that taxes affect interstate industrial location. However, as Prof. John F. Due, of the University of Illinois, has indicated, within a general region taxes can have a deciding role "in the selection of the precise site in a metropolitan area (property taxes being the ones of chief concern)."

Thus the existence of many units may hold tax rates and collections below levels that might have otherwise been obtained if only one unit levied taxes for the entire SMSA. In short, this is one instance where the whole (the tax revenues that could be collected by a unified taxing area) may possibly be greater than the sum of its individual parts.

As a large portion of local expenditure in growing communities will be devoted to capital outlays, attention should be directed toward the financing of the outlays.

Unlike current operating expenditures, which usually are financed on a pay-as-you-go basis, a large part of the capital outlay is financed by borrowing. Local governments borrowed 39 billion dollars of the 62 billion dollars devoted to capital outlay in 1952–1960.

Borrowing these funds, rather than obtaining them from current taxes, is a way to shift part of the costs of the new facilities to future residents. This shifting of costs forward in time commonly is justified on the grounds that the future residents should be called upon to pay part of the costs because they will share in the benefits arising out of the new facilities and because the additional expenditures may have been made in anticipation of the arrival of new residents.

Local governments that have to borrow large sums very likely are subject to State-imposed limitations on borrowing.

The restrictions vary from State to State, but generally appear in one of three forms: A limit on indebtedness expressed as a percentage of the local government's property tax base (its assessed valuation); a limit on the rates that can be imposed specifically for debt service or for various purposes, including debt service; or the requirement of a local referendum (which may call for some kind of special majority) to authorize the issuance of bonds.

The restrictions tend to be especially burdensome to rapidly growing communities. Large sums may be needed almost immediately, but the growth in taxable property values takes place more slowly. Part of the future rise in property values can be attributed to the new capital facilities.

The Advisory Commission on Intergovernmental Relations, an advisory body created by the 86th Congress, has commented on the difficulty in justifying the restrictions, which were imposed primarily to prevent abuses in local borrowing. The Commission pointed out that the restrictions pertain to present or past conditions, rather than those of the future, and that local economic capacity to service and repay the debt is measured in reference to only one revenue source, the property tax, which has been declining in importance as a source of local revenue this past half century.

THE RESTRICTIONS have encouraged a search for loopholes. Two methods have been used.

First, the restrictions apply only to the debt backed by the full faith and credit of local governments and not to nonguaranteed local debt, such as revenue bonds. The funds to service and repay revenue bonds must come from earnings of the particular project financed by these bonds, in contrast to the servicing of guaranteed debt from general revenues. For example, revenue bonds may be issued to finance the building of a toll road, and the liquidation of the bonds depends on the tolls collected. The use of nonguaranteed debt has been increasing, in absolute amount issued as well as a proportion of new State and local security offerings. The 206 million dollars of revenue bonds in 1946 constituted 17.1

percent of total issues; in 1955, the 1,710 million dollars issued was 29 percent of total new issues.

The use of revenue bonds instead of full faith and credit debt tends to increase the costs of borrowing. It has been estimated that the interest costs of revenue bonds issued to finance water and sewer systems have been about 0.5–0.6 percent greater than the rate of interest charged on general obligation bonds.

In terms of total cost, an increase in the rate of interest paid by a 30-year serial bond from 3 to 3.5 percent would increase total interest costs by 19 percent.

Another factor that affects the rate of interest and the total interest cost is the length of maturity of an issue. The more distant the date of repayment, the greater is the charge. Revenue bonds generally have longer maturity periods than do most general-obligation bonds. The increasing use of this form of debt therefore will result in greater costs than would have arisen from full faith and credit bonds.

Secondly, the financial restraints placed on local finance provide an incentive for the proliferation of special districts.

The Advisory Commission on Intergovernmental Relations, in studying this tendency to create additional units of government to circumvent legal restrictions on local debt, concluded that, "The dispersion of local government responsibility among multiple layers of specialized units is often a handicap not only to consistent planning and administration, but also to citizen understanding and control of local government as a whole."

Needless to say, poor planning or lack of planning will result in raising the costs and increasing the financial problems of the units concerned.

We should be aware also of the general uptrend in the interest costs of full faith and credit bonds. Because the income an investor receives from those securities is exempt from Federal income taxes, the interest charge on them has been lower than on comparable privately issued debt. Since the end of the Second World War, interest rates on tax-exempt securities have increased faster than almost any other comparable interest rate. The differential in costs between tax-exempt and non-tax-exempt securities has narrowed in this period.

Roland I. Robinson, in a study published by the National Bureau of Economic Research, concluded that the increased costs of State and local borrowing result from the greatly increased volume of offerings, plus the need to attract new investors to whom the tax exemption is less important.

Another detail brought out in the study was that the spread in interest rates between high-quality State and local securities and those of intermediate quality continued to be about as wide in 1956 as in 1946. On the other hand, the differential between different grades of corporate securities narrowed over the same period.

The fact that the interest rate gap between different grades of Government securities did not narrow led Professor Robinson to conclude: "The financial problems of State and local government in the future may be even more acute than some forecasters have suggested since an increased volume of borrowing inevitably means some reduction in the quality of the securities issued. On this basis it may be expected that there will be increasing problems in financing State and local government capital improvements."

All these circumstances point to a need for considerable attention on the part of the various State governments to the problems of financing local capital improvements.

Existing State restrictions appear to be creating financial problems for local units, rather than preventing them, and are therefore in need of change. The States may ease the financial problems of growing communities through various programs, such as State loans to local units, State payment of local debt service, or perhaps increased use of grants-in-aid and shared taxes, which would reduce somewhat the need of local governments to resort to borrowing.

STATE GRANTS-IN-AID and shared taxes, an increasingly important source of local revenues, rose from about 6 percent of total local general revenue in 1902 to slightly more than 28 percent in 1957.

State aids usually are granted for a specific purpose, such as for support of a particular local function or to "equalize" expenditures or revenues between the poorer and more prosperous governments.

Shared taxes generally are State-collected levies, which in many instances are returned to the origin of collection. The specific amount to be returned usually is based on a predetermined portion of some State tax.

In general, it appears that shared taxes will not provide much help to the growing communities that have the most pressing financial needs. Shared taxes that are distributed on the basis of origin generally tend to favor the wealthier communities that may not need these funds. Distribution of State revenues on this basis may also encourage the wealthier residents in some sections of the community to create new municipalities to reduce their taxes. This course of action will add to the financial difficulties of the entire community.

Sharing taxes on the basis of population appears to offer greater promise of assistance to growing communities. This method, however, suffers from some serious administrative difficulties. One of them is the desirability of determining annually the population of all the units that are sharing these revenues to insure the growing communities an equally proportionate share of the funds from year to year. State grants-in-aid appear to be better designed to help growing communities than do shared taxes.

Prof. Alan H. Smith, of Marquette University, in a study of State-local financial relationships, found that more than 93 percent of State aid for specific functions was given for education, highways, and public welfare. Expenditures for the first two items will probably account for most of the capital outlay of a growing community.

A Bureau of the Census publication, *State Payments to Local Governments,* indicated: "Aid for the support of specific local functions is distributed with reference to some measure of local need or activity—for example, for education, school age population, enrollment or attendance or actual local expenditure; for highways and miles of road, number of vehicles or particular local requirements; for public welfare programs, actual or estimated local expenditure."

Growing communities can anticipate receiving additional sums under such programs. Grants-in-aid are especially helpful when wide variations exist in financial abilities of local governments, because many programs are given with the object of equalizing costs of providing certain services in the separate units. This distributional method may offset partly the encouragement given by many shared-tax programs to set up tax enclaves.

IN CONTRAST to the various programs that rely primarily on State funds, the States could also aid their local units by loosening some of the revenue-raising restrictions they placed on local governments.

Specifically, the States could permit local taxation of nonproperty sources. There has been some movement in that direction since 1930. Several States have granted additional taxing powers to their local units.

The degree of freedom they permit varies widely. At one extreme, only one local nonproperty tax (motor fuel) is used in Wyoming. Missouri permits local use of several nonproperty levies but restricts the use of the income tax to St. Louis. Pennsylvania allows its local governments to tax anything that is not taxed by the State

government. Eight different taxes, including one on personal property, are used to finance local activities.

In general, the most productive local nonproperty tax sources have been the levies on sales and income. On a nationwide basis, local sales and gross receipts taxes accounted for about 7 percent of total local tax revenue in 1961, and local income taxes produced about 1 percent.

Milton C. Taylor, of Michigan State University, has written, "For the particular local governments levying an income tax, this levy has become a principal source of revenue." The local income tax often has yielded greater sums than the property tax.

Twelve States in 1961 permitted the local use of the sales tax; 5, the income tax; 9, tobacco taxes; 1, liquor taxes; 8, motor fuel taxes; 11, admissions taxes; and 8, the local telephone service tax. Six States permitted municipalities and counties to operate liquor stores. Local governments in 23 States imposed telephone taxes.

Regarding the use of local nonproperty taxes in rapidly growing communities, I should stress that their ability to raise revenue may be dampened considerably under certain circumstances. For example, a growing residential suburb will obtain little, if any, revenue from a local sales tax. Similarly, a low-income community may not derive much benefit from a local income tax. In short, local nonproperty taxes do have considerable revenue-raising abilities, but their use is not a financial panacea.

The use of local nonproperty taxes presents several problems.

An important lesson can be learned from the experience California had with a local sales tax. California originally allowed its local units—including counties—to determine their own rates. The result was that the rates were not uniform across the State. Sales for delivery outside the taxing locality were exempted, and a use tax was levied on items purchased outside of the taxing localities by its

Professor Taylor suggested the use of the county as the administrative agent for local income taxes.

In an even more detailed report, the Advisory Commission on Intergovernmental Relations recommended a local supplement to a State tax in the States in which both levels of government use a similar tax. In States where the nonproperty tax is used exclusively by local units, the Commission suggested that the State act as the administrator or authorize local governments to join together and create an administrative agency. Another suggestion was that the States minimize such variety in local taxes as differing rates and bases.

THE DIFFICULTIES involved in financing the expanding demands of residents for local government services in the rapidly growing suburban fringe will continue to be a serious problem in coming years.

residents. The consequences were that the administrative difficulties were increased greatly. Retailers, if they had branches in different tax jurisdictions, had to file separate forms in each one and in the process compute the different tax rates. Furthermore, they had to determine the residence of their customer because of the exemption, and that complicated compliance and administration of the tax. Finally, the use-tax provisions were practically unenforceable.

A new tax law, which became effective in 1956, corrected the difficulties by standardizing the tax rates throughout California and inducing a more widespread use. The exemption to nonresidents was eliminated as sales were taxed at the place of the sale regardless of the point of delivery—with the single exception of out-of-State sales. If a city and the county within which it was located both employed a sales tax, the county tax could be paid with the credits from the city tax.

This experience indicates that the States should not give their local units complete freedom regarding use of nonproperty taxes. Collection and enforcement should be centralized as much as is possible for reasons of efficiency and administrative economy.

Communities no doubt will continue to devise new ways of coping with the problem. For example, wider use may be made of the method of financing such new capital facilities as roads and streets by adding the cost to the price a new resident pays for his house.

Alternatively, additional revenues might be raised through an increased use of fees and service charges.

Continuing financial pressures may well lead communities to give more serious consideration to the possibilities of governmental reorganization, with the aim of creating more efficient forms of government.

Perhaps, as a result of efforts directed toward the consideration of such alternatives, new organizational and financial arrangements will be devised to help local governments fulfill their responsibilities better.

HARVEY SHAPIRO *is an economist in the Tax and Rural Governments Section of the Department of Agriculture. He has given particular attention to problems of supplying and financing public services in rural areas. He received his doctorate in economics from the University of Wisconsin.*

BERNARD F. HILLENBRAND

HOW COUNTY GOVERNMENTS
ARE BEING MODERNIZED

AFTER nearly 300 years of service to rural America, the venerable county is also becoming the leading local government for our urban America. A few years ago, when predictions of the death of county government were in vogue, few would have dreamed that we would see American cities contract with counties to provide urban services within the city.

Those who maintained that county government was as obsolete as a buggy must be astounded now to see county water, sewage, and refuse systems; county industrial development units; countywide police and fire services; and even county renewal projects.

Mourners at the county graveside also decried the inability of existing local units to meet our urban needs. They demanded new units of metropolitan government. They could hardly envision that today the only metropolitan governments in existence are Dade County in Florida and Davidson County in Tennessee. Both are county units reorganized and revitalized.

These examples of resurgent county government have captured the popular fancy, but the real story of the revival goes deeper. Counties are taking on new functions one at a time in nearly every community in the United States. Counties are assuming responsibility for parking, traffic control, libraries, park and recreational facilities, airports, community colleges, mental health clinics, hospitals, urban transportation, and planning. Perhaps the key to our governmental future is the word *planning*—and increasingly Americans are turning to the county to plan the orderly development of their urban and rural communities.

Statistics on county growth are impressive. During 1952–1957, the latest years for which we have census figures, county expenditures increased 7.4 percent annually, capital outlay increased at the annual rate of 9.4 percent, wages and salaries went up 57 percent, and county debt rose from 2 billion dollars to 3.5 billion. For comparison, the population has been increasing at an annual rate of about 1.75 percent.

If we are to understand what has already happened and what is likely to happen to county government, we must understand the manner in which America is becoming urban. More than half of our 3,043 counties are declining in population; 1,960 counties lost population during 1950–1960. We quite properly are concerned with growth in the urban areas, but we must be equally concerned with the more difficult problems in the localities that are declining in population.

There are, for example (by one definition), some 2,700 nonurban counties.

Typically they have fewer than 50 thousand inhabitants, but 250 counties have fewer than 5 thousand residents. Yet the 2,700 nonurban counties are fractionalized governmentally into an average of 5 incorporated municipalities, more than 5 townships, 15 school districts, and 4 special-purpose districts.

Their citizens have serious problems of economic survival. They must find ways of preserving farm income, retaining nonfarm income, and attracting new economic growth. Education and the other governmental functions must be continued and financed, often on a shrinking tax base.

The trend there runs strongly in favor of having the county provide areawide services, such as rural libraries, health and welfare offices, police services, civil defense, and control of air and water pollution. School districts are consolidating to become coterminous with the county boundaries. Counties are establishing countywide tax assessment, tax collection, and data-processing services for all the governments within the county.

Great numbers of these nonurban counties have established county machinery for economic development with the help of the Area Redevelopment Administration and are formulating overall plans to effect total community development.

Sometimes a single county has proved inadequate, and the programs have become multicounty. For example, some 13 counties participate in an economic development plan in Georgia.

Even the traditional agricultural functions of counties are being adjusted to meet changing needs. Franklin County in Massachusetts, for example, has joined its sister counties of Hampshire and Hampden to form a regional extension program. The broader tricounty approach has opened the way to increased specialization to the benefit of all the farmers of the region.

To UNDERSTAND the impact on the counties that are gaining in population, we should consider the nature of the growth.

Nearly two-thirds (17.1 million of 26.4 million) of our increase between 1950 and 1960 has occurred in 200 metropolitan areas. The growth has been mostly in 300 urban counties and largely outside the central cities. Of the five American cities of more than a million, only one, Los Angeles, gained in population. The others—New York, Chicago, Philadelphia, and Boston—and most large cities lost population during the decade—some sharply.

Refining population shifts still more, we find that the rural migrants, the minority groups, the very old, and the very young have been concentrating in central cities. They require the greatest number of the most expensive governmental social services.

By the same token, the new factories, more expensive houses, and the other taxable wealth are moving with the more well-to-do to the suburbs. Thus, in the 300 urban counties, we are getting increasingly a sharp division between those who most need services and those who can best afford to pay for them. Both groups, however, are governed by their counties, and in 62 percent of the cases the entire city and suburban area is in a single county.

This economic factor is responsible for pressure from the central city for the county to share the costs of the services and facilities that benefit an entire community but in the past were financed solely by the city. The cost can be shared by dual cost-sharing, joint operation, and contractual operation or a combination of them. Since most counties have areawide jurisdiction, however, the commonest response is that the county assume full responsibility. Therefore we have countywide programs now in public health, welfare, community colleges, and other services and facilities.

Another factor accounts for county growth in urban areas: The proliferation of tiny units of government in nearly every community. It varies from place to place and will surely be affected by continued growth of the United States. At least five functions must be performed or carefully supervised on an areawide, countywide basis—urban transportation; water supply; waste disposal (sewage, refuse, and air pollution); planning; and civil defense. The trend has been toward a county or multicounty approach to these problems.

ALTHOUGH URBANIZATION has been a prime reason for the greater importance of county government, other factors have had a part.

Automation, data processing, and other technological advances commonly found in larger units of government have caused county growth. Increasing complexity of operations, demands for more efficient and abundant service, and specialization of American life also have tended to cause citizens to turn from smaller units to the larger county for service.

While factors outside the control of citizens or their county officials have been responsible for their new importance, counties offer several advantages in dealing with these responsibilities.

First is geography. More than 133 million Americans are governed by counties. (Most of those outside county jurisdiction are in big cities, like New York and Philadelphia, which have become coterminous with county boundaries and are really city-counties, but are usually omitted from statistical analysis of county government.) Even in places where regions spill across county lines, the county offers promise as a coordinating unit. The New York

metropolitan region is encompassed in 22 counties in three States. A countywide approach to regional problems is simpler than attempts to deal with the smaller units in a region.

Counties also offer a broad tax base, which takes on new importance with the shift to the suburbs of industry and other taxable economic activity. Attempts by the central city to tax this wealth by levying city income, payroll taxes, or sales taxes on suburbanites create resentments and upset governmental harmony.

Usually the county has taxing jurisdiction countywide, and the direct county approach to administering and financing areawide functions seems the fairest way to proceed. This and countywide property tax assessment and collection could produce uniform tax administration at less cost to taxpayers.

Counties have political accountability. They are the basic units of organization for our political parties. Every citizen of the county, whether he resides in a city, town, village, or unincorporated area, is served by his county, pays taxes to his county, and selects and controls his county officials.

All too often, residents of cities have thought of the county as the farmer's government. Because the city resident has an additional set of city officials, he has shown relatively little interest in his county and has participated less vigorously in its affairs.

Fortunately for county government, its increased cost is bringing new awareness of it among citizens. The failure at the polls of many attempts at local annexation, consolidation, and reorganization have focused the spotlight on the county as the unit to accomplish the desired result without upsetting historical political patterns and relationships of the citizen with his government. In other words: To have the county, which represents all the people, build an airport causes no particular political problems; to try to reach the same end by consolidating all the local governments is futile.

The States and the Federal Government are going to be increasingly involved in local government affairs. Again, the county, a field office so to speak of the State and local administrative unit for several Federal programs, has closer ties with these larger units.

Our national agricultural, public welfare, and road programs generally are administered at the local level (often in cooperation with the State) by counties. In the recent past, the Federal Government has started aid programs in airports, urban renewal, water pollution, air pollution, planning, public works, hospitals, soil conservation, flood control, civil defense, mass transit, and preservation of open space. It is much easier for the Government to deal with 50 States and 3,043 counties than with thousands of smaller units.

LEST I DEPICT too bright a future for counties, let me point to a dark cloud on the horizon. Counties, generally speaking, are not now properly organized to discharge their new responsibilities. The main question is one of time.

We know that our counties are getting their administrative houses in order, but is it fast enough?

The main danger is that impatience with the seeming slowness to change in urban counties may cause a popular reaction that will lead to creation of new units of government (often not popularly controlled) or resort to direct State or Federal action, or both.

County officials, who daily operate with obsolete administrative machinery, know full well that we must reorganize our counties and establish the general organization patterns already firmly established and tested in our Federal, State, and most municipal governments.

We need to separate legislative, executive, and judicial functions; establish an elected or an appointed administrative head; and to streamline our administrative machinery. Where do we begin?

Several reorganization plans have attempted to eliminate the elected judges, clerks, recorders, treasurers, sheriffs, auditors, commissioners, assessors, and coroners. This way wastes the troops needlessly, and it usually fails.

Perhaps if we were creating county government from scratch, we would appoint rather than elect those officials. But they have been established in the public mind for a long time, and the incumbents usually have long tenure and a strong political following. If the positions were appointive, the incumbents most likely would get the job. The positions were created by the State, and the incumbents administer important statewide functions, such as elections, property assessment, justice, and keeping records. There is little local discretion.

County reorganization must be aimed at creating a genuine home rule, local government. It should take the form of State enabling legislation to allow counties to undertake new local functions, such as planning, zoning, and waste disposal. Most important, it should aim to make the county governing board a genuine legislative body and should place administrative responsibility in an elected or appointed executive.

Once that is accomplished, it is relatively less difficult to bring about the other refinements, such as personnel reform, executive budgeting, capital budgeting, central purchasing, and other modern administrative improvements. Power to reorganize departments and create new ones, I think, should rest with the county governing body.

The proceedings of the 1962 Home Rule Congress of the National Association of Counties outlined in detail the principles of county home rule and the actions necessary for accomplishment. It is an action handbook for county officials who are anxious to respond to our new challenges.

MANY PERSONS unfamiliar with the operation of local government in their

State have questioned whether abolition of the counties in Connecticut by
action of the State legislature on
October 1, 1960, was not the forerunner of similar action in other States. I
think not. A good case can be made
that Connecticut never tried county
government as it is known in other
States. Note, for example, that the
three county commissioners in each of
the eight counties were not elected;
they were appointed for 4-year terms
by the State general assembly.

Only the county sheriff was and still
is elected, and this position continues.
The commissioners made the budgets,
but they had to be approved by the
State senators and representatives of
the towns within the county. Connecticut counties had no direct taxing
authority and were limited to making
levies against the towns.

Through the years Connecticut had
absorbed nearly all the important
functions of counties, and at the end
the counties functioned principally as
keepers of the county jails. They were
taken over by the State, and the 400
county employees were frozen into
the State personnel system.

We should remember also that the
town in Connecticut is the unit that is
much more comparable to the typical
American county.

The 169 towns in Connecticut contain every square inch of Connecticut
territory and are responsible for local
welfare administration and other functions performed by counties in other
States.

IT IS IRONIC THAT even Connecticut
with its relatively small area finds
that the towns are too small and the
State too large to administer matters
of public health, sanitation, and
flood control that are regional in
nature. Regional planning and flood
control commissions and metropolitan
districts are being created, and speculation is that by 1966—the 300th
anniversary of the legislative establishment of Connecticut counties—
this fine old State may create regional

units comparable to the counties in
the rest of the Nation.

REFORMERS have pointed out that
many counties are too small to perform
efficiently (as are many of our 17,500
cities) and have urged county consolidation. Again, this generally will
be unacceptable to the local electorate.
The same result can be obtained, however, by having the multicounty approach to the individual functions.

Examples abound of the uniting of
several counties for public health,
library, fire protection, sewer and
water, prison operation, and other
areawide functions.

Thus the farmer, the city dweller,
and the suburbanite look to their reorganized county government as the
complexities of modern life force us to
readjust our Federal system to meet
changing times.

The new vitality of the American
county is reflected in the new vision
of the county officials themselves. A
visit to the schools or conferences for
county officials sponsored by our State
associations of county officials in 44
States will illustrate the dedication and
determination of the elected and appointed county representatives.

Our oldest form of local government
is suddenly becoming our newest and
most exciting.

BERNARD F. HILLENBRAND *became
executive director of the National Association of Counties in 1955. He received the
degree of master of public administration
from Syracuse University. He previously
served as assistant director of American
Municipal Association and has held positions in State administration in Wisconsin
and New York and as assistant director of
research for the city of Syracuse.*

For further reading:
National Association of County Officials,
American County Platform. Washington, D.C.
——— *County Finance Congress.* Washington,
D.C., 1960.
——— *County Home Rule Action Program.*
Washington, D.C., 1962.
——— *The Urban County Congress.* Washing-
ton, D.C., 1959.

WILLIAM G. COLMAN

RESPONSIBILITIES
OF THE STATES

THE States have responsibilities as well as rights under our American Federal system. Nowhere is this truism truer than with regard to the problems facing all levels of government in the growing urban areas, many of which embrace more than one county. The leadership, assistance, and supervision of State government therefore must be brought to bear on the urban areas and their surrounding environs, which may be agricultural today but will be urban tomorrow.

In 1906 in an address before the Pennsylvania Society, Elihu Root observed:

"It is useless for the advocates of states' rights to inveigh against the supremacy of the constitutional laws of the United States or against the extension of national authority in the fields of necessary control where the states themselves fail in the performance of their duty. The instinct for self-government among the people of the United States is too strong to permit them long to respect anyone's right to exercise a power which he fails to exercise. The governmental control which they deem just and necessary they will have. It may be that such control would better be exercised in particular instances by the governments of the states, but the people will have the control they need, either from the states or from the national government; and if the states fail to furnish it in due measure sooner or later constructions of the constitution will be found to vest the power where it will be exercised—in the national government."

The Advisory Commission on Intergovernmental Relations, established by act of Congress in 1959, made up of representatives from all levels of government, and charged with continuing study directed toward strengthening relationships among National, State, and local levels of government, has made a number of recommendations for action by the State governments in coping with the problems generated by the rapid increase in the population, geographic scope, and complexity of the Nation's urban areas.

At no point in the structure of the

American Federal system of government are problems of intergovernmental relations so marked, varied, and difficult as in the large metropolitan areas, where the activities of all three levels of government function in close proximity.

Within such areas, Federal, State, county, and municipal agencies, often supplemented by a small host of special-purpose units of local government, must carry on their functions, subject to a complicated framework of Federal, State, and local laws and administrative regulations.

In its studies of these problems, the Commission has echoed the admonition to the States set forth by their own Council of State Governments in its 1956 study for the Governors' Conference:

"Although the roles of local governments and the National Government are indispensable, the States are the key to solving the complex difficulties that make up the general metropolitan problem. To achieve adequate results the State governments—the legislative and executive branches and the people—need to exert positive, comprehensive, and sustained leadership in solving the problem and keeping it solved."

Possibly one of the most difficult tasks facing State governments is an active reappraisal of State constitutional and statutory restrictions on local governments. For example, many State constitutions include provisions that prevent or make it extremely difficult to reduce the number or enlarge the size of local units of governments; specify the details of electing governing bodies and of carrying on the executive management of local governments; and prescribe terms of office, salaries, duties, and residency of elected and appointed local government personnel.

No SINGLE, easy solution exists for easing the problems of political and structural complexity of local government in the Nation's metropolitan areas. Rather, the Commission has proposed the enactment by State legislatures of a package of permissive powers to be utilized by the residents of those areas as they see fit.

The Commission also has proposed that States establish within the structure of State government a dual function of oversight and also technical assistance to local units of government, thereby asserting a determination to assist continually and to intervene where necessary to help with political jurisdictional problems in the metropolitan areas.

FIRST, A modification of the traditional home rule concept is in order, to wit: Local home rule for strictly local problems and metropolitan home rule for areawide problems, but with the State free to legislate and otherwise act with respect to problems that cross county boundaries and cannot be solved through interlocal cooperation.

The States would be well advised to lose no opportunities in the normal processes of constitutional change to make sure that constitutional home-rule provisions are so modified as to insure that the authority of the State with respect to its metropolitan areas is not unduly restricted.

Liberalized municipal annexation and control of new municipal incorporations should be provided by State legislatures. Many of the problems in our older cities can be attributed directly to the difficulty in the annexation of unincorporated territory and the ease with which small new and often "defensive" incorporations are effected. The result all too often is a central city ringed with incorporated places and continuing civil war between the large city and its suburbs. The proposal I cited is no cure if the disease has progressed far, but it is a healthy preventive in cases that are just emerging into a sizable urban situation.

Authority for city-county contracting, joint enterprises, and for the voluntary transfer of functions from cities to counties, and vice versa, should be provided by State legislatures.

This type of legislation is strictly permissive and forces no one to do anything. On the other hand, it provides legal authority for interlocal arrangements between city councils and county commissioners to cope with many functions of government that the population explosion has carried beyond the lines of original jurisdictions.

In many States, existing constitutional and statutory restrictions on the borrowing powers of local governments in terms of the assessed valuation of locally taxable property, coupled with requirements for specific referendum approval of proposed bond issues, actually handicap local governments in supplying their citizens and industries with community facilities indispensable to growth and prosperity. They constitute a serious impediment to any local self-government, handicap the self-reliance of local communities, and impel them toward increased financial dependence on the State and the Federal Government.

States are urged to repeal constitutional and statutory restrictions limiting local government debt services by reference to the local base for property taxation. Legislation enacted in their place should relate realistically to the ability of local governments to meet debt service requirements.

States are urged to vest authority to issue bonds in the governing bodies of local governments, subject to permissive referendum only, on petition, and with participation in any such referendum available to all eligible local voters and, except under unusual circumstances, with results determined by a majority vote on the question.

Local government should be provided with necessary machinery for carrying out complicated "business type" operations.

Many local governmental services, particularly those financed largely from user charges, defy economic handling on a fragmented or parochial basis within large metropolitan areas.

The State legislatures should provide permissive authority for the creation, either by action of local governing boards or by initiative vote on the part of the people, of multifunctional service corporations which carry out urban functions spread over an entire metropolitan area and which demand handling on an areawide basis.

Such corporations should depend on a vote of the residents of an entire area for the addition of new functions.

Furthermore, the board of directors of such a corporation or authority should be made up of elected officials of the local governments concerned so that the instrumentality is directly responsive to the people of the area.

The people residing in urban areas should be endowed with the privilege and the machinery for self-determination with respect to the structure, form, and functions of their government.

The Advisory Commission on Intergovernmental Relations has urged that State legislatures enact legislation authorizing the establishment of metropolitan area charter commissions for the purpose of developing proposals for revising and improving local government services.

This body should be created, optionally, by either mutual and concurrent action of the governing bodies of the local units within the area, or by initiative petition and election of the voters of the metropolitan area. Its eventual proposals should be placed before the electorate for approval or rejection.

Similarly, the Commission has recommended that States enact legislation authorizing the creation of metropolitan area planning bodies to give people the opportunity to establish a comprehensive planning body.

To PERMIT is not enough. The State must also lead, assist, and intervene.

In the light of widespread support for a Department of Urban Affairs, it is paradoxical that only a handful of States have provided within their own State government organization an office or a focal point for attention to urban problems, especially when one considers that 46 out of the 50 States have within their borders at least one standard metropolitan area, as defined by the Bureau of the Census, and that 42 of the States have more than one.

IN ITS SPECIFIC proposals to State legislatures, the Commission has suggested that a State office of local affairs or other similar unit might profitably have the following functions:

One, to assist and advise the Governor in coordinating those activities and services of agencies of the State which involve significant relationships with local governments.

Two, to encourage and, when requested, to assist in efforts of local governments to develop mutual and cooperative solutions to their common problems.

Three, to study existing legal provisions that affect the structure and financing of local government and the State activities that involve significant relationships with local government units. Particular attention in such studies and recommendations shall be given to problems of local government for metropolitan areas and other areas where major changes in population or economic activity are taking place.

Four, to serve as a clearinghouse, for the benefit of local governments, of information concerning their common problems and concerning State and Federal services available to assist in the solution of those problems.

Five, when requested, to supply information, advice, and assistance to governmental or civic groups which are studying problems of local government structure or financing for particular areas.

Six, to consult and cooperate with other State agencies, with local governments and officials, and with Federal agencies and officials, in carrying out the functions and duties of the office.

State financial and technical assistance to urban areas is badly needed. In most States the flow of technical assistance to their urban areas is much larger from the Federal Government than from their own State government.

The pattern of land use and of the potential growth of the urban area is tied closely to the public transportation system and to building highways and expressways. It is imperative that at this time, when the Federal Government has programs of assistance for both highway building and mass transit, the State governments expand their traditional role in these fields.

State policies with respect to taxation of transportation properties and the regulation of transportation rates and service have an important bearing upon the ability of private and public enterprise to provide adequate mass transportation service to cities.

The State government is also in a strong position to help resolve problems among conflicting local jurisdictions in providing coordinated mass transportation facilities and supporting adequate transportation planning on an areawide basis.

To accomplish these purposes, the Governor should have staff facilities to: Advise and assist in the formulation of overall mass transportation policies; make necessary studies and render technical assistance to local governments; consult with the appropriate State, local, and private officials who carry out programs affecting mass transportation; participate in regulatory proceedings that affect mass transportation; and develop proposals for retaining urban and commuter transportation facilities.

The State also occupies a strategic role in the allocation of water and the regulation of its use for urban purposes. The spread of urban development, the need to go farther afield for water supplies, and the increased capital requirements for such development, all reduce the abilities of individual municipalities to obtain and develop future sources for water on a unilateral basis.

Other fields in which States should provide assistance and leadership include urban planning, urban renewal, modernization of building codes, civil defense, air pollution, and organization and finance of local government.

The provision of open spaces in and around large metropolitan areas is a challenge to all levels of government.

FINALLY, States must not hesitate to intervene in resolving disputes among local units of government where such disputes are resulting in delayed or inadequate services to their citizens.

In the absence of the establishment of areawide units of government, no authority exists short of that of the State to resolve disputes between or among counties or cities within metropolitan areas.

This is not to suggest that the State endeavor to impose a particular form of government upon a metropolitan area, but rather to use its authority and good offices in the resolution of residual problems after the local governments in the area have utilized all of their available methods of local self-determination.

The Commission believes that these legislative and administrative proposals would, if placed into effect, constitute significant steps forward in the improvement of Federal-State-local relations with respect to metropolitan areas and would provide a base for far-reaching improvements in the adequacy and efficiency by which governmental services are provided to the 113 million people now residing in our 212 metropolitan areas.

The problems are so interrelated, however, that no single proposal, standing alone, can be considered an effective approach toward this objective. Rather, concurrent and persistent efforts on a number of fronts by each of the levels of government concerned are considered by the Commission to be necessary to sound progress in this segment of our overall structure.

The Commission, therefore, has urged that legislators and officials at all levels of government give sympathetic consideration to these proposals, recognizing that each level of government and each branch of government may find some propositions here with which they heartily disagree as well as some they can endorse.

The Commission believes that the problems of governmental structure, organization, planning, and cooperation in the metropolitan areas are so urgent and critical as to require the ushering in of an era of reciprocal forbearance among all units.

For example, unless counties and cities are willing to yield some autonomy to each other and unless the States take necessary, though controversial, action along a number of fronts, the final result can only be a much wider assertion of direct Federal action and control than either States or local government officials or the people themselves would be willing to accept under normal circumstances.

That result will come about if the battlelines among levels of government continue to harden and there is continued thwarting of the desires of the people for adequate and efficient local government in the metropolis.

Wholesale assumption by the Federal Government of functions of metropolitan areas is now recommended by few, if any, thoughtful people, but it will surely come to pass if the only alternative is chaos, disintegration, and bickering at the local level and disinterest at the State level.

To those who question the justification for the degree of increased Federal responsibility I described, the Advisory Commission would point out that moderate Federal action now, designed to stimulate more effective State and local action, is much to be preferred to a more unitary approach at a later date.

WILLIAM G. COLMAN *is Executive Director of the Advisory Commission on Intergovernmental Relations. He has previously served as Executive Assistant to the Director of the National Science Foundation and as Assistant Director of Research for the Kestnbaum Commission on Intergovernmental Relations and has held a number of executive positions in State government.*

JOHN E. STONER

COOPERATION AMONG UNITS OF GOVERNMENT

SERVICES often cannot be supplied because of lack of money and lack of jurisdiction. Their capital costs may be so large as to put them beyond the reach of small units of local government acting alone. When the units pool their resources, however, they are able to build water storage facilities and sewage treatment plants or other facilities, because the per capita costs generally decline with the increase in number of people served.

Lack of jurisdiction and how co-operation eliminates the lack can be illustrated by conditions in the Fox River Valley of Wisconsin. The north-eastern shore of Lake Winnebago and the next 15 miles of the upper Fox River Valley are densely populated and highly industrialized in parts.

The region lies in two counties, and 14 other local governments exercise jurisdiction in it. The only government with power to plan in the whole ter-ritory is the State of Wisconsin. But planning with respect to utilities, land use, and the location, width, and con-struction of local roads usually is con-sidered to be a local function.

Eleven of the local governments (four cities, three villages, and four townships) created a commission to plan for the region. The plans could then be adopted by each of them. Thus for the purpose of formulating

plans, boundary lines are erased; for purposes of action, each local unit adopts the plans and so retains its au-tonomy, the equivalent of eating the cake and keeping it, too.

Cooperation is carried on in many ways. We can group them somewhat arbitrarily into six classifications.

The simplest type, the exchange of information, ranges from chance per-sonal contact to carefully structured arrangements. Police officials supply information across jurisdictional lines. County A does not pay overtime to its road crew; instead, a record is kept of the extra time the road crew works during emergencies, such as snow-storms; compensating time off is per-mitted during slack periods. Officials in Counties B and C hear of this procedure, and they adapt the practice to their own use.

Officials in one unit may be puzzled

about how to pay for a needed service and ask the others how they finance it. The result may be action by a single government. Or two units of government have a similar problem. For example, their employees are about to organize and affiliate with a union. After consultation, both decide to adopt the same policy. This is parallel action.

A slightly more structured arrangement is the regular meetings of the officials of a number of municipalities around Wisconsin Rapids. The executive heads of the local units and a number of their department heads meet together in the morning, and in the afternoon the mayors meet together, the clerks meet in another room, the engineers in another, and so on.

Still more structure is seen in the creation of an organization for the purpose of furthering cooperation. Some years ago Park Ridge, Ill., and six other suburbs along the commuter line of the Wisconsin division of the Chicago & Northwestern Railway formed an organization known as the Northwest Municipal Conference.

According to Charles Hetrick, assistant city manager of Park Ridge, the organization was set up to assure "cooperation by association" and "to serve as an instrument of an exchange of ideas for understanding and cooperation between the municipalities."

Also outside the formal governmental structure is the web of associations of local officials, the municipal leagues, the associations of mayors, of county officials, finance officers, sheriffs, firemen, and so on. These organizations, established primarily to secure more strength in the political power struggle, perform a singularly important function in fostering a flow of information among local officials. The channels are the personal contacts of the officials themselves, the activities of the executive secretaries of the associations, the newsletters and the journals they edit, and their direct relations with member officials.

A SECOND general classification may be called mutual aid. Much of it occurs in emergencies.

Cities send their equipment to neighboring cities to fight fires too large to be controlled by one of them alone. The *Municipal Year Book* reported in 1947 that of 851 cities queried on the point, 630—74 percent—replied that their fire departments responded automatically to calls from another locality. Sometimes agreements to do so are tacit. Sometimes they are formal. Eighty percent, or 950 of 1,064 cities, reported that they had mutual aid agreements, according to the *Municipal Year Book* for 1954.

Equipment commonly is exchanged on a temporary basis and in emergencies among road jurisdictions. Police officials often get help from officers in other jurisdictions when they make arrests there. The service performed for other jurisdictions may or may not be compensated.

Mutual aid involves no change in administrative structure and no new employees, but a greater use of equipment that otherwise would be idle.

THE THIRD classification includes cooperation through contracts. An example: A city provides fire protection for rural governments or towns.

This device is used for many other services, such as water, sewerage, garbage and refuse disposal, and construction and maintenance of streets and roads. Contracts also are used for recruiting, examining, and training employees.

Sometimes the contract is an understanding developed through many years of use. A city may send its fire equipment to neighboring units on call and submit a bill for the service.

Sometimes the practice has continued year after year without any conference among the officials of the units concerned. At other times, officials sign a formal agreement that specifies the kind and amount of services, the payments to be made, and the length of time the contract is to run.

The widest use of such an agreement I have discovered is for fire protection among small units of government in Wisconsin. Since I found in my surveys no town or village without some sort of cooperative firefighting arrangement, I conclude that most of them have it.

A locality generally uses contractual arrangements to obtain services that a larger place is already providing for its own citizens. Often the service is a new one for the smaller place. Then it is simply an extension of service beyond existing boundary lines.

Distance makes such arrangements impracticable in northern Wisconsin. Consequently towns (townships) and towns and villages contract with each other. In such cases, it is a new service, requiring the acquisition and maintenance of equipment and the organization and training of a body of men to operate it.

Two factors contribute to the widespread use of cooperation in Wisconsin.

One is the structure of county government, which brings chairmen of town boards and village chairmen together on the county board. Responsible officials from different jurisdictions serve on the same committees and consider county business together, and so it is a simple matter to pool resources when a job beyond the reach of one needs to be done.

Another is equalized assessments, which tend to produce uniformity in assessed valuation of real and personal property throughout the State. Consequently, when a judgment as to comparative ability to pay is required, facts are available to base it on.

ANOTHER KIND of cooperation is through the sale of services. It is somewhat like the contractual arrangement I described.

Many smaller places buy water from a neighboring locality much as any other user purchases it.

A variant is the transfer of a student to a school in another district, his own district paying his tuition. Some Wisconsin towns also make loans or grants of money to the school districts.

The classes of cooperation we have examined thus far—exchange of information, mutual aid, contracts, and buying and selling services—have a common characteristic: They require no structural changes in the participating governmental units.

A minor exception is the new administrative organization necessary when two units (for example, Wisconsin towns) together develop a new service, such as firefighting.

THE FIFTH category is joint action.

An example is the sharing of buildings—the city-county building of Marion County and Indianapolis, Ind.; the city-county building of Dane County and the city of Madison, Wis.; and two tuberculosis hospitals in Wisconsin, one of which is owned and operated by two counties and the other by three counties.

The hospital owned by the three counties is managed by the hospital board, to which each county board appoints one member. The hospital board organizes itself and appoints a director. The county boards maintain contact with the hospital through their own finance committees, and their chairmen meet with the hospital board at budget-making time. The finance committees serve as a two-way channel of information and action. They are able to relay the wishes of the county boards to the hospital board when the budget is being made, and they also can relay information about the hospital to the county boards when the budget is being enacted by the full board.

Frequently, though not always, large amounts of capital and long-term commitments are involved in joint action. An example is the city-county building in Indianapolis, for which a 40-year bond issue of 32 million dollars was made. It is a 28-floor structure with more than a million square feet of floorspace. Its annual operating cost has approximated 1.2 million dollars. The three-county hospital in Wisconsin has been in existence for more than 40 years.

Not all joint-action ventures involve large construction, however. Purchasing, for example, is done cooperatively in many places. Among the cities with populations of more than 10 thousand, the *Municipal Year Book* for 1957 reported that 106 had arrangements for joint purchasing.

Another type of joint action occurs sometimes when two or more local units of government in Pennsylvania establish an authority.

Not all of these authorities are illustrative of the joint-action principle, because a single unit of government may set up an authority as a kind of special type of special district. But when the authority is created by two or more municipal units acting together, it may then perform the services for which it was created, much as if it were a special district. Indeed, some persons classify authorities as full-fledged special districts. In any event, though, the creation of one of them by two or more local governments is joint action.

The State associations of local officials, State municipal leagues, and State associations of county officials must be mentioned again. In addition to fostering an exchange of information, as I mentioned earlier, they perform services for the local governments, which seem to be in a class by themselves. They are private organizations. Neither they nor their officers have governmental powers. A principal activity is representation in behalf of local governments. They support what they consider favorable legislation and oppose bills they consider detrimental in the State legislatures. The associations perform other services for their member governments. For example, they set standards; the Michigan Municipal League administers a purchasing service.

THE FUNCTIONS performed cooperatively, by and large, look like a list of local government functions.

Guthrie S. Birkhead, associate professor of government in Syracuse University, conducted a study of interlocal governmental cooperation in New York for the Governor's Committee on Home Rule in 1958. Dr. Birkhead found 1,142 instances of cooperation among local units of government in the performance of nine functions.

An earlier study by Sidney Wise, of Franklin and Marshall College, under the auspices of the Department of Internal Affairs of Pennsylvania, *Selected Areas of Intergovernmental Cooperation*, set forth the legal authority for interlocal cooperation in Pennsylvania. He put 18 functions in his selected list.

Another study, undertaken in 1961 under contract between the United States Department of Agriculture and Indiana University, had the aim of finding what functions were being carried on cooperatively by local governments in five States. The States examined and the four professors who conducted the fieldwork were: Alabama, Robert Highsaw; Pennsylvania, John Ferguson; Nebraska, A. B. Winter; and Indiana and Wisconsin, John E. Stoner. Clarence J. Hein was named to represent the Department of Agriculture in the project.

After analysis of the statutes and consultation with authorities in each State, the men devised a list of functions that was comprehensive but short enough to be usable in a questionnaire to all local governments in the five States.

This list is not inclusive of all the functions performed cooperatively, but it does indicate their range and variety: Airports, assessments, buildings, civil defense, comfort stations, conservation, docks, drainage, elections, fire protection, flood control, garbage, health, hospitals, housing, industrial development, institutions, joint ownership (tax-delinquent property), lease equipment, legal services, libraries, lighting, personnel, planning, police protection, public works, purchasing, recreation, parks, roads, streets, bridges, sewage, tax collection, urban renewal, utilities (gas and electric), war memorials, water supply, welfare, and zoning.

The nature of a service provides little evidence as to whether it may be performed cooperatively. The test seems to be whether the need for it extends beyond political boundaries.

LEGAL AUTHORITY for local units has been considered necessary for some kinds of cooperation.

Ever since the Attorney General of Washington in 1913 (State of Washington, *Report of the Attorney General 1913–1914*) held that two local units of government could not operate a ferry without special authority to do so, authorizations of three kinds have been used. One is constitutional. Two are statutory.

The State constitutions of Alaska, California, Florida, Georgia, Hawaii, New York, Missouri, and Ohio contain references to interlocal cooperation.

The authority ranges from permission to the legislatures to delegate cooperative power to local governments to a direct grant of power to local governments. For example, article VI, section 17 of the Missouri Constitution provides that "any municipality or political subdivision of the state may contract and cooperate with other municipalities or political subdivisions thereof. . . ."

Of the two kinds of legislative authorization, the first is a general grant, which permits local units of government to cooperate. Wisconsin in 1939 and Minnesota and Pennsylvania in 1943 have enacted such a statute.

The Council of State Governments printed a draft bill in its annual *Suggested State Legislation Program* for 1957. Its key clause was: "Any power or powers, privileges or authority exercised or capable of exercise by a public agency of this state may be exercised and enjoyed jointly with any other public agency of this state. . . ."

It also defined public agency to include the local units of government. Another clause was meant to safeguard State interest in the administration of cooperative functions by specifying the basic contents of agreements to cooperate and by requiring the approval of designated State officials before the agreement became valid.

Indiana and Kansas adopted this bill in 1957.

The clause I quoted is similar to the one adopted 18 years earlier by Wisconsin. About a dozen States have used this general type of authorization.

This legislation changes the powers already possessed by the local governments not a whit except to permit them to do together what they already could do separately. The initiative for cooperation, the extent, and the functions covered are left to the discretion of the participating governments.

This kind of general grant of power to local units of government to cooperate with respect to the performance of any service has not been used extensively in Indiana. For example, in that State, proposals to cooperate are to be presented to the attorney general for his review and approval. From 1957 until 1963 he received few such proposals. Evidently the legislature itself was skeptical of the usefulness of the act of 1957 because it enacted another in 1961 authorizing local units to contract with each other for services.

One reason for the nonuse of the general grant is that the bond opinion, the accepted legal firm, which reviews most bond issues in the State, is hostile to a general grant of authority. When it approves the legality of a bond issue, it prefers that authority for it be found in a specific grant to perform a specific function. The bond opinion used by Wisconsin municipalities takes the same general position.

WHAT THE FUTURE holds for interlocal governmental cooperation will be determined in part by what local officials themselves think of it.

Evidence gathered in the survey of

PERCENTAGE OF TOWNS, VILLAGES, CITIES WHOSE ROAD AND STREET WORK BY FUNCTION IS PERFORMED BY THE COUNTY HIGHWAY DEPARTMENT [1]

Total number: Towns, 1,277; villages, 379; cities, 177

Type of work	Towns			Villages			Cities		
	Regularly Percent	Occasionally Percent	None Percent	Regularly Percent	Occasionally Percent	None Percent	Regularly Percent	Occasionally Percent	None Percent
Winter Maintenance	40.2	29.8	30.0	24.3	29.6	46.2	7.3	29.9	62.7
Summer Maintenance	38.3	13.9	47.8	21.9	35.9	42.2	6.8	24.8	68.4
Construction:									
Grading	43.5	17.4	39.1	36.9	26.1	36.9	12.4	29.9	57.6
Sand gravel lift	40.2	11.7	48.0	25.8	14.5	59.6	9.0	24.8	66.1
Aggregate for surfacing	41.0	18.1	41.0	32.2	24.8	43.0	18.1	28.8	53.1
Surface course and surface treatment	57.9	13.5	28.7	55.1	24.3	20.6	37.3	30.5	32.2
Structures (over 20-foot span)	27.7	9.4	62.9	7.1	11.6	81.3	2.8	7.3	89.8

[1] There are 71 counties in Wisconsin, but one, Menominee, is not included in this table because its road and street system is operated as a county unit. Discrepancies in the percentages are due to rounding errors. Compiled from A. J. Thielen's records, June 1962.

five States indicated strong support of such cooperation.

A. J. Thielen, executive secretary of the Wisconsin County Boards Association, requested information from each county highway department in Wisconsin on the construction and maintenance of town roads and village and city streets. Of the 71 counties, 64 performed regularly some of the construction or maintenance functions for towns, and 49 did so for village and city streets.

It is general knowledge that there has been a great deal of cooperation among county road departments and other local units that perform road or street functions, particularly in States whose townships continue to exercise road functions. For example, Minnesota counties provide standby service for townships and frequently carry on the road maintenance work.

The extent of cooperation in Wisconsin as shown by the survey in an accompanying table is substantial.

IN SOME CASES it appears that cooperation is good commonsense. Small rural units can pool their resources and increase fire protection; a water system is an improvement over the rain barrel each householder had long ago. So also with hospitals, libraries, bookmobiles, garbage handling, police protection, the construction of buildings, drainage systems and structures, and many more.

If services are to be supplied to rural communities, obvious choices are available: Local units may cooperate, or they may be abolished and their powers and duties transferred to another unit that has political boundaries that do encompass the needs for the service.

Both of these choices have been used. The number of townships has declined and so have their functions.

The Bureau of the Census ceased to count townships in Iowa in 1957 because substantially all their functions had been absorbed by the counties. In Michigan and Indiana, township road functions have been transferred to the counties. The Indiana Legislature in 1959 set in motion a movement to take the responsibility for schools away from townships.

The creation of special districts is a third choice if the local unit cannot provide the service because of lack of resources or because the political boundaries fail to include the area of need for services. Between 1942 and 1957, the number of special districts increased from 8,299 to 14,405, many of them in rural areas.

Other choices become available in built-up areas, such as annexation, various kinds of adjustment of political jurisdictions through federation, and separation or consolidation of cities and counties.

When small places incorporate on the edge of a city to avoid being included in the city, cooperation tends to create problems. It may enable small, uneconomic jurisdictions to survive and strangle the large city. Some States, notably Minnesota and Wisconsin, have attempted to control this by making incorporation more difficult and annexation easier. Consequently cooperation in urban areas may not have so much utility as in rural areas, or it may have a different kind of purpose than in rural areas.

Two factors are likely to boost the attractiveness of cooperation.

The first is political. Because local units (as political parties and State legislatures are now constituted) have positions of great power, local governments are not likely to have the initiative taken from them, barring some major development that could bring about revolutionary changes.

The question then becomes one of how local officials will react to the pressures for more services. This reaction may be different for differently situated officials. Those in large cities surrounded by smaller places, for example, may prefer to use the means being developed in metropolitan areas; in smaller places and in rural governments it seems likely that officials will prefer to keep their relative positions and status. For these latter ones, cooperation will often be the answer.

The second factor is the emulative character of change in local government. Local officials, particularly rural officials, seem to me to be more impressed by actual performance than by theory or argument. Success succeeds with them.

As the facts of cooperation become known and as the pressures for finance drive local governments together and strengthen their associations, the attractiveness and the inherent practicality of cooperation as a means of doing a job will increase its use.

JOHN E. STONER *is professor of government in Indiana University. Dr. Stoner, who holds degrees from Manchester College and the University of Chicago, joined the faculty of Indiana University in 1938. He was chief adviser to the Institute of Public Administration of Thailand in 1958–1960.*

For further reading:
   Blanford, John B., Jr., "Administrative Organization." *Municipal Year Book*, 1945, pp. 239–243.
   Carrell, Jeptha F., "Learning to Work Together." *National Municipal Review* (November 1954), pp. 526–533.
   Gill, Norman N., "Intergovernmental Arrangements." *Municipal Year Book*, 1936, pp. 140–147.
   Goodwin, George, *Intermunicipal Relations in Massachusetts.* University of Massachusetts, Bureau of Government Research, Amherst, 1956.
   Hillenbrand, Bernard F., "Urban Counties in 1957." *Municipal Year Book*, 1958, p. 56.
   National Association of County Officials, *The County Officer*, Vol. 26 (No. 6, June 1961).
   New York State Department of Audit and Control, *Interlocal Cooperation in New York State—Extent of Cooperation and Statutory Authorization for Cooperative Activity.* Prepared for the Governor's Committee on Home Rule, Albany, 1958.
   Selected Areas of Intergovernmental Cooperation, Sidney Wise, editor. Commonwealth of Pennsylvania, Department of Internal Affairs, Bureau of Municipal Affairs, Harrisburg, 1957.
   Sherwood, Frank P., "Administrative Management: 1955 Developments." *Municipal Year Book*, 1956, pp. 241–247.

NORMAN BECKMAN

THE FEDERAL GOVERNMENT AND URBAN DEVELOPMENT

THE Presidential Commission on Intergovernmental Relations—known as the Kestnbaum Commission—in a report in 1955 set forth several general principles, which may serve as a guide in evaluating Federal responsibilities and activities in urban development when other levels of government do not act.

"*When the National Government is the only agency that can summon the resources needed for an activity.*" For this reason, the National Government from time to time has assumed responsibility for assisting in the redevelopment of areas of chronic unemployment and urban slums.

"*When the activity cannot be handled within the geographic and jurisdictional limits of smaller governmental units, including those that could be created by compact.*" Regulation of water pollution in interstate waters and control of air traffic are examples.

"*When the activity requires a nationwide uniformity of policy that cannot be achieved by interstate action.*" Sometimes there must be an exclusively national policy, as in the planning of a system of interstate and defense highways and surveillance of radiological fallout.

"*When a State through action or inaction does injury to the people of other States.*"

On this ground, national action may be justified to prevent the unrestrained exploitation of exceptional park and recreation areas and to help protect urban water supplies.

"*When States fail to respect or to protect basic political and civil rights that apply throughout the United States,*" such as the free movement of people across State lines.

Several factors that seem to justify Federal activity in urban development stem from these general criteria.

If social or economic problems were to cause a breakdown in the normal operation of urban areas, the constitutional responsibilities of the National Government could no longer be met.

Additionally, some 74 of our 212 metropolitan areas not only spill over the boundaries of local political jurisdictions, but border on or cross State lines, thereby bringing certain problems into an interstate category.

The Federal Government likewise has responsibility to see that its activities do not "unbalance" attempts to meet urban problems. Ongoing programs must be evaluated against trends and developments in the domestic scene and measures taken to adjust to those facts. Thus a Federal highway program has an inevitable impact on local and private ability to provide mass transportation facilities.

Related to the problem of achieving a balanced approach is the interest of the Federal Government in coordinating its practices that affect metropolitan areas to assure that its funds are not wasted and that the national goals enunciated by the Congress are achieved.

SUPREME COURT doctrine in the past several decades by and large has removed the judicial branch as a possible obstacle to the carrying on of Federal activities in urban areas and has primarily devoted its attention to the guardianship and protection of human and civil rights.

Thus the Federal Government has a wide range of constitutional authority and economic resources to achieve national goals. The only restrictions in the exercise of this authority lie in the United States Constitution and in the self-restraint of the Congress and the President.

This evolution in Court doctrine may have gone further than is generally recognized in meeting problems of urban growth. For example, as William H. Whyte has noted in his book, *Securing Open Space for Urban America: Conservation Easements*, public agencies have far-reaching authority under Federal and State legislation pertaining to urban renewal:

"They can take a man's property—all of it—and then re-sell it to somebody else, and at a cheaper price, too. Not so many years ago the very idea would have been thought outrageous, unconstitutional, communistic; and so, indeed, it was. Now it's part of the status quo, for the public has realized the overriding need for such action if the larger community purpose is to be served."

In a decision having application for communities throughout the United States, the Supreme Court in *Berman v. Parker*, 348 U.S. 26 (1954), upheld an action of the Urban Renewal Agency of the District of Columbia. In the majority opinion, Justice Douglas established an expanded view of the public welfare when he wrote:

"The concept of the public welfare is broad and inclusive. The values it represents are spiritual as well as physical, aesthetic as well as monetary. It is within the power of the legislature to determine that the community should be beautiful as well as healthy, spacious as well as clean, well-balanced as well as carefully patrolled. In the present case the Congress and its authorized agencies have made determinations that take into account a wide variety of values. It is not for us to reappraise them. If those who govern the District of Columbia decide that the Nation's capital should be beautiful as well as sanitary, there is nothing in the Fifth Amendment that stands in the way."

Constitutionally, if not politically, direct Federal-local relations are carried on by acquiescence of the State governments. In almost all instances, municipalities and other public bodies participating in Federal programs must first have State legislative authorization.

In practice, States generally control such a participation in considerable detail, and, of course, in all cases the State is free to aid, modify, reduce, or eliminate the relationship and manner of participating of any local jurisdiction in Federal programs.

Thus, under the Federal urban renewal program, sometimes cited as an example of direct Federal-local relations, no local agency, city, or town can participate in the national program without State enabling legislation.

A number of States prohibit participation by all or certain of their local jurisdictions in the Federal urban renewal program. Other States provide grants to supplement Federal contributions to localities.

Finally, the State, in setting legal limitations on the taxing ability and other financial powers of local jurisdictions, determines the type of local governments that may exist, the range of functions they can perform, and the method of cooperating with other jurisdictions in metropolitan areas.

MOST FEDERAL aids are channeled through the States, but a number of programs, notably public housing, public facility loans, urban renewal, airports, and metropolitan planning, are not generally channeled through or directly controlled by the States.

In addition, through State sufferance or consent, some Federal programs have encouraged or tended to result in the creation of new special districts or public authorities in such fields as public housing, urban renewal, watershed control, and soil conservation. Either Federal or State action could have provided that these local services be assigned directly to existing local units of government.

National concern and legislative support for meeting rural problems has not declined as a result of the increasing amount of Federal resources devoted to meeting existing and emerging urban needs.

Many of the programs of fundamental importance to urban population, such as highways, housing, hospitals, and grants and loans for public works, are of equal importance to rural populations. Federal appropriations for rural electrification and telephone service, secondary roads, and rural library services have increased in recent years.

The viability and well-being of the rural and urban economies have always been interdependent.

Likewise it should not be assumed that Federal assistance to urban areas is concentrated in assisting the larger metropolitan population complexes.

Many of the Federal aid programs to areas are centered in the Housing and Home Finance Agency. In a number of instances, the HHFA programs, at the express direction of the Congress, are required to assist small rather than large municipalities. Thus the program for loans for public facilities is limited to communities of less than 50 thousand population.

Almost 600 thousand mortgages had been insured up to 1962 by the Federal Housing Administration in counties outside standard metropolitan statistical areas. More than 40 percent of the communities with low-rent public housing projects are cities of less than 5 thousand population. The Federal share for slum clearance projects is increased from two-thirds to three-fourths for communities having a population of under 50 thousand.

Federal programs that affect the planning and development of urban areas have lagged behind the growth of such urban areas. Not until the thirties did the Federal Government initiate economic and public works assistance on any large scale in an effort to reduce unemployment in the cities.

The major impact of Federal aid programs on central city, suburban, and rural fringe areas in general has come about since the end of the Second World War—for example, the Federal interstate highway program, urban renewal and public housing, grants for building plants for sewage treatment, and the construction of large airports. Thus the problems of coordination of national policy, organization, Federal-State-local relations, and impact on rural communities near cities are relatively recent.

The President's budget message for fiscal year 1960 stated: "The Federal Government is helping local communities meet many of the major problems of community development created by increasing population and growing urbanization. Federal expenditures for grants and long-term loans to assist 14 major types of capital improvements alone will reach an estimated $2.1 billion in 1960, or almost double the amount actually spent for these programs in 1958."

The President's budget for 1963 contained proposed grants and loans for these 14 major types of capital improvements in amounts more than 4 times that of 1958. The impact on a typical municipal capital budget is striking. The capital program of the city of Philadelphia for 1959–1964 was estimated to require 821 million dollars, of which 417 million dollars were Federal funds and only 317 million dollars were local funds.

The Housing and Home Finance Agency, in a study in 1962 of a sample metropolitan area, that of Atlanta, Ga., identified some 29 separate programs involving more than 117 million dollars and administered by 12 major Federal agencies. This total covered: Direct grants and matching funds for such projects as road construction and airport construction, 35.8 million dollars; direct Federal expenditures of 2.3 million dollars for water resource, defense, and recreation projects; direct loans for housing, small business, public works planning, and so forth, of 594 thousand dollars; and various types of insuring programs for housing, totaling 79 million for the year.

THERE IS STILL a surprising lack of regular reporting on the amount of Federal funds by program going into urban and metropolitan areas and the individual or total influence of these programs on urban and rural areas. Such information cannot be found in the annual Budget of the United States or the periodic census of governments.

Testifying on the role of the Federal Government in metropolitan areas before the Senate Subcommittee on Intergovernmental Relations of the Committee on Government Operations in December 1962, the Housing Administrator estimated that the total impact of Federal programs to assist urban development is in the nature of some 20 billion dollars annually. When one considers the multiplier effects of such expenditures, the total significance and impact of these activities to urban areas is even greater.

Virtually every Federal program has a significant effect on urban areas.

The American Municipal Association, in its publication, *Federal Aids to Local Governments*, contains 11 major classifications under which 36 separate Federal aid programs are listed—including area redevelopment, civil defense, community development, community facilities, special public works, public health programs, school assistance, surplus property donations, training courses for municipal personnel, airports, mass transportation, highways, and juvenile delinquency.

IN CARRYING OUT its urban development programs, the Federal Government faces a number of obstacles in attempting to contribute to the orderly and coordinated development of our urban areas and in being assured that these aids are used effectively in accomplishing the objectives of the programs.

First is the sheer growth of urban population. Between 1950 and 1960, while rural population remained static, urban population increased at an average rate of 29 percent, although growth rates varied widely by region.

Suburban populations are dispersed and at the same time are extremely mobile within the metropolitan area, and so make heavy demands on transportation facilities. Social frictions are intensified by racial and economic disparities between central city and suburb.

Fragmentation and overlap of governments exist in urban areas. Provision of physical facilities by these governments often is uneconomic and meets only short-term local needs.

AIR AND WATER pollution, locations of major highways, facilities for mass transportation, and the urban water supply affect the dweller on the urban fringe and the resident of the central city and must be dealt with on a regionwide basis. Many urban services benefit directly or indirectly an entire metropolitan area, but the cost of construction may be primarily confined to a single jurisdiction—for example, the central city for rapid rail transit. There has been a lag in State reform of archaic financial, organizational, and functional restrictions on local governments.

IT IS IMPORTANT that the timing, nature, location, and objectives of federally assisted development activities be compatible with each other and with desired community goals.

Yet Federal programs that affect urban areas by and large have been developed and administered independently of each other and of State, local, and private decisions regarding development.

Federal statutes in the past generally have failed to recognize the urban area as a whole. Rather, in both statute and administration, the orientation of many Federal programs has been to the State, the rural area, the individual county, or municipality, and only rarely to the metropolitan area.

Now many of the new Federal programs and some of the older ones are being redirected to recognize urban areas as social as well as economic entities.

The programs set up performance standards that provide, as a condition of Federal aid, that projects be consistent with other Federal, State, and local development activities and with comprehensive plans for the development of the area.

I DESCRIBE these performance standards and summarize the major Federal programs that contribute to urban development.

The Housing and Home Finance Agency has the most direct legislative mandate to assist in urban and community development. A unified housing agency was first established in 1942 to coordinate existing housing programs and was reorganized and put on a permanent basis in 1947. The Federal Housing Administration, the best known of the HHFA constituents, insures lenders against loss on mortgage loans covering new or existing residential property and on loans for improving homes.

The Community Facilities Administration administers two programs directly related to urban development. Public facility loans are available at low interest for local public works, except schools. Communities must be under 50 thousand population to qualify. Communities with a larger aggregate population that wish to join to provide a common public facility are ineligible for loans. Advances for public works planning are available to communities. The advances are repayable when and if construction is undertaken. Applications for planning advances must show that the public work will conform to a general plan approved by a State, local, or regional agency; or otherwise must state that no general plan exists.

The Urban Renewal Administration administers programs relating to slum clearance and urban renewal and provides Federal grants for two-thirds or more of the net cost of urban renewal projects. Before a community can qualify for Federal assistance for urban renewal or public housing and liberalized FHA mortgage insurance for housing in urban renewal areas, it must prepare a program—known as the "Workable Program"—for community development. This requirement is the community's own plan for using both public and private resources to eliminate and prevent slums and blight. It involves comprehensive community (but not areawide) planning, the adoption and enforcement of modern building and housing codes, the analysis of slum and blight problems, and effective administrative organization and adequate financing, a program for relocating families displaced by all types of governmental action, and participation and support of the citizens.

Under the Urban Planning Assistance program, Federal grants covering two-thirds of the cost of planning projects are made to metropolitan and regional planning agencies and to State planning agencies to serve communities with a population of less than 50 thousand. This program is designed to help the local jurisdictions and the area as a whole to view specific programs and projects for urban renewal, public facilities, and public works—including schools, airports, transportation, sewers, water supply systems, and the like, whether federally assisted or not— against an overall plan for the future development of the community.

The urban planning grant program has been expanding rapidly. During fiscal 1962, contracts covered a total of 18.2 million dollars, 3 million dollars more than the total of all approvals for the six preceding fiscal years. Of the contracts approved in 1962, 220 were to provide assistance to 700 small communities, 52 were for metropolitan and regional planning, and 20 were for statewide planning.

THE FEDERAL Open-Space Land program provides a financial incentive by increasing its matching grants from 20 to 30 percent where the public body receiving the grant has authority to acquire open-space land for the urban area as a whole or for all or a substantial portion of an urban area pursuant to an interstate or intergovernmental compact or agreement.

In order to qualify at all for open-space grants, a program of comprehensive planning for the urban area must be in effect. In addition, the open-space land to be acquired must be important to the execution of a comprehensive development plan.

If such a plan has not been completed, an application may be approved on the basis of a comprehensive plan for the locality within which the open-space land is situated.

The open-space-land proposal must be reviewed by other public bodies that have responsibilities for compre-

hensive planning and related phases of the open-space program.

Finally, the Housing Agency administers a program authorized by the Housing Act of 1961 for grants and loans for the planning and development of urban mass transportation facilities. In order to qualify for Federal mass transportation assistance, there must be in existence or under active development an effective program for the development of a comprehensive and coordinated mass transportation system for the urban area served by the applying public body. To be acceptable, the mass transportation program must be part of an official program for the development of a coordinated urban transportation system (including highways) and be designed to contribute to the planned comprehensive development of the urban area.

OTHER FEDERAL programs of major significance I mention briefly.

The Area Redevelopment Administration in the Department of Commerce provides loans for industrial or commercial facilities and loans and grants for public facilities in certain economically depressed urban and rural areas. The act requires that before a community in a redevelopment area can qualify for any of the loans, grants, or other Federal assistance, it must prepare an "Overall Economic Development Plan" and have it approved by the Area Redevelopment Administrator. The OEDP generally covers an "economic unit"—a county, metropolitan area, labor market area, or even a region. The plan must include a description of the redevelopment area, the local organization responsible for the program, an assessment of the labor skills, natural resources, physical facilities, and so on, and a program of action for creating new employment opportunities.

The Bureau of Public Roads of the Department of Commerce administers the interstate highway program, which provides 90 percent Federal matching funds (more than 2 billion dollars were authorized for expenditures for 1962) and construction of primary and secondary and urban highway systems, based on 50-percent Federal matching.

The President in his 1962 transportation message to Congress recommended that after 1965 interstate highway locations in metropolitan areas be required to conform to comprehensive development plans for those areas. A modified version of this planning requirement enacted by the Congress provided that after July 1, 1965, a highway project in an urban area of more than 50 thousand population must be based on a continuing and comprehensive transportation planning process carried on in the area.

The Department of Health, Education, and Welfare administers programs of school aid to federally impacted areas, hospital and related health facility construction grants on a matching basis, and research on air pollution. Construction grants are made for municipal facilities for sewage treatment. As amended, the Water Pollution Control Act of 1961 permits the pooling of grant funds (not to exceed 2.4 million dollars) by communities to build joint treatment projects. Grants to individual communities may not exceed 600 thousand dollars, or 30 percent of project costs, whichever is less. At least 50 percent of the Federal grant funds must go to communities of less than 125 thousand population. In practice, some 91 percent of the grant funds have gone to such communities.

The Corps of Engineers of the Department of the Army is responsible for water and related resource development, including local flood protection, flood control reservoirs and multipurpose projects, development of navigation, beach erosion control, and planning of water resources.

The Bureau of Reclamation of the Department of the Interior carries out similar water resource construction and operation activities in 20 Western States.

The Federal Aviation Agency operates the Nation's air navigation system and administers a 50–50 grant program for construction of local airports.

The Department of Agriculture administers several programs of significance to urban dwellers. They include planning and construction of watershed protection projects for conservation of water supplies and recreation; soil surveys, which are helpful in selecting sites for urban and residential development; and a capital investment program in rural and urban fringe areas for municipal electric plants and telephone services.

THE CONGRESS in a number of instances has given advance approval for use of interstate compact machinery to facilitate the coordination of urban development activities. Advance congressional consent has been given to interstate compacts for the promotion of safety on the highways, construction and operation of airports, development of civil defense plans, and the operation of metropolitan planning agencies that cross State lines.

The Congress has extended the interstate compact device further by providing for Federal participation in the Delaware River Basin compact— a comprehensive Federal-interstate agreement for the planning and development of water and related land resources in the highly urbanized basin.

A NUMBER of changes in Federal organizational machinery have been proposed or made to achieve a coordinated approach to urban problems among the Federal agencies and between the Federal and the State and local governments.

Among the most significant developments have been proposals to create a Department of Urban Affairs and Housing and establish a unit in the Executive Office of the President for urban development. Actions taken before 1963 included the assignment of a Special Assistant to the President for Intergovernmental Relations, the creation of regional Federal Executive Boards, and the activities of the Advisory Commission on Intergovernmental Relations.

The President transmitted legislation to the Congress in April 1961 to create a Department of Urban Affairs and Housing.

The Director of the Bureau of the Budget, in his testimony before the Senate Committee on Government Operations, reported that creation of such a new department is needed:

". . . to provide the most effective framework for the consideration of urban area problems and for administration of major programs designed to assist in their solution. . . .

"Most Federal programs, to a greater or lesser extent, affect our urban and metropolitan areas. The proposed legislation vests in the Secretary of Urban Affairs and Housing responsibility for bringing problems of urban development to the Cabinet and providing leadership in the coordination of the many Federal activities affecting urban areas. There is a need to encourage the departments and agencies whose programs have a major impact on local planning to recognize metropolitan areas in their program development and to adapt their program administration to State and local needs to the extent possible. There is also need to improve procedures for review of Federal and federally-supported projects at the metropolitan-area level."

The new department, which under the President's proposal would contain those programs now administered by the Housing and Home Finance Agency, would establish a base of political support for increasing attention to meeting urban development needs.

Robert Wood, of the Massachusetts Institute of Technology, in an article, "The Case for a Department of Urban Affairs," described the strength that Cabinet status would bring:

"By and large, it is through a seem-

ingly endless process of negotiation, cajolery, reasoning, bureaucratic intrigue, the scrambling for positions of access, consultation, and harassment that the urbanists today work toward their ends of a coordinated Federal approach to urban and metropolitan affairs. One senses in their testimony before the Congress a deep dissatisfaction with the roles they play: an urge to be done with the appearances of bootlegger, agitator, and diplomat, a desire for a command post all their own."

This legislation and a subsequent reorganization proposal were not adopted by the 87th Congress.

Several proposals have been made to create a staff agency in the Executive Office of the President that would be concerned with coordination of federally supported urban development activities either in place of a Department of Urban Affairs or to complement its work by providing staff assistance to the President for urban policy guidance and reconciliation of conflicting agency positions.

Two political scientists, Robert H. Connery and Richard H. Leach, in their book, *The Federal Government and Metropolitan Areas*, have recommended that the Executive Office unit "should have no authority to coordinate Federal programs [but] it should have power to collect data, ask questions, and make recommendations to the President."

Other staff functions might include developing proposals for national policy with respect to urban areas; identifying emerging problems; encouraging agencies to recognize the complexity and problems involved in urban development in their own formulation of programs; and administering these programs so as to meet coordinated local needs to the extent possible.

Under President Eisenhower, the position of Assistant to the President for Intergovernmental Relations was established to serve as a focal point on intergovernmental matters within the executive branch. President Kennedy's administration established a similar position of Special Assistant to the President.

The President in November 1961 directed that a number of regional Executive Boards be established in major cities to strengthen the coordination of Federal field activities in many metropolitan areas. Certain cities house upward of 100 separate Federal offices and installations, which administer Federal programs that affect local governments in the surrounding region. Heads of Federal field offices comprise the boards.

These Federal Executive Boards were directed to serve as a forum for the interchange of information about Federal programs, to seek coordinated approaches to interrelated activities, and to establish "a relationship with State and local officials which will contribute to better mutual understanding and support of the roles and purposes of their respective governmental jurisdictions and which will aid in solving problems that may arise in providing services to the public."

THE CONGRESS in 1959 established on a permanent basis the Advisory Commission on Intergovernmental Relations, a 26-member Commission with representation from the executive branch, the Congress, private citizens, and executive and legislative officials from the State and local governments.

The Commission has several continuing responsibilities: To bring together representatives of Federal, State, and local governments to consider common problems; to assist the executive and legislative branches in reviewing existing and proposed legislation to determine their effect on the Federal system; and to recommend the most desirable allocation of governmental functions, responsibilities, and also revenues among the three levels of the government.

The Commission has directed much attention to the problems resulting from the rapid growth of urban areas and made a number of recommenda-

tions to the Congress as well as to State and local governments for expanded and integrated activity by the Federal Government, including strengthening the role and effectiveness of metropolitan planning bodies and improving the coordination of Federal programs that affect urban areas.

The Commission has devoted attention to following through on behalf of its recommendations for Federal and State legislative and administrative action for easing problems of governmental structure in meeting urban needs.

A NUMBER of changes and approaches may be anticipated in the future to make more effective the role and efforts of the Federal Government in urban development.

In addition to a strengthened organization in Washington and the field, there is a need to formulate national policies on urban area development, to strengthen urban and metropolitan planning activities as a framework for relating Federal to local development, to expand research to permit better understanding of the dramatic changes taking place in the composition of our urban society, and to enact State enabling and facilitating legislation to promote Federal-urban area coordination.

The Federal Government has not yet fully come to grips with the implications of its many programs that affect urban areas. The Department of Agriculture, explaining its Rural Areas Development program, can state in a publication that "The Department of Agriculture and other departments and agencies of the National Government have joined with the States to make balanced farm, industry, and community development in underdeveloped rural areas a principal objective of National policy." A comparable statement cannot be made by the Federal Government on national policy objectives for urban development.

Two kinds of goals are needed: The

spelling out of national policy objectives and the development of policy standards for administering Federal programs to accomplish the national objectives better.

Luther Gulick, of the Institute for Public Administration, has proposed a number of "goals for metropolis," which might serve as a starting point for development of goals of national policy.

He advocates that each urban resident should have maximum opportunity for a number and range of human contacts and for freedom of choice of the individual; decent housing; clean air and surroundings; protection from disease; reasonable opportunities for education, work, recreation, and cultural satisfactions; and community activities, community commitments, and community institutions within our large urban complexes.

By the enactment of Public Law 86–527, the Congress and the President laid down a policy that the management of the District of Columbia and of all Federal agencies and activities shall be coordinated with the development of the other areas of the Washington metropolitan region, so as to contribute to the solution of the community development problems of the region on a unified metropolitan basis.

A similar declaration of Federal interest in the relationships of its agencies to the proper development of the other rapidly growing metropolitan areas of the United States would be a modest but appropriate pronouncement of national policy.

Other guides in the development and administration of Federal programs may include:

Requiring local planning on an area-wide basis for the major Federal urban development programs as a prerequisite for receiving Federal funds for projects;

Promoting coordination of federally supported projects with locally prepared comprehensive development plans and programs for the metropolitan area;

Encouraging coordination among Federal agencies administering interrelated direct, or federally supported, projects within metropolitan areas;

Avoiding the creation of Federal impediments to restructuring local governments into more adequate units for meeting the metropolitan needs or causing the creation of single-purpose area authorities, which add to fragmentation of local government structure in urban areas; and

Encouraging appropriate cooperative or joint implementing action by two or more local and State units of government within the confines of a metropolitan area through use of financial and other incentives or requirements.

WE NEED a better understanding of the problems of urban growth and development.

A national program of research in urban development is needed to complement the rapidly increasing Federal, State, local, and private funds that contribute to this development. Such research would provide systematic study of the problems and challenges facing our urbanized and soon-to-be-urbanized populations. Federal support of such research has been minimal, and an expanded program of support for research would fill a gap in our urban development program.

The present picture of uncoordinated development and sprawl in our urban areas comes at a time when we as a Nation have the opportunity—if we knew how to best use our human and natural resources of private and public capital and tools of organization—to achieve almost any kind of urban community that we wish to have. Yet lack of basic understanding of the complex phenomenon of urbanization can be costly in both dollar and social terms.

As Harvey S. Perloff, director of the Regional Studies and Urban Economics programs of Resources for the Future, Inc., noted in his report, *A National Program of Research in Housing and Urban Development:*

"We have already seen that hurried 'solutions' can be self-defeating at times: new highways built to relieve urban traffic congestion have in some cases increased congestion; attempts to improve housing have sometimes intensified the housing problems of certain groups, often those least able to help themselves. . . . This complexity of urban problems requires that action programs rest on a foundation of research and experimentation aimed at deepening and broadening our knowledge of urban affairs."

The establishment of effective areawide comprehensive planning agencies is important from the standpoint of general national interest as well as a necessary aid to State and local efforts to achieve an orderly pattern of urban development.

There is a need for strengthening coordinating and general policymaking machinery at the national level. Little, however, is likely to be achieved by such organizational innovations at the Federal or State level until grassroots coordination of Federal-State-local and private programs of development is achieved in the urban area itself.

THE FRAMEWORK for orderly area development is an approved plan, an ongoing planning process, and a determination that the future development contribute to the accomplishment of that plan.

The many uncoordinated sources of Federal development activity and the number of local jurisdictions and special districts in metropolitan areas make reliance on areawide planning increasingly necessary.

As John Gaus, professor emeritus of Harvard University, has phrased it, comprehensive urban planning is simply an "effort to improve the making of decisions."

Metropolitan planning agencies in urban areas, if properly geared into the political decisionmaking process and responsible to elective officials in the area, can serve as an effective mechanism for formulating area goals and developing comprehensive plans for future development, and for relating specific Federal development proposals at the local level to such plans and area goals.

Rural areas lying in the path of urban development have an obvious interest in the character of such development, the demand it creates for public services, and its revenue-raising potentialities.

There is still time in rural communities that have just joined a metropolitan area to avoid the economic and social effects of unplanned and uncontrolled development.

Population growth and urbanization generally present a challenge and opportunity to achieve convenience and attractiveness if they are controlled to conform with agreed upon development goals.

To that end, the Advisory Commission on Intergovernmental Relations has recommended (and the Housing and Home Finance Agency has since modified its regulations to provide) that Federal grants be made available to provide continuing support to the operations of metropolitan planning agencies in preparing general development plans, conducting basic studies of the physical features and economy of the area, composition and change in population, transportation, and so forth. Such agencies had been established in 1963 in fewer than half of the existing metropolitan areas.

The Commission has also proposed legislation to require that Federal grant-in-aid applications for urban development projects be reviewed and commented on by such planning agencies for conformance to general development plans.

Finally, many of the States have taken action to help local governments meet the accelerating needs of urban development through financial and technical assistance and authorization for joint local action. More State assistance and leadership are needed if national objectives are to be met and Federal funds are to be spent effectively.

The need is for a continued Federal concern to meet responsibilities towards urban areas in cooperation with State and local action in attacking these problems.

The obstacles of rapid growth of population, fragmented local government, and central city suburban stratification are too great to permit us to ignore existing regional governments—the States.

As national urban policies are adopted, cooperative federalism, involving an active partnership among the levels of government—which has been successful in the past in meeting problems of agriculture and developing resources, health, and transportation—can be applied increasingly to meeting the problems of urban development.

NORMAN BECKMAN *is Assistant Director (Metropolitan Areas) of the Advisory Commission on Intergovernmental Relations. He has previously served as a staff member of the Bureau of the Budget, concerned with Federal organization for urban development and housing, and before that held positions in the Public Health Service and in New York State government. He received his doctor's degree in public law and government from Columbia University in 1957.*

For further reading:
Advisory Commission on Intergovernmen-

tal Relations, *Governmental Structure, Organization, and Planning in Metropolitan Areas.* U.S. Government Printing Office, Washington, D.C., 1961.

"City-Federal Relations." *Proceedings of the American Municipal Congress*, American Municipal Association, Washington, D.C., 1958.

Connery, Robert H., and Leach, Richard H., *The Federal Government and Metropolitan Areas.* Harvard University Press, Cambridge, Mass., 1960.

The Editors of Fortune, *The Exploding Metropolis.* Doubleday Anchor Books, Garden City, N.Y., 1958.

The Federal Government and the Cities. George Washington University, School of Government, Business and International Affairs, Washington, D.C., 1961.

Fiser, Webb S., *Mastery of the Metropolis.* Prentice-Hall, Inc., Englewood Cliffs, N.J., 1962.

Housing and Home Finance Agency, *Workable Program for Community Improvement.* U.S. Government Printing Office, Washington, D.C., 1961.

Johnson, Thomas F., Morris, James R., and Butts, Joseph G., *Renewing America's Cities.* The Institute for Social Science Research, Washington, D.C., 1962.

National Resources Committee, *Our Cities, Their Role in the National Economy.* U.S. Government Printing Office, Washington, D.C., 1937.

Perloff, Harvey S., *A National Program of Research in Housing and Urban Development.* Staff Study, Resources for the Future, Inc., 1961.

Planning and the Urban Community, Harvey S. Perloff, editor. University of Pittsburgh Press, Pittsburgh, 1961.

U.S. Congress, House of Representatives, Committee on Government Operations (87th Cong., 1st sess.), *Government in Metropolitan Areas: Commentaries on a Report by the Advisory Commission on Intergovernmental Relations.* U.S. Government Printing Office, Washington, D.C., 1962.

―― Senate, Committee on Government Operations (87th Cong., 1st sess.), *Hearings To Establish a Department of Urban Affairs and Housing*, June 21–22, 1961. U.S. Government Printing Office, Washington, D.C., 1961.

―― Senate, Committee on Government Operations, Subcommittee on Intergovernmental Relations (87th Cong., 2d sess.), *Hearings on Problems of Federal-State-Local Relations*, September 18, 1962. U.S. Government Printing Office, Washington, D.C., 1962.

United States President's Commission on National Goals, *Goals for Americans.* Prentice-Hall, Inc., Englewood Cliffs, N.J., 1960.

Urban Government, Edward C. Banfield, editor. Free Press of Glencoe, Inc., New York, 1961.

Wood, Robert C., *1400 Governments.* Harvard University Press, Cambridge, Mass., 1961.

RECREATION; RE-CREATION

THE words are much the same. Recreation has become a basic ingredient of American life because of higher productivity, more leisure, a shorter workweek, and more income. We work hard; we need to play, walk, sit, think, and so to re-create body and mind. But where? Parks in cities need to be established, enlarged, or refurbished. Plans for play places are needed in growing suburbs. Farm forests, under multiple use, offer opportunities for farmers and visitors. In the "scatteration" that attends urban expansion, land may be bypassed and abandoned to weeds; it can be precious open space for recreation and considered growth. Our seashores, lakeshores, and riverbanks, long neglected, demand constant vigilance against exploitation. Our new system of highways can serve purposes besides transport—rest stops, picnic grounds, places to learn more about man and Nature. Our national parks and forests are within reach of more and more travelers. We need to cherish and protect them. A good environment for man must include some areas that are wild; for them, let us have enduring policies and programs.

297

RALEIGH BARLOWE AND
MILTON H. STEINMUELLER

TRENDS IN
OUTDOOR RECREATION

UNTIL recent decades, most Americans held to a work ethic. They regarded hard work and the act of being busy as a virtue. They disdained idleness. Most people were so occupied with the process of making a living and getting ahead that they had little time for outdoor recreation.

Many things have happened to make outdoor recreation, time for play and relaxation, and satisfying uses of leisure time an attainable goal in American life. Average productivity per man-hour has increased to a point at which it is no longer necessary for the average worker to toil long hours to acquire an acceptable or even a high level of living for his family.

People have decided that they would rather have more leisure than the income and products they could obtain from additional hours of work. Consumption activities have taken their place alongside production as a major function of our economy. People still adhere to a work ethic, but work has acquired aspects of play and play aspects of work, and many workers think of labor as a means to the attainment and enjoyment of leisure.

Leisure is the time one has free from his income-earning responsibilities and from personal and family housekeeping activities, such as eating, sleeping, keeping house, personal grooming, shopping, and similar activities that are necessary for day-to-day existence.

Recreation involves leisure-time activities that people engage in from choice or, as Dr. Marion Clawson says, free-time "activity (or inactivity) undertaken because one wants to do it."

How much leisure time Americans really have is a matter of question.

Statistics indicate that the average workweek in the United States dropped from 69.8 hours in 1850 to 60.2 hours in 1900, 49.7 hours in 1920, 43.3 hours in 1940, and 39.7 hours in 1960. One may conclude that the average American worker now enjoys 30 more hours of free time each week than his great-great-grandfather did in 1850.

That conclusion is subject to challenge.

The statistics on length of the aver-

299

age workweek are illusory in that they do not provide a complete measure of the actual time the average fully employed person works each week. Moreover, much of the increasing amount of time not counted as part of the workweek is used for nonleisure activities.

As Sebastian de Grazia indicated in *Of Time, Work, and Leisure,* a book published by the Twentieth Century Fund in 1962, factors like a longer journey to work, "moonlighting," overtime, time spent on household chores, and do-it-yourself projects have narrowed the amount of additional leisure actually enjoyed by the average person.

To some ways of thinking, genuine leisure may be viewed as a rarity in times past and as a near illusion today. Insofar as our nonworking hours are crowded with the thousand-and-one necessary details of modern life, we might well feel with Dr. de Grazia that, "Never before have so many Americans had so *little* time to call their own."

A look at the facts, however, shows that the average person does have more free time at his disposal.

UNTIL RECENT decades, genuine leisure has been primarily the province of a small segment of society. America supported a small leisure class, while the bulk of the population enjoyed what bits of leisure were available to them on an occasional and generally sporadic basis.

Today the benefits and satisfactions of leisure are available in greater volume to a much larger portion of the population. Leisure has become a privilege of the average man, and outdoor recreation has become a favored method of using one's leisure.

Man has long enjoyed outdoor work and play. Until about a century ago, the average adult American worked on a farm or in some other outdoor employment. With the rise of industrialization, much work moved indoors, and outdoor sports and recreation began to come into their own.

Perhaps the demand for outdoor recreation sprang from a realization of the shortcomings of urban life—from some inner urging, some basic desire for opportunity to commune with Nature and to play in the out of doors.

Frederic L. Paxson wrote in the *Mississippi Valley Historical Review* in 1917: "It was the open frontier that kept America young during its first century of national existence. . . . When the frontier closed in the eighties, the habit of an open life was too strong to be changed off hand. The search for sport revealed a partial substitute for pioneer life."

Baseball became a national pastime during the second half of the 1800's. Roller skating started in 1863. Bicycling, tennis, and polo were introduced in the 1870's. America's first golf tournament was held in 1894. Football and other college sports started coming into vogue near the turn of the century. The automobile started a new era in outdoor recreation.

Facilities for recreation have come with the rise of sports. The farsighted leadership of a few people brought the establishment of our first National, State, city, and local parks during the 1800's.

The acquisition and dedication of additional areas for public parks and places of recreation has continued; the Outdoor Recreation Resources Review Commission reported in 1962 that 283 million acres, 12.2 percent of the Nation's land area, had been designated for public recreational use.

Meanwhile, substantial private investments have gone into the development of golf courses, resorts, and commercial recreation facilities. Shelters, stadiums, scenic drives, and a host of other facilities have been provided both by public and private investment. Recreation has become a major business, which caters to the desires of millions and provides seasonal and permanent employment for thousands of individuals.

Among the several factors that have contributed to our increasing interest and participation in outdoor recreation are the growing population, the trend toward a shorter workweek, rising levels of individual and family income, changes in individual mobility, a revision of our attitudes regarding recreation, and the advertising and the publicity given to recreation.

Population numbers must always be regarded as a major component of demand. The population of the United States doubled between 1860 and 1890, doubled again between 1890 and 1930, and increased half again by 1960. This upward spiraling has added greatly to the number of potential users of outdoor facilities and has thus contributed to the overall increase in interest and participation.

The shorter workweek allows workers and their families time for outdoor play and relaxation. Shorter working days make it possible for workers to enjoy family activities in their yards, picnics in the park, or scenic drives during the week. The 5-day week permits weekend camping and fishing trips and Saturday excursions to the beach, to a ball game, or to nearby scenic areas. More and longer vacations with pay enable families to make transcontinental tours and trips to historical sites and scenic wonderlands.

Average productivity per man-hour in the United States (measured in constant 1950 dollars) was about 41 cents in 1860, 76 cents in 1900, 93 cents in 1920, 1.32 dollars in 1940, and 2.42 dollars in 1960. The increase has been reflected in rising real incomes; with higher incomes, many families have found it both possible and desirable to allocate larger shares of their incomes to recreation.

A revolution in communication and transportation facilities also has had an effect. Bicycles, automobiles, roads and expressways, speedboats and liners, and airplanes have fostered mobility. One can travel hundreds of miles in a few hours. Wonders of Nature that once seemed far away are just around the corner.

Individual participation ranges from little or no activity by some people to major emphasis on outdoor recreation by others.

An incomplete tabulation shows that around 5 billion dollars were spent for outdoor recreation in 1960. No allowances were made in this total for the cost of the automobiles, travel expenses, luggage, food and beverages, clothing, lodging, and the souvenirs people on vacation buy. These items may well have put overall expenditures between 15 and 25 billion dollars.

No set relationship exists between money spent on recreation and the amount of participation and enjoyment obtained therefrom. In outdoor recreation, it is often true that "the best things in life are free." The most popular activities—driving for pleasure, participation in outdoor games and sports, swimming, sightseeing, and bicycling—do not cost very much.

According to the Outdoor Recreation Resources Review Commission, the average person of 12 years or more participated 92.2 times in outdoor recreation activity in 1960. Slightly more than a third of the total—33.6 occasions—came during the summer.

Important relationships exist between participation and age, income, education, occupation, and place of residence. Youngsters, persons in families with annual incomes of 6 thousand dollars or more, families headed by college graduates and by professional people or by workers with paid vacations, and suburbanites have the highest rates of participation.

Annual visitation rates have been climbing steadily at our national parks and forests and at State, regional, and local parks. Sales of hunting and fishing licenses continue to climb. Camping, swimming, and boating enthusiasts are making intensive use of the increasing facilities provided for them.

This trend has caused the National Park Service and several State and local park agencies to embark on public land acquisition programs to provide additional park and recreational areas. It has caused the Forest

Service, the Fish and Wildlife Service, the Bureau of Reclamation, the Bureau of Land Management, the Corps of Engineers, and numerous State land management agencies to reevaluate their administrative policies and place increasing emphasis on recreation as a desirable multiple-purpose use of their land and water holdings.

Increased interest in outdoor recreation also has prompted adjustments in our thinking regarding public and private rights in natural resources. The forests and parks of Europe in times past were held largely as the private domain of the nobility. Our policies stress the public ownership of some areas and the need for obtaining and maintaining public access to extensive private lands for hunting, hiking, and other related uses.

New legal devices, such as the acquisition of conservation easements for the preservation of scenery and open spaces, have been developed. Public interests have been asserted in the use and enjoyment of lakes and streams; public access points have been acquired. Beach areas have been acquired and developed for public use, and wilderness areas have been established to preserve nature in its primeval state.

How MUCH outdoor recreation we will have in years to come will depend on world peace, population trends, individual choices, the willingness and economic ability of people to spend time and money on recreation, and on our foresight in providing facilities.

Projections of future trends vary with one's assumptions. Marion Clawson indicated in an article, "The Crisis in Outdoor Recreation," in American Forests in 1959, that the "increase in recreational demand might be as small as five times or as great as fifteen times" the demand of the midfifties by 2000. A more conservative fourfold increase was assumed by the Forest Service in its Operation Out-of-Doors program. Outdoor Recreation Resources Review Commission, in turn, has projected a threefold increase by the end of the century.

Fulfilling this demand calls for the development of additional facilities, some of which will require the acquisition of new sites, although many can come on lands already in public and private recreational ownership. The greatest need for new acquisitions likely will come with agencies operating in and near large cities.

Effective development and management of outdoor recreational areas is one of the key problems we face in preparing for the future. With good management, our future needs can be handled without major increases in park and recreational area acreages.

Significant problems can arise with the shifting of lands out of farms and forests into public and private recreational uses. For the operators involved, these shifts will involve a simple problem in economics. Private operators or public agencies will see opportunities to use land areas to advantage for the provision of recreation. They will offer the going prices for the lands they need, and the owners of the farm or forest land will sell if the circumstances please them.

Around cities, the acquisition of rural lands for parks or private recreational investments will attract or will be associated with other types of investment. Rural land values will be bid up as lands are bid off for subdivision and other uses. Speculation will bring the idling of large acreages. Lots will be laid out and developed. Demands for police and fire protection, for more roads, schools, and other public services will mount. Tax assessments and local millage rates will rise.

TWO TYPES of park and recreation lands come to mind when one thinks of rural recreation. One involves the large areas of resource-based lands in our national parks and monuments, in many State parks, in Federal and State forests, and in some other areas. The second type involves park and recreational lands located within a

2-hour drive of their major user populations. These areas can be described as intermediate-use areas.

Most of the lands in the resource-based areas find their present uses in recreation, forestry, and grazing. Little use is made of them for farming, and there is little prospect that they will be used for this purpose in the immediate future. Many that will be developed for intermediate uses have scenic values and are currently used to produce timber or grass. Their development, however, will call the shifting of some lands out of farming.

Generally speaking, attempts will be made in most of the resource-based areas to preserve natural resources—scenery, flora and fauna, and natural conditions—in their present state. Notable changes involving the creation of artificial lakes, the development of new vistas, the planting of trees and shrubs, and the like can be expected in many of the intermediate-use areas. Improvements involving the building of roads, the provision of parking areas, and the development of concession and service areas will affect both types.

Some of this development activity will be objected to by purists who maintain that the natural landscape should be preserved. Most people agree though that roads are needed to make areas accessible to the public. A better road is usually a safer road; a developed swimming area is often superior to the facilities provided by Nature; and facilities are needed to accommodate visitors.

Many places will suffer from use. Changes will occur because people stand on or walk over the land surface. Care will be needed to prevent upsets in ecological balances and to prevent erosion, the disappearance of plant and wildlife species, and the loss of esthetic values. Imagination and hard work will be required if resource managers are to prevent wholesale destruction of the things people expect to find in parks and recreational areas.

Designation of forested and grazing areas as parks and recreational lands can bring important changes in rural land use. Commercial forestry and grazing activities may be curtailed in some areas and thereby limit the economic base of some communities. A shifting of farmed land into intermediate-use areas also could lead to losses of rural economic base and local population.

The new developments, however, will generate other types of business and job opportunities.

People will be needed to develop, administer, and maintain the recreational areas. Motel, restaurant, and other service businesses will be needed to serve the needs of tourists and visitors. Insofar as desired recreational facilities are provided, the developments will probably buoy up local land values, bring new markets for local farm products, and provide employment possibilities for rural people.

Employment opportunities may develop along three major lines.

First, people will be employed in the construction, operation, and maintenance of new and expanded public and private recreation areas.

Second, possibilities for self-employment will occur in the operation of privately developed recreation businesses.

Third, there will be opportunities for employment in private developments or with firms which supply goods and services to recreationists.

Obviously, as public recreation areas grow in number, size, and use, more employees will be needed. Also, we can expect that many areas will be developed for more year-round use. And we can expect a greater amount and variety of private concession operations within the public areas. Although some of the new positions will require professional and skilled people, rural people have the qualifications for many of the positions which will become available within the recreation areas.

Self-employment possibilities will develop for many rural people. For some, however, the possibilities may be quite limited. Not every person owning a tract of land along a highway leading to a recreation site has a gold mine in terms of a potential motel, restaurant, or service station. Everyone on a reservoir does not have a potential marina or swimming beach. Every wooded area is not a potential campground. These kinds of developments require investment, business skill, and a certain amount of luck as well as a suitable location.

The role of private enterprise in supplying recreational resources has been discussed widely. There is little doubt that there will be many profitable opportunities—governments cannot do it all. People who can obtain capital and who have the necessary motivation and skill will often be able to establish private businesses that cater to recreational demands. Rural people will discover a growing number of employment opportunities in these kinds of firms. Not all of these will offer high wages nor will all of them offer year-round jobs. But the number of income-earning alternatives should increase for many rural people living in those parts of the Nation where recreation becomes more important.

Institutional adjustments involving changes in the laws, customs, and governmental organization of many rural communities may also be expected. With more visitors to both public and private recreation areas, local communities will often find themselves facing new problems. Informal and formal zoning regulations within recreation areas may be needed. Limitations on numbers of people will become more common. Restrictions on motorboats, water skiers, scuba divers, fishermen, and swimmers will be adopted to protect the safety of visitors.

Outside the recreation areas, local communities and political units will experience problems of obtaining desirable land use patterns. Planning and zoning can be used to guide development and insure against unwanted activities and structures. These measures will bring new adventures for many communities. Appropriate enabling legislation and competent advice is available in most States, but mistakes will be made nevertheless.

Increased road maintenance, pollution control, and police and fire protection problems will spring up in some communities almost overnight. Solutions to these problems will cost money—tax money. Who should pay, and how much, are questions that will receive increasing attention.

When a longer view is taken, the question arises: Is the action taken today sufficient and will it provide for the situation 10, 20, or 30 years from now?

With our 20–20 hindsight, we can see a number of missed opportunities that occurred in years past. A few more dollars invested in recreational developments then would pay off handsomely now. And a number of adverse impacts on our rural resources would have been avoided.

Many of the probable and possible impacts we have discussed seem so obvious as to scarcely need mentioning. Yet a consideration of past adjustments that affect rural communities shows that the impacts of earlier changes were not sufficiently anticipated and that strategically timed action was not taken. The impact of this force we call recreation is likely to be as far reaching in its effect in many areas as some important adjustments, such as the development of a highway system, in the past.

Successful adjustments to changing conditions will depend largely on the efforts by local resource owners and local community leaders to predict and analyze potential opportunities and impending problems. Action will be required to capitalize on opportunities and to avoid problems. There is no substitute for these steps. Mistakes will be made, but they will be of a smaller magnitude than if nothing is done.

RALEIGH BARLOWE *is professor and department chairman and* MILTON H. STEINMUELLER *is assistant professor, Department of Resource Development, Michigan State University.*

LAURENCE I. HEWES, JR.

RECREATION
AND RURAL PEOPLE

THE range of recreation services available to many farm people is relatively limited. Lack of money, a comparatively higher age, and lack of mobility, prevalent among some farm residents in particular localities, tend to restrict their participation in recreational activities, even if they had opportunities to do so.

Such are the conclusions one can draw from Study Report 19 of the Outdoor Recreation Resources Review Commission, "The National Recreation Survey," which presents data about the outdoor recreation of different segments of the population.

The report listed 20 activities, of which picnicking is the most popular.

In the summer of 1960, 53 percent of the people more than 12 years old and 54 percent of metropolitan and rural nonfarm residents but only 48 percent of the rural farm population went picnicking. The average rural nonfarm person (who lived in small towns or country residences) picnicked two or three times. Americans generally and city persons averaged a little more than two times. Persons who lived on farms averaged fewer than two picnics a year.

Higher percentages of farm and rural residents went fishing than Americans

generally and city residents. Somewhat higher percentages of the rural nonfarm population, however, engaged in boating (other than canoeing or sailing), camping, hiking, and water skiing than the other residential classes, including farm people.

The proportion of rural nonfarm residents engaging in camping was considerably higher than metropolitan or rural farm residents. The farm group had the lowest proportion.

A smaller proportion of farm residents than metropolitan or rural residents took part in boating (other than sailing or canoeing), water skiing, swimming, hiking, picnics, outdoor games, walking for pleasure, driving for pleasure, sightseeing, and attending outdoor concerts and theaters.

The activity repeated oftenest by farm people was swimming—an average of slightly more than two times during the summer of 1960.

Higher frequency among rural non-farm participants was reported for swimming (5.09), camping (0.86), picnics (2.41), outdoor games (3.05), driving for pleasure (5.93), and attending outdoor sports events (1.23). In no instance, except horseback riding, was there a marked difference in the frequency rate for rural nonfarm from either metropolitan or national average frequencies. On the other hand, farm frequencies were consistently lower than rural nonfarm frequencies and, in most instances, lower than national and city averages.

No single explanation for the characteristic preferences of farmers vis-a-vis the farm people and city people is possible. Perhaps farm people like horseback riding and fishing because facilities are closer and those sports cost them less. But that would not explain why they seldom go hiking. A possible reason for that is hiking may seem to be more like everyday work than recreation.

In the 12 months to May 1961, farm residents older than 12 years spent an average of 27.20 dollars for all outdoor recreation activity away from home; rural nonfarm residents spent an average of 45.80 dollars; city people spent 77.80 to 119.60 dollars; and the national average expenditure was 74.90 dollars.

When we list participation and frequency of participation in the major regions, we have a somewhat different variation.

In some regions, particularly the West, markedly higher proportions of rural farm and nonfarm people engaged in some sport.

Fishing is a favorite activity everywhere. More rural farm and nonfarm persons than Americans generally go fishing. Westerners especially like to fish. Rural southerners go fishing oftener than other Americans do.

Boating has a high score in the Northeast and West among the non-farm population, but not the southern farm group.

Three somewhat passive activities—walking for pleasure, driving for pleasure, and sightseeing—have relatively high scores in the Northeast among rural nonfarm residents.

We can draw several conclusions from the figures.

Generally speaking, higher proportions of rural nonfarm than of rural farm residents engage in outdoor activities. Except for fishing, overall minimum rates are generally in the South among rural farm residents.

The proportion of western rural nonfarm residents engaging in outdoor recreation activities is markedly on the high side relative to other regions, except for the more passive activities, in which northeastern nonfarm resident proportions are higher. Thus rural nonfarm residents engage at relatively higher rates for the more vigorous activities, particularly in the West. Overall rural participation is low, except for fishing in the South.

Preferences for 11 activities were analyzed in the survey.

General preferences were expressed by larger proportions of rural residents than by residents of large cities (or the country as a whole) for fishing, boating (other than canoeing or sailing), camping, and driving for pleasure.

Only for fishing, however, was the preference markedly higher among rural people than among residents of large cities or the total population.

Preferences were expressed by a slightly smaller proportion of rural residents for picnicking (32 percent) than by city residents and the Nation. For playing games, the preference of rural residents was 6 percent; cities, 9 percent; and the Nation, 8 percent; for swimming, rural (32 percent); cities (52 percent); and the Nation (42).

Preferences for fishing were expressed by a higher number of rural persons in the South (56 percent) than for rural persons in any of the other regions; the same is true of swimming in the Northeast (49 percent).

Driving for pleasure, sightseeing, and

attending outdoor games and sports tended to have higher proportions among rural residents in the north-central region than among rural residents in other regions. In general, percentages of rural preferences by regions did not differ much from the national rural preference rankings.

With few exceptions, boys and men prefer recreation that requires physical exertion, but girls and women tend to equal or exceed male participation in such activities as sightseeing, driving for pleasure, and picnicking.

A person tends to prefer the activities that he is familiar with and are easily available. An example is the preference of westerners for camping and of rural southerners for fishing. Even so, the percentage of participation may be a better indication of opportunity—a particular activity for which abundant opportunities are available may become commonplace. Thus, the high proportion of participation in several activities in the West may be taken to mean that opportunities for them are present and are used intensively.

Taken together, the lower western rural preferences for sightseeing (20 percent) and a participation of 46 percent among western farm residents could mean that many westerners have done all the sightseeing they want to do.

On the other hand, when the preference rating is high and the proportion of activity is low, we may guess that the facilities for that particular activity are inadequate. In the north-central region, for example, camping has a low percentage of participation and a considerably higher preference—perhaps a reflection of the low availability of public camping facilities.

The study group of the Outdoor Recreation Resources Review Commission tried to devise a means of rating opportunities for recreation. The general conclusion was: "High [opportunity] ratings were most frequent in the West; northeast and the north-central regions were next; and the

South had the lowest ratings on the whole. It was also noted that rural residents seemed to favor those recreation activities which involve 'roughing it.' "

Thus the rural group participates in outdoor recreation at rates close to the national averages. Yet several differences appear when rural residents are divided into rural farm and rural non-farm classes and by regions. The first difference arises from the observation that the rural farm group participates in outdoor recreation at a particularly low rate. The outstanding influences, aside from sex, on the rates of participation are age and income and not residence. Race is also a factor. Consequently, markedly lower proportions of participation by the rural farm group can hardly be attributed to rural residence alone, because, if it could be so attributed, the percentages of participation of farm and rural non-farm residents would tend to converge.

They do not. Rural farm rates are consistently and sometimes much lower than rural nonfarm rates.

The likeliest explanations of the differences are that the rural farm class includes substantial numbers of lower income families; that the average age of farmers may be relatively high; and that some facilities are not available to or used by Negroes, particularly Negro farmers.

That farm residents do not seem to

be able to engage in outdoor recreation as often as other residential groups may signify that on-farm rural persons do not receive or cannot achieve the same scope and variety of recreational services as city people.

It also may be that many individuals in the rural farm group are less mobile than metropolitan or rural nonfarm residents. To get to a place to fish, hunt, sail, and swim, one almost has to have an automobile; public transportation is not available in some rural sections. Low-income city people also must depend on public transportation and they have to use recreation centers near their homes.

It seems likely that the recreation services required by many farm people are those that are easily accessible to low-income people, white and Negro, of advanced years, who do not own automobiles, and who do not have access to the opportunities for recreation available to their fellow citizens in other groups.

It is hard to explain differences as to outdoor recreation among residential sectors in terms of cultural differences. The recreation services sought by rural people are like the opportunities sought by urban people. The desire for hunting, fishing, horseback riding, and camping, and so on can be satisfied more easily by some rural people than by some urban residents. This may account for somewhat higher rural participation in those sports. But that is by no means the universal condition.

It is possible also that the recreation pattern of farm families is affected by the seasonality of farming operations. From late spring to early fall, farm families in most regions are busy and have no leisure for recreation.

The quality of recreational facilities seems to be discounted if the impulse is strong. Thus an ocean beach and salt-water bathing may be no more used than the backwater of a small inland stream. On the other hand, in the West, an array of recreational resources of high quality seem to stimulate relatively large numbers of separate activities. This may also be related to the relatively milder weather in much of the West over a series of months each year, particularly in California.

Additional support for the conclusion that rural people have about the same recreational interests as other people is given in unpublished studies of the Farmers Home Administration on efforts of farm people to establish commercial recreation enterprises. In a number of instances, initial motivation for establishing a recreation enterprise was to provide recreation for the farm family and its neighbors. The enterprises include golf courses, water impoundments for swimming, boating, and fishing, and hunting preserves. The ability to develop such resources would be limited by cost and landownership.

It is likely, also, that smaller rural communities cannot afford to set aside extensive areas or to develop resources for such activities as picnicking, hiking, nature walks, and camping. To the extent that such services are available to farm people, it seems probable that they result from the favorable location of national and State parks and forests with respect to such rural residents, or, perhaps, from favorable location and access to public recreation establishments financed by larger nearby communities. But here again the factor of mobility is important, and the lack of adequate transportation would tend to keep some farm residents from deriving the benefits available to more mobile and affluent groups.

As a general attack is mounted against rural poverty, insecure old age, and racial discrimination, the therapeutic and morale-building qualities of outdoor recreation should be enlisted as part of rural reconstruction.

LAURENCE I. HEWES, JR., *joined the Office of Rural Areas Development, the Department of Agriculture, as Assistant to the Director in May 1962. Formerly he was Chief, Forecasts and Economic Studies Group, Outdoor Recreation Resources Review Commission.*

HUGH A. JOHNSON AND MAX M. THARP

MEETING THE DEMAND FOR OUTDOOR RECREATION

NINE-TENTHS of the American population participated more than 4 billion times in one or another of 17 forms of outdoor recreation in the summer of 1962. Very likely the participation will be three times greater than that before the year 2000, when three-fourths of all Americans may be living in cities and may have more leisure and money for recreation.

Studies made for the Outdoor Recreation Resources Review Commission pointed up the fact that the total demand for recreation is a complex mixture. People differ in their wants and needs, physical abilities, the time they have available, mobility, and funds.

Eva Mueller and Gerald Gurin reported in a study for the Commission that: "At present outdoor recreation seems to satisfy a need to acquire physical and manual skills. It offers a pleasant change from the urban environment. And it seems to play an important role in the social life of the American people, which is likely to imply further increases in participation."

They emphasized that desires for active types of recreation change with age. There are regional differences in preferences. Suburbanites take part in a greater variety and amount of outdoor recreation than do residents of city centers or the open country.

They said also: "Participation in outdoor recreation rises with income up to the $7,500–$10,000 income group and then declines slightly. Apparently among the lower income groups, lack of money now imposes some limitation on outdoor recreation activity. We therefore would expect an increase in participation rates over time as more people move into the income brackets over $7,500.

"Money is not the only factor at work, however. Participation in outdoor recreation also rises with improvements in educational and occupational status. It has been said that over the past two decades the middle and upper classes have been leaders in the trend toward a new life style, characterized by informal living. Outdoor recreation is part of this new life style.

"In the next few years, as lower income people become increasingly af-

309

fluent, as the level of education rises, and as more people are engaged in skilled occupations, it is likely that there will be more widespread participation in this new way of living. But when looking into the more distant future, we must recognize that popular tastes may change."

SIMPLE RECREATION activities are the most popular—driving and walking for pleasure, swimming, and picnicking—regardless of income, education, age, or occupation.

The Commission projected an increase of 228 percent in recreation occasions between 1960 and 2000. Driving for pleasure is expected to increase 184 percent; picnicking, 209 percent; swimming, 300 percent; boating (other than sailing or canoeing), 317 percent; water skiing, 476 percent; hiking, 511 percent; and hunting, 91 percent—if the quality and quantity of facilities available on a per capita basis is improved adequately.

Playgrounds and open space, picnic areas, and beaches and pools for swimming are the facilities most important for day use by large populations. They can be provided relatively easily from the standpoint of space, since a few acres can accommodate many people, but the space may be costly, especially in the central cities. It is possible, however, to provide such facilities, generally at reasonable costs, in expanding communities on the rural-urban fringe if proper plans are developed early and implemented along with the building program.

Bicycling and hiking also are popular. If trails for them were available in the right locations, children could bicycle to school safe from the hazards of traffic, and older people could use them, too.

On that subject, the Commission said in its report to the President: "The most basic thing that can be done is to encourage the simple pleasures of walking and cycling. It is something of a tribute to Americans that they do as much bicycling and walking as they do, for very little has been done to encourage these activities, and a good bit, if inadvertently, to discourage them. We are spending billions for our new highways, but few of them being constructed or planned make any provision for safe walking and cycling. And many of the suburban developments surrounding our cities do not even have sidewalks, much less cycle paths."

Outdoor recreation is seasonal. It ties in with school recesses, which also establish times for adult vacations.

A result is that seasonal patterns of recreation might cause crowding—picnic tables are not available, campgrounds are full, and beaches are overpopulated. During secondary peaks in the seasonal pattern, on weekends and holidays, roads to recreation areas often cannot accommodate all of the people who want to use them. Launching ramps, marinas, and beaches often are crowded far beyond their capacity during peak periods of use.

Information about visits was obtained by the Commission on about 5 thousand major nonurban public outdoor recreation areas of 41 acres or more. They had more than 500 million daytime visits in 1960. The overnight visits were about a tenth of the daytime visits. Some 11 thousand roadside parks, waysides, and picnic areas had a great number of short visits.

Nearly half of all daytime visits to the larger areas during the average weekend day in the season of greatest use were to State-operated areas—about 70 percent to State parks. About a third of the visits were to Federal areas (particularly national forests) and a fifth to parks and playgrounds owned by municipalities.

More than one-half of all overnight visits were to Federal areas, and most of the remainder were to State areas. The national forests accounted for two-thirds of all overnight visits to Federal areas, while parks reported the largest share for State-operated areas.

The total demand for recreation reflects the mixture of the many outdoor recreation activities. To satisfy the demand is a complex problem in logistics and economics. It is not easy for recreation planners to achieve a workable balance, for balances change, and changes make the best plans go astray.

An upsurge in sales and use of outboard motors, for example, led to a great demand for boating facilities, including places to operate the boats. Launching ramps, marinas, and access to available water itself became limiting factors. Then a new dimension was introduced. Scuba diving and water skiing became popular and increased the pressures at the larger lakes and impoundments, rivers, and seacoasts.

OUR SUPPLY of recreation resources, in the broadest sense, is the 2.3 billion acres of land and water of the United States. Space and scenery are attributes of land and water. Sightseeing, a popular form of recreation, depends on no standardized type of land, resource management, or ownership pattern but on individual tastes. More active forms of recreation are possible only on parts of the total acreage of land and water.

About 234 million acres of land and water in 48 States in 1960 were in nonurban, public, designated recreation areas, the equivalent of more than one-eighth of the total area. They included the entire acreage of National, State, county, and local parks, monuments, historic sites, memorials, geologic areas, archeological areas, forests, recreation areas, public hunting and shooting grounds, water access areas, fish hatcheries, and wildlife refuges where the public was permitted to engage in recreation activities. Highway waysides and rest and picnic places also were included in the total. Highway areas were small, totaling about 21 thousand acres for the 11 thousand such areas of which the Commission made an inventory. About 200 thousand acres of access areas, State, county, and other local forests and recreation areas also are included in the national total.

Besides these public designated areas, other millions of acres, private

as well as public, are used for recreation. For example, some 3 million acres of defense land in 48 States are open to various forms of recreation, mostly hunting. In the West, nearly 170 million acres of public domain land are available for limited recreation use. About 28 million acres of Indian land were reported open for various types of recreation in 1960. Much private forest land and farm and ranch land is open to recreation seekers, particularly hunters and fishermen.

This seeming abundance of recreation land fails to provide outdoor recreation opportunities adequate for the public. One of the major factors limiting its effectiveness is location. Much of the public recreation land is located where population density is least. The Northeast region, for example, with about 25 percent of the population, had only 4 percent of the public recreation area in 1960. The West, with 15 percent of the population, had nearly 73 percent.

Vast acreages in the western mountains are not available for use for general recreation. Concentrated populations are too far away to utilize them for day use or short visits.

Acreage thus is a poor indicator of the number of recreation opportunities available. The most popular forms of recreation often require little land. For example, picnicking and swimming require relatively small areas to service large numbers of people. Land and water resources designated for recreation often are usable for several recreational and nonrecreational activities. A lake, for example, may provide opportunities for fishing, boating, and swimming. Seasons of use and time of the day or week influence the number of recreation opportunities available.

Management also limits effectiveness of resources to satisfy demands. Management decisions can increase the effective supply of outdoor recreation resources without a corresponding increase in acreage. A change from low-density use emphasizing natural environment to high-density use emphasizing facilities creates more recreation opportunities in the same area. Areas managed for wilderness values necessarily must be large enough to provide space for the enjoyment of those values. Areas to be managed for picnicking can be smaller and provide a greater number of opportunities.

Nearly 85 percent of the public recreation areas in 1960 was managed by the Federal Government. State agencies were responsible for recreation management on about 14 percent of the total recreation acreage. Local government agencies controlled the remainder. More than 80 percent of Federal recreation land was in national forests. About 9 percent was in national parks, monuments, and other areas of the National Park Service.

Of the State recreation areas, forests accounted for 55 percent, fish and wildlife areas for 27 percent, and parks for 11 percent of the recreation land. Most of the local recreation land was in forests (79 percent), parks (9 percent), and fish and game areas (8 percent).

More than half of the Nation's total land is in farms. Most farmland can provide some kinds of recreation opportunities. Hunting and fishing are probably the most important. Farms and ranches contain thousands of ponds and numerous lakes and reservoirs, and they include thousands of miles of streams that produce fish and provide nesting areas for waterfowl. In many areas, farm ponds and streams supply a considerable portion of the total available fishing opportunities.

Outside the Western States, farmlands produce most of the huntable game. Under the Agricultural Conservation Program, millions of additional acres of "conservation" land will provide good wildlife habitat.

Farmlands also provide opportunities for hiking, picnicking, and camping. This phase has developed rapidly as a farm enterprise in some sections.

The leasing of deer-hunting privileges on farms and ranches, fee fishing in farm ponds, and ski tows are examples of recreation as an added farm

business. In some instances, farms have been converted wholly to serve the recreation trade, as, for example, the large number of hunting preserves for shooting stocked game birds that have sprung up in recent years. These instances are but suggestive of the potential for farmers and ranchers to increase their income by providing recreation facilities and services. With many rural communities facing a declining economy and with the urgent need to convert substantial amounts of cropland to other more profitable uses, the recreation possibilities should be fully evaluated. And, fortunately, much of the farmland of the Nation lies close to population centers where recreation is most urgently needed.

AN INVENTORY in 1960 indicated that about 4 million persons could be accommodated at one time for three types of day use. Overnight facilities on the public areas, campsites, cabins, trailer areas, lodges, and such had capacity for 1 million persons.

Estimates of potential capacity on public recreation sites were obtained for two time periods for selected day-use and overnight facilities. The short-time period covered the 1960–1964 development plans for existing recreation areas. A longer estimate extending to 2000 would require major changes in access, water supply, and so on.

Short-term potentials for expansion of picnic facilities were estimated to be about 40 percent more than the 1960 capacity. The long-range capacity, however, was expected to be about 2.6 times that of 1960. Combined short- and long-term increases would triple the picnicking capacity on the public recreation areas if the full potentials were reached.

The capacity of swimming beaches and pools was expected to increase by 70 percent in the short-term period and by 3.9 times the 1960 capacity over the longer period. This would create a combined short- and long-term increase of about 4.6 times the 1960 capacity.

Capacities of winter sports sites were expected to increase by 40 percent and 740 percent in the two periods.

The capacity of campgrounds, the only overnight facility for which potential developments were obtained, was expected to increase about 70 percent above 1960 in the short-term period. The long-range potential capacity, however, was expected to increase more than 11 times.

These estimated potentials indicate that the existing nonurban public recreation areas have the physical capacity to meet future demands for these types of activities. Public action will be needed to insure that the potentials will be reached. New acquisitions in specific localities and for certain types of facilities will be needed where full development of existing public areas will not meet the future demands. Acquisitions of recreation land and water areas for specific purposes may be urgently needed in metropolitan regions and rural-urban fringe communities. Shorelines are an example of a resource type in short supply relative to public demand.

THE MAJOR DIFFERENCES between public and private development for recreation hinge on economics.

Values in public recreation seldom if ever are measured in terms of potential profits. Investments are made in response to political or administrative decisions. But private developers must decide whether the recreation business will pay for itself. The analysis may be relatively simple if one specialized kind of operation is involved. It becomes complicated as the number and variety of services to be provided are increased.

Industries and corporations that have large holdings of land or bodies of water that may be developed for recreation must extend their economic analyses a further step. The chances are that recreation is unrelated to their primary business and represents a considerable investment, whose only tangible return is through the fleeting values measured in public goodwill.

In the Commission's Study Report 17, "Multiple Use of Land and Water Areas," the American Forestry Association stated industry's case thus:

"Multiple use of private land differs from multiple use of public property in that more emphasis must be placed upon economic returns by the private owner. This necessity usually focuses more attention upon some major use and limits the extent to which minor uses may be permitted. . . . Multiple use of industrial forests [is] the accommodation of a maximum of other compatible uses with the growing of trees for successive timber harvests."

WHETHER A PRIVATE owner can make money by using his property to provide recreation facilities depends on whether he can furnish the services people will pay for and its location.

A location near public recreation facilities can be a help and a hindrance. Public developments attract visitors, but because they are free or inexpensive, private enterprise, which must charge for use of facilities, may not be able to compete with them.

A public park or forest might provide camping and picnicking areas but only limited housing accommodations. Private owners can provide motel, hotel, and cabin services for people who want facilities different from those in the public areas or who lack access to what is available. They can provide a variety of other goods and services unavailable at the nearby public facilities—food, gasoline and repairs, outfitting and guiding, specialized land and water sports, and other services.

Most people looking for recreation differentiate between public and private ownership only as ownership affects the opportunities available and the expenses involved. In practice, public ownership and development generally involve land with relatively few other economic uses and facilities and services that private enterprise cannot or will not provide.

The terrain and vegetation do not

change because of ownership. The economics of ownership, however, operate selectively to concentrate ownership of some land used for recreation in the public sector and others in the private one.

Large areas whose use usually is extensive and intermittent tend to be in public ownership. Smaller areas capable of intensive use are more apt to be privately owned. Operations such as outfitting and pack trips often depend on a public-private combination with public ownership of land resources and private ownership of equipment, livestock, and some facilities.

Sylvia Porter, an economist who writes a syndicated column, wrote in September 1962 on the economic climate for business ventures. "The birth trend of new businesses is down," she said, "and the death trend is up." She cited a study by Dun & Bradstreet of the causes of business failures in 1961: Inexperience, 46.9 percent; incompetence, 44.4 percent; neglect, 3 percent; fraud, 1.3 percent; disaster, 0.8 percent; unknown, 3.6 percent.

She noted: "As always, the highest mortality rate is among business babies—a death rate of 56.2 percent in businesses in existence five years or less in 1961—but the toll is rising among older ones too."

The mortality rate among new outdoor recreation enterprises probably is among the highest and very likely is due mostly to inexperience and incompetence of management.

The recreation industry often runs aground on another kind of shoal—the public's fickleness. Fads for certain sports or for certain areas come and go.

Unseasonable weather or a temporary breakdown along the transportation system frequently spells disaster for a highly seasonal business.

Some enterprisers no doubt can provide some recreation services on a financial shoestring, but most businesses require large amounts of capital and high levels of managerial ability.

Some advocates of recreation as a cure for the ills of regional under-

employment and to meet a need for new enterprises in the country apparently ignore this fact. As agriculture once was expected to absorb the urban unemployed during depression, outdoor recreation apparently is being prescribed as a panacea for maladjustments in land uses.

Only disillusionment and waste can result when planning is absent.

Average data on investment may have little meaning because of the variations in what the investment covers, but replies from more than 2 thousand operations give us a guide.

The average investment in 152 resorts was 740 thousand dollars; in 64 dude ranches, more than 200 thousand dollars; in 44 commercial beaches, more than 530 thousand dollars; and in 13 resort hotels, more than 1.5 million dollars.

One motel operator estimated the average investment was 10 thousand to 15 thousand dollars per room, depending on the kitchen facilities and number of public rooms.

Investment in 157 ski areas, many operating on leased land, averaged 250 thousand dollars; many of their operators reported plans for expansion, which would increase the average.

The average investment of trail riding and pack trip operators in one State was about 100 thousand dollars in horses, equipment, camping accommodations, and so forth, even though most of their trips and activities occur on public lands.

A study of regulated shooting preserves in Pennsylvania in 1957 showed an average investment of about 58 thousand dollars in land, buildings, equipment, machinery, birds, dogs, and other needed items.

MANY FARM sections have an adequate combination of wildlife game and potential hunting demand to make possible at least a modest income from the sale of hunting rights.

More and more farmers are coming to feel that the trespass privilege for the purpose of hunting is valuable and that they should realize some income from it. This may be in the form of a seasonal lease to a sportsman's club or a daily fee charged to each hunter. These ventures are most successful when conducted on a fairly large acreage. Some farmers can easily band together for this purpose. In one midwestern county, 50 farmers pooled their land for deer hunting. Hunters are charged 10 dollars a day. In 1961, this land provided 1,600 man-days of hunting and brought each farmer an income of 320 dollars. Some of the farmers also provided rooms and meals for hunters.

Many marginal farms provide opportunities for new enterprises in recreation—but not without costs, which rise sharply as the shift to new enterprises is made.

Many large, old farmhouses have room for guests, and the farm operations could be organized to provide activities interesting to visitors. But many of the houses require intensive repairs and remodeling, purchase of modern equipment, and other investments before they will attract visitors as a paying proposition.

Where adequate facilities exist or can be provided, vacation farms or ranches provide an opportunity for city families to enjoy modest-cost, unsophisticated vacations outdoors, together with an opportunity to see something of farm life. Usually vacation farms provide pleasant and quiet surroundings in an agreeable climate, home cooking, and a few simple accommodations. They may include facilities for swimming, horseback riding, fishing, hiking, picnicking, and nature study.

Many farms can accommodate this kind of enterprise. A small farm in the Northeast furnishes an example of a successful operation. This place was occupied by a retired craftsman, who sought to supplement his income by accepting summer guests. Most of the guests are elderly city couples. The farm can accommodate about 15 persons. Guests are accepted throughout the year, but most of them come from May through September. About 50 or 60 couples are accommodated annually. Most of them stay about a week. This farm is near an established vacation area and provides little in the way of recreation facilities except cards, TV, a large library, and croquet. The operator and his wife do most of the work related to the business. The enterprise nets this farmer about 3 thousand dollars a year in addition to a modest regular income from farm operations.

Thousands of farm ponds built for other purposes can be used for fishing, swimming, and boating, but many ponds are hard to reach, and others cannot be managed without sizable outlays.

An example is the experience of a farmer in Schuylkill County, Pa., who built a 5-acre pond that his family, employees, and friends could use. He stocked it with fish, built picnic tables, and landscaped the area. A few group picnics and carloads of visiting fishermen convinced him that his pond was a liability if he did not restrict its use carefully. Visitors broke up his picnic tables for firewood and left the grounds littered with trash. He learned also that he would be financially liable for any accidents.

On the other hand, hundreds of similar ponds provide thousands of hours of recreation for farm families and friends. The smaller ponds usually have very limited productivity for commercial operations, but larger ones frequently provide the central core for active commercial enterprises run concurrently with the farm business or as a substitute for farming.

A midwestern farmer with a small, 85-acre farm realizes about 1,500 dollars net income each year from a fishing enterprise. Two ponds were constructed on the farm, together with access roads and a few structures including a minnow pond and a snack bar. The farmer also sells bait and fishing tackle. The two lakes can accommodate a maximum of 75 poles. Charges for a day's use of a pole range from 1 dollar to 3 dollars. The operator, his wife, and seven children provide the necessary labor.

The Rural Areas Development Newsletter for September 1962 described a "one-man rural areas development recreation project," developed when one farmer sold his dairy herd, constructed a 9-hole golf course, added a 12-lane bowling alley, and converted his milking parlor into a restaurant. This shift in enterprises cost 400 thousand dollars to start with; plans for further developments may boost the total capital costs to a million dollars.

Another type of income-producing project is the sports center which may be based upon a lake or pond, providing swimming and boating facilities, or horseback riding, winter sports, or some other popular activity. The development of these enterprises may be quite expensive, particularly if a pond has to be constructed or if stables and other equipment needed for horses have to be built. They need to be within easy commuting range of population centers.

AN EXAMPLE of a cooperative possibility for providing recreation is a Town and Country Recreation program. This is a program to tie together the needs of urban areas for open-air recreation with the resources available in nearby farming areas. The urban population would benefit by being able to participate in the development of recreational facilities and the enhancement and protection of rural scenic areas.

Boys' and girls' clubs, nature groups, civic associations, and others could actually participate in the work. Farmers would also enjoy the recreational facilities and would obtain financial benefit from Federal cost sharing for improvement of land and water resources that would enhance recreation. They also would realize some direct income benefits, as the increased flow of urban visitors would make possible the establishment of riding stables, roadside produce stands, and other enterprises. Enjoyment of

the recreational facilities would be open to the general public.

The program would be developed somewhat as follows:

A few metropolitan areas would be found that were interested in cooperation with local associations of farmers in an outdoor recreation program. The urban unit might be a city, a borough, a suburb, a park authority, or similar entity. The association of farmers might be a soil conservation district, a watershed association, or a special recreation district.

An agreement would be worked out that would provide that the urban area would raise funds and furnish volunteer workers for recreational development and the rural area would provide certain natural facilities, and preserve certain amenities such as scenery. The Federal Government, in cooperation with State and local agencies, would provide technical aid and share costs of some developments, such as tree planting, establishment of wildlife habitat, pond construction, land acquisition, and basic facilities.

Farmers would be assisted to obtain loans for development of supplementary income-producing recreational enterprises.

Limited funds frequently prevent the development of new enterprises and their later expansion. Bankers as a rule are skeptical of proposals for recreation development. Losses have been high for the family-managed operating units. Corporations and larger scale developments usually have long-term financing from sources other than banks and can arrange short-term loans for seasonal operating costs.

BUT OUR increasingly metropolitan population must get most of its recreation near home.

We can classify recreation areas as user-oriented, intermediate, and resource-based, or as local areas, all-day, and overnight and vacation areas.

Local or user-oriented areas as a class probably start with one's own backyard—or, too often, play in the city streets when backyards are absent—and radiate outward in time and distance to areas used for an evening's or an afternoon's recreation. Next are areas and facilities one would visit only on an all-day outing. The last class can be visited only on overnight and vacation trips.

Built-up areas generally are short of spaces set aside for any kind of recreation. Many suburban areas also lack actual facilities. The potential for development often remains, however, if the community is willing to use lands still available for the activities. Somewhat farther out, in zones where subdivisions still are growing, prospects for outdoor recreation still are bright, although they grow steadily dimmer as communities fail to preempt remaining resources well suited for recreation.

Programs to acquire land and develop facilities almost always must be a public responsibility in built-up areas because of cost and the management problems involved. The public hand probably also must be firm in suburban areas to assure that land is acquired and facilities developed by public agencies for some recreation uses and that incentives are provided private enterprise to develop others.

A common claim has been that rapidly growing urban-suburban areas were swallowing land resources needed for recreation uses. While this generality is a partial truth insofar as sound regional planning is concerned, observation of suburban areas casts doubt on this argument. Frequently whole farms, bypassed as the suburbs leapfrog outward, remain physically available for recreation or other enterprises. Similarly, tracts too small for modern mass development methods and areas too steep, too wet, or too stony remain as open areas inviting future use for recreation.

Not all such acreage would be suitable for parks and playgrounds, but much of it could be used to help piece out the scarce public areas. Many of the tracts are the remaining spaces available for playgrounds, sports fields, and picnic areas adjoining or lying between residential subdivisions.

Similar situations frequently occur as remnants of subdivisions. Steep slopes, flood plains, and gorgelike areas near small streams are unsuited for housing. The developers often are willing to donate these "useless" lands to the community. Public planners are learning to demand better bargains. Ordinances on the development of subdivisions more and more include setback lines and regulations as to flood plain use, dedicated open spaces in proportion to developed area, and other concessions to amenity values.

Better bargains for public recreation probably can be struck in the future when more planners recognize the requirements for recreation that can be adapted to lands marginal for building purposes. They should be able to set aside strips and blocks of land that are big enough and comprise parts of an integrated framework to meet the community's needs for recreation land.

Progress can be made when public representatives and developers are willing to negotiate on the basis of best uses for land from the public viewpoint as well as the best development plan from the business viewpoint.

An analysis we made in 1958 said: "In sections in which peculiar values do not upset the generalized pattern, about 4 acres of rural land are affected for each acre actually developed for urban use—at least 2 acres on the edge of activity enter a nonuse, ripening stage; nearly an acre inside the area of activity is undeveloped; and about an acre is used."

A survey in northern New Castle County, Del., in 1962 disclosed that 5 percent of the total area was in privately owned vacant tracts of 10 acres or more lying outside cities and subdivisions. Nine of ten of the holdings had a poor potential for immediate development because of the size of the tracts, limitations in soil characteristics, distance from public facilities, such as water and sewer lines, and other factors that make them economically marginal for the proposed uses. The soils on many of the tracts were unsuited for crops. The mixture of old fields and woods, level to rolling topography, and wet to good drainage make these same lands ideal for a variety of recreational uses.

The Economic Research Service in a study of potential new sites for outdoor recreation in 10 Northeastern States showed that land use within a band reaching from the essentially urban built-up areas outward for 25 miles contained about 55 percent forest; 9 percent idle land, much of which was reverting to forest; 7 percent pasture; and 29 percent cropland and other uses.

Five types of recreation sites were defined to include factors of cover, slope, and area needed to provide opportunities to develop a recreation unit. These site types were called: Gorge-ravine; ridgetop-headwater; stream, river, lake, or pond; small stream; and potential pond sites. By definition, most of them would occur within wooded lands, fields lying idle or in pasture, and generally on the rougher topography.

Within this 25-mile zone near urbanized areas, a carefully drawn sample showed that one or another of these basic types of sites occurred an average of once per 129 acres of forest, once per 258 acres of idle land, and once per 320 acres of pasture.

For the rest of the 10-State region lying farther afield, the rates of occurrence were once per 132 acres of forest, once per 303 acres of idle land, and once per 645 acres of pasture. The occurrence of any one of the five types of sites varied more widely, of course, depending on the geologic conditions of the areas. A high percentage of all sites occurred in land use capability classes IV, VI, and VII—not recommended for sustained economic agriculture or generally suitable for urban development. Sites identified on the better soils of classes I, II, and III usually were in areas previously farmed but now idle or reverting to forest.

A wide range in physical opportunities for recreational developments of this nature would be expected in different parts of the country. The study demonstrates, however, that unsuspected potential resources for recreation still remain even in densely populated regions.

The problem is to get the potential changed to actual use for recreation.

The Outdoor Recreation Resources Review Commission, in its recommendations for a development and management program to provide needed recreational facilities in the future, stressed the need for realistic planning and conscientious followthrough by public agencies—from Federal to local. It emphasized also that private enterprise can have an increasingly important part in it if it is given a chance.

The Commission developed a system for classifying outdoor recreation resources "encompassing the full range of physical resources needed for all kinds of outdoor recreation activity and specifying the types of management required for optimum recreation uses of each category." The six categories range downward in intensity of resource use from class I, "high-density, recreation areas" (for mass use), through class V, "primitive areas" (limited and specialized uses), and VI, "historic and cultural sites."

The classification system is based primarily on physical features and is designed largely to spur programs of public agencies.

In the words of the Commission: "While the specific management policies recommended are most applicable to public areas, the underlying concept of recreation zoning has relevance for private areas as well."

Case studies conducted for the Commission's reports disclosed the dangers to private interests when public agencies and individual public employees at times seem to have acquired virtually dictatorial powers for policy decisions and program development or require excessively rigid compliance with minor regulatory details, or establish conditions which private operators cannot meet economically.

The Bureau of Outdoor Recreation was created in 1962 as a semiautonomous body located administratively in the Department of the Interior. One of its important functions is to provide leadership, guidance, coordination, and assistance necessary to assure adequate planning for recreation development. One of its responsibilities is to encourage a proper, functioning balance at all levels of public responsibility for recreation programs and a desirable combination of public and private enterprise to assure the best possible array of opportunities.

Surveys of Federal and State agencies with responsibilities for recreation programs suggest that planning frequently leaves much to be desired. Customary programs are adapted to anticipated incomes. Landowning agencies may frown on approaches for cooperative use by "program" agencies. Some administrators may be unfamiliar with laws and regulations that frequently could be used effectively to improve the agencies' services.

But on the other hand, the surveys brought out the imagination, long-range planning, public relations, and new ideas other agencies were using to enlarge their recreation programs.

Progress is possible.

New York voters in 1960 authorized a bond issue of 75 million dollars to be used for acquiring more public land for parks, beaches, and uplands. The people of New Jersey approved a similar bond issue for 60 million dollars in 1961. Wisconsin launched a 50-million-dollar program. Other States, including California, Massachusetts, and Michigan, have begun to develop comparable programs. Various methods of financing recreation have been under consideration in other States and by the Federal Government.

Some States are using easements to acquire use of land at a considerable saving over purchase in fee simple.

Wisconsin has purchased scenic easements along many of the State's highways, particularly along the Great River Road. Funds were included in Wisconsin's 50-million-dollar 10-year resource development program to acquire scenic easements on an estimated 450 miles of Wisconsin highways by 1964 and for more than 3 thousand miles of highways by 1971.

Easements are also being proposed by many metropolitan areas to provide open space and greenbelts around their rural-urban fringes.

Greater use will probably be made of such devices in the future to insure more recreation opportunities for urban and suburban people.

IF THE DEMAND for recreation grows as we expect it to, planning authorities will need all the workable ideas that can be collected.

The problem will be to provide the necessary services and facilities on lands and waters owned both publicly and privately.

Public access can be assured by public action through a variety of legal tools, such as acquisition of full right in the resources, acquisition of rights less than full ownership, regulatory devices, and assessment and tax policies.

Less formal arrangements often can be negotiated with owners of private property to allow access to some areas if users follow prescribed conditions.

A few State fish and game agencies have made notable progress against "No Hunting or Fishing" signs. They have promised private owners that visitors will adhere to certain standards of conduct. The game wardens have vigorously patrolled the areas to enforce compliance.

Another kind of planning involves joint programs of public agencies and private business to assure adequate and varied services and facilities for a well-rounded recreation area.

The concessionary system followed by some agencies is a step. Private enterprise teams up with government to provide facilities and services on government-owned land. The public gets the services, government money is saved, and opportunities are created for private investments to earn income.

Efforts by some agencies to acquire development rights or restrictive zoning in areas adjoining the approaches to their holdings are another way.

Still a third device is to license guides, pack trip operators, tour managers, and others to use roads and trails, campsites, and other facilities on public holdings.

But practically the whole range of possibilities for cooperation in recreation resource development remains to be explored.

We know that private operators tend to cluster around public facilities— that is where the tourists and recreationists are.

We know that free public campgrounds or subsidized overnight facilities in areas where privately owned facilities would be possible reduce the economic feasibility of private development.

But we do not know what the total opportunities for both public and private developments in a given situation may be, nor do we know which should be publicly controlled and which privately.

In other words, recreation planners need to consider the benefits (both cash and noncash) that might accrue when public and private interests cooperate in providing recreation facilities that complement each other. When this is done, facilities can be provided by those best equipped to do the job within an overall development program and social benefits tend to be maximized.

The problem of meeting the demand for outdoor recreation is not one of choice between public or private enterprise. Its solution will involve both public and private activities. Public policy and the policy of public agencies strongly affect the conditions under which private enterprise can operate.

The real problem, then, involves questions of who can do what best, and where, when, how much, and under what conditions.

Emphasis on economy frequently has concentrated public holdings in areas of low land values, far removed from population centers and only partially adapted for the proposed uses. Housekeeping expenses, including planning, operation, and maintenance, are continuing but necessary drains on budgets. While they preserve the status quo, these worthwhile expenditures add little to the recreation resources.

A study by the staff of the Outdoor Recreation Resources Review Commission found that operation and maintenance expenditures accounted for approximately 64 percent of total direct outdoor recreation expenditures made by the States during 1951–1960, compared with 26 percent for development and construction, and 10 percent for land acquisition.

As reported in the Commission's Study Report 25, expansion of the State park systems and related projects came in the thirties. Total expenditures in 1933–1934 were approximately 6 million dollars by State agencies in 28 States. Twenty States had not established park systems. The 48 States in 1951 reported direct outlays for outdoor recreational opportunities, facilities, and services of 117 million dollars. By 1960, States reported outlays 58 percent greater than the 1951 level. States provided 187 million dollars for outdoor recreation in 1960.

Federal agencies in 1951 reported financial outlays of 54 million dollars for provision of outdoor recreation. By 1960, 189 million dollars was reported by Federal agencies.

Outlays for outdoor recreation were estimated to be more than 8.5 billion dollars for the 1951–1960 period in terms of 1960 dollars. Direct Federal outlays for recreation during the 10 years were 1.2 billion dollars. State agencies reported similar outlays of 1.5 billion dollars. Local outlays were estimated at about 5.8 billion dollars.

Development for use frequently has lagged through lack of appropriations or has been eked out from secondary sources such as license fees, gate receipts, or use taxes, such as on ammunition.

The concession system used by State and Federal agencies is a modification whereby private business provides services on public lands that the public agencies cannot provide.

The National Planning Association, in a report, "Paying for Recreation Facilities," said that the concession system has provided almost all the commercial and quasi-commercial facilities now in national parks, national forests, at Federal reservoirs, and other Federal recreation developments.

The same report said also:

"Private capital is largely attracted through the concession system in which private persons, in return for a franchise fee or rental, are allowed to conduct a business for profit on public property, under such rules and regulations as are laid down by the responsible government agency. The reason for the dominating role of the concession system is simple: It has been the most practicable and most efficient way of supplying the facilities. Sometimes both the capital and the management of the facility are from the private sector. In many other cases, public funds are used to construct the facilities but management is turned over to a private firm.

"Such arrangements allow facilities to be constructed and operated with less public capital and with fewer public employees than would otherwise be the case. It is in accord with the widely held view that the government should not provide services that the private sector can supply. In recent years, moreover, techniques have been devised which have led to the establishment of several hundred small, private, independent business enterprises in connection with public recreation, a development which has widespread approval."

But by no means all recreation and even less of the services occur on public lands. Private enterprise usually can be observed clustered around approaches to public lands. Probably many times more investment for facilities and services occurs near public lands than on them.

No estimate of total private investment in recreation resources is available. But the amount would be staggering. Privately owned farmland used primarily for other purposes contributes its bit to the recreation whole—as do weekend retreats, cabins and camps, gas stations, and hotdog stands—in their proper places.

In concluding our thoughts on ways to meet the demand for recreation, we concur with Ayers Brinser, School of Natural Resources, University of Michigan, when he wrote:

"If recreation is to be given equal consideration in budget decisions it is necessary that the calculation of costs and returns from recreation investments be estimated in such a way that they are comparable with similar projections for alternative investments with which recreation must compete in budget decisions. As an equal claimant in public budget decisions, recreation must be defined in a way that differentiates what is properly an opportunity for public investment in contrast with opportunities for private investment in recreation."

The array of potential demands is infinite. The opportunities appear to be legion. The challenge is clear. We, as a Nation, can have a better, richer life than ever before if we only will use our potential for recreation wisely.

Hugh A. Johnson, *a research agricultural economist, is Leader, Urban Impact Investigations, Land and Water Branch, Economic Research Service. He was project director of two studies conducted by the Economic Research Service for the Outdoor Recreation Resources Review Commission.*

Max M. Tharp, *a research agricultural economist, is Leader, Southern Area Development Investigations, Economic Research Service. He was formerly Chief, Inventory and Evaluation Group, Outdoor Recreation Resources Review Commission.*

R. C. WILSON AND GEORGE VITAS

MULTIPLE USES
OF FAMILY FORESTS

ONE of rural America's great opportunities lies in the improvement and development of farm woodlands. Our small woodlands cover a quarter of a billion acres. They contain one-third of the sawtimber volume and much of the most accessible and best timberland in America. They can supply nearly one-half of the timber that will be needed by forest industries and an ever-increasing income from public outdoor recreation—camping, picnicking, hunting, fishing, and other services.

Four and one-half million Americans own tracts of woodland that average 60 acres. These family forests comprise about 55 percent of the country's commercial forest land. Three of every four farms have family forests.

Yet, as an inventory of the Nation's forests has revealed, they are growing only one-half or one-third of the volume of good forest products they are capable of growing. They are producing far less than their potential of other benefits and services if the fullest multiple use were made of woodland properties.

Multiple use is the management of wooded and related areas so as to conserve the basic land resources and produce sustained yields of timber, recreation, water, and wildlife in a harmonious combination that meets the landowner's objectives. The objec-

tives could be a regular annual income, a deferred periodic income, the build-up of capital value, the preservation of a favored grove of trees, the development of better hunting and fishing opportunities, and the maintenance of esthetic qualities.

Multiple use may be applied much more intensively to a family forest than to any other forest holding, for its effective application implies that many people have access to the benefits contributed by a parcel of land and that several benefits are derived from it.

Most family forests are on farms, and most farms are in populous States or close to primary transportation routes. Accessibility favors the use of the resources on family forests by large numbers of people.

Use of the timber is easy because of the relatively short distances over

322

which logs or other harvested items need be transported to the mill.

People must go to the forest to experience returns from such other values as recreation and wildlife values, but in this respect also the family forest is situated more favorably than are most holdings in other ownerships. It may be within motoring reach of thousands of people in a matter of a few hours.

THE DIFFERENCES in the values attached to the various benefits and use of family forests merit examination against the background of management opportunities that are suggested by the changing and varied attitudes of owners of small woodlands.

Some owners favor nonuse and view their timberlands as preserves on which the only logging they allow is that necessary to remove dying or dead trees. Others liquidate all realizable values or deplete forest productivity by inviting the first timber buyer to cut whatever trees he chooses regardless of consequences to the forest.

Some owners have a wait-and-see policy. They may permit restricted cutting but are undecided as to what course to follow, partly because they do not fully understand the opportunities available.

Still others seek to manage the woodlot for maximum dollar returns from wood production without impairing the site for other uses.

These viewpoints suggest that many owners of family forests would be interested in managing for multiple use if the full potentials of returns from all land uses—timber harvests, recreation, game management, and minor forest products—were set forth.

TIMBER HARVESTS often provide the quickest means of converting forests to dollars. Today, when wood can be manufactured into several hundred different useful products as varied as tissue paper and telephone poles, almost any tree represents cash if it is not defective, is large enough for processing, and can be marketed.

Some trees may not bring enough returns to pay for costs of logging. Others may command high prices regardless of whether they are logged immediately or held for cutting at a future date.

An example: Using published price reports as references, a forester in an Eastern State may appraise the values of three white oaks, each 3 feet in diameter and containing about 1,500 board feet, at nothing, 60 dollars, and 200 dollars, respectively, on the stump. His experience tells him that the first tree is so crooked and contains so much rotten wood and so many knots or other defects that it cannot yield a single merchantable log or bolt. The second tree contains two high-grade sawlogs and two other merchantable logs, which in the aggregate should be worth about 100 dollars when logged and delivered to the mill. The third tree, choice in form and quality, contains two veneer logs and two sawlogs that should bring nearly 250 dollars at the mill.

The forester would probably recommend killing the rotten, unmerchantable oak (along with other culls or undesirable trees) to release growing space for younger trees. He may also prescribe reserving for future cuts some presently merchantable trees having good growth potential. He knows that there always will be a demand for high-quality hardwood suitable for choice furniture and paneling.

The owner of a family forest may not be able to put his tract under intensive forest management immediately, but it is to his advantage to devote at least some effort to his woodland to protect it from fire and destructive cutting until he can invest in other management measures. Even this minimum of effort can do much to keep his woods stocked with desirable trees.

Timber stands can be improved in a number of ways: Killing cull trees by girdling, poisoning, or felling to release growing space for desirable trees; thinning of overcrowded stands to increase growth; removal of brush or other undesirable ground cover to favor establishment of tree seedlings; interplanting to fill gaps in a stand; pruning fast-growing but limby trees to improve wood quality; and conversion cutting to replace an undesirable stand with a desirable one.

The proper treatment can be prescribed best by a professional forester, since the need for treatment varies with the species, age, quality, vigor, and like factors.

THE COSTS of planting trees and possible returns from plantings are of particular interest to landowners who have nonforested idle land suitable for growing trees.

Costs and returns depend on the particular situation, but an analysis of prospects within the range of one important commercial species may be helpful as an illustration. Within the native range of loblolly pine on the average site, one forestry expert estimated the planting costs at 10 to 20 dollars an acre, depending on whether the trees are planted by machine or by hand, the spacing between trees, terrain, and local wage rates.

Regardless of the planting site, recurring annual expenses for taxes, fire protection, and professional advice may be perhaps 75 cents an acre.

The time between planting and final harvest and the number of intermediate partial harvests varies as to whether sawlogs, poles, piling, pulpwood, other products, or combinations of them are to be produced. If the primary objective is to grow pulpwood (for which markets continue to expand), the harvest may be scheduled when the stand is 30 years old. Intermediate cuts of merchantable material may be made when the stand reaches 20 and 25 years of age.

The prospective pulpwood harvest is estimated at 30 cords an acre on the average site when plantings are spaced at 6 and 8 feet. This harvest includes about 13 cords estimated to be removed during the two intermediate cuttings. A possible range in prices

for pulpwood stumpage (the value of standing timber) during the next 30 years is 4 to 7 dollars a cord, although the actual range will depend on the location of the tract, growth of forest industries, and the value of future dollars. If the stumpage is 7 dollars and the land cost is 20 dollars an acre, for example, the prospective rate of return (computed by compound interest formula) would be 6.5 percent when planting costs are 10 dollars an acre. If the stumpage is 4 dollars and the costs of the land and planting are the same, the rate of return would be only 4 percent. Significantly higher costs of land or planting therefore would make an operation marginal during a long period of low stumpage prices.

The land cost may be assumed to be nothing when the owner is not considering sale of his tract but is trying only to determine what alternative crops might be planted on idle acres. In this situation, the prospective rates of return with a stumpage price of 7 dollars would be 8 percent and 10 percent, when planting costs are 20 and 10 dollars an acre, respectively. In the same situation, with stumpage at only 4 dollars a cord, the respective rates of return would be somewhat more than 5 percent and 7 percent, respectively.

A careful professional evaluation of each situation is highly desirable, before proceeding with a program. An appraisal of the site (the timber-growing capacity of the land) may determine whether investments in planting offer excellent prospects or only marginal prospects. For example, on good sites—as contrasted to the average sites we have assumed—with stumpage at 7 dollars a cord and with a zero land cost, the rate of return could range between 10 and 12.5 percent within the spread of assumed planting costs. Even with a stumpage price of only 4 dollars a cord, the returns on good sites could be 7.5 to 9.5 percent on the investment.

Since trees are not perishable as ripe food crops are, the owner need not make annual harvests of timberland. He has the option of delaying harvests beyond periods of low prices until the demand for wood products is active— just as an owner of common stock attempts to sell only when the market is bullish. Trees, unlike stock certificates, however, continue to grow in value during economic slumps.

THE OWNER of timber reaps another advantage from this flexibility in timing his harvests.

He can change his objectives of management within reasonable limits. He might aim initially at management for production of pulpwood, for example, by starting out with a plantation of loblolly pine. But if prices for pulpwood are in a slump during the year scheduled for a harvest, he could postpone cutting for several years or longer and wait for rising prices. Much of his timber would continue to appreciate in value even beyond the 30-year period between planting and harvest which was assumed previously.

Although this postponement of cutting might result in a decrease in average growth of all material most suitable for pulpwood, it would increase the volume in trees that could be used for more valuable products, such as veneer, sawlogs, or poles.

If the final harvest is deferred until a fair proportion of trees in the stand reach 15 inches in diameter (at an age somewhat beyond the 30-year period needed to grow a crop of pulpwood on the average site), one 15-inch tree, at 1963 stumpage prices, would be worth 9 dollars if sold as sawlogs or 10 dollars if sold as a utility pole. Such a tree would be worth no more than one-half that amount if sold as pulpwood.

Product objectives of management need not be inflexible, but it is important to set them intelligently and follow them through a rotation if possible without much modification, because ideal silvicultural measures vary with the objective.

One course of action is management aimed at producing a diversity of products. Under such a policy, intermediate thinnings of rather small material could be sold as pulpwood. In the final harvest the choicest parts of largest trees could be sold as sawlogs, veneer logs, piling, or utility poles, and the residues could be marketed primarily for pulpwood. In some instances, two or three products could be taken from a tree. By such a procedure, each portion of every tree is manufactured into the most valuable product it is suitable for.

RECREATION looms large in the potential contributions of family forests.

Demands for outdoor recreation will increase more than 100 percent by 1975 as measured by expenditures, according to a projection by the Outdoor Recreation Resources Review Commission in 1962. By the year 2000 an increase of more than 300 percent is forecast.

Some 1.7 billion dollars was estimated to have been spent in 1960 in the United States on all outings that were of a day or less. Within the next four decades, the total annual expenditure for such outings may aggregate nearly 6.5 billion dollars. These short trips into the country—totaling more than 800 million a year—are the kind of visits on which owners of family forests might easily capitalize, if suitable picnic facilities are developed.

Many owners of woodlands might also help meet needs of people who are making longer trips if they have facilities for overnight camping.

One reason for the projection of large increases in vacations, trips, and outings in the next few decades is the expected shortening of the workweek and lengthening of vacations. That should extend the average leisure time of people by nearly one-third before the end of the century. When combined with the projected increase in population, this means that the time away from home should increase from some 2 billion man-days a year in 1963 to 3 billion by 1975 and to nearly 6 billion by 2000.

The outdoor recreation business on family farms and forests can take many forms. It may be a "vacation farm" enterprise in which the clients live at the farm or ranch during their stay and participate in farm chores and the other activities of farming.

A picnic or sports area will normally draw people for a day or less.

Fishing waters are always an attraction, as in Bullfrog Park, Oregon City, Oreg. Here Clarence Hitchman, a former farmer and logger, built two 3-acre ponds on part of his 150-acre forest. He equipped the area with picnic tables for a thousand persons. There is plenty of running water. Facilities are modern. A buffer zone of natural woodland around the park adds to its beauty.

Another example is the Foster Lake Club, Alfred, N.Y., a day-use membership club, in central New York. Eddy Foster, the owner, constructed two earth dams at opposite ends of a natural saddle in a 200-acre plantation of Christmas trees. The resulting 25-acre lake is stocked with trout, bass, and bluegills. He installed a swimming area and boating facilities. Family memberships are 15 dollars a year, and an initiation fee is 5 dollars. There were 164 family memberships in 1963. The capacity is about 200.

A growing interest in family camping also offers opportunities to the landowner for development of campgrounds. Enterprising owners of woodlands in every section have found that campers willingly pay fees of a dollar or more a day for space to peg a tent.

The sale of recreation lands and recreation use rights (that is, sites for summer cottages) can be another source of income. The list of outdoor recreation activities, which can include skiing, horseback riding, and nature trail hiking, is a long one.

All possible activities should be carefully considered by the owner in land use planning for multiple-use management of his property.

Game production on forest land can be a profitable activity to fill a substantial part of the demand for outdoor recreation and can be a significant source of income from multiple-use management on the family forest as well.

The importance of hunting is indicated by a survey for the Fish and Wildlife Service, which shows that 12 million persons engage in this sport annually. Three-fourths of those who hunt are after squirrels, rabbits, quail, and partridge—the kind of small game that can be managed in abundance on or adjacent to the typical family forest without conflict with other uses.

If the ratio of hunters continues to be the same—one of every five American men—there undoubtedly will be great pressures on every bit of field and woodland that will support game animals and may be opened to hunting.

Because accessible public hunting grounds are overcrowded, there should be no lack of paying customers for many an owner of a private forest who is willing to cater to hunters. If his land is reasonably close to a city and he has made a successful effort at game management, he may be selective in choosing the men he wants to help harvest the game.

The landowner who is willing to accommodate hunters may engage in a variety of enterprises. Day hunting for a fee is especially practical where he has several hundred acres or where he has combined his land with that of his neighbors to form a logical hunting complex.

For most hunting enterprises, nearness to large population centers is important. The rates charged depend on the abundance and kind of game and waterfowl. Whenever the landowner has invested some effort in improving wildlife habitat, he is in a much better position to cash in on his wildlife crop.

Special services to hunters can be another source of income. Examples are board and lodging; sale of hunting equipment and supplies; and rental of vehicles, saddle and pack animals, camping equipment, guide services, trap, skeet, and archery facilities, hunting and retrieving dogs, and waterfowl shooting blinds or boxes.

The hunting preserve is another venture. It normally calls for the use of pen-raised game. Hunters using the preserve are guaranteed the opportunity to shoot and to take game home. Fees vary and may be based on the number killed. Many preserves are near rather large cities and cater to business executives. The landowner engaged in this business may find it profitable to give the major part of his time to this enterprise at the expense of farming.

Hinegardner's Hunting Lodge, near Dover, Ark., is an example of a woodland hunting preserve. It consists of a 440-acre wooded area, enclosed with wire-mesh fence. The specialty is hunting wild hogs. Charges are 40 dollars a hog killed.

SPECIAL FOREST products—products other than sawtimber, pulpwood, and the like—should be given full consideration by the owner.

Opportunities depend on the area, the kinds of trees and other plants in the forest, the season, and the market.

Small, well-shaped evergreen trees can be harvested as thinnings after Thanksgiving and sold as Christmas trees. If pruning is deferred until a couple of weeks before Christmas, the evergreen branches produced in pruning, instead of being left to rot, can yield extra income when fashioned into Christmas wreaths or when merely bundled as greens.

Pine cones may also be collected and sold for decorations or to nurseries for seed production. Nuts, wild berries, maple sirup, medicinal plants, decorative floral plants, shrubbery, and numerous other special products—the list numbers several hundred—can be utilized to enhance the owner's income while his trees mature.

Whether the land use plan includes a strong special products section or not

can make the difference in whether or not the owner succeeds in making his woodland a full producing part of the farm property.

LAND USE planning for multiple-use management of a private woodland requires the services of a professional man experienced in this work. Foresters, by virtue of their training and experience with land resources, are well acquainted with land use planning.

The forester, after consulting with the owner and after making an analysis of the woodland, can make a plan that embraces all the potential multiple uses that can be utilized to meet the goals and needs of the landowner. The plan should contain the basic forest management recommendations needed to bring the forest into a high state of productiveness from the standpoint of species composition, timber quality, and volume of timber growth. Then, without impairing those goals, it may include appropriate provisions for development of outdoor recreation facilities, fishing, hunting, and the production of special forest products if the owner approves. In other words, the needs and desires of the owner would be harmonized with the potentials and limitations of his woodland.

To realize recreation values, for example, the forester may recommend that a relatively low-value grove of beech trees be the site of a campground or picnic area development. A natural depression running through a field at the edge of a plantation of Christmas trees may be a good site for a dam and a pond that can be developed for fee fishing or for development for summer homesites. The north slope of relatively unproductive pasture at the edge of the woods might lend itself to the development of a ski run. If the woodland contains a sizable acreage, it may be improved for hunting of upland game and birds. A marshy area on a flyway might be the ideal spot for hunting wild ducks and geese.

Only after a basic plan for multiple-use management is made can the direction and need for a more detailed survey and plans for individual uses be appraised. A recreation planner might be called in, for example, to develop the details for a campground or picnic area. When it comes to the detailed planning for water, fishing, and hunting development, a wildlife management specialist may be needed to prescribe certain measures. The detailed plan for the production of timber crops and special forest products would be prepared by the forester himself. A soil conservationist could advise on the development of ponds.

ADVICE on land use planning for multiple-use forest management can be obtained from professional foresters employed by Federal, State, and local public agencies. The forest industries and consulting foresters are other sources of help.

Competent private consulting foresters often are available at reasonable fees. There are more than 350 such self-employed foresters in the United States. State forestry personnel are familiar with the consultants in their States and can recommend one or another of them to the owners of woodlands.

The forest industries conduct a number of programs to promote good forestry on private lands, such as Keep America Green, to prevent forest fires, and the Tree Farm Program, to recognize private timber owners who practice good forestry and pledge themselves to continue the practice. The Tree Farm Program has been in operation since 1941 and included 25 thousand certified tree farms in 1962. The area in the program has tripled since 1950.

Among the public agencies giving the greatest amount of on-the-ground service to woodland owners are the State forest services of America. One of the key programs which the State forester conducts is the Cooperative Forest Management Program, a cooperative State-Federal activity to provide the private landowner with technical advice and assistance in management of his forest land for continuous production and profitable operation.

State-employed professional "service" or "farm" foresters, of which there are 660, meet with the owner and give him on-the-ground woodland advice. For forest management assistance, the timberland owner should get in touch with the State forester, the county agent, Soil Conservation District, or any one of the other public agricultural agencies. They can give the name and address of the nearest service forester.

The Federal Extension Service cooperates with the State extension service in conducting forestry education and demonstration work with farmowners and rural youth. There are 80 State extension foresters in the Nation. Landowners desiring extension forestry assistance should call their local county agents.

The Agricultural Stabilization and Conservation Service provides costsharing forestry assistance under the Agricultural Conservation Program. The program in most counties shares with owners the cost of improving existing stands of trees and the cost of planting trees and shrubs on their farmlands for forest, windbreak, shelterbelt, and erosion-control purposes. The nearest ASCS office should be consulted for information.

The Farmers Home Administration makes loans for forestry purposes on private woodlands for periods up to 40 years at a low rate of interest. These loans are made to accomplish the work recommended by a professional forester to bring a farm woodland into fuller production. Eligibility for such loans depends on the landowner's needs, finances, ability to obtain credit, and the contributions of his woodland to total income.

THE FOOD and Agriculture Act of 1962 provided authorization for new programs, which should be of interest to owners who may wish to put their family forests under multiple-use management.

The Soil Conservation Service has the responsibility for leadership in assisting rural people to establish income-producing recreation enterprises on farmland. The Farmers Home Administration received authorization to implement the development of these income-producing enterprises. The agency can lend money to farmers and ranchers to establish recreation businesses as part of their farming, and can provide credit to groups of farmers and rural residents for changing land from crop production to recreation use. The local offices of the Soil Conservation Service and the Farmers Home Administration can furnish further information to owners of farm woodlands.

Under the new act, the Agricultural Stabilization and Conservation Service is responsible at National, State, and county levels for the development and administration of the land-adjustment programs authorized in section 101 of title I of the act. State and county Agricultural Stabilization and Conservation committees are responsible for the day-to-day operation of the programs. The programs enable farmers to expand grassland, expand and improve woodlands, and develop recreational use of private lands. Local offices of the Agricultural Stabilization and Conservation Service can furnish information about land use adjustment opportunities for landowners.

Title IV of the Food and Agriculture Act, in addition to providing loans for income-producing recreation enterprises, also permits the Farmers Home Administration to broaden its definition of farmers to include persons engaged in fish farming to qualify for credit assistance. It also permits credit assistance to other farmers to develop fish production as an additional enterprise to supplement their incomes and thus expand the application of multiple-use management to their lands. Local Farmers Home Administration offices should be consulted by landowners interested in loans for fish farming.

The farmer can get the technical help of the Soil Conservation Service in choosing a pond site, designing dams and spillways, and managing the pond for fishing. The Soil Conservation Service also gives on-the-farm technical assistance to farmers and ranchers in planning, applying, and maintaining conservation farm and ranch systems. This planning includes anticipated actions for soil and water management, recreation and conservation, and use of cultivated land, grassland, and woodland.

Although all these varied programs offer landowners more help than ever to increase returns from family forests, there also is greater need than ever for careful planning.

For the many woodlands that lie within the zone where suburbs are crowding into rural areas, the competition between alternative uses for land is keen. Inevitably some of the most accessible forests will be cleared to make way for expansion of residential areas, superhighways, reservoirs, and other nonforest developments. We hope that most woodlands will survive this expansion. Planning by owners and communities will help to safeguard them and their many values.

R. C. WILSON *became Chief of the Forest Survey Branch, Division of Forest Economics and Marketing Research, of the Forest Service in 1958. He has worked at forest experiment stations in California, North Carolina, and Oregon.*

GEORGE VITAS *is a member of the Division of Information and Education of the Forest Service. He is the author of* Forest and Flame in the Bible *and* Every Forester a Timber Owner *and other publications.*

For further reading:

U.S. Department of Agriculture, *A List of Aids for Rural Areas Development.* 1962.

———— *Forest Recreation for Profit.* Agriculture Information Bulletin No. 265, 1962.

———— *Outdoor Recreation in Small Watershed Projects.* Program Aid No. 500, folder, 1962.

ARTHUR A. DAVIS

THE USES AND
VALUES OF OPEN SPACE

THREE forces—population growth, the trend toward urbanization, and the horizontal expansion of cities—have been gobbling up land at a prodigal rate. The resulting sprawl has been marked by haphazard location of residential subdivisions, dull and inefficient suburbs, and the merging of adjoining towns and cities into strip cities that embrace hundreds of square miles. Lewis Mumford has described this process of "scatteration" as producing a "large mass of undifferentiated low-grade urban tissue."

The haphazard urban development leaves behind it an astonishing amount of open land. It is estimated that in the New York metropolitan area, which embraces 22 counties, 550 municipalities, 1,467 local governments, 7 thousand square miles, and 16 million persons, only 25 percent of the lands have been developed. The urbanized area of the six counties in northeastern Illinois that have Chicago for their urban hub is estimated at 28 percent.

These open spaces offer opportunities for shaping the development yet to come in urban regions. They provide a resource base for meeting needs for public parks and recreation, preserving watersheds, providing a habitat and cover for fish and birds, and serving a variety of historic, scientific, and esthetic purposes.

Open-space lands may be large or small, public or private, permanent or temporary.

They are predominantly undeveloped. They may be used for agriculture, timber, grazing, and recreation or to help limit and define city growth. They are not valueless wastelands; on the contrary, they have positive values for meeting a variety of community needs.

Land held permanently open for regional parks, greenbelts, green wedges, or buffer areas can prevent inefficient sprawl and unplanned development.

Regional parks and greenbelts usually are as large as several thousand acres. Their size and shape depend on topography, particular local requirements, and the existing pattern of city development.

Greenbelts that follow such natural features as ridges and valleys can influence community growth in harmony

330

with the land and do much for the attractiveness of a city. The economic aspect is that a disregard of natural features and soil conditions may mean higher costs of roads and bridges, suburban homes that sink or slide on improper foundations, and local flooding and poor drainage.

Open tracts can serve to limit boundaries and so promote the efficient concentration of community facilities and separate incompatible urban land uses. The noise, smoke, and fumes of an industrial area, for example, may be isolated and screened by a greenbelt.

Open space can be used as safety and noise-reducing zones around airports, as natural floodways, and as buffer strips between major arterial roads and residential development.

Lands reserved for future development give communities a powerful lever to assure rational patterns of growth. For example, a city may anticipate a future demand for sites for industry, commercial centers, and public facilities. To avoid the loss of such sites to undesirable or incompatible developments, the land can be acquired and perhaps held for sale or lease later.

We have been slow to recognize that open-space lands can be life insurance policies for our communities. Too often we permit our highways to become billboard alleys or commercial strips at the city fringe to mushroom into a jangle of Neon signs and drive-ins. Once lovely rural towns are tarnished by the loss of trees and green space to make way for some more "modern" or "urgent" facility.

Parks and green spaces that remain are threatened continually by one or another kind of encroachment. These open lands seem ideal for highways, airports, school sites, and residential or commercial development. If park land proper is somehow kept intact, there is a constant battle to stave off shoddy or incompatible development at its edges. There seems to be less interest in providing buffer areas around green space than there is in acquiring the open space itself. Yet open spaces can not serve their purpose well if hemmed in by billboards, gas stations, roadhouses, and auto graveyards.

European countries long ago recognized the need for preserving green space. In the Netherlands, for example, the use of land reclaimed from the sea is planned carefully. Acres are precious, and urban sprawl cannot be tolerated. New towns are planned with careful attention to recreation and open space needs—bicycle paths, walkways, and parks. Greenbelts are retained in agricultural uses to prevent the merging of expanding towns into the kind of metropolitan behemoths common in the United States.

In Washington, D.C., a Year 2000 Plan proposes that open spaces be used to provide a radial network of green wedges extending outward from the center of the city like the spokes of a wheel. They would separate residential from business and commercial districts, and a mass transportation system and highway network would be integrated with them.

Ottawa, the capital of Canada, has purchased lands to create a greenbelt 2.5 miles wide to define the limits of the metropolitan area. Much of the land has been leased for farm purposes.

Philadelphia uses public parks and greenbelts to separate its ten major districts.

But it would be largely accidental if these plans and patterns were found to be equally useful elsewhere, because the need for space for shaping urban development relates closely to local conditions. Factors to be considered are economic, social, and physical characteristics of the city; the amount of land now in an open condition; and present and projected population density.

ABOUT OPEN space for recreation, the New York Regional Plan Association, Inc., said in a report, *The Race for Open Space*: "[It] provides a setting for a variety of popular activities and for the satisfying of a host of basic human physical and emotional needs. The activities range from games and swimming to walking and bird watching. The human needs include relief of tensions; keeping physically fit; satisfying the impulses to explore, to learn, to be alone, to express oneself; aesthetic experience; and the need for fruitful and pleasurable leisure."

Small parks, school parks and playgrounds, residential commons, and the banks of small watercourses are examples of neighborhood open-space areas. City parks are larger, and may provide golf courses, swimming and boating facilities, picnic and other day-use facilities, fishing, hiking and horseback riding, nature centers, and botanical gardens. The aim is to serve all or a large part of the community.

Regional parks often cover several thousand acres, and provide recreation opportunities generally similar to those available at State parks and forests. Beach and shoreline areas, large natural areas suitable for overnight and vacation use, fishing, boating, and facilities for youth, church, and social organizations usually are available.

WE USE A number of rules for estimating the space needed for public recreation. They have value only as general precepts. Factors like terrain, the type of recreation activities, character of existing urban development, and the kind and location of available and planned transportation facilities will be the final determinants.

If we use as a standard the figure of 10 acres per thousand persons, the acquisition of more than a million additional acres will be required to meet needs in 1970. A standard of 20 acres for county and metropolitan regional park and recreation areas would require an additional 4.3 million acres. To meet total needs for statewide recreation and natural areas, with 45 acres per thousand persons as a standard, an additional 11.2 million acres would be required. By 1975, then, the 1963 acreage of city parks and playgrounds would need to be tripled; that in regional, county, and metropolitan areas

would have to be expanded eightfold; and State parks would have to be tripled.

The cost of meeting these recommendations will be high. It has been suggested, for example, that the needs of the Tri-State New York Metropolitan Region for about 860 square miles (550,400 acres) at 1960 prices would mean a public expenditure of about 1.9 billion dollars. It has been estimated an additional 54 thousand acres of open space for recreation uses were needed in the Chicago region in 1962 and a total of 89 thousand acres will be needed by 1980.

Scientific and historic values are related to recreation needs. Such areas usually are site oriented—the character of the site proper is important to its use for the intended purpose. A stand of virgin hardwoods is of interest because of ecological conditions that exist in old timber. Battlefields are lessons in history; once destroyed, they can never be replaced. Tracts of scenic and esthetic value may not involve active use and often do not require public ownership to preserve their attractiveness.

Open spaces can provide many of the conservation benefits derived from retaining an area in a relatively undeveloped condition. Such lands serve as sponges to absorb excess runoff. They provide natural sumps and catch basins that assist in stabilizing ground water levels and promoting proper drainage. Large forests are cooler in summer, and in winter they break the force of winds. Watershed areas help reduce erosion and sedimentation. Flood plains along rivers are a part of the natural channel and can be developed only at risk to life and property. The Corps of Engineers has estimated that at least 2 thousand urban areas should consider reserving flood plains from further development.

The proper selection and management of urban open space can contribute greatly to meeting our need for water, which may be three times greater in 1980 than in 1963.

To PRODUCE these diverse benefits, open spaces must be selected with regard to human needs and resource capabilities. They must meet two basic tests.

They must be useful for the purposes they are to serve. A public park, for example, must be accessible by public or personal transportation. It needs to be big enough to provide the recreation it is intended to offer in an attractive and uncluttered setting. It should have the natural physiographic features appropriate to a park or be capable of development to create such surroundings by landscaping.

They must be integral elements of the community pattern of land use. The requirements of location and terrain for many uses are not so critical as for urban development, but that does not mean that bits and fragments of undeveloped land, or rocky, broken, or swampy terrain unsuited for other purposes will always be useful for open space. The notion that open spaces are land left over from urban development denies at the outset the tangible and intangible values they can contribute to orderly community development.

Acquisitions of larger open spaces should follow stream valleys, watercourses, ridge lines, and other features.

Smaller tracts may be acquired to prevent developments of certain kinds in particular areas. Suburbs ordinarily should not be permitted on swampy or impermeable soils. Aquifer recharge areas should remain undeveloped to preserve their value for regulating streamflow and stabilizing water levels. Flood plains should be reserved from costly public or private developments.

Where rural and urban influences meet, planning and appropriate action are particularly important. Public acquisition often is not needed or desirable to maintain attractive pastoral settings close to cities. Scenic and esthetic values can be preserved by public acquisition of development rights, conservation easements, and similar arrangements. Agricultural zoning may be appropriate in some areas.

CITIES throughout the country have reported plans and studies to acquire open spaces to serve various purposes and values.

Up until the end of June 1963, the Federal Open-Space Land Program, which I describe later, assisted 110 public agencies to acquire open lands in accordance with their comprehensive plans for park, recreational, and conservation uses. Grants approved totaled more than 18 million dollars and assisted in the acquisition of more than 57 thousand acres of land. Many tracts serve multiple purposes.

In Sacramento, Calif., 262 acres of additional open space along the American River protect flood plains from development, expand recreational opportunities in existing parks, and help shape the growth of the city.

The Maryland National Capital Park and Planning Commission received a grant to aid in the acquisition of more than 4 thousand acres in two counties near Washington, D.C. The 41 sites include several large regional parks, greenbelts, and smaller facilities within walking distance of suburban residents.

The Huron-Clinton Metropolitan Park Authority acquired more than 800 acres along the Huron River to provide day-use, camping, and other facilities to serve the Detroit region.

A grant to Morris County, New Jersey, made possible the purchase of 50 acres of stream valley land along the Passaic River for recreation and conservation. Facilities are provided for hiking, nature instruction, bicycling, and picnicking.

Several grants involved intergovernmental cooperation. Madison, Wis., bought lands as part of a long-range park and open-space plan prepared by the city in cooperation with surrounding communities and with the assistance of several State agencies.

In Massachusetts, the State Department of Natural Resources received a grant to assist in purchasing a park and recreation area near the city of Taunton. The 647-acre area preserves a picturesque remnant of the cranberry bogs that once covered much of this part of the State. The site, developed for recreation, conservation, and nature study purposes, is accessible to a population of more than 300 thousand.

States are taking increased interest in preserving open space. In New Jersey, a "Green Acres" program was approved by the voters in November 1961. A bond issue of 60 million dollars provided for the acquisition of recreation and conservation lands by State agencies and local governments. Twenty million dollars was earmarked for reservoirs, a like amount for forest and park lands, 5 million dollars for expanding existing areas, and 15 million dollars for assistance to municipalities, counties, and other local governments on a 50-percent cost-sharing basis.

New York voters in 1960 approved a bond issue of 75 million dollars for the purchase of open-space land. An additional issue of 25 million dollars was approved by the voters in 1962. Under the original program, funds were allocated for acquisition of State park areas (20 million dollars); for other conservation and recreation lands (15 million); and for aid to counties, cities, and towns to acquire open lands (40 million), the State contributing 75 percent of the cost.

Wisconsin in 1961 enacted a 50-million-dollar program financed by a 1-cent increase in the cigarette tax and designed to develop a statewide system of conservation and recreation areas. The State can pay up to 50 percent of the cost of obtaining local or county open-space areas.

Other States that have drawn up programs include Pennsylvania, California, and Connecticut. Among the States that have enacted enabling legislation for the acquisition of open space are California, Connecticut, Maryland, New Jersey, New York, Pennsylvania, and Wisconsin.

TWENTY-EIGHT Federal programs contribute directly or indirectly to the acquisition and preservation of open space. Among them are programs concerned with planning, housing, development of water resources, watershed protection and soil conservation, management and disposal of public domain lands, national parks and recreation areas, national forests, agricultural stabilization, pollution control, fish and wildlife, area redevelopment, and interstate highways.

Most Federal programs relate only incidentally to open space, since Federal land and water managing agencies initiate projects or administer lands for particular purposes authorized by law.

An exception is the Open-Space Land Program, administered by the Urban Renewal Administration, a unit of the Housing and Home Finance Agency. The program, authorized by title VII of the Housing Act of 1961, has for its purposes ". . . to help curb urban sprawl and prevent the spread of urban blight and deterioration, to encourage more economic and desirable urban development, and to help provide necessary recreational, conservation and scenic areas. . . ."

The program provides technical and financial assistance in the acquisition by State and local public bodies of open-space lands in urban areas for park, recreation, conservation, scenic, or historic purposes. No land is acquired by the Federal Government. Instead, grants are available for up to 20 percent of the cost of acquiring land or permanent interests in land. Public agencies acquiring open land for an urban area as a whole, either on their own authority or under terms of intergovernmental agreements, may qualify for grants of up to 30 percent.

Lands to be acquired must be predominantly undeveloped, and their permanent dedication to open-space uses should have a substantial effect on curbing urban sprawl, and encouraging a desirable urban development. Grants apply only to costs of acquisition. Any proposed development for recreation, conservation, or other uses compatible with maintaining the open-space character of the area must be undertaken by local agencies.

Lands to be acquired must be important to the execution of comprehensive plans for urban areas. An urban area is defined as an area which is urban in character, including those surrounding areas that form an economically and socially related region. Consideration is given such factors as population trends and patterns of urban growth, location of transportation facilities, and distribution of industrial, commercial, residential, and institutional activities.

Since open-space needs are related to urban growth and development, the program requires that comprehensive planning must be going forward actively in the city and surrounding towns or suburbs. There also must be a comprehensive plan for the entire metropolitan area, which should include elements dealing with open space, recreation, and land use.

State and local governments can be assisted in meeting the planning requirements for the Federal Open-Space Land Program under the urban planning assistance program authorized by section 701 of the Housing Act of 1954. The program, also administered by the Urban Renewal Administration, provides cost sharing for urban planning undertaken by smaller towns and cities, metropolitan and regional areas, and for State comprehensive planning.

To assure coordination of efforts, evidence must be submitted that the proposal of the applicant agency has been reviewed by other governmental agencies responsible for planning and related phases of the program. Applicants must demonstrate that they are preserving a maximum of open space at minimum cost through such means as use of existing publicly owned land, zoning and subdivision regulations, special tax provisions, the acquisition of easements, and other available tools for the preservation of open space.

THE INTEREST in this program has been encouraging. We have received hundreds of inquiries from States, cities, and towns all over the country. Nor has interest been limited to the big metropolitan areas. Counties and smaller cities account for a substantial share of the applications received. Regional agencies concerned with parks, open space, and other functions for portions of States also have applied for assistance, and 12 States have expressed interest in participating in the program.

More than 200 applications, received by the end of June 1963, involved land to be acquired in all but 14 States. Applications ranged from 10 acres with acquisition costs of a few thousand dollars to several thousand acres, involving millions of dollars.

The diversity of lands for which grant assistance is requested reflects the many kinds of needs of different communities. Some cities wish to expand and consolidate their present parks and holdings of open space. Counties are concerned with preserving lands for open-space uses on the rural-urban fringe. Regional plans usually involve large acreages that can have an effect on shaping urban development.

Most applications are concerned with providing accessible outdoor recreation opportunities close to where people live. Often lands acquired with Federal assistance will be improved for recreational purposes by the installation of facilities with local funds. Artificial lakes, trails, picnic areas, and playing fields are a few of the kinds of improvements planned.

Watershed protection and other conservation measures frequently are listed as major open-space purposes. Acquisition of stream valleys and public ownership of ridges, steep slopes, wooded draws, and marshes and wetlands are proposed in many plans. Occasionally a city wishes to convert lands to open-space uses, as in the case of strategically located railroad rights-of-way surplus to railroad needs. Such lands must be predominantly undeveloped to qualify for Federal assistance. Interest also has been expressed in preserving historic sites, such as portions of battlefields, and in securing additional buffer lands to prevent encroachments on existing historic sites.

We have been particularly pleased at the number of regional open space action programs. Nearly half of the grants approved by the end of 1962 qualified for 30 percent Federal cost sharing because the applicants represented entire urban areas. Seven programs involved intergovernmental agreements that call for joint action by several jurisdictions to preserve open space in an entire urban area.

Local park and recreation programs have been operated by cities and counties for many years. The concept of a total approach to meeting open-space needs is relatively new, however, and embraces a number of objectives in addition to park and recreation. To develop a complete plan for open space, it is necessary to have also a plan of developed space—land needed for all kinds of urban improvements and facilities. Then the two plans can be balanced and meshed together, so that a single plan of land use emerges.

A number of research projects are in operation which should help in setting standards and criteria for preservation of open space. Also, there are available several legal tools, financial methods, and tax benefit arrangements, which are being tried in different places.

THE ACQUISITION of open-space lands is a private as well as a public concern. Park and recreation associations, conservation groups, fraternal and religious organizations, nonprofit foundations, private trusts, and other community interests have shown appreciation of the needs and values of open space. Some of the groups have taken direct action to acquire such tracts. Others have led community efforts for State and local park, recreation, and open-space programs. Of course, final support for open-space programs must come from the individual citizen who is responsible for approving bond issues for recreation and open-space programs, seeing to the enforcement of zoning and other appropriate land use controls, and making urban planning an effective tool for orderly community growth.

As urbanization continues, and our population grows, the problem of allocating natural resources equitably will become increasingly difficult. Choices will become more sharply defined, and decisions once made more difficult to vacate. Gradually, the lands and resources most intimately related to meeting the needs of people are being permanently dedicated to serve one or another purpose of a modern society.

It is necessary to act now to assure that essential open-space values are preserved while there is still time to make the necessary choices. The problem is critical particularly in and near metropolitan centers, where the bulk of our citizens live, work, and play.

ARTHUR A. DAVIS *became Director of the Open-Space Land Branch of the Urban Renewal Administration, Housing and Home Finance Agency, in 1961. Previously he was Chief of the Programs and Policies Staff of the Outdoor Recreation Resources Review Commission, a temporary joint commission created to recommend policies and programs to meet outdoor recreational facilities needs for the American people through the year 2000.*

For further reading:
   Clawson, Marion, Held, R. Burnell, and Stoddard, Charles H., *Land for the Future.* Resources for the Future, Inc., The Johns Hopkins University Press, Baltimore, 1960.
   The Open Space Land Program Fact Sheet. Urban Renewal Administration, Washington, D.C., 1962.
   The Race for Open Space. New York Regional Plan Association, Inc., New York, 1960.
   Siegel, Shirley A., *The Law of Open Space.* New York Regional Plan Association, Inc., New York, 1960.
   Whyte, William H., *Open Space Action.* ORRRC Study Report 15, U.S. Government Printing Office, Washington, D.C., 1962.
   —— *Securing Open Space for Urban America: Conservation Easements.* Urban Land Institute, Technical Bulletin No. 36, 1959.

JEANNE M. DAVIS

GETTING AND
KEEPING OPEN SPACE

Open space has three dimensions. It is a use of land, water, and air, to which the functions of open space are related and on which they partly depend. Open space is not vacant space. The former term implies use; the latter, nonuse. In order to be considered an open space, a tract of land must fulfill three requirements.

It must be relatively free of manmade structures and give the appearance of a natural landscape. Only areas with 25 percent or less of the total site covered by buildings, parking lots, and roads are sufficiently uncluttered to be considered as possible open spaces.

It must be relatively free of vehicular traffic.

It must meet acreage requirements that vary in proportion to the intensity of use and the density of development in surrounding areas. For example, a half-acre park in a city's center is a true open space, yet a half-acre lot in the suburbs or the country, where building density and intensity of use are low, is merely a vacant lot.

One of the most important aspects of open space is that it is a link between Nature and people.

Open space can provide room for service facilities, such as parks and recreation areas, institutions, and other extensive land using activities. (In unplanned development, the land needs of these service facilities frequently are unmet.)

Open space can provide amenities, such as fresh air, quiet, and a change from the monotony of cityscapes.

It can provide the required physical conditions for watershed protection, soil conservation, flood prevention, and preservation of wildlife and other natural resources, including preservation of the best lands for crops and forests in economically significant acreage.

Permanent open spaces can be used to separate neighborhoods, communities, towns or cities, metropolitan areas, and regions. By providing a framework for development, open space is a means of controlling urban sprawl.

Properly planned open spaces can serve all these purposes simultaneously.

Just two decades ago, rural open spaces were within easy access of most people—even those who lived in the large metropolitan areas.

TODAY, even when one gets to the countryside, he may not find true open space. Strings of subdivision-type houses clutter many once-rural areas. These strings of settlement often connect villages, frequently with no apparent break between them. The string-type development usually is only one house deep, but it ruins the countryside as open space.

The rural-urban fringe—the transition zone between the built-up area and the predominantly open countryside—contains much land that is not built on. Once it may have been farmland but now is idle and may be held for speculation. It may be land bypassed for development because the landowners placed excessive price tags on the parcels or because new roads or water and sewer lines prematurely opened up tracts still farther from the city where land costs are lower. But this land is not necessarily open space.

Many of the large estates in the rural-urban fringe that once provided pleasures for Sunday drivers from the city have been sold. The extensive grounds now may be dotted with the buildings of private schools or covered with boxlike houses and postage-stamp lawns. So, too, many country clubs.

Each year the open spaces beyond the city limits have been diminishing in numbers and acreage, until the only ones we can be sure of preserving are those owned or controlled by the public—parks, recreation areas, publicly owned forests, wildlife sanctuaries, arboretums, and reservoirs.

Open spaces in the residential areas of cities and suburbs still exist, of course. Parks and recreation areas, golf clubs, some schoolyards, and the grounds of some public or semipublic institutions are such, but each year more of the institutions, golf clubs, and private schools move farther from the city center. These once-open spaces are used for housing developments that increase population densities of neigh-

borhoods or for high-intensity uses, such as shopping centers. Rarely are such sites acquired for park or recreation areas.

Some vacant lots exist in the cities and suburbs, but most of them are not true open spaces because they have no semblance of a natural landscape.

Many are weed covered and trash littered. Yet the space itself is enticing to trespassing children if there is no other place large enough for them to play. Many vacant lots are large enough and are so located that they could be converted easily to neighborhood parks or recreation areas.

Center city, or downtown, open spaces have changed the least. Small parks, paved squares that give a brave show of flowers and shrubs in boxes, the green "front yards" of some old churches, malls, and onetime village greens become more precious with the years.

Whatever its origin and size, the center city open space is a breathing space—a place keyed to the human scale, a visual break in the cityscape, and a haven from traffic. It is as true an open space as the neighborhood park or recreation area, the arboretum in the fringe, or a farm.

How MUCH open space is needed? Only the people living in each State, each region, each county, each city and town can answer the question.

Suggested acreage standards for a few open-space uses, such as parks and recreation areas, have been established by a number of organizations.

Standards established in Philadelphia in 1957 call for neighborhood playgrounds of three sizes and service areas. These vary from playgrounds of 3 to 8 acres, intended to serve an area of one-fourth mile radius in areas of highest density (175 persons or more per net acre) to playgrounds of 6 to 8 acres, serving a radius of one-half mile in areas with a density of fewer than 75 persons per net acre. For sections with no private yards and therefore no relief from endless buildings and streets, recommendations call for greenways and small parks of trees, lawns, and places to sit. Playfields of 8 to 20 acres serve each five or six playground population areas. District parks of 20 to 100 acres are within a mile of most homes. The Philadelphia standards also suggest at least one regional park of 300 to 2,500 acres within 40 minutes' traveltime of most homes in the region and at least one regional reservation of a thousand acres or more within 2 hours' traveltime of each home in the region.

Standards established in 1959 for Arlington County, Va., suggest a total of 19 acres of open space per 1 thousand of population. This would include 4 acres per thousand for neighborhood parks, playgrounds, and playfields; 5 acres per thousand for urban parks; and 10 acres per thousand for other open land.

The Baltimore Regional Planning Council's Technical Advisory Subcommittee on Parks and Recreation in 1960 recommended that town and county boundaries should be ignored and standards be based on the neighborhood and the region. This decision was reached because adults, as well as children, need parks nearby to walk in or sit in, and they also need places for active recreation. City and even suburban yards generally are too small to provide opportunities for active recreation for other than small children. The neighborhood standards recommended were 4.5 acres per 1 thousand of population—one-third for playgrounds, one-third for playfields, and one-third for parks. The committee recommended also that within the region 15 acres per thousand be provided for waterfront parks, active-use parks, and golf courses, and that wherever possible within the region an additional 25 acres per thousand be provided for natural parks of at least 500 acres each.

California's *Public Outdoor Recreation Plan, Part II,* published in 1960, established four zones of recreation demand, based on travel distance and recreation activities. Zone 1 includes the neigh-

borhood (with a population of 3,200 or less and having a service radius of one-half mile), the community (population to 25 thousand and service radius of 2 miles or less), and the district (population to 100 thousand and service radius of 5 miles or less). Zone 2 is "an area within approximately 40 miles of the dwelling accessible on 1-day round trips." Zone 3 is subdivided; one area "within approximately 125 miles of the dwelling for overnight trips of 1 to 3 nights," and another "within approximately 250 miles of the dwelling, for vacation trips of 4 to 9 nights." The fourth zone is "an area extending beyond zone 3 for vacation trips of 10 nights or longer."

The California report showed the supply and predicted demand for several outdoor recreation facilities in the State. For example, 481 group picnicking grounds were available in 1958; the minimum 1980 requirement is for more than double that number— 1 thousand, and the 1980 optimum number is 1,783. For swimming, the "effective feet of shoreline" in 1958 was 246,253, and the 1980 minimum requirement is more than double— 500 thousand, with the optimum 961,543 feet, or about four times as much shoreline as in 1958.

The New York Regional Plan Association, Inc., in its 1960 report, *The Race for Open Space,* recommended that for local recreation areas the National Recreation Association's long-established suggested minimum standard of 10 acres of local recreation space per 1 thousand persons be met or exceeded wherever possible. Achieving even this minimum standard is impractical in much of the region, which is already densely developed. Goals more likely to be obtained by 1985 were set, based on the average density of each community. (Population per net residential acre equals density.)

The recommended goals for all local recreation areas ranged from 1.8 acres per thousand of population in extremely high-density apartment areas such as Manhattan (with an average of 450 persons per acre) to 5 or 6 acres per thousand population for low-density apartment areas (30 to 79 persons per acre). For high-density sections of one-family houses (10 to 29 persons per acre), 8 or 9 acres per thousand was the standard suggested for all local park and recreation areas, and 11.5 to 12.5 acres per thousand was recommended for these uses in low-density residential areas (average population density below 10 per acre).

Besides these goals for local recreation places, a standard was set for county parks. It calls for "12 acres . . . for every 1,200 of the county's 1985 population, or 5 percent of the county's total area, whichever is greater."

How CAN WE acquire open space for the center city, for existing residential areas, and for residential areas now being built?

For the center city, the needed open spaces usually can be acquired only by buying buildings, demolishing them, removing the rubble, and landscaping them as small parks or squares.

Open space in existing residential areas can be acquired in several ways. Neighborhoods may be able to provide small open spaces by converting a street in one block to a park or play area, as was done in Baltimore.

In neighborhoods where rehabilitation has already become necessary, small parks and play areas can be provided by razing two or three derelict houses or stores no longer fit for use and least likely to be rehabilitated. In neighborhoods needing complete renewal, several kinds of open spaces should be provided while there is an opportunity to do so. These include neighborhood and community parks, children's playfields, and recreation centers for adults.

Open space is more difficult to provide for the older suburban areas. Vacant and idle lots are acquired most easily. Another possibility is to buy the less well-maintained buildings, such as small, rundown, little-used rows of shops, and demolish them for parks.

In suburbs built since the war, probably the only early opportunity will be to buy and raze buildings near schools and enlarge the small spaces at the schools into more practicable sizes. The tracts of bypassed land between subdivisions may be turned to community assets by buying them for park purposes, if the terrain is rough, or for recreation areas, if the land is suitable.

In all these residential areas, privately owned open spaces should be considered for acquisition for public use when the owner wishes to dispose of his property.

I see no great problem in finding sites in the city fringes. Tracts to be kept open should be selected and proper uses for them determined. Consideration should be given to whether parks and recreation areas should be next to schools or separate, and whether it is possible and desirable to plan the open spaces to form a greenbelt, which could act as a buffer between subdivisions and between possibly conflicting land uses, such as residential and commercial or residential and industrial.

Providing open spaces within country towns may be considered in much the same way as providing open spaces in the center city, the suburbs, and the rural-urban fringe—depending on the parts of the towns that need open space. There may be little difficulty in towns of less than a thousand population. The problems increase as the towns grow.

The problem of open space in rural areas is one of preservation. String development destroys open countryside. Means are needed to preserve some areas for cropland, pastureland, forest land, or other agricultural use. Land especially suitable for growing specialty crops, such as oranges or grapes, should be high on the priority list of land to be kept in agricultural uses.

WHAT OF THE future? How can we prevent a repetition of past mistakes?

If we are to have areas comparable to New York's Central Park in what we are now building, we must decide now what we want and need.

Our plans need to recognize that we are living in a rapidly changing world. We cannot foresee the direction, rate, or magnitude of all changes. If we are to have livable cities and viable agricultural areas in the future, open space of sufficient size and quality for these uses must be planned for and preserved.

A primary need of each community whose people are interested in having a life tomorrow as good as or better than today is knowledge of what it already has. It needs an inventory of present land uses.

For a State or other large area, the inventory may be generalized and include such categories as built-up or urban land, park and recreation areas, and agricultural lands.

For a county, the inventory may be more detailed and include residential, commercial, industrial, public, and semipublic land uses; public parks, public recreation areas, and privately owned recreation areas; cropland, pasture, forest land, and idle land.

For still smaller areas, a more detailed inventory may be desired.

We need to know and have maps for the locations of areas best suited for development—which may also be the same lands that are best suited for agriculture.

We need comprehensive studies to show us where the lands most suited to agricultural use are located. The land use capability classes I, II, and III of the Soil Conservation Service may fit these needs well.

We need also to know, and have maps for, the areas best suited for retention in greenbelts for use as natural parks or recreation areas. Class VI, VII, and VIII lands may be excellent for natural parks, but possibly, because of location, some better land well suited for agricultural use and also well suited to development might be needed for parks and recreational use.

Using all these data, people in each community can establish a logical policy of land use and decide how much land is needed for which types of uses and where these uses should be.

For example, in determining acreage requirements for recreation, they can answer such questions as: "Is there adequate space within each neighborhood for children to play?" "Is the space in regional parks adequate to meet all but peak requirements?"

Concerning residential developments, people may ask:

"Is there adequate provision for housing within the town for older citizens who prefer not to leave this town but no longer wish to live in the large houses in which they reared their families?"

"Does this community need space for housing more people within the next 10 years?"

"Where should this development take place? What type of development should this be? How should it be separated from other residential developments and from industrial areas?"

"What transportation and community facilities are needed to serve this area? When should the development take place?"

Concerning changes in the agricultural use of land, people may ask:

"Is it possible to keep the land around Smalltown in cropland? What will Smalltown's population be in 1980? Where and how will additional people be housed? Should residential expansion take place on the north side of town, in an area where potatoes now are produced, or on the south side, where there are some fine apple orchards? If some of the orchards are sold for residential development, is there another part of the county suitable for growing apples? If these orchards are destroyed, will the applesauce cannery and the vinegar works be able to import enough apples from the next county? Or will these industries go out of business because the raw materials will no longer be available?"

Once the policy is agreed on, the community can prepare a program for the acquisition of open space in areas already developed. It also can prepare plans for the orderly development of the lands to be built on. Plans for preservation of rural and rural-urban fringe lands to be kept open permanently and those to be kept open for the present, but possibly to be built on in the future, also are needed.

Scheduling the approximate time an area is to be developed—1964, 1970, 1980—facilitates orderly development. The needed facilities (water and sewer lines, roads, and such) and needed services (fire and police protection, and so on) can be provided in an orderly manner. Scheduling can guide growth.

OPEN SPACES can be preserved in several ways. These range in degrees of rights acquired from fee simple purchase through acquisition of easements to zoning regulations.

Other proposed methods are based on the provision of tax incentives to owners of land earmarked for use as open space.

One method is preferential assessment, or the valuation of such property on the basis of present, instead of possible or potential, land use. Several States have adopted laws of this type, but generally they have not been tied in with any overall land use plan.

Another is the deferring of taxes on land in open uses until the land is sold for nonopen-space use. Several States have adopted or have considered such proposals.

A combination of preferential assessment and tax deferral administered as an adjunct to a general plan for open space and development appears to offer more hope than does either alone.

NEW WAYS of developing residential areas, and, indeed, entire new towns, have occurred in the United States. Each offers the possibility of preserving some open space that otherwise would not be saved. They include the superblock, cluster development, variable density development, and planned-unit development.

Zoning changes almost always are needed for any of them. One important needed change is from the old-fashioned concept of zoning for a residential area so that each lot has a uniform, fixed, minimum size, to zoning for a specified overall density for the area.

Zoning for overall density makes it possible to use smaller lots, to group houses in superblocks or in clusters, and (in order to maintain an average, specified size of lot) to retain as open space the land not used in individual lots. The density of development may be increased, yet areas developed in superblocks, in clusters, and in planned units can appear more spacious than do tracts of the same size with the same number of dwelling units developed by ordinary, lot-by-lot subdivision methods.

In superblock development, the open space saved is within the block. Many variations of this type of development have been used in Europe. A few have been built in the United States.

CLUSTER DEVELOPMENT is a new name for a concept similar to that used in the 1920's by Clarence Stein and Henry Wright in the design of the community of Radburn, N.J.

In well-planned cluster development of a tract of land, whether it is 10 acres or 100, the size of each lot and the amount or proportion of the street frontage are reduced. The houses are clustered—grouped—together and the land saved by reducing the lots plus the land saved through reducing the length (and sometimes the width) of the streets is set aside for use as common open space.

Cluster development has other advantages. These include lower costs for installation of water and sewer lines; less expense in providing and maintaining electric, gas, and telephone lines; fewer street lights, storm sewers, and fireplugs; and lower costs for police patrol, garbage collection, and street maintenance, including snow removal.

Such planning and developing on a town, community, or neighborhood basis offer opportunities for building an interesting variety of housing types, so that people of different ages and incomes can live happily together.

Only with large-scale planning and development can the ingredients necessary for a viable neighborhood or a town be an integral—instead of a tacked on—part of the area. For example, neighborhood needs include neighborhood service shops (so one need not drive 5 miles for a loaf of bread); an elementary school; and some recreation facilities.

Community needs include a junior high school; a doctors' and dentists' office building; churches; and a community center for arts, crafts, dances for teenagers, and meetings.

Town needs include a senior high school; library; post office, fire department, and other service facilities; hospital or clinic; commercial center; and industrial areas.

Provision also can be made for open-space buffers or separators between residential areas and conflicting (but necessary) land uses. Separators also can serve between neighborhoods, communities, and towns so that each is a distinct unit. Distinctly separate units help people identify the places where they belong—the "my community," "my town" feeling many sociologists believe necessary for good human development.

Andover, Mass., was one of the first communities in the United States to permit cluster development. The permissive zoning article permitting special developments (that is, clusters) was approved during a town meeting on March 12, 1960. Five cluster developments were under construction in Andover in 1962.

The first developer-builder to take advantage of this zoning concept was able to make a better subdivision of 130 acres on land previously zoned to require approximately an acre for each house. The overall density for the tract remains the same, and the lots still are spacious. But cluster development, by reducing street frontages and lot sizes and clustering the houses in seven groups, saved one-third of the tract for open space to be used by all residents.

A second developer in Andover deeded 15 acres, a little more than one-third of the tract he was developing by the cluster method, to the Andover Village Improvement Society. Another developer began a cluster-type residential area for 56 houses on about 75 acres of wooded land. In this instance, the one-third of the acreage to be kept in open space has been divided among the lots, so that each lot is larger. The developer keeps control of the use of the extra land in each lot by including restrictions in the deeds to the lots. The developer spent extra time and money in planning the site, so that a minimum number of trees were cut, and telephone and electric lines were put underground to preserve the natural beauty.

Apple Hill is a 29-house subdivision atop a steep hill in St. Louis County in Missouri. More than half of the 33-acre site is a recreational tract held in common by homeowners. The rocky terrain made costs of land development relatively high, but the developers saved at least 25 percent by using the cluster plan.

A larger cluster-plan neighborhood, Ville du Parc, was started near Milwaukee, Wis. Under 1-acre zoning and because of the hilly terrain, only 253 homes could have been built on a 300-acre tract. The planner designed a neighborhood in which more than one-half of the total site was left for open space. The lots are in two major clusters. Each is surrounded by a green, wooded area. Each also has a number of small, landscaped courts. The greenbelt has space for a golf course, swimming pool, clubhouse, and riding trails. A shopping center has been planned. Imaginative planning provided all this and 270 homes, or 17 more than could have been developed according to a conventional subdivision. Development of the site according to the cluster method reduced the basic cost of lots to only three-fifths as much as for lots developed conventionally.

PLANNED-UNIT development refers to planned development of an entire neighborhood, community, or town.

Forerunners of this concept in the United States were Greenbelt, Md., near Washington, D.C., and Greendale, Wis. Both were built to provide work and to provide good dwellings in green surroundings for people with moderate incomes.

People have always liked to live in Greenbelt. Many who started out in the original Greenbelt townhouses and apartments have since built larger, better homes there rather than move away.

Two developer-builders in 1962 began constructing new housing at Greenbelt. One community, on a 390-acre tract in the northwest section of Greenbelt, was planned to include about 5 thousand dwelling units in townhouses and high- and low-rise apartments. The second planned community, on 450 acres, includes clusters of townhouses and single-family houses on curving streets ending in culs-de-sac.

Fremont, Calif., was one of the first cities in the United States to provide the legal tools for the development of planned units to avoid the monotony of suburbia.

The objectives of planned-unit development, as stated in a memorandum of the city manager to the city council of Fremont, are to achieve flexibility; provide a more desirable living environment than would be possible through the strict application of ordinance requirements; encourage developers to use a more creative approach in the development of residential, commercial, and industrial land; encourage a more efficient and more desirable use of open land; and to encourage variety in the physical development pattern of the city.

Besides providing homeseekers with greater variety in the types of housing and lots, land has been saved for neighborhood parks.

Roy Potter, the director of planning in Fremont, stated in January 1963:

"We now have approximately 70 acres of land that have been dedicated to the city at no cost for public park purpose. This has enabled us at least to meet much of our neighborhood park needs in the Fremont area. About 18 acres of land have been developed and approved for homeowner parks, with the city retaining an open-space easement over these particular areas. This has been made possible through lot-size reduction, cluster development, and the movement of the planting strip between the sidewalk and the curb into the park area so that the overall density of any particular tract would remain the same."

Other California cities have started to follow the Fremont plan. In San Carlos, a plan would permit building 238 row-type houses on 47.8 acres, of which 25.3 acres would be a greenbelt.

Among the planned communities under construction in 1963 was Marin Bay, on a peninsula in Marin County, Calif. It has sites for garden apartments and houses for an eventual population of 20 thousand. Five different neighborhoods have been planned, each with its own special recreation spaces and facilities. A 400-acre natural preserve on a wooded hilltop was set aside by the developers for the use of all residents of Marin Bay.

El Dorado Hills, near Sacramento, was planned for a population of nearly 75 thousand in 12 villages on more than 9,800 acres of rolling land. The villages are separated by parks and arterial streets. Each village has a recreation club and at least one school.

Paths through the parks connect houses with schools; children cross no arterial streets. The design for the community retains 20 to 30 percent of the total acreage as open space. All utilities are below ground. A water purification plant with distribution lines and a sewage treatment plant and lines are included. Shopping facilities are provided in each village. Land was reserved for major shopping centers to be built when demand warrants them.

University Community, near San Diego, combines a 1,100-acre University of California campus with a 3,500-acre residential area. The completed community is planned to cover 10,600 acres and to have 100 thousand residents. In the plans are 25 thousand dwelling units, including houses and apartments. Numerous neighborhood parks will be scattered throughout the community. There will be 18 elementary schools, 3 junior high schools, a senior high school, and the university. Facilities for all necessary commercial enterprises will be available, and an industrial area is planned. Another new town is to be developed around the new University of California at Irvine.

A planned development in Pittsburgh also is noteworthy. East Hills, under construction in 1963 on a 130-acre site, was planned as a residential district to include garden and elevator apartments, duplexes, and one- and two-family houses. Space was allocated for schools, churches, shopping facilities, and private and common open space.

Plans for a new community, Reston, in Fairfax County, Va., near Washington, call for development to be completed by 1980, at which time the community is expected to have 75 thousand inhabitants. More than 40 percent of Reston's 6,800 acres is to be retained as open space.

To SUM UP: Space—land—is needed for residential and for other uses—for housing, commerce, industry, transportation; schools, hospitals, other facilities; parks, recreation areas, zoos, museums, and art galleries. We must have space for agriculture. But space—horizontal space, land space, open space—is limited.

We could centralize, put all these space uses—except agriculture, some transportation, and some outdoor recreation—into a few cities of skyscrapers, or even into a few of the one-building Mile High Cities conceived by the late Frank Lloyd Wright.

We could spread development out more than we have already done—in decentralized arrangements, with each dwelling on its own acre lot, such as the Broadacre City, also conceived by Mr. Wright.

WE COULD GO ON as we have been going, and just push the urban area and the rural-urban fringe farther out into the rural areas each year. Eventually—and not so many years from now as one may think—transportation and communications would become virtually impossible. The journey to work might take half the working day. Recreation out of doors might be restricted to one's immediate environs because travel to a park would be too much of a struggle.

Are these fantastic examples? No. Broadacre City could easily be built. Mile High City, or something like it, is feasible with today's construction materials and methods.

We cannot afford to sit back and let new residential subdivisions, new shopping centers, and new industrial parks grow up wherever a few people want to put them. We need to start thinking about the best use of our land—not just the use that will bring the highest cash returns. We need to learn about the many possible ways of planning, developing, and building that are better than the urban sprawl that costs each one of us, no matter where he lives, so much in dollars, effort, and time.

Imaginative, balanced, planned development will work as well for small rural villages, county seats, and small cities as it will for large cities and metropolitan regions. Planning for reasonably compact development and for preservation of open space is a problem and a challenge for each of us—for each community.

JEANNE M. DAVIS *is an urban planner in the Land and Water Economics Branch, Resource Development Economics Division, Economic Research Service. She was formerly a consultant to the Baltimore Regional Planning Council.*

HOWARD ZAHNISER

WILDLANDS, A PART
OF MAN'S ENVIRONMENT

A GOOD environment for man will always include some areas that are wild. Whether man thinks of himself as a descendant from first parents who started life on the earth in a Garden of Eden that was an actual area of pristine Nature or as the beneficiary of an evolution traced back to savage, amphibian, or even earlier conditions, still he knows that home for his ancestors was savage, wild, and intimate with trees and other plants and animals, but without the shelter and protection from the harsh elements of Nature for which he has now sacrificed a companionship with the elemental forces and forms of life and Nature.

An awareness of such a background of inheritance, an intimation of nostalgia for the distant ancestral conditions, and an immediate joy in living and learning that is experienced in the wild and natural areas that remain have given modern men a consciousness of the values of returning to the primitive for recreation, for inspiration, and for knowledge.

Even areas of the wilderness itself have come to be valued *as wilderness*—areas that, in contrast with those parts of the earth's landscape that are dominated by man and his works, are untrammeled by man; areas where man is himself a member of the natural community, a transient whose travels leave only trails.

The earth's wilderness in any cosmol-

ogy is the great mother of resources—man's source of all his materials, as well as his own ancestral home. Out of the wilderness have come man and all that he knows. Out of the wilderness he has fashioned his civilization. It is the raw material of his culture.

It is no wonder then that men sigh for the wilderness as they see it disappearing. It is no wonder that so many respond to a mention of the wilderness with a nostalgia from deep-seated, half recollections of something they want to see again.

Americans know an especially keen poignance as they think of wilderness, for as Americans they have always known something of the wilderness.

To their immediate generations of ancestors the wilderness was all-en-

346

compassing, and it still persists in remnants, some of magnificent extent.

When the European world of our origins was well settled, even crowded as our ancestors thought, we Americans found a new continent where the wilderness was still pristine. We started all over again. We fashioned the wilderness anew. It refashioned us, too. And this time, before the wilderness was all made over into civilized, mechanized, humanized areas, it was itself valued, and it began to be cherished. The mother of resources was last to be recognized as in need of protection, but in the United States the recognition did come—and it came before the wilderness had all vanished.

The wilderness in America is still living. It is different to us, but it has not vanished. It no longer seems to contain mankind, as outer space does now seem to. We ourselves seem rather to contain the wilderness. The dear Mother who gave us origin, nurtured us—chastised us, too—lives with us now, lives, as we might say, through our care, but still lives.

ONE OF the first Americans to sense the values of wilderness as wilderness and the possibility of its preservation in the public interest—Henry David Thoreau—perceived these values not only as recreational in a common sense but also as profound. "In Wildness," he wrote, "is the preservation of the World," capitalizing both "Wildness" and "World."

Before the 19th century was half gone, Thoreau had asked for the preservation of wilderness areas "for our own true recreation," and had urged a primitive forest for every town and a committee to see that the beauty of the town received no detriment. He had also interpreted the human need for wilderness.

"The wilderness is near as well as dear to every man," he wrote in 1849 in *A Week on the Concord and Merrimack Rivers.* "Even the oldest villages are indebted to the border of wild wood which surrounds them, more than to the gardens of men. There is something indescribably inspiring and beautiful in the aspect of the forest skirting and occasionally jutting into the midst of new towns, which, like the sand heaps of fresh fox burrows, have sprung up in their midst. The very uprightness of the pines and maples asserts the ancient rectitude and vigor of nature. Our lives need the relief of such a background, where the pine flourishes and the jay still screams."

In his classic *Walden,* published in 1854, Thoreau predicted that "our village life would stagnate if it were not for the unexplored forests and meadows which surround it."

He went on to exclaim in a rhapsody of understanding:

"We need the tonic of wildness,— to wade sometimes in marshes where the bittern and the meadow-hen lurk, and hear the booming of the snipe; to smell the whispering sedge where only some wilder and more solitary fowl builds her nest, and the mink crawls with its belly close to the ground. At the same time that we are earnest to explore and learn all things, we require that all things be mysterious and unexplorable, that land and sea be infinitely wild, unsurveyed and unfathomed by us because unfathomable. We can never have enough of nature. We must be refreshed by the sight of inexhaustible vigor, vast and titanic features, the seacoast with its wrecks, the wilderness with its living and decaying trees, the thundercloud, and the rain which lasts three weeks and produces freshets. We need to witness our own limits transgressed, and some life pasturing freely where we never wander."

ROBERT MARSHALL, who a century after Thoreau, in the 1930's, led a wilderness preservation movement from his position as head of the Division of Lands and Recreation of the Forest Service, knew and expressed values that for him made the wilderness unique esthetically.

"The wilderness," Robert Marshall

wrote, "furnishes the best environment for physical adventure," the lack of which "is responsible for much unhappiness, for a considerable portion of the crime which is so often committed as a means of self expression, and, if we are to believe William James and Bertrand Russell, even for war."

In wilderness Marshall also found "ideal conditions for developing physical hardiness" and at the same time "the perfect environment for peacefulness and relaxation."

He found the wilderness "also unique esthetically in that it stimulates not just the sense of sight, as does art, or the sense of sound, as does music, but all of the senses which man has."

"The traveler wandering at evening to the shore of some wilderness lakelet," Marshall wrote, "senses through his sight the pink sunset sky and the delightful pattern which the deep bay makes through the spruce trees which rise from its shores; senses through his hearing the lapping of the water against the rocky shore and the evening song of the thrush; senses through his smell the scent of balsam and the marsh flowers at the water's edge; senses through his touch the gentle wind which blows on his forehead and the softness of the sphagnum beneath his feet."

"The wilderness," testified Marshall, "is all of these senses harmonized with immensity into a form of beauty which to many human beings is the most perfect experience of the earth."

Immensity indeed was for Robert Marshall the wilderness's dominant value.

"All these esthetic values," he said, "are present, but they are blended with the dominant value of being a part of an immensity so great that the human being who looks upon it vanishes into utter insignificance."

On such convictions as these, the forester Robert Marshall based his strenuous and effective efforts for wilderness preservation and his establishment of a trust fund that has succeeded remarkably in its purpose to increase the knowledge and appreciation of wilderness as a resource of the American people.

NOT ONLY, however, are wilderness values superlative. They are essential. The exquisite is also a requisite. We have a profound, a fundamental need for areas of wilderness—a need that is not only recreational but spiritual, educational, scientific, essential to a true understanding of ourselves, our culture, our own natures, and our place in all Nature.

It is a need that any modern man may know, whether his residence is urban, suburban, or rural.

This need is for areas of the earth within which we are without our mechanisms that make us immediate masters over our environment—areas of wild Nature in which we can sense ourselves as dependent members of the interdependent community of living things that together derive their existence from the sun.

By very definition this wilderness is a need. The idea of wilderness as an area without man's influence is man's own concept. Its values are human values. Its preservation is a purpose that arises out of man's own sense of his fundamental needs, an awareness that comes only when man's communities of dwelling places and his farmlands have become so urban, suburban, mechanically rural that man himself feels crowded, regimented, and in all his mastery the tool of his own inventions.

It is not surprising that recreational values generally are understood as representing the dominant importance of wilderness in our modern civilization. Only in a society that produces the erosion of human beings, the wearing away of soul and body and spirit that is so familiar in modern circumstances, does the concept of recreation appear.

Wilderness is the antithesis of all that produces the conditions that recreation remedies. It provides the kind of recreation most needed by the increasingly large numbers who now seek wilderness. It affords a background for the kind of outdoor recreation for which conveniences and accommodations are provided—the frontier where those who do not wish to experience the rigors of wilderness living and travel may still know in some degree the tonic benefits of its wildness.

Some of the benefits of wildness, fortunately, are realized in areas that are not wilderness—areas that are not large enough to be wilderness or that are modified by timber cutting, roadbuilding, dwelling places, or other intrusions that destroy wilderness yet leave areas where the quality of wildness lives on.

"Wildness" and "wilderness" are common terms in their distinguishing nature, yet not synonymous.

Wildness is a quality. Wilderness is an area of certain character.

Wildness is the essence of wilderness, yet it characterizes also that which is not wilderness, including many natural and wildland areas that are not wilderness.

Wildness is the quality of that which is fresh and independently vital, undomesticated, uncontrolled, although close to and even surrounded by man's civilization.

The house cat, in its indoor feline independence and its untrammeled caterwauling outdoors at night, maintains its essence of wildness despite its domestic surroundings.

Wilderness is something more than wildness, yet not comprehensive of all wildness.

It is indeed not only for absolute wilderness that modern men and women and their adventurous children leave the city in a return to wildness.

What they seek is the quality of wildness—the wildness in which Thoreau saw the preservation of the world.

They seek and find this quality of environment in many of the areas near at hand—areas not truly wilderness though more or less free from the trammels of man's domesticating genius.

We call the areas within which the quality of wildness is present and perceptible, even though modified by other qualities, "the wildlands." So distinctive are these areas in the midst of our civilized, domesticated landscape that they are designated by this unit term, the one word, "wildlands"—not simply lands that are wild but areas that are distinctive, the wildlands.

Arthur H. Carhart, a landscape architect and land use planner with long experience in wild country, has applied to the consideration of conflicting uses of wildlands the zoning skills that have become so effectual in dealing with similar conflicts for the use of areas within our cities.

In a book, *Planning for America's Wildlands*, Mr. Carhart in 1961 proposed an orderliness in wildlands management to meet all needs reasonably and at the same time protect in various zones the quality of wildness and provide also for the preservation of the ultimate areas of wilderness.

As one of his urban colleagues might view a well-planned city from the Residential Zone A, Mr. Carhart looks out from the heart of the true wilderness toward, and through, zones of increasing use for purposes that more and more modify the natural scene.

The B Zone of our wildlands, which he calls "Wilderness Buffer," and the C Zone, designated "Primitive Camping," have a closeness to the Wilderness Zone A that is like the approaches of the B and C Zones in city planning to the ideal protected in Residential A.

D, E, F, and G Zones encompass all the other wildlands, even to the edge of the city, or perhaps as wildland "islands" in the parks of the city itself. (These, in Mr. Carhart's nomenclature, are the Dude Ranch Zone, the Summer Home-Lodge-Group Camp Zone, Intermediate Resort and Camp Zone, and the Semisuburban Zone.)

"Physically," says Mr. Carhart, "wildlands begin wherever we face away from the man-dominated landscape of farm, town, city, or any landscape grossly modified by human occupancy maintained for any purposes. From this spot the wildlands extend in graduated degrees of lessening human influence in the natural landscape, outward, to reach their type climax in the wilderness. Thus the term 'wildlands' is more than a synonym for the term 'wilderness'; wildlands are the wilderness plus all the surrounding lands that lie between genuine wilderness, as exemplified by the totally natural landscape, and those landscapes where man's control and manipulations are immediately evident."

ESPECIALLY NOTABLE among or within the wildlands are the natural areas set aside for scientific purposes. These are areas of widely varying sizes, areas that would occur in any of the zones which Arthur Carhart has visualized. They are sections not only within which natural conditions may be studied but also areas that may themselves be used as "check" zones in connection with studies of management practices. Their distinctive value is in their freedom from human manipulation and modification.

"We take it for granted," Luna B. Leopold, Chief of the Geological Survey's Water Division, told the Sixth Biennial Wilderness Conference in San Francisco in 1959, "that there is some social gain in the erection and maintenance of a museum of fine arts, a museum of natural history, or even a historical museum. Sooner or later we ought to be mature enough to extend this concept to another kind of museum, one which you might call the museum of land types, consisting of samples as uninfluenced as possible by man."

It may be that the scientific values will come to be considered the greatest of all the values of wilderness and wildland natural areas.

Scientific values of wildlands are similar to those of historical importance in depending on the preservation of areas as they existed, and exist, without the influences of modern man,

pieces of the long ago that we still have with us.

Scientific and historical values are related also to the study and observation that are essentially educational in their purpose. Wildlands, including the smaller natural areas and also the extensive wilderness, should be preserved for the sake of the field study that they make possible for students, generation after generation. They serve this purpose for the summer camps of youth organizations, for field stations of college summer school classes, and also for the more advanced excursions of graduate students.

Perhaps the most profound of all wilderness values in the modern world is an educational value.

As the so-called conquest of Nature has progressed, men and women—separated by their civilization from the life community of their origin—have become less and less aware of their dependence on other forms of life and more and more misled into a sense of self-sufficiency and into a disregard of their interdependence with other forms of life.

In the areas of wilderness that are still relatively unmodified by man, it is possible for a human being, adult or child, to sense and see his own humble, dependent relationship to other creatures, plant and animal.

In and from these areas are the opportunities for gaining an understanding of our past, ourselves, and our world, which will enable us to enjoy the conveniences and liberties of our urbanized, industrialized, mechanized civilization and yet not sacrifice an awareness of our human existence as spiritual creatures nurtured and sustained by and from the great community of life that comprises the wildness of the universe, of which we ourselves are a part.

Paradoxically, the wilderness which thus teaches modern man his dependence on the whole community of life also can teach him a needed personal independence—an ability to care for himself, to carry his own burdens, to provide his own fuel, prepare his own food, furnish his own shelter, make his own bed, and even transport himself by walking.

WITH THESE LESSONS comes the understanding that physical, psychic, and spiritual human needs are such that wilderness recreation should always be available and, in fact, should be enjoyed to a much greater extent than it now is.

Wilderness vacations have overtones that make them more than narrowly recreational. They are more likely to be joyous than merry, more refreshing than exciting, more engrossing than diverting. Their typical rewards are satisfactions.

Philosophers of education who describe their goals in such terms as "life adjustment" and "personality development" may find in the wilderness a most valuable resource where recreation becomes profoundly educational.

In a culture like that which we call modern, we can be sure that it will be increasingly important for students, of the present and of future generations, to know what the wilderness has to teach—through their own experiences; through educators who are informed and corrected by wilderness experiences; and through photographs, paintings, writings, and other educational and informational materials with a validity insured by a still living wilderness.

As long as wilderness areas exist in reality, providing actual resorts for human beings, giving a sense of actuality to pictorial and literary representations of the wilderness, and affording the scenes for further research, so long will the safeguards against an urban, industrial, mechanized ignorance of the facts of human life be effective.

To know the quality of wildness in the wilderness or even in lesser wildlands is to have a portion of the vitaminlike essentials without which mankind weakens into the want that comes with a bread-alone existence.

IT IS FORTUNATE that our bounty of land and water resources is so great that we can have our natural areas of wildland, including our great remaining stretches of wilderness, without sacrificing the material benefits derived from the products of land and water areas exploited for commodities.

We can, for example, have our forest products and wilderness, too, although, of course, we cannot take the products from places cherished as wilderness.

We need commodities that only the forest provides. We need also the undeveloped, unexploited areas of forest wilderness.

Just as man cannot live by bread alone, though the very statement recognizes bread as essential, so we cannot afford to use the forests for products only, though we recognize clearly that forest products are essential to us.

The needs are not single or simple. They are many and complex—multiple.

Indeed, the principle of multiple use of resources is a remarkably apt one for application in a program for wildland preservation.

Used by some especially interested groups and individuals as a euphemism to describe programs that exclude wilderness preservation, the term "multiple use" has had wide publicity in controversy as an ideal opposed to preservation of areas. Those who resist a policy or program that would preserve an area which they may wish to exploit for commodities (or think they or their successors might so wish to exploit at some possible future time) have idealized their own single purposes with a "multiple-use" label.

This has been notable not only in arguments advanced during controversies but also in formal nomenclatures. Thus the vice president of a paper company speaks publicly in New England as director of the Association for the Multiple Use of Maine Timberland, and a lumber company's managing forester in Idaho speaks as chairman of the Inland Empire Multiple Use Committee.

This polemic use of the term to idealize commercial purposes that are in conflict with wilderness preservation proposals has confused some into concluding that such proposals are inconsistent with the multiple-use principle.

The truth is to the contrary.

Not only is wildlands preservation consistent with the multiple-use principle. The best apparent hope for success in the preservation of such areas, including wilderness, is indeed actually in application of the multiple-use principle. This is particularly true in areas in public ownership.

The Forest Service has defined multiple use as that combination of uses of any area that is best suited to public needs.

The Multiple Use Act of 1960—Public Law 517 of the 86th Congress—which declared, "The establishment and maintenance of areas of wilderness are consistent with the purposes and provisions of this Act"—defined the term as follows:

" 'Multiple Use' means: The management of all the various renewable surface resources of the national forests so that they are utilized in the combination that will best meet the needs of the American people; making the most judicious use of the land for some or all of these resources or related services over areas large enough to provide sufficient latitude for periodic adjustments in use to conform to changing needs and conditions; that some land will be used for less than all of the resources; and harmonious and coordinated management of the various resources, each with the other, without impairment of the productivity of the land, with consideration being given to the relative values of the various resources, and not necessarily the combination of uses that will give the greatest dollar return or the greatest unit output."

"The combination that will best meet the needs of the American people . . . not necessarily the combination of uses that will give the greatest dollar return or the greatest unit output" is a combination that

within many forests and in many areas provides for wildland preservation.

Under such provisions, the designation within our forest lands of some areas as wilderness is obviously sound multiple use, and within the areas that are designated as wilderness there are various combinations that are consistent with preservation of the wilderness character of the areas.

Watershed protection, for example, is a most important use of nearly all our areas of wilderness—so important in some that recreational uses may be prohibited during dry seasons when the fire hazard from campfires would jeopardize the vegetation and soils on which watershed protection is dependent.

Research and study uses of areas to realize their scientific values are likewise among the multiple uses in a wilderness combination.

Camping, fishing, hunting, picture taking, and other recreational uses are of dominant importance from the viewpoint of many, and these uses can be as consistent with wilderness preservation as they are in some respects dependent on areas of wilderness.

Only those uses are excluded from a wilderness combination that would destroy an area's wilderness character—timber cutting, roadbuilding, and resort operation, for example.

Both in the broad, overall selection of a reasonable portion of our land and also in provision for the use of the specific areas classified for preservation there is a harmony with the multiple-use principle.

Application of the multiple-use principle will facilitate wildlands preservation.

The principle is important to wilderness and other wildlands preservation because the areas to be preserved are within areas already devoted to some other purpose and the lateness in our history of land use would make difficult indeed the realization of a category of lands for wildland use only—the single purpose posed by the would-be exploiters who consider the production of commercial commodities the essential multiple-use nucleus.

The fact that there still are wildlands, even areas of wilderness, within lands devoted primarily to various other uses than wildland preservation indicates that such preservation is compatible with various uses of the land. To realize the preservation in perpetuity it is necessary only to manage the lands for other purposes in such a way as continuously to preserve the wildlands character. The multiple-use principle provides well for meeting such a need.

It seems apparent that no land within the United States is to be left unused. There is no hope, thus, on this assumption, that wildlands will persist by escaping utilization by man. Areas to be preserved by man will have to be used by him positively, to meet the needs for wildlands that he recognizes—managed to be left unmanaged.

Furthermore, with increasing pressures on limited land areas it becomes more and more important to use all available land for all recognized needs. Wildland preservation must be an aspect of a total program that meets all needs.

To preserve some areas free from timber cutting will require adequate timber production on other areas. Preserving natural areas undeveloped with recreation facilities will require adequate provision of developed areas with the access and facilities needed by the large numbers seeking outdoor recreation with conveniences.

The multiple use of the total land resource must be so planned and managed as to include the preservation of wildland, if it is to be complete.

MOST OF THE wilderness still remaining within the United States is in Federal ownership.

Nearly 15 million acres within national forests outside Alaska have been designated administratively for preservation as wilderness in 84 units, which vary in size from a little more than 5 thousand acres to more than 1.2 million acres. Perhaps, including Alaska, an additional 15 million acres within the national forests would qualify for such designation but for conflicting potential uses. Including these *de facto* areas, there actually are thus some 30 million acres in the national forests.

Within some 49 areas in the national park system there are about 20 million acres of wilderness, including the areas in Alaska and Hawaii and omitting 2 million acres as the estimated total area within the 49 areas involved in roads and facilities for visitors.

National wildlife refuges and ranges include 23 units, which contain nearly 25 million acres of wilderness, about 19 million of which are in Alaska.

Areas administered by the Bureau of Land Management and some other agencies may bring to 80 million acres the total of the wilderness in Federal ownership, most of it in Alaska and the Western States.

In the aggregate, some 3 million acres of wilderness in a dozen or so separate areas are being preserved by the States. The largest State total is in New York's total of nearly 2.5 million acres in the forest preserve within the Adirondack and Catskill Parks. More than 200 thousand acres are in the Katahdin wilderness of Baxter State Park in Maine.

Private holdings within the United States also include significant areas—great stretches, for example, of the paper companies' 1,800,000 acres in Allagash country in Maine.

No wilderness inventory has ever been made of the entire United States. The total area of land in a wilderness condition in 1963 may be estimated at less than 90 million acres, out of our total land area of more than 2.3 billion acres.

The Wilderness Act passed by the United States Senate in 1961 specified for consideration, as units of a proposed National Wilderness Preservation System, Federal areas that in the aggregate total some 62 million acres, of which the measure's sponsor, Senator Clinton P. Anderson, estimated between 35 and 45 million acres would survive the review program provided for in the act and come to constitute the Nation's wilderness resource.

NO ESTIMATES are available or apparently possible for the number or the average or aggregate sizes of other wildland areas, but it seems clear to those who value such areas that they are already too few, too small, and increasingly subject to pressures that threaten their natural conditions.

Anyone who has custody over any area of wildland should preserve it if at all possible in meeting other needs, so precious and scarce are such areas becoming.

Throughout the land, whether in urban, rural, or wildland surroundings, the continued existence of areas in unspoiled natural condition must be the result of deliberate, determined action. No extensive areas of wilderness will long survive except as they are positively valued as wilderness and deliberately so preserved. Nor will natural conditions prevail within city and suburban parks or indeed in even the rural landscape unless the quality of wildness is adequately appreciated before it has vanished and protected by whatever governmental unit has custody.

Fortunately, the human need for experiencing natural surroundings has been felt so extensively and understood so well that there is reasonable hope that some of the same circumstances which threaten such surroundings will help in realizing the developments that will preserve them.

The result has been not only numerous and increasingly serious threats to the wilderness that yet remains, but at the same time a growing demand for wilderness as a refuge from the pressures and distractions of our urbanized, mechanized environment.

This interest has found expression also in a concern for the areas, though smaller, that are more numerous, often nearer home, and, though in private ownership, still available as an important part of the whole wildland heritage that we enjoy.

The variety and extent of available areas can still match the multiplicity and degree of uses that are desired.

It is still possible to see such a balance continued indefinitely—a challenge not only to land planners but also to all citizens who participate in the formulation of public policy and the establishment and maintenance of programs.

For it must be emphasized that no areas of wilderness will persist except as they are designated for preservation as such and are so protected. Nor will any natural area or other wildland tract retain its quality of wildness except as this is deliberately valued and safeguarded by excluding the developments that would sacrifice its wild character.

TO BE REALIZED in our culture, wildlands preservation must be the result of a deliberate purpose, implemented through policies and programs that can be expected to endure.

If private lands are to be handled and bequeathed as wildlands they must be preserved through dedications that have legal force and are perpetual, or the time will surely come when their wilderness character will be lost.

A sound and adequate total policy and program of land use must provide for so handling those areas devoted to production and development as to permit also the preservation of the wildness within the maximum possible number of areas of maximum possible size in their natural condition.

A good environment for man will always include some areas that are wild.

HOWARD ZAHNISER *became executive secretary, The Wilderness Society, Washington, D.C., and editor of its magazine,* The Living Wilderness, *in 1945. Previously he was head of the Information and Editorial Division of the former Bureau of Plant Industry, Soils, and Agricultural Engineering in the Department.*

LAWRENCE N. STEVENS

SEASHORES, LAKESHORES,
AND RIVERBANKS

THE Nation's seashores, lakeshores, and riverbanks are a priceless possession. From Plymouth Rock to Cape Canaveral, they have been a deep foundation of history. They have provided the harbors that serve our commerce and sites for basic industries. Great cities have been built on their shores. They have grown in importance as a prime resource for recreation.

We are fortunate in the extent and variety of our shorelines: The rugged coast of Maine and its myriad islands; the beaches and the dunes of North Carolina's Outer Banks; the keys and everglades of Florida; the Golden Gate and San Francisco Bay; the fiords of Puget Sound and Alaska; the gemlike beaches in Hawaii.

We have more than oceans. The Great Lakes are inland oceans. Winnipesaukee, Champlain, Winnebago, and Tahoe are among thousands of lakes that have been magnets for many years. We have scores of new, manmade lakes, such as Lake Mead, Lake Texoma, and the reservoirs of the Tennessee Valley.

Our streams are our arteries—the mighty Mississippi, the wide Missouri, the historic Potomac, the lovely Shenandoah, the busy Delaware, the motherly Ohio, the ambitious Columbia, the grand Colorado, the challenging Rio Grande, the lyric Suwannee. And the smaller ones—the Zumbro, the Minnesota, and the Chattahoochee—where we swam, and picnicked, and dreamed.

Yes, it is a magnificent heritage. But what we have done with it is a sorrowful, shameful, selfish blot upon the record of a proud Nation.

The coastlines, shorelines of lakes, and the banks of many rivers have been neglected, underdeveloped, and polluted. The rights to the shorelines have been left for acquisition by whoever wanted them.

The Outdoor Recreation Resources Review Commission estimated that less than 10 percent of the Nation's ocean and Great Lakes shoreline was in public recreation areas in 1961. A small percentage is restricted for military use. Most is under private control.

The magnificent stretches of beach and sparkling surf that remain in their

355

original and wildly beautiful state, where oceanside overlooks invite campers, picnickers, and naturalists, are dwindling rapidly as other uses encroach. Public access to river, sea, and lake shores often is severely limited. The cost of acquiring such access, high now, rises constantly, especially near cities.

The limitations on public access to shoreline recreation areas exclude many persons from waters legally open for common use. Sometimes land surrounding such waters is privately owned or controlled. Sometimes there are no roads or paths by which people can reach the water.

Water pollution, a growing hazard, in many places endangers health, may destroy aquatic plant and animal life, frequently creates conditions offensive to eye and nose, and eliminates many areas from recreational use. Pollution may stem from domestic sewage, industrial wastes, mine drainage, pesticides, insecticides, fertilizers used on nearby lands, sewage and refuse dumped from private boats, and soil erosion in the watershed. (Nearly 7 million tons of suspended sediment are carried past St. Louis in the Mississippi River each year.)

Although many cities are within easy driving distance of the oceans or the Great Lakes and many of the larger inland cities are on major rivers, we often have failed to consider the recreation potential in planning reservoirs and other water development projects, and to bear in mind that recreation developments along our larger rivers offer a flexibility of distribution not paralleled by other water resources.

Most projects of water development have been planned and built for purposes other than recreation. Opportunities for swimming, boating, picnicking, and similar activities have been incidental rather than a major consideration. Frequently provision for the acquisition and development of places for recreation associated with these projects has been inadequate or lacking. As a result, recreation use has

been less than could have been provided with a little additional cost.

These serious problems have been due partly to the lack of a national focal point at which to coordinate policies, activities, and programs.

RECOGNITION of this fact was among the reasons that led the Congress in 1958 to establish the Outdoor Recreation Resources Review Commission.

The Commission, made up of eight Members of Congress and seven Presidential appointees, conducted a 3-year study of the outdoor recreation needs of the American people and of the resources available to meet the needs.

In a report in 1962 to the President and the Congress, the Commission emphasized that recreation pressures on shoreline resources had become critical and that all subdivisions of Government as well as private persons and groups would of necessity become involved increasingly in the problems.

One reason therefor is that nearly half of our population prefers water-based recreation to all other forms; roughly one-third of all Americans fish for sport; boating is among our most popular outdoor pastimes; water skiing and skindiving, spectator sports short years ago, now attract millions; swimming, already high on the list of outdoor activities, promises to top all others before many years have passed.

The Commission limited its studies to recreation, as it was set up to do, and this chapter confines itself to that matter, but a reminder is needed that lakes and streams serve other functions, too—commerce, water supplies, irrigation, sanitation.

The Commission's report recommended the establishment of the Bureau of Outdoor Recreation to serve as such a clearinghouse in the Federal Government. It recommended also the formulation of a national outdoor recreation policy; the establishment of guidelines for managing recreation resources; the expansion, modification, and intensification of existing programs to meet increasing needs, and a Federal program of grants-in-aid to help States plan, acquire, and develop the resources.

President Kennedy, in a message to the Congress on March 1, 1962, recommended that a Bureau of Outdoor Recreation be created. He also announced his intention of appointing a Recreation Advisory Council to provide a means of coordinating national recreation policies.

Secretary of the Interior Stewart L. Udall established the new Bureau of Outdoor Recreation on April 2, 1962. Later that month President Kennedy appointed the Recreation Advisory Council, which comprises the heads of executive agencies that have major responsibilities for recreation resources.

In his message, the President applauded the congressional action that led to creation of the Cape Cod National Seashore and urged favorable consideration of proposals for 10 new national recreation areas, 6 of which would offer water-based activities. Later in 1962, the 87th Congress authorized the establishment of national seashores at Point Reyes, Calif., and Padre Island, Tex.

Concerning water, the President said: "This Administration adheres to the policy . . . that our available water supply will be used to provide maximum benefits for all purposes—hydroelectric power, irrigation and reclamation, navigation, recreation and wildlife, and municipal and industrial water supply."

The Bureau began studies of a number of areas where water-based recreation could be provided in harmony with other uses. They include the Shasta-Trinity-Whiskeytown Reservoir area in northern California, Pictured Rocks in Michigan, the Allagash River in Maine, the Allegheny and Raystown Reservoirs in Pennsylvania, the Lewis and Clark Trail across the West, and Assateague Island on the Atlantic coast. Each represents a different type of opportunity, ranging from wilderness to relatively heavy day use.

The Commission and the Bureau urged Federal and State action to obtain tracts before they are preempted for other, less important uses.

The President on February 14, 1963, sent to the Congress a bill to establish a Land and Water Conservation Fund to provide grants-in-aid to States on a matched-fund basis for statewide comprehensive planning, acquisition, and development of recreation resources, and for the acquisition of certain needed recreation lands by the Federal Government. The fund would be based on fees assessed users of Federal recreation lands, waters, and facilities and on other sources of revenue. It is expected that acquisition and development of shoreline recreation areas would have a high priority in both State and Federal programs financed by the fund.

One way of helping to meet the increasing need for water-based recreation is to provide for multiple use of publicly owned waters, such as water-supply reservoirs which have been closed to outdoor recreation and can be opened to selected activities that will do no harm to the public interest they were designed to serve. Portland, Maine, for example, draws its water supply from Sebago Lake, which is extensively used for recreation.

The best efforts of all agencies concerned also are needed. They must work closely together in planning and developing the shorelines, classifying rivers and lakes for recreation purposes, acquiring and maintaining the access routes to water recreation areas, and controlling pollution.

Most of all, it is a task for all people. Citizens who are aware that our seashores, lakeshores, and riverbanks are a priceless possession will use and enjoy them, take care of them, and guard them against exploitation.

LAWRENCE N. STEVENS *became Associate Director of the Bureau of Outdoor Recreation, the Department of the Interior, in 1962. Previously he was Deputy Director for Studies, Outdoor Recreation Resources Review Commission.*

MAX M. THARP AND HUGH A. JOHNSON

MULTIPURPOSE DEVELOPMENT AND HIGHWAYS

THE highways that were planned, being built, or finished in 1963—41 thousand miles of high-speed, limited-access, scenic highways that link more than 90 percent of the cities having populations of 50 thousand or more; more than 800 thousand miles of primary and secondary highways; and more than 2 million miles of local rural roads—are a tremendous public investment and a public trust.

Of their several purposes and uses, one should be to extend everyone's opportunities for recreation; that can be done with imagination and modest modifications. By recreation we mean not only exercise and fun. We mean also knowledge and understanding of the country, a broadening of one's appreciation of its work and accomplishment, an awareness of its beauties and possibilities—lessons, that is, in patriotism and our environment.

Our thesis has the support of time. The Land Planning Committee of the National Resources Board, in a report in 1938, declared:

"The automobile in the space of 30 years has evolved from an experimental curiosity into a vital element in our existence. . . . It has been little more than a decade since a trip of 500 miles or more by automobile was an uncommon experience, and even today

358

[1938] it is probable that comparatively few people have made more than a dozen trips of a thousand miles or more. . . . Present day statistics estimate that only 40 percent of all motor travel is for commercial and strictly transportation purposes. This indicates that 60 percent of all motor travel is largely recreational. . . . This demonstrates the important place the automobile holds in our national recreation scheme. . . ."

Much can be done to provide recreation facilities in the national highway system. We recognize the restrictions of law and custom, but they change as conditions, autos, roads, our ways of life, and our needs change. The law and policies can be changed, if the program warrants. Engineering design obviously need be no limitation.

The fact is that encroachment by public and private uses, including highways, is a continuing threat to public outdoor recreation areas.

RECREATION PLANNERS long have warred with highway builders because park and recreation land is often devoured in the process of highway construction. Individuals and organizations have done their best to prevent such encroachment, but usually, in the end, park or recreation land is taken instead of rerouting the roads or acquiring other land.

It is not always necessary to buy desirable land along rights-of-way or adjoining access roads for certain recreation purposes. For example, scenery can be protected through the use of easements that allow only desirable uses of land adjoining highways.

This legal device has been used with good results on land bordering the New York State Thruway and the Great River Road in Wisconsin.

The New York State Thruway parallels the Hudson River from the eastern part of the State to Albany. From there it turns west through the Mohawk Valley and terminates at the Pennsylvania State line. The breathtaking scenery along this great highway has been preserved for the enjoyment of the motoring public.

The proposed Great River Road will follow the Mississippi River from the headwaters to the Gulf of Mexico. When completed, it will be the longest scenic highway in the Nation. It will open up a vast panorama of scenery along the bluffs of the river, through the productive Midwest farm country, to the rich deltas of the South.

Scenic easements can and are being used to preserve the natural scenic beauty paralleling these highways. Conservation values are protected, and forest and other vegetative cover is preserved to prevent undesirable developments that would result in eyesores and detract from the natural beauty of the countryside adjoining the highways. Recreation values are enhanced, and driving becomes a more pleasant and recreative experience. The scenic ease-

ments provide a way of preserving these recreation values at less cost than if the land had to be purchased.

Such scenic easements may not permit public use of the land, but they can produce conservation values as well as provide recreation values for pleasure driving. Often the land protected through scenic easements would remain in the use it had, particularly if it were in forest or pasture.

Federal-aid funds were not available for recreational activities along the Interstate System except for safety and rest areas, which may be developed for picnicking but are not intended for more extensive recreational use.

No developments of any other kind may have direct access to the Interstate and Defense Highways System. It is possible that development of waysides and scenic lookouts would be possible under these conditions on the Interstate System. Other types of recreation areas would have to be developed off the Interstate System, but could be located near interchanges.

SO FAR, WE have emphasized relatively local and nonmonetary arguments for greater consideration of recreation needs. What about the benefits to a region?

In a paper entitled *Highways and Recreation*, presented before the Federal Inter-Agency Committee on Recreation, February 1, 1960, Sidney Goldstein, Bureau of Public Roads, U.S. Department of Commerce, said:

"It has been demonstrated that an area with outstanding natural attributes will attract people to it, provided reasonable means of transportation are available. In fact, a national park's popularity is often tied in with availability of transportation. This fact is amply illustrated in the case of Yellowstone National Park where, between 1895 when the park was opened and 1917, no automobiles were permitted to enter. During the span of years the largest number of visitors to this wonderful area was less than 52,000. During the 12 years, 1917–1929, when cars were permitted to the area, the number of visitors increased to some quarter of a million annually. In 1957 alone about 1.6 million persons visited this park and over 87 percent of them came by private automobile. The park itself contains over 500 miles of paved highway and a network of improved highways in Montana, Wyoming, and Idaho afford direct access to the park from all principal highways."

Yosemite, Grand Canyon, and the Great Smoky Mountains National Parks have all had increases in number of visitors, almost all of whom have come in their own automobiles.

The Chesapeake Bay Bridge has opened a recreation potential on the Eastern Shore of Maryland. The number of motorists crossing the bay at the point where the bridge spans it doubled soon after the bridge was opened.

Baltimore, Washington, and some nearby metropolitan areas in Virginia have provided a large share of the traffic over the bridge to the Eastern Shore recreation areas.

The New Jersey Garden State Parkway provides an example of how a modern highway can affect the recreation areas it serves. This 173-mile parkway has been a great aid to tourists, who use it as an access to nearby resort areas. The parkway has also served as a major factor in integrating recreation activities with other developments, including residential and commercial developments in the areas it serves.

A CAREFULLY PLANNED recreation program integrated with the highway systems, in which the needs and activities of both are balanced, is indicated.

The recreation system should be incorporated into the Interstate and Defense Highways System and thus become an integral part of the major parkway, State, and county highway networks. Different types of recreation facilities, depending on landscape, terrain, and other natural features and the limitations required for traffic management, could be developed at stated intervals to meet the present and expected future demands. This would be the practical application of the principles of multiple purpose and balanced use.

We discuss four types of facilities for meeting much of the traveler's demands—highway waysides and scenic lookouts, rest parks, recreation areas, and rural-urban recreation centers.

Waysides and scenic areas are small areas that provide limited facilities adjacent to a highway. They provide parking, comfort, safety, and enjoyment. They may be spots that allow a few drivers to pull off the main highway for such purposes as mapreading and changing tires or for emergencies; or they may be more elaborate roadside parks, like those provided in Ohio, Texas, and other States, where picnic and sanitary facilities, historical markers, telephone services, and so on are provided.

Many States have provided more than 11 thousand wayside areas on highways. They are designated as table sites, turnouts, overlooks, waysides, roadside rests, picnic areas, safety rest areas, and roadside parks. They may be one-tenth acre up to 40 acres, and average about 2 acres.

Besides picnic tables and parking facilities, some have fireplaces, playgrounds, trash barrels, drinking fountains, toilet facilities, and shelters.

Waysides are available on many roads, but there is need for more of them to provide for the millions of travelers on the new Interstate System. The new ones may be of less than an acre and have only turnoff facilities. Larger ones of 5 or 10 acres would also be welcome to give tourists a chance to stop, walk around, and stretch. They could be installed every 25 to 40 miles—or closer if conditions warrant.

Scenic lookouts would provide opportunities for taking pictures and enjoying the view. Extensive parking areas would not be needed. The lookout facilities would be designed for only brief stops.

The areas of historic interest would provide other types of desirable sites.

Recreation facilities would ordinarily be quite simple and in good taste. Wayside facilities near points of interest also are desirable, with signs that point out the historical significance and interesting facts of geology, land use, economy, and past developments. Motorists can stop at them; often they cannot pause to read ordinary markers.

In a Midwestern State, one drives a long distance on a straight, monotonous stretch of Federal-State highway. At one point, attractive signs welcome travelers to a nearby wayside, whose main feature is a borrow pit, from which came sand and gravel for the highway. Once ugly, it now has been shaped and developed into a place of beauty, a cool pond, which is the home of ducks and fish. An access road leads around the pond to parking areas shaded by trees, so trimmed that cool breezes can move through them and tourists can walk about.

About 2 hours' driving time west of San Juan, P.R., the well-paved road passes through sugarcane and pineapple country. The sun is hot, and a motorist would welcome a stretch stop. It is there. On what probably was a service area when the highway was made, the Commonwealth built a small, roofed, open-sided shelter and three or four picnic tables atop a small ridge. People have worn winding, informal trails into the nearby low-growing vegetation. Visitors are tempted to linger and enjoy the views as waves roll in from the sea toward a crescent-shaped beach cupped between the hills.

These examples are not uncommon. Our plea is that their number be multiplied and their attractions be emphasized. One's attitude toward Nature, resources, and life itself can be affected positively by experiences made possible by such small evidences of thoughtfulness.

HIGHWAY REST PARKS would usually use basic physical resources similar to those used for waysides, but there would be difference in location, facilities, and size.

The parks can be off the highway and spaced farther apart. Access to them would be provided by feeder roads at appropriate interchanges. The areas would be back from the highway a relatively short distance—1 to 3 miles, depending on terrain and availability of appropriate sites. Generally the areas would be screened from the main highway by plantings or natural geologic features.

They would be larger than waysides and have space for a wider range of activities. They should probably be 40 acres or larger.

Facilities at highway rest parks would include restrooms, drinking water, simple shelters, picnic tables, hiking trails, and play areas. A manmade pond or reservoir would be an attractive adjunct. The parks would emphasize conservation by developing borrow pits into recreation attractions, stabilizing cutbanks with trees, and other plantings, and providing bird and wildlife sanctuaries. Highway fills that dam up natural waterways could be made into reservoirs for recreation on many such sites.

The right kinds of shrubs and trees would attract birds and small animals, which would be an added source of pleasure to visitors. Markers could be used to point out features of interest, the kinds of birds and animals frequenting the area, and when and where they are likely to be found. Concession facilities could be provided if the number of visitors created sufficient demand for them but there would be no overnight facilities.

HIGHWAY RECREATION areas are near major highway networks. They are similar to many of the better developed State parks in size, facilities, and opportunities for recreation.

They could sustain a large and varied amount of activity, including camping, picnicking, fishing, water sports, nature walks, and outdoor games. They may have several hundred acres and provide opportunities for day, weekend, and vacation use—campgrounds, lodges, cabins, trailer parks or other types of overnight facilities, restaurants, snackbars, service stations, telephones, and showers and laundry facilities. Entertainment might be provided at peak seasons of use, and an interpretative program would be a feature of such areas.

The nature of the resources and their natural setting must be taken into consideration in planning the areas. How the areas are to be used and at what intensity they are to be developed will depend on these factors. In northern areas, winter sports might be developed as a major feature to supplement the summer season and provide year-round use. Likewise, where the climate permits, opportunities for swimming and water sports might be provided throughout the year to balance out patterns of seasonal use.

Population density would determine their placement along a highway, but one every 200 to 350 miles would provide overnight facilities.

HIGHWAY RURAL-URBAN recreation centers are strategically placed close to the metropolitan complexes. They provide mass recreation facilities primarily for city dwellers on a daytime and weekend basis. Campsites, however, would be featured in some areas to provide for weekend and short-time camping. The sites are of particular use for Scouts and other organized groups. They may require a heavy capital investment.

Their distinguishing feature would be their location outside but close to central cities. The new interstate highways, city bypasses, and circumferential highways provide access to them.

They would be relatively small, intensively developed, and geared to the needs of city people. They would provide for a full range of high-density types of recreation facilities, including swimming, picnicking, playgrounds, and hiking. Adequate parking facilities would be essential.

Hiking trails or paths would connect the parking areas with the various types of recreation facilities. The facilities would be developed in clusters around specific parking areas. Dispersed parking areas would be oriented to the various major uses. This would help eliminate the illusion of mass crowding, yet would provide for large numbers of visitors. Limits on number of users may be required to keep a balance between uses of the areas.

Educational programs for the young people could be developed in connection with weekday participation. These areas would substitute for in-city recreation areas, where land prices are high. The money and social costs involved in moving the visitors to the recreation sites may be less than the cost of providing the facilities within the metropolitan boundaries.

Buses could be provided on regular schedules to carry the recreation seekers to the recreation area. Bicycle and hiking trails could be provided so that children could visit them without getting out on highways or streets. Provision for organized groups, such as Scouts and Campfire Girls, would be taken into consideration in planning the use. Weekday public transportation schedules could be designed to take care of children and adults who wish to use the facilities and weekend transportation schedules could be increased to take care of the great influx of weekend visitors.

A major population center might well be served by a series of them to provide easy access for all the people with a minimum of travel. Adequate parking facilities and adequate access roads to get the cars to and from the major highway network would be essential and would require a great deal of imagination among planners.

PAYING for these additional services depends on the basic purpose of the facility. If it is highway safety—relaxation from driving tensions, rest stops, refueling—financing is a part of the highway program.

If recreation is the primary purpose, financial and administrative responsibility shifts by degrees from that of the transportation agency. It may remain a public responsibility and be financed from the public treasury, or some phases may be public and some private. Basic necessities of recreation undoubtedly should be assured through the public means. Entertainment and special services should be provided privately.

The acquisition of highway recreation sites on Federal highways might best be financed from Federal funds. Development of facilities may be Federal, State, or local, or through a combination of types utilizing private enterprise and private capital for some facilities and the types of recreation services people should pay for.

Assistance in the form of grants-in-aid may be sought from the Bureau of Outdoor Recreation, if legislation authorizing such grants is enacted. Or the Small Business Administration, Housing and Home Finance Agency, or other lending agencies serving the private sector may be authorized to move into this field.

The development of waysides and scenic lookouts could be integrated with the highway departments, and maintenance should probably be their responsibility. Highway rest parks could be developed jointly by the State highway and State and local park or recreation agencies. The maintenance should usually be taken over by one State or local agency.

Maintenance of highway recreation areas probably would best be the responsibility of a major State recreation agency in cooperation with the highway department. The rural-urban-highway recreation areas might well be maintained and operated by the metropolitan centers whose population uses it most or be administered by a public agency and operated through a concession system.

Establishment of fee schedules and collection from users, whenever practical, would help to make the highway recreation areas and the highway rural-urban-recreation areas self-sustaining. The schedule of fees could be designed to recapture operating and maintenance costs. If the use warrants, revenues above operation and maintenance might be used to repay investment costs of facilities and acquisition. Fees for the simple types of recreation opportunities ought not be set so high as to discourage the largest possible use of the areas.

ARE SUITABLE sites available? Many people think not, especially in metropolitan areas. To gain insight about the situation, the Outdoor Recreation Resources Review Commission turned to the Department of Agriculture for a study of potential recreation sites on private lands in the Northeast.

Five basic types of recreation sites suitable for picnicking, day camping, swimming, some fishing or the general enjoyment of the outdoors, a water body such as a stream or pond, shade, suitable terrain, and access were used.

In a 25-mile zone adjacent to the area of dense urban development near Boston, New York, and Philadelphia-Camden, the number of potential recreation sites in private ownership was surprisingly high. The analysis indicated that opportunities for developing defined kinds of recreation sites occur at about the rate of 1 per 129 acres of forest, 1 per 258 acres of idle land, and 1 per 320 acres of pasture still in private ownership. A very high percentage of all these sites occur within 0.5 mile of some type of road, ranging from private roads to major highways. Actual access, generally, would be a minor physical problem.

A high proportion of the sites occurred on land capability classes not suited for economic agriculture or for urban or industrial development. In total, it was estimated that more than 50 thousand of these sites were close to dense urban developments. Also, for a majority of the sites, the adjacent land is all in forests, idle farmland, or land formerly in an agricultural use that is reverting to forest.

In the construction of the highways of the interstate network, many farming areas have been bisected, often resulting in the splitting up of existing farms. Because of limited access on these roads, it may mean that parts of many farms are separated by 3 to 5 miles or more from the operating headquarters. Some of these parts of farms may be combined with adjoining acreages, but for others this may not be feasible. In many instances, these parts of farms cut off from the original headquarters might be acquired to provide some of the outdoor recreation areas outlined above. This would be particularly true for the least productive areas, because the rougher terrain, including streams and possible small reservoir sites, make good potential recreation areas but are not suited for commercial crop production.

BICYCLE AND HIKING trails are important to many people.

In the eastern part of the country, the Appalachian Trail affords an excellent hiking facility that extends from Maine to Georgia. Simple shelters and campsites provide hikers overnight accommodations on the trail. In the West, the Sierra Club is an example of an organization that helps maintain mountain trails into wilderness and remote recreation areas.

With only limited additional cost, cross-country and local bicycle and hiking trails could be provided on many of the highways already built or authorized. The rights-of-way are generally wide enough for these trails, and—with the limited access highways grade or road crossings would not be a hazard. Such trails would be of particular value near the cities and through the rural-urban fringes into the open country.

As the Outdoor Recreation Resources Review Commission report pointed out: "Europe, which has even greater population densities, has much to teach us about building recreation into the environment. Holland is constructing a national network of bicycle trails. Car ownership is rising all over Europe, but in the planning of their roads and the posting of them, Europeans make a special effort to provide for those who walk or cycle."

Tying a system of bicycle and hiking trails into our highway network would open up the possibility for expanding our youth hostel program similar to that in Europe. More than 70 hostels are chartered by the American Youth Hostels, Inc., of New York. Hostels provide overnight facilities and most of them are in scenic rural sections of recreational significance. In some areas, the hostels are close enough together so that hostelers can take hiking or bicycling trips, spending each night in a different hostel. Providing highway-oriented bicycle and hiking trails would encourage our citizens and foreign visitors to take time to see our country and to enjoy its scenic attractions and points of cultural and historical significance.

ALTHOUGH the main reason for highways is transportation—the movement of people and commodities safely and quickly—recreation and other possible allied uses of the highways system should not be overlooked. Highway recreation potentials can be realized by making minor modifications in highway plans and construction. Such modifications will be in the public interest.

Our plea is that we should stop selling recreation short in developing our highways. An integrated program can greatly increase the benefits that accrue from highways. Concerted action is needed to assure the benefits.

MAX M. THARP, *a research agricultural economist, is Leader, Southern Area Development Investigations, Area Economic Development Branch, Economic Research Service. He formerly worked for the Outdoor Recreation Resources Review Commission.*

HUGH A. JOHNSON, *a research agricultural economist, is employed in the Economic Research Service.*

WHAT TO DO?

WE can resolve the problems we have considered so far. Units of government can give us advice and some financial help. But the completion of the great tasks of rural renewal, easing adjustments in farms, insuring orderly growth, programing facilities, and fulfilling related obligations depends on the citizen and community. Several means are at hand. One, planning for communities and regions, is an extension of a person's and a family's own planning. Zoning is widely used and sometimes abused. Capital programing can be a democratic procedure for creating humane and efficient communities. The development commission brings an array of services, but it must depend ultimately on its own sense of responsibility. Underlying all is the need to husband what we have. In the words of Congressman Jamie L. Whitten of Mississippi: "Events have proved, since the beginning of our Nation, that we have wasted more natural resources in a shorter period of time than any nation in history. We can see that unless all of us, through the instrument of Government, set the pace we will go still further downhill."

ISRAEL STOLLMAN

THE USES AND PRINCIPLES OF PLANNING

CITY and regional planning is the name now commonly given in the United States to the work of designing a unified plan of development for a community. The design embraces proposals for the arrangement of all land uses, for the ways to ship goods or travel about, and for public facilities like parks, dams, sewers, airports, or schools. It is a bulky name, often shortened to city planning. This shortening is encouraged by the history of planning activity; most of it has been planning for cities; little of it has been planning for regions.

The parts of a planning region are linked by common problems, common resources, or common opportunities. The people of the region are interdependent, economically and socially; they do business with each other, read the same newspaper, use the same hospitals, decline or prosper together. With widely diverse careers as individuals, people nevertheless share, in some measure, a single regional destiny.

To achieve a destiny which will be of our choosing, we have come to accept the need to plan our environment. We are accepting planning despite an ingrained urge to decide individually how each plot of ground is to be used. We find it less possible to make individual decisions stick. Many changes among people and in jobs and technology have been taking this power

of decision away from individuals. Through community planning we are trying to regain control over the way our land resources will work for us.

The uses to which we put land have become more demanding in standards of quality, location, and extent.

Robert M. Reeser, of Ohio State University, applied these standards to the future development of Ohio. He found that 22 million people in Ohio by the year 2000 (the 1960 population was near 10 million) would require more than 33.5 million acres to supply space for agriculture, industry, houses, roads, recreation, shops, and other land uses. This is 7.25 million more acres than there *are* in Ohio, or will be.

Will we reduce our future population? or lower standards? or invent new ways to get along with less land? or squeeze

367

out some uses of land? or change our forecasts?

Events will give us an answer if we let the future happen to us. If we prefer to exercise choice among the possible answers and work for a combination of alternatives that suits us, we will undertake to design regional plans and to perform them.

THE PARTITION between urban land problems and rural land problems is broken. We live in one large room and need to follow the planner's habit of looking at problems whole if space is to be wisely shared. Much of what is called "rural planning" takes place at the fringes of metropolitan areas. Some planners fear that the term "city planning" implies attention only to the central city of a metropolis. They prefer to use the term "urban planning" to recognize that problems spill over political boundaries into suburban areas.

But the urban-rural partition in the words we use is longer lived than any partition in the problems of land use that we face. One urban planner labeled a category of land use "agricultural, vacant, or unused." He changed this label when he found that the county for which he was planning was among the State's leading agricultural producers.

To pay him back, there is a classification of major land uses in the United States, used in agricultural reporting, which lumps "urban, industrial, and residential (land) outside farms" with a miscellany including "ungrazed desert, rock, swamp, and other unused and waste land." It is a sound instinct with which city planners have persisted in calling themselves city and regional planners. The British, using a language very much like our own, have not found a short, sharp word to express the seamlessness of our physical environment, either; they call it "town and country planning."

THE MANY USES OF A PLAN may be put under six general purposes. The first purpose is to create a unified set of goals for the development of a city or region. It is easy to compile a list of disunited goals in a community. The usual concern with community development gives single-minded attention to one goal: The development of industry, or the preservation of agricultural lands, or the expansion of recreational opportunities, or the construction of efficient highways, or adequacy of the water supply, or quiet enjoyment of a residential neighborhood. Each goal may be worthy; taken together, they come into frequent conflict.

The supporters of separate development goals will compete for the same location, object to the character of a neighboring land use, try to preempt space enough for maximum future needs, and ask a high priority of public expenditure for facilities to support their goals. They will ask at once for the protection of public regulation and for exemption from public regulation; for more public services and less public cost. Planning seeks a best accommodation among these conflicting demands upon our stock of land resources.

A second purpose requires that the plan be relied upon as a central source of proposed public projects. Every community can make a list of improvements that are wanted if given the money to build them. Projects are listed in response to new crises or old dreams. They satisfy a demand that is currently popular or insistent.

Many of the public works built to serve the needs of travel, health, safety, education, recreation, or transportation are admirable community assets. Many others elicit the question: "Now, why didn't somebody think of that before they built it?" These are the schools or sewers or roads that incorporate the seven follies: They turn out to be too big or too small; they are built too soon or too late; they were not really needed at all or they were put in the wrong place; their design does not match their actual use.

Even commendable public works which have escaped these follies miss important civic opportunities if they must be built without reference to a general plan. A plan will seek to exploit opportunities to coordinate all public construction to insure that each project contributes in moving the community toward its adopted goals. It will find opportunities to squeeze a maximum of accomplishment from each public construction dollar. It will examine public works with an eye toward cultivating beauty in our environment.

A third purpose of a plan is to restrain the public regulation of private land within fair limits. This purpose has usually been put the other way around: That the purpose of land regulations is the execution of a plan. But regulations have apparently become more popular than plans. American communities have been quick to adopt zoning ordinances—the best known form of land use regulation—to deal with immediate problems. Zoning is too powerful a tool and too restrictive a regulation to justify putting it to work for short-run objectives. Our courts have supported the use of zoning in the name of long-range plans which the zoning laws are presumed to be putting into effect. The courts, however, have commonly accepted, as plans for the future, various rationalizations of the present.

When a community wields the tools of planning without having a plan, the property owner finds his rights managed arbitrarily. He may be kept from putting an industry on his land, although later planning will show it to be the right place for industry. He may be asked to demonstrate, with great care and detail, the merits of a new use of land that he proposes, although the restriction that he asks to change was itself not supported with care and detail when it was adopted. He is assured that regulations will protect his enjoyment of land, or his profitable use of it, from adverse happenings. But the assurance is empty if the regulation fits an unreal estimate of future development: His well may yet be polluted; his road may yet be glutted with traffic.

Regulations-without-plan may win some small victories by hardening the pattern of land uses where it is good enough to continue with little change. It is, however, with some hope of evolving better arrangements of land use, where change is great, quick, and endless, that we accept the burden of land regulations. The burden of regulation is unjust if it comes without the hope of a plan.

A fourth purpose of a plan is to guide private landowners in making individual plans to develop their property.

The unique character of land, as a kind of property, makes ineffective the methods that work in managing other kinds of property. Once committed to a chosen use, land does not yield to the daily adjustments that are possible in fitting other kinds of commodity to the tugs of the market. Land investments are long run and not quickly reversed; it takes great expense to modify them. The private landowner needs information that tells him the total direction of development his community will take. He needs information on roads, parks, or dams projected by public agencies. He needs information on what other landowners are up to.

Some of the regions in which large amounts of land are being retired from agriculture, for example, are looking at the possibility of developing outdoor recreational facilities as a source of income to the rural economy. A canvass of opinion may show each farmer interested in opening a fishing pond; how many will succeed? Success will require a plan that has worked out answers to the questions: How many customers? what kind of recreation? how good is access? how attractive are the public parks of the region? does it fit in with water management plans? Giving these answers is one purpose of a good regional plan, because a private bankruptcy in the use of land is also a public calamity.

A fifth purpose of a plan is to appraise unexpected problems or opportunities. No plan can anticipate every turn in our changing patterns of land use. No plan should be drawn so rigidly that it cannot respond to the continuing challenge of change.

Without a plan, however, the unexpected is always an emergency: We scramble for scraps of information; hold hurried meetings; debate quickly conceived alternatives; flock to the best rhetoric; and adopt decisions because we are pressed to act, or to adjourn. An accumulation of emergency solutions, whether executed in bricks or in ordinances, makes a burdensome part of the problem whenever planning does, at last, begin.

A plan, instead, will give us an analysis of fact, and a considered set of policies, with which to assimilate the unexpected to our advantage, turning problem into opportunity.

The sixth purpose of a plan is to preserve the more fragile among desirable land use arrangements. Some land uses can take care of themselves better than others, because they make intensive use of land and can pay higher land prices or because they command more popular approval. Preserving land for agriculture when housing, let us say, is an alternate use is difficult to accomplish, even with a plan. A great deal of thought is being given to this difficulty.

Elements of beauty in the landscape will find it harder to survive as our country becomes still more populated and as the people move still more freely and frequently across it. Long-established biological relationships on the land will easily be disturbed and destroyed. Combine these characteristics in a land form or use that is extensive, beautiful, and based upon some natural balance and you will have the scene set for a campaign to save the dunes! save the bluegrass! save the orchardland! save a bit of marsh!

It is unlikely that we will find it essential to save every acre meeting this description. Analogous urban campaigns to save a pleasant street, a historic mansion, or a park do not always win. A plan should show whether we are winning often enough and in the right places. It should show whether a loss is a necessary one to achieve all the objectives of a balanced land use plan. It should show how to harmonize the sometimes conflicting desires of preserving an asset in our landscape and enjoying it, too.

THE PRINCIPLES OF PLANNING are of two kinds.

One kind deals with planning procedures. These principles are few.

They are also general and can, with variations, be applied to industrial planning, or governmental planning, military planning, community chest planning, or any other specialized planning. They govern planning as a process that allocates and arranges any set of resources in order to achieve a set of goals.

The second kind of principles deals with planning design. These principles govern design relationships among the resources planned—as in city and regional planning, land use relationships. Principles of this kind are numerous. They may be grouped in families of related principles.

Consider, as an illustration, the city planning principle: "The journey from home to work should be short, economical, pleasant, and safe." The offspring of this principle includes such subsidiary principles as: "Local streets should be designed to give access to the residences on them, and to carry no through traffic"; or "pedestrian and the vehicular traffic should be separated."

The planner, practicing in a specific community, often finds himself applying simultaneously several design principles that are in conflict with each other. By going all out to satisfy one principle, he gets in the way of satisfying another.

A short journey to work, for example, may not jibe with the principle that a community's size will fit the level of services and job opportunities that is forecast. In using his professional skills to design a plan, the planner creates a reconciliation among these conflicts.

Some of the design principles in city

planning are touched upon in a later chapter. Discussion of design principles in regional planning, including new ones that are emerging, is scattered throughout this book. Let's look more closely at the principles of planning procedure.

COMPREHENSIVENESS is the central idea among the principles of planning procedure. The word "plan" is used for a multitude of diverse reports and proposals, most of which are not comprehensive. Some—like a plan to attract industry or a plan for construction of a highway—deal with an aspect of community development but lack the comprehensiveness that must be a characteristic of the city plan or a regional plan.

A comprehensive plan for a city or region is comprehensive by virtue of following four principles:

First, the plan applies to all land use and circulation systems.

Second, the plan covers the entire geographic area affected by common problems of development.

Third, the plan is designed to meet long-range consequences, which will show up in 15 years, say, or in 50 years.

Fourth, the plan is part of a continuing process, in which all the essential steps are taken of studying facts, making plans, and executing plans.

The first principle requires simultaneous planning for all uses and functions of land. It will not do to collect a pile of reports, each dealing with but one function, if these have been prepared independently of each other. Water resource planners, for example, may propose to cover with a lake the same piece of ground that is proposed by highway planners as part of a new right-of-way.

The requirements of a reservoir location are more restrictive, generally, than the requirements of a new highway location. But the future demands upon our highways have been recognized, with legislation and financing, more extensively than the future

demands upon our water supplies. When it is prepared in isolation from a comprehensive plan, a highway plan may be executed before plans for other facilities are even made; highways may then preempt sites needed for reservoirs, and may influence future land use in unsought ways.

The comprehensive planner does not plan or design a dam. By dealing with all land uses in their general relationships only, he makes a plan that knits and fits and interweaves them into a consistent arrangement that will best serve all our purposes.

The second principle requires that a comprehensive plan be made for an area of land large enough to contain a full understanding of the problems and large enough to make the proposed solutions effective. A great deal of notice has been given to the discrepancy between political boundaries—which describe areas that adopt plans, pass laws, and approve budgets—and metropolitan boundaries or regional boundaries—which embrace common problems, needing integrated solutions.

Comprehensive plans can be made without altering political boundaries. They cannot be comprehensive, however, unless there is sufficient cooperation to make the territorial scope of the plan equal to the scope of the land use problems that are to be solved.

There have always been land use problems extending throughout a region and involving all its resources. The proper relationship between city and country has always been one of the central issues in planning. Today, the changing rural-urban relationships described in this book—pulling the homes of city people into the country; pulling the jobs of country people into the city—enlarge the claim for plans that comprehend the entire region.

The third principle requires long-range forecasts of changing needs, goals, and resources. A comprehensive plan must stretch over a sufficient period of time just as it must stretch over a sufficient area of space.

We are inured to the experience of

tearing down buildings before their time is fairly up; to making do with the wastes of inadequate arrangements; to accepting as unavoidable the excuse beginning: "Who could have foreseen . . .?" If we cannot literally foresee, we can nevertheless forecast future probabilities to a high degree of usefulness. It is not necessary to predict with unvarying accuracy to produce a kind of knowledge of the future that will illuminate our current decisions. Everybody belittles the weatherman, but nobody turns away from tomorrow's forecast.

Techniques and information needed in forecasting population, employment, and technological changes are developing rapidly. (As our forecasting methods improve, we are also becoming more cautious in using the forecasts, shrinking from the ambitious word "prediction" and adopting the modest word "projection.")

More accurate forecasts make it possible to design plans that will more closely fit the future facts. Someone labeled this use of forecasts, "cooperating with the inevitable."

There are also forecasts that are accurate only in the sense that a continuation of present trends and policies will make them true. Forecasts of this second kind are far from inevitable. Sometimes the future they represent is in conflict with the future we want. We can deflect forecasts of this kind by changing our policies.

A number of writers, for example, have recently popularized the terms "megalopolis," "interurbia," "stripcity," and "exploding metropolis" to dramatize the fact that our cities are growing to such an extent that sometimes the suburbs of one metropolis reach out to touch the suburbs of the next.

The force of this growth is strong enough to intimidate us into accepting the developing pattern of metropolitan growth as a future event that is beyond the reach of human plans and policies. Some of the consequences of this pattern, if unwelcome, need not be accepted fatalistically as a wave of the future. The long-range view of a comprehensive plan contributes to distinguish those forecasts that must rule us from those forecasts we would rather overturn.

The fourth principle requires that the process of planning be complete—studies and surveys, but also a plan; plans and proposals, but also their implementation.

The most popular part of the planning process is the implementation of plans. It is more popular than making the plans themselves; therefore, we are often implementing plans that do not exist. The implements of zoning, of subdivision regulation, or of capital improvement programing are put to work in many localities that have not taken the time to make a plan. In the name of planning, many action programs are begun to accomplish limited objectives of construction, development, or regulation without asking why build? why regulate?

We are results-minded and turn quickly to immediate action. The time needed to make a plan seems to be a needless delay of action and progress; sometimes it seems to be a downright risk in the face of an emergency. Yet—without a plan—is it progress in a direction of our choosing? By acting quickly in the midst of quick change do we become prone to emergency? Planners have ironically expanded the strength of planless action by making available new tools to put plans into effect. The tools should be kept subservient to the plans.

The action minded are encouraged to ignore plans by a corollary fault—plans that are not carried out. Some of these plans may deserve to be overlooked. Other plans are not put into effect because no care was taken to have them understood, to develop financing plans, to check legal requirements, or to create the public and private organizations needed to carry out planning proposals.

A complete planning process should bring together the long-range planner, who is now worrying about the year 2000, and the short-range planner, or action man, who is worrying about what goes under contract in 1964 and 1965. Planning must make a continuous chain between this year's daily decisions and the general plan adopted for realization over the decades.

The making of a plan, in turn, seems to be more popular than discovering the facts upon which a plan should be based. "Survey before plan" was the advice of one of the founders of modern planning. Plans go quickly awry if they are not based upon knowledge of who people are, how they make a living, and what the nature of the land they occupy is. The place of extensive survey has often been taken by the planner's personal observation and insight. Now that economists, other social scientists, and statistical geographers are devoting more study to the life and work of the region, there is no proper cause for merely cursory attention to the factual basis of a plan.

HERE, THERE is also a corollary fault: Surveys without a plan. The facts relevant to a problem are marshaled, analyzed, and translated directly into a decision without lingering for a plan. Any plan must have a degree of flexibility in absorbing the amendments required by changed facts or new facts.

In the midst of quickly changing conditions, the greatest flexibility can be had by skipping from facts to decisions; skipping the planning stage, however, must also mean skipping the attainment of any fixed purposes. To the wry slogan, "Don't confuse me with the facts; I have already made up my mind," we can add a companion: "Don't slow me down with a plan; I'm too busy getting out of the mess I'm in now."

A variation of the planless survey is the planless forecast. The planless forecast comes in the guise of a plan. It forecasts that whatever is happening today will continue to happen and offers, as a plan for the future, a mere extension of the present.

As we enlarge our ability to garner facts, and as we refine our forecasting methods to find the range of future probabilities more accurately, we will be tempted oftener to supplant a plan with a forecast. The ingredient that would thereby be lost is the imaginative vision that must characterize a plan. The planning profession recognizes its work as "art and science," containing a creative element that is not attained by way of fact or method.

Two comments by John Dewey are apposite: "The first intimations of a better future are always found in works of art." "Art is a mode of prediction not found in charts and statistics," and insinuates possibilities "not to be found in rule and precept, admonition and administration."

RURAL COMMUNITIES need stronger planning organizations to carry out their purposes of development effectively.

Planning organizations that serve the urban regions of the country have been widely established or dramatically strengthened during the forties and fifties. The effectiveness of urban planning is continuing to grow as the basic need of organizing to do planning work is being replaced, in attention, with questions of how well it is done. The basic need of organizing to plan for resources regions is, largely, still unattended.

It is possible that the decade of the sixties will record a spurt in the establishment of effective organizations to plan for resources regions.

How effective they will be will depend on the care taken to build cooperating programs for the performance of planning work at the local, State, and Federal levels; to keep the responsibility for doing planning work distinct from the responsibility for current operations; and to recruit citizen planners and professional planners of high competence.

At local levels, adequate organization has been developing most rapidly where a resource region is just one step more beyond the acknowledgment of a metropolitan region. The Northeast Illinois Metropolitan Area Planning Commission is an example.

IN RURAL AREAS that are not close to metropolitan centers—where people, economic development, and tax resources are spread thin—local planning can also be accomplished through regional planning agencies. Regional agencies can be organized, if provisions are made in State law, to serve a group of counties that find themselves with common problems of development.

State planning agencies can also provide planning services to rural areas, but two reservations must be noted. One is that, in the early sixties, State planning agencies are themselves in the beginning stages of revival, reorganization, strengthening, or establishment. This has happened in Hawaii, California, Wisconsin, Tennessee, and Delaware, for example. In most of the States, however, a State planning agency must first be established or must first be given an adequate range of duties.

The second reservation about the State planning agency is that it should not displace local government in taking the responsibility for local development plans. State planning should instead help the establishment of local and regional planning agencies. State planning agencies should also work to coordinate local plans, cooperate with local planning agencies in the development of State plans, and offer technical and research services.

The same need to look at the problem, rather than at the political boundary, will produce cooperative planning arrangements among the States to deal with regions that straddle State lines. Such arrangements have been put to effective use in adopting joint operations for a variety of interstate services. Interstate compacts, interstate agreements, and parallel legislation adopted in adjacent States have brought an accumulation of experience with cooperative work on transportation, transit, parks, water resources, and other specific functions.

Some cooperative interstate planning has also been accomplished, but has been limited to planning for one or another of these specialized activities. These interstate arrangements are available, although now largely unused, for joint comprehensive planning by the States or by local governments. Local governments can undertake joint efforts with neighbors across a State line on their own initiative, provided there are statutes that permit it, as in a number of States.

Another responsibility of State planning programs will be to balance sound urban development with sound rural development. Urban areas are increasing in dependence upon rural product and urban people will want the conservation of farmland, of open space, of forests, of well tended but lightly developed countryside. Rural areas are increasing in dependence upon urban areas and rural people will want to see their urban centers prosper as creators of jobs and markets. Both are concerned with the form of cities and the edges of urban development where rural and urban land use problems become, most vividly, one problem. A narrowly urban view of land use problems can be tempered by the comprehensive view of a State planning agency.

At the Federal level, paradoxically, it is more attention to sound urban development that is needed to achieve a more balanced land use policy. A Federal department of urban development would have as a key assignment the devising of policies that can discipline our enormous urban growth into patterns less wasteful of the countryside.

The second requirement of effective organization for planning requires a clear view of the responsibility of a planning agency. Planning is an activity that is hard to sell. It is abstract; it deals with the future more than with the present and with general ideas and policies rather than with specific plans to build something. The planner's clientele is continually asked to visualize a possibility; concrete examples offered for inspection are often examples of what not to do.

A PLANNING PROGRAM is burdened also with the necessity of exposing community conflicts. Differences of goals and opinions within the community are blurred and covered over in reaching expedient daily compromises. All these differences must be discovered, examined, debated, and publicly reconciled in producing a long-range plan.

These difficulties have frequently persuaded community leaders to gain acceptance for planning by diluting its abstractness and its tendency to go out looking for trouble.

Comprehensive planning has been diluted by assigning it to an agency with responsibilities for building public works or for providing a highly visible public service. Currently, it is popular to attach the planning function to the function of promoting economic development.

Planning has been also diluted by dividing it among a number of operating agencies: A recreation department does all the recreation planning, a highway department does all the highway planning, a natural resources department does all of the water supply planning. Coordination among these plans is effected by loose, informal means or—for the aspects of the plans that become capital budget items—by a department of finance.

Planning agencies require much smaller budgets and fewer personnel than do the operating departments of government. As a small corner in a big operating department, planning will be swamped by assignments of current administrative problems and it will be colored by the specialized viewpoint of its department.

To forestall conflict over the goals of a plan, some community leaders have postponed consulting community opinion until the plan is completely developed and ready for publication. This procedure may save time spent in hard discussion and may save some pet proposal, but it is likely to cost in public support for the continuing planning program and in relevance of the plan to what people need of their community.

Civic-minded men have often contributed private funds to the preparation of a plan when government was slow to approve spending money for it. The results have often been stimulating to community thought but less effective in accomplishment. This procedure also suffers from the handicap of bypassing the necessary involvement of the public. Elected officials will have the responsibility of supporting a plan with laws and funds; they must be closely involved in preparing the plan.

It is reasonable to expect some dilution of the comprehensive planning process as community leaders labor to establish support for planning. Careful organization, however, can achieve more support with less dilution. While planning is an executive function of government, for example, there should be formal means for legislative participation in planning because the adoption of the policies recommended in a plan is a legislative prerogative. As another example, the planning agency can inject many kinds of concrete, immediate services if it is organized to embrace the full span of its job, including the execution of its plans; daily decisions of the doers and builders will be associated closely with the flow of information and recommendations from the planning agency.

THE PERFORMANCE of planning tasks needs people—citizens and public officials who will burden themselves with hours of extra work, talk, and study; professional planners who will do the technical work.

Some communities have sought to dispense with the technician and try to do-it-yourself. This follows the normal impulse to save money by concluding that no expert outsider knows the local problems as well as amateur insiders. So many other communities have been hiring professional planners that the man with training and experience is scarce and hard to attract.

Planning requires complex skills and extensive knowledge. The profession is now faced with problems of extending that knowledge much further, training many more planners, and conserving the trained manpower that we have. Technical services for thinly populated regions can be provided effectively by pooling staff in a central regional, or State, planning office.

Planners with special competence in working for a resource-oriented region are much scarcer than urban planners.

The practice of regional planning will continue to evolve through the coordination of scattered planning work done by special-purpose operating agencies—irrigation districts, soil conservancy districts, water conservancy districts, park and recreation commissions, highway departments, industrial development boards.

One State authorized the establishment of local conservation commissions to plan for recreational and natural resource development. This step will encourage regional planning, but seems to combine the disadvantages of attaching a planning fragment neither to an operating agency nor to a comprehensive planning agency.

The lack of coordination and the duplication of work now common in regional planning needs replacement by stronger comprehensive planning for all resources.

ONE OF THE greatest sources of strength in American city planning has been the mingling of diverse talents among planning practitioners. The young planning profession has attracted the loyalties of men trained and experienced in many related fields, such as architecture, municipal law, civil engineering, public administration, land economics, public finance, geography, urban sociology, and landscape architecture. The varied skills and knowledge of these people merged in common devotion to comprehensive planning. People from these many fields are continuing to enrich planning by entering the graduate planning schools.

Regional planning will be greatly enriched if a stream of resource specialists were to begin to flow into the planning profession; when some students of agronomy, forestry, hydrology, rural sociology, agricultural economics, ecology, or geology decide to devote themselves to a career in planning.

The greatest influence on the quality of regional planning will be the quality of mind and character brought to it.

ISRAEL STOLLMAN *has been head of the City and Regional Planning Division in the School of Architecture at Ohio State University since 1957. He was previously the planning director of the city of Youngstown. Earlier, he was a staff member of the Cleveland City Planning Commission and lectured on city planning at Western Reserve University. He was graduated from the City College of New York and took the degree of master in city planning at the Massachusetts Institute of Technology.*

For further reading:
Black, John D., and Westcott, George W., *Rural Planning of One County, Worcester County, Massachusetts.* Harvard University Press, Cambridge, 1959.
Council of State Governments, *Planning Services for State Government: A Summary of the Need and Suggestions for Organization.* Chicago, 1956.
———— Subcommittee on State Planning of the Governors' Conference, *State Planning: A Policy Statement.* Chicago, 1962.
McDougal, Myres S., and Rotival, Maurice E. H., and others, *The Case for Regional Planning with Special Reference to New England.* Yale University Press, New Haven, 1947.
National Resources Committee, *Regional Factors in National Planning and Development.* U.S. Government Printing Office, Washington, D.C., 1935.
National Resources Planning Board, *Public Works and Rural Land Use.* U.S. Government Printing Office, Washington, D.C., 1942.
Perloff, Harvey S., *Education for Planning: City, State, and Regional.* The Johns Hopkins Press, Baltimore, 1957.
———— and others, *Regions, Resources, and Economic Growth.* The Johns Hopkins Press, Baltimore, 1960.

WILLIAM S. BONNER

PLANS FOR

SMALLER PLACES

M ORE than a generation ago, the Department of Agriculture issued a publication, "Rural Planning—The Village," that people have forgotten and ignored these many years. Its very neglect, though, gives it meaning: We have precedent for what some think is a dynamic, brandnew (and therefore, to some, suspect) and challenging idea; we must have patience in our plans; an idea, like a publication, dies if people do not care enough to act.

From the old pamphlet, I quote a particularly acute warning that is true of life today:

"City planning for convenience, efficiency, health, and social well-being has become a pressing public problem, especially since the rapid increase in urban population. Hundreds of cities have their own planning boards, and others are studying or putting into effect the city plan prepared by the experts to overcome intolerable conditions caused by congestion or undirected growth. Attempts to recover from past mistakes or neglect, from carelessness or inertia, are costing cities millions of dollars annually."

Our emphasis in planning now has shifted to embrace small places, as well as metropolitan centers, for there are several thousand cities of less than 50 thousand population that are out-side metropolitan areas, contain a substantial part of our population, and serve a sizable segment of the Nation. We have not paid enough attention to planning by the small cities, villages, and the countryside around them.

Despite the Department's warning of a generation ago, planning still is relatively immature.

For example, in Arkansas, a State which has only three cities with populations of more than 50 thousand, there were only six known city planning commissions in 1950. In 1962, there were more than 80 planning commissions, of which 6 were county or joint city-county commissions—a substantial increase in number, but the commissions in 1962 were only beginning to develop adequate plans and regulations for the growth of their communities, and not one county had developed a comprehensive plan to guide its

377

future. The situation was much the same in most of the other States.

Two THINGS have intensified interest in planning in small places and counties—the efforts of State industrial development agencies to convince localities that they must plan in order to be attractive to industry; and the availability of planning grants, through the Federal Housing Act of 1954, to State agencies to help cities develop comprehensive plans. The grants were first made available to communities with populations of less than 25 thousand and, since 1959, to those with populations of less than 50 thousand.

Forty-five States had agencies to help with local planning in 1962. Eight had adequate staffs to do the technical planning for cities and counties. Seven had limited resources for direct assistance. The other States relied on planning consultants to undertake the preparation of comprehensive plans.

I need not go into detail again about the many changes in our society, industry, population, small communities, agricultural technology, and so on, or repeat the problems the changes have brought—of commuters, the almost helter-skelter making of farms into subdivisions, the serious lowering of the ground-water level and the pollution of drinking water in places where wells and septic tanks are installed, the increase in ground-water runoff and the flooding of new areas, an increased demand for services in subdivisions that once were farms, and rises in taxes.

The small communities—or "cities," as many of the traditionally rural-oriented centers now desire to be called—are also facing problems as they find they can no longer depend for their economic existence on their traditional function as trade and service centers to their surrounding territories.

Many of them must look to industry to provide a supplemental economic base, regardless of the changes and problems that the demands of industrialization bring in terms of traffic, parking, land use, land development, and utilities and services, including adequate housing, schools, and recreational facilities. In all this, planning is essential.

THE AIMS in planning for small cities and rural places should be:

To insure that urbanization and the resulting urban land uses are directed to serve better the needs of people without placing an unrealistic or uneconomic burden on the farmer.

To insure sound growth of the small city with respect to its physical layout and the provision of adequate community facilities and services.

To preserve the basic character and resources of the rural areas.

The aims are simple and desirable but are not easy to reach.

One reason is individualism, which is still a strong characteristic among Americans.

The concept that no person should use his land to the detriment of owners of adjacent land conflicts with the individualist's belief in his right to use his land as he sees fit. A primary objection to planning is that its controls will limit complete freedom.

Many persons are in favor of planning as long as it gives them desired protection, permits them to achieve economic gain, and does not affect them adversely. If they begin to be afraid they will lose their freedom of action in regard to the uses of land, planning is bad, un-American, socialistic.

Another reason for inertia may be a lack of adequate means for planning. Limited funds may make it difficult to initiate and sustain a planning program and hire technical and professional competence to make proper plans.

A third reason is that land in small cities and rural areas has been less intensely utilized, and there is less friction therefore between inharmonious uses. When land is not intensely used, people may not recognize the need to put uses in proper relationship to one another.

Lack of interest in planning also can be laid to the declining or stationary characteristics of the populations of many localities during the past two or three decades. Awareness of the need for planning is lacking, since actually there appear to be no really pressing needs for guiding growth and development. People know that most small cities are not going to become big cities.

A further reason for indifference is that the future cannot be assessed in terms of its impact on the small city and open country. If there is no apparent role to be played in the changing scene, there is no need to plan to play it.

Yet, despite all these rationalizations, we need to plan. The land area of the United States must be utilized to its best potential if the Nation is to remain vital.

Planning must begin with recognition of total resources and needs. The States must accept a vital role in the inventory of their resources and the recognition of their needs in respect to the national picture.

State planning agencies need to develop basic inventories of the social, economic, and natural resources of their respective States and overall plans for utilizing their resources. Each should identify regions and, if necessary, sub-regions of the State in order that the small cities and the counties will plan within a context that has meaning.

COMPREHENSIVE planning consists of four major elements:

Study and analysis of such factors as population, economy, physiography, land use, natural resources, street and roadway networks, and public facilities and utilities.

Preparation of a development plan that includes a statement of objectives, a land use and roadway network plan, and a plan for public facilities.

Preparation of programs to implement the comprehensive development plan, including zoning, control over development of land, protection of roadway facilities, and programs of priority for public improvements.

Coordination and administration of planning activities both locally and with State and Federal agencies, including the application of planning principles in day-to-day community problems, keeping information current, and updating the comprehensive development plan.

Comprehensive planning is important to local government, to residents, and to those who invest money.

To local government, it helps to insure adequate services and facilities, an adequate roadway system, and harmonious uses, thus permitting the most efficient use of tax money.

To the resident, comprehensive planning insures stability of areas and values so that the individual can plan for the future with reasonable certainty in respect to his residence or his business.

For the investor, planning sets the framework for development, providing that all must meet basic requirements and standards.

Planning for small cities and rural areas must be regarded as preparation of a guide or blueprint for change.

Change is continuous; only the amount—positive or negative—is problematical. By having a plan, local governments can be in position to meet an "impact" situation that may result, for instance, from the unpredicted location of an industry.

In developing the guide for change, it would be fallacious reasoning for a community of 2 thousand inhabitants to plan in anticipation of a population of 10 thousand to be realized in a decade when it may not be much larger or smaller at the end of the 10 years than it is today. This does not mean it should not plan nor does it mean that the community cannot become a better place for the 2 thousand inhabitants to live in over the 10-year period—if plans are made and the means to implement them are realistic.

Comprehensive planning should also be utilized to maintain the agricultural economy of an area—that is, to maintain land in its highest productivity. Planning can assist this aim by preventing premature urbanization of rural areas with its resultant increase in demands for urban services and facilities and the higher taxes to support the facilities.

PLANNING is a continuous process, which can be accomplished most efficiently by acquiring and applying knowledge and skills to do the job.

To make planning effective there is a need for:

An understanding of the intent and purpose of the various statutes pertaining to planning.

An understanding of court decisions that apply to planning.

The ability to interpret present conditions in order to estimate future needs.

The preparation of a community development plan.

The adoption of effective implementing measures.

The adoption of rules of procedure and effective enforcement.

The undertaking of an effective educational program, which will keep the people informed of the value of planning.

The last of these items is the key to effective, continuous planning. Without the understanding and support of the people, planning will be just another word.

In planning for cities, attention is primarily on urban uses—residential, commercial, industrial, and public— on the facilities and utilities to support those uses, and on a street system to tie them together.

In planning for rural areas, attention turns first to natural resources and productivity of land, values for recreation and tourism, the nonfarm-resident population, and the roads that link them.

In planning for cities there is sufficient history and knowledge to do an adequate planning job, given adequate legislation. In planning for rural areas, however, planners' experience has been that often there is no legislation adequate to permit comprehensive planning. Even with adequate legislation, planning efforts have been primarily concerned with urban, not rural, aspects of planning.

To illustrate: In planning for cities, a major street plan is a common element. Streets are classified according to functional use, and a major street plan is developed to serve present and potential urban needs. But little consideration has been given to the development of a county roadway plan based on a functional use classification. Many planners seem to think county roads are merely extensions of city streets.

In Arkansas, the first comprehensive study of a county road system was made by the Arkansas Highway Department in 1961 for Phillips County. Its purpose was to classify the roads and to recommend measures for defining and developing a modern system that would serve the county adequately, economically, and efficiently, and could be provided within a reasonable time and within the ability of the county to obtain funds for improvements.

Phillips County had 813 miles of county roads, of which 126 miles were providing arterial service. The arterial routes put almost every residence in the county within 2 miles or less of a State highway or a county arterial. Below the arterial classification were 205 miles of collector-feeder roads. The remaining 486 miles were called land-service roads and provided service to one or two families to the mile. The daily travel over these roads averaged only 11 vehicles a day. No one mile of the roads carried more than 24 vehicles a day. The land-service roads at best never averaged more than one vehicle an hour.

The study revealed that the arterial system in Phillips County accounted for 15 percent of the county mileage but handled 40 percent of the average daily traffic. The collector-feeder roads accounted for 25 percent of the

mileage and handled 44 percent of the traffic. The land-service roads accounted for 60 percent of the mileage but carried only 16 percent of the daily travel over the system.

The study also indicated that there were only 3.57 miles of pavement on county roads and they came from relocated State highways and donations.

The Arkansas State Highway Department made several recommendations in a report, "A Study of the County Road System of Phillips County, Arkansas." The roads should be classified in three functional subsystems—county arterial, county feeder roads, and county land-service roads. Supervision of the roads should be delegated to a superintendent qualified in road engineering management. The county road segment of the Federal-aid secondary system should be reviewed for the purpose of revising obsolete routes to fit present and anticipated road-use patterns. As families leave the farms, the land-service roads that lose their function as public roads should be dropped from the county road system. Land-service roads that serve fewer than three rural units evenly spaced to the mile are regarded in many States as not being public roads but private lanes. Arkansas law states that a road does not become public until it reaches that point where it

serves at least 10 families or is otherwise a mail or schoolbus route. A 15-year program should be adopted as the goal for developing a modern county road system in the county.

The recommendations and the report could be the basis for an action program when Phillips County has an organization to carry out the recommendations and the planning function.

Adequate statutory authority to plan and agencies willing to help plan—the Arkansas State Highway Department and the University of Arkansas, as a designated agency for local planning assistance—were available in 1963, but local leadership was lacking to do the job. It is an example of the failure of the people of a community to convince themselves and the responsible authorities that planning does have an important place in day-to-day decisions and in long-range development.

As an excuse for not initiating planning, people often say, "If only we had started planning 10, 20, 30 years ago, we wouldn't be in this situation." There is no logic in that. The logical attitude is to consider the changes that will come in the next 10, 20, or 30 years: Will change be left to chance, or will change be directed toward the goal of general welfare?

One would think that any community which knows that a major change is coming would make plans to meet the situation, to minimize possible ill effects, and to make the most of the opportunities it may offer. Often the community does none of these things.

For example, in all the reservoir projects undertaken by the Corps of Engineers, I know of no local government that has attempted to plan for the changes that the creation of a reservoir is bound to cause. The efforts of residents end with obtaining such projects; no effort or interest is carried over to planning for the effects of the projects.

Lack of time is no excuse; there is enough time for planning. Once a reservoir project is approved and the Corps of Engineers begins work on what is known as the design memorandum stage, the local units of government have 18 months to 3 years to plan for both the impact of construction of the dam and for effects resulting from the presence of the reservoir itself. This planning should be concerned with meeting the housing requirements of the construction workers and their families. While these temporary residents are present, there will be additional demands on schools and other public facilities. Construction of reservoirs disrupts the normal road system, alters the characteristics of school districts, and causes sale of land for nonagricultural purposes. These are all a concern of planning.

To repeat: Here are two specific situations—the construction of a dam or reservoir, and the acquisition of a new road system—in which local units of government are seldom aware of the impact effect on their communities or the special opportunities such changes offer them for advantageous planning.

Planning and its tools can be utilized in various ways. One of them, zoning, can help to keep urban uses in specified areas and prevent the location of unwanted urban uses in rural areas so as to retain the best land in agriculture. To be fully effective, though, zoning has to rest on a sound policy of taxa-

tion and assessment, which recognize the differential in ability of urban and rural uses to support needed public facilities.

Zoning, for example, has been used to protect forestry and recreation, two compatible uses. Zoning has been utilized in Wisconsin to keep farm and forest lands separated. Michigan has made use of the recreational district to advantage in fostering recreation values.

Planning for small cities and rural areas has several prerequisites if it is to be successful.

Legislation is needed that will permit cooperation in area planning by cities and counties. It should be permissive and flexible. Once a joint planning agency is created, other public agencies, such as school boards, park commissions, and improvement districts, should be permitted to become members.

Competent technical assistance must be available. State planning agencies may provide it, as in Arkansas, Kentucky, North Carolina, Tennessee, Oregon, and Rhode Island. A planning agency that has a broad structure can have its own planning staff or consultants to prepare and administer plans.

The need for planning must be understood by all residents.

Effective administrative and enforcement procedures must be established. Many small cities and counties are not able financially to hire planners by themselves, but they can do so by joining forces.

WILLIAM S. BONNER *is professor of city planning and head of the City Planning Division in the University of Arkansas. He is a member of the American Institute of Planners and a member of the Board of Trustees, American Planning and Civic Association.*

For further reading:
Nason, Wayne C., *Rural Planning—The Village.* U.S. Department of Agriculture, Farmers' Bulletin No. 1441, 1925 (Rev. 1935).

ERLING D. SOLBERG

OLD AND NEW
PRINCIPLES OF ZONING

MODERN zoning was foreshadowed by protective measures passed in colonial times. First, dangerous uses were isolated. Then nuisances were barred. Uses termed "injurious" were set apart later. Laws for the public safety in the 17th century banned gunpowder mills and storehouses to the outskirts of the tiny settlements, and laws that restricted the location of slaughterhouses and distilleries were applied to Boston, Salem, Charleston, and other market towns.

As cities grew, the realization grew that many industries and occupations were harmful if allowed anywhere in the city. A result was the adoption of "nuisance ordinances," which permitted injurious activities to be carried on only in certain areas. They ostracized activities that were actually or potentially noxious or harmful regardless of location and other activities that might become nuisances if they were carried on in congested or residential areas.

Nuisance regulations and zoning regulations derive from the same broad community power, called the police power—the power to safeguard and promote public health, safety, morals, or the general welfare. Both types of measures involve the regulation of land uses. Some early zoning ordinances were primarily nuisance regulations.

Burgeoning urban growth brought new problems. New laws were shaped to correct newly emerging evils. After the nuisance ordinances came enactments creating fire zones. The construction of frame buildings in congested areas was prohibited. Then tenement house codes were adopted to prevent overcrowding. Later came building codes, sanitary codes, and height ordinances, because tall buildings shut out light and air.

The need for use districts was being realized. The tests of time showed that no one of these protective measures nor any combination of them was adequate to cope with the ills of high-density urban areas. New measures were needed. There arose a demand that the use of property should form the axis around which new remedial measures could be shaped.

The new creation came to be known as the comprehensive zoning ordinance. It was shaped by weaving together selected parts of earlier remedial measures around the new use axis. The first such ordinance was adopted in 1916 by New York City. It divided the city into use districts, or zones, to keep conflicting land uses apart. It prohibited manufacturing uses from moving into retail districts or residential zones.

Zoning received a great boost in the early twenties when the Department of Commerce published a model zoning enabling act. It was a pattern to guide the States in granting their cities and other local governments the right to zone. A second boost came in 1926 from the Supreme Court of the United States. The Court, in the Euclid Village decision, held zoning to be a valid practice.

Most of the States pattern their zoning enabling laws after the model act, but there is little servile adherence. Changes were made and continue to be made as new problems of land use arise.

Only the local governments—cities, counties, towns, or townships—that receive zoning powers may pass zoning ordinances. Only the powers granted may be exercised.

THREE MAIN TYPES of regulations are authorized by nearly all zoning enabling laws.

The most important are use regulations by which a community can be divided into several kinds of zoning districts. Separate districts can be established for farming, homes, business, industry, forestry, recreation, and so on. In each kind of district, only the uses of land, buildings, and structures that can remain side by side in harmony need be permitted. Other uses that may cause harm can be excluded. Unwise mixtures of land uses in the future can thus be avoided; land uses that may conflict can be kept apart.

Use regulations, the core of zoning, generally are reinforced by two related groups of regulations—building-tract (area) regulations and building-size regulations. The first establish restrictions as to the minimum size of lots or tracts, minimum setbacks, side and rear yards, and permissible lot coverage. The second establish restrictions as to the height, number of stories, and size of buildings.

Regulations for tracts and size of buildings may be used to influence population densities and to assure adequate light and air around buildings. Large lots and one-story houses mean low densities of population. Small lots and multistory houses permit higher densities.

TWO METHODS of applying use regulations in zoning districts are resorted to in drafting zoning ordinances. One yields exclusive-type zoning districts. The other produces cumulative-type zones.

In exclusive-type districts, only the classes of uses indicated by the names of the districts (residential, farming, business, or industrial), plus certain related uses that complement and foster the basic uses of the district, are permitted. For example, only agriculture and related uses are allowed in farm zoning districts of the exclusive type. Similarly, in exclusive-type residential, business, and industrial zoning districts, only the basic and related uses of each kind of zone are allowed.

Cumulative-type zoning districts permit a mixture of land uses. The broad makeup of the mixture allowed in a district often is revealed by its position in the list of zoning districts established by the ordinance.

Districts may be arrayed in the following order: Residential, agricultural, business, and industrial. Each district in the list permits the uses allowed in the preceding one. That is, uses permitted in each successive district from the most to the least restricted are cumulated as follows: In residential districts, the most restricted zone, only homes and related uses are permitted; in agricultural districts, homes plus farming are allowed; in business districts, homes plus farming plus trade are allowed; and so on. The name of a cumulative district is descriptive of the least restrictive of the array of uses allowed in that district.

RESIDENTIAL districts for one-family houses usually are of the exclusive type, whether established under exclusive- or cumulative-type ordinances. Business and industry are barred. Very often livestock and poultry farming are excluded as well. These excluded uses are often detrimental to the use of the district for homes, because of odors, fumes, noises, traffic, and so on.

Although residential districts are protected from invasion by harmful uses, homes are allowed next door to the same kinds of objectionable uses in agricultural, business, and industrial districts of the cumulative type. Harmful uses may not come to the homes, but homes may go to the harmful uses. This seems inconsistent.

Residential district regulations may be varied to serve local needs and wants. Many kinds of districts have been created.

Separate districts have been established for one-family dwellings, two-family dwellings, and apartments. Residences in these districts are separated on the basis of housing types.

Other residential districts permit the mixing of a variety of housing types. Under this approach, housing types are cumulated in successive zones from the most restricted one-family zone to the least restricted apartment zone.

Many communities have one or two kinds of residential districts. Others may have four or five or more.

In one-family residential districts, only detached homes and accessory and related uses that complement residential uses are permitted. The related uses include churches, schools, parks, and libraries. Several districts with identical use regulations may be established, but they differ as to minimum sizes of lots permitted. Lots of various sizes are prescribed for small or large dwellings and for areas served by water main or

private wells, sewers, and septic tanks, or some of them.

Another variation of residential zones is the planned development district. Its purpose is to allow variety in large-scale developments. A substantial acreage or even an entire community is sometimes planned and developed as a unit. In planning building groups for these developments, a diversity in the relationship of various buildings, structures, and open spaces is allowed. Usually the limitation on height of buildings may be varied.

Zoning to encourage cluster development is one promising innovation. Typical zoning requires rigid spacing of houses on minimum-size lots. In cluster developments, on the other hand, houses are placed closer together in attractive patterns. The remainder of required lot space is dedicated to park land or open space to be used in common. Fewer miles of streets and service facilities are needed. Less urban sprawl is threatened.

FARM ZONING districts may be of the exclusive type or of the cumulative type.

Exclusive agricultural districts have been developed in California, Colorado, Hawaii, Illinois, Indiana, Iowa, Kansas, North Dakota, Ohio, Utah, Washington, Wisconsin, and Pennsylvania.

Agriculture is the primary land use permitted in farm zoning districts of the exclusive type. Other permitted uses are secondary and accessory. Among the latter are a few related activities that further the use of land for farming. Also permitted are certain public and semipublic uses. Residences are allowed only as an accessory use to agriculture. Nonfarm residences, nonfarm business, and industrial activities are barred.

As an added safeguard against non-farm development, minimum tracts of 5, 10, 20, or 40 acres, and even 80 acres or more, are required.

Similarly, in farm zoning districts of the cumulative type, all kinds of agricultural activities and structures usually are permitted. Nonfarm homes and related uses are allowed also.

Cumulative-type farm zoning districts often serve as transition zones from agriculture to residential uses, including subdivisions. The transition may be facilitated by lowering requirements as to the minimum size of lots to one-half acre or less, or it may be discouraged by specifying larger tracts of 1 to 5 acres or more.

ZONING DISTRICTS for business may consist either of a mixture of business, residential, and other kinds of uses or of selected business uses only.

Mixed land uses often prevail in older business areas in cities and towns, a natural result of expansion over the years. Zoning cannot unscramble the mixture, but it can help to guide future growth.

Zoning districts for business only are growing in favor. These districts, and their use regulations, often are designed to serve and protect shopping centers—neighborhood, community, and regional. Offstreet parking space is a standard requirement in all districts regardless of size. Future traffic problems may be avoided by a wise selection and zoning of areas for coming shopping centers.

Roadside zones are special kinds of business districts. A wide range of uses is permitted in them. One group was designed primarily to serve the traveling public. Only businesses that provide automotive services, food services, and lodging are allowed. In a second group, commercial recreational facilities are included. Other roadside business districts serve both the local people and the traveling public. An additional wide range of retail business activities is permitted in these zones.

INDUSTRIAL DISTRICTS, the country's workshops, often are noisy and dirty places to live in. Mixed-use industrial districts are common, but a growing number are of the exclusive type. The only residences allowed in them are those needed for the caretakers and watchmen.

Some industries are objectionable in residential, commercial, and even in certain industrial zones because of noise, smoke, odor, dust, dirt, glare, heat, fire hazard, noxious gases, traffic, or industrial wastes.

Objectionable industries often are placed in districts away from other uses and districts that may be harmed. Many industries are no longer bad neighbors, because their offensive qualities have been lessened or ended, and they need not be isolated. The test is their effect on their surroundings. The effects of noise, odor, and of other offensive qualities can be measured.

Zoning ordinances can prescribe performance standards, and industries that comply have a wider choice of possible sites.

Many factories have moved to rural areas. They bring jobs for farm and nonfarm people. Rural communities try to attract new industries. A usual practice is to zone for industry the good industrial sites that are needed in the future for expansion of the employment base and the property tax base.

Another growing practice is to establish industrial parks. Site plans must meet certain conditions, such as an efficient and harmonious design of buildings, properly arranged trafficways, adequate parking and loading facilities, appropriate landscape treatment, and adequate sanitary and other facilities. The entire area must be attractively arranged and have no adverse effects on nearby developments.

FORESTRY and recreational values also can be fostered and protected with zoning. A variety of districts, both exclusive and cumulative, depending on local needs, have been created.

Many forestry and recreational zoning districts were formed in the thirties in the cutover counties in the Northern Lake States, where a large acreage is marginal for farming but valuable for forestry. Restored forests have added to the recreational attraction of numerous lakes.

The earliest forestry zoning ordinances in Wisconsin created districts for forestry and recreational activities only, plus certain extractive and hydroelectric facilities. All other land uses were barred, including the establishment of new farms and residences for yearlong occupancy. Later ordinances created zoned districts, in which family dwellings were allowed so that owners could protect their investments during the entire year.

Recreational districts, in which agriculture is a desirable secondary use, have been formed in many States. The districts are of the cumulative type. Uses permitted often include most, if not all, uses normally allowed in one-family residential districts and in farming districts. Permitted also is forestry and a selected list of recreational uses and activities. Some ordinances require that site permits be obtained for some specified uses and facilities, such as riding academies, bathing beaches and bathhouses, motels and trailer camps, stores and establishments to service recreation, and a variety of institutional uses.

Zoning can protect mountainous, riverbank, lakeshore, or other areas that have natural or potential recreational features. Recreational zoning districts can be designed to keep areas as nearly as possible in their natural wooded condition or to guide the development of commercial resorts. Between these extremes are many shadings.

FLOOD PLAIN and watershed zoning districts are fairly new.

The flood plain zone under one ordinance comprises all land covered by streams and all land subject to overflow. Another ordinance establishes two types of districts—flood plain zones enclosing areas adjacent to rivers, streams, drainage channels, and ponds that are in danger of flooding; and floodway zones, consisting of the beds of watercourses and of those portions of the adjoining flood plain that are required to carry and discharge the floodflow.

Land uses allowed in these zones vary. Usually all agricultural uses, including forestry, are permitted unconditionally. Extraction and processing of mineral resources and a variety of recreational facilities generally are allowed, but special location permits may be required. Similar location permits are required also for sanitary fills and dumps, sewage plants and incinerators, radio and TV towers, parking areas, and other facilities not susceptible to major flood damage. Buildings, gradings, and fillings that unduly obstruct floodflow generally are prohibited.

One-family residences are allowed in some flood plain zones after approval of location and design. The ground surface and main floor must be at stated heights above probable flood levels. Foundation walls, footings, and construction must be able to withstand flood conditions.

WATERSHED ZONING districts reserve mountainous and hilly land for water production, forestry, wildlife, and recreation. Regulations aim to protect these lands from fire, erosion, soil compaction, pollution, and spoiling of scenic attractiveness.

Forestry, agriculture, and grazing are deemed desirable principal uses in these zones. The types of recreation that need large acreages are suitable secondary uses.

Approval of location for a variety of land uses is a common requirement. Special permits are needed in one or more districts for nonfarm residences, recreational facilities, extractive industries, sawmills, airports, and private schools and hospitals. Similarly, permits are needed for some kinds of farming, including poultry and hog farms, feedyards, dairies, and plants for processing agricultural products.

Minimum lots of 1 acre, 5 acres, and even 40 acres have been required, depending on the proposed land use.

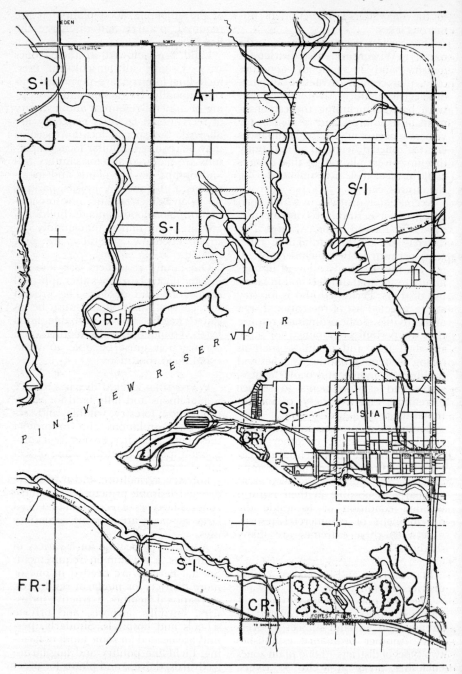

This example of a zoning map includes part of Upper Valley, Pineview Area, Weber County, Utah. Most of the area shown is zoned for recreation. Shoreline zones and four smaller commercial-resort-recreation zones border Pineview Reservoir. Zoning districts include agriculture (A–1), forest-recreation (FR–1), shoreline zone (S–1), commercial resort recreation (CR–1), and subresidential-agriculture (S–1A).

Conservation zoning districts may enclose watersheds or flood plains or both. Their purposes are to protect water sources and to avoid loss from improper use of land that has high water tables or is subject to periodic flooding.

Agriculture, forestry, and recreational uses are allowed, as in watershed and flood plain zoning districts. Yearlong habitation is barred in one such district. Clearing of new land for cultivation or pasturing is forbidden in another. The feeding and spreading of garbage is prohibited in a third. Special permission must be obtained in several districts before locating sand and gravel pits and related operations, sanitary fills, and certain utility and municipal land uses.

OPEN-SPACE zoning districts are new creations. Depending on the locality, their purposes are to reserve rural areas of trees and plants on the urban fringe for future generations, to provide permanent open space, or to protect natural watercourses.

Usually, crop and tree farming, grazing, and recreation requiring large acreages are allowed. Additional uses and facilities ordinarily included are flood control channels, water pumping stations, reservoirs, irrigation canals and public rights-of-way, settling and water recharging basins, and parkways.

Zoning to preserve and to protect buildings and places of historic interest is done in a number of States.

Such districts help to safeguard our heritage by keeping history visual. They serve educational, cultural, and recreational ends. They stabilize or improve property values and foster the vacation travel industry.

The regulations pertain to buildings and structures of some significant architectural period. The concern is with exterior features only, including design, arrangement, texture, materials, and color. No building or structure may be erected, reconstructed, altered, or restored without approval of an historic district commission.

SPECIAL COMBINING districts and regulations are included in some zoning ordinances.

These special districts are intended for combination with other districts. The special regulations are in addition to or instead of certain regulations of the other districts. Design control zones, for example, add regulations concerned with the exterior appearance of improvements, including layout and landscaping of the building tract. Other examples are districts with regulations as to camps, agriculture, and highway frontage.

Additional uses allowed in camp combining districts include campgrounds, tent and trailer camps, automobile courts, and other uses of the same general type.

Agricultural combining districts are suited for uniting with other districts that are experiencing a residential growth. The added regulations often limit the number and kind of farm animals that may be kept on residential-size tracts and restrict the location of farm buildings on the tracts.

Flood plain combining districts provide regulations for restricting land uses, especially homes, in areas that flood. District regulations may also require official approval of location, structural design, and elevation of proposed improvements. These districts are designed for combining with other districts that contain overflow lands.

Regulations of highway frontage combining districts concern the arrangement and use of properties along the roadside. These districts are convenient for combining with other districts that contain important highways. Regulations may govern size of lots, setback and height of buildings, type of signs, parking facilities, and use of land and buildings, or some of them.

Other kinds of combining districts include building-site districts, building-height districts, parking districts, buffer zones, airport approach height zones, public safety districts, special civic districts, and rural professional districts.

ZONING DISTRICTS—agricultural, residential, commercial, industrial, and so on—helped to avoid conflicts between incompatible land uses. Their aim was to keep conflicting land uses apart. But many conflicts between uses within districts continued. One remedy was to create several subclasses of each main class of districts. For example, many zoning ordinances establish three or more types of residential zones.

Another remedy is to create zoning districts of a more exclusive type and fewer cumulative zones.

A third and relatively new way to avoid conflicts is accomplished through further separation of land uses within districts. For example, churches and schools normally are allowed in residential districts, but all locations are not equally suitable. In fact, some locations may be objectionable.

Hence, special permits are required for locating churches and schools in many residential districts. Further conditions are frequently added. Building sites containing a stated minimum acreage, for example, may be required. Offstreet parking space may be prescribed.

Similarly, a few agricultural activities, including some livestock and poultry operations, could be objectionable if located near nonfarm homes. There may be unpleasant noises, odors, and flies. Here also, special permits are sometimes required before locating these farming activities. The permit may require farm buildings and roaming yards to be at stated distances from highways, property lines, or boundaries of residential zoning districts.

The list of special-permit uses keeps growing. The list includes certain agricultural activities and many commercial and industrial uses; it includes public and semipublic properties, institutions, and utility facilities, extractive operations, and many kinds of recreational facilities. Even residential uses are included by some ordinances.

Special permits may be required in any type of zoning district. The ordinances give them a variety of names. Among them are special-use permits, special exceptions, location permits, conditional permits, and commission permits.

Permits may be granted with or without a prior public hearing, depending on the proposed land use or improvement involved and the provisions of the particular ordinance.

The issuing agency also varies with the types of uses and ordinances. Permits may be issued by zoning administrators, zoning boards of appeal, planning and zoning commissions, legislative bodies, or by more than one of these, as provided in the ordinances.

Zoning continues to grow. Each year new rural areas are served by old and new zoning techniques. The changing problems of land use and conflicts spur the shaping of remedial zoning measures. Zoning is becoming less rigid and more flexible. This is one result of the special-permit technique. At the same time, conflicts among land uses normally allowed within zoning districts are avoided or diminished.

The future promises zoning in new ways to achieve new ends. The use of property is likely to remain the axis around which tomorrow's zoning measures are shaped.

ERLING D. SOLBERG *is an agricultural economist in the Resource Development Economics Division, Economic Research Service, the Department of Agriculture.*

For further reading:
By Erling D. Solberg: "Countryside, U.S.A." *The Residential Appraiser*, Society of Residential Appraisers, October 1959, pp. 14–24. *Land-Use Planning and Zoning in Arkansas Rural Areas* (with Albert M. Witte and Lee R. Martin). University of Arkansas, Agricultural Experiment Station, Bulletin 657, June 1962. *New Laws for New Forests. An Evaluation of Wisconsin's Forest-Fire, Tax, Zoning, and County-Forest Laws in Operation.* University of Wisconsin Press, Madison, 1961. *The Why and How of Rural Zoning.* U.S. Department of Agriculture, Agriculture Information Bulletin 196, U.S. Government Printing Office, Washington, D.C., 1958. *Zoning for Rural Areas.* U.S. Department of Agriculture, Leaflet 510, U.S. Government Printing Office, Washington, D.C.

SELDEN LEE TINSLEY

PLANNING FOR CONSERVATION IN THE SUBURBS

EVERY month Mr. and Mrs. Robert Scott of Alexandria, Va., make another payment on the mortage of a 30-thousand-dollar house near Washington's Mount Vernon. The payments are to continue for 15 years. A difference between the Scotts and millions of other young Americans with mortgages is that the house is not their home. It seemed secure when it was built in 1957.

In April 1960, the hillside above, its marine clay soil saturated with water, began to slip toward the Scotts' house.

Drier summer weather halted the glacierlike movement, but on February 1, 1961, heavy snow saturated the hill again. It slipped and did not stop until the Scotts' house was leveled and the homes of nine neighbors were damaged seriously. A pile of rubble at 419 Bluebill Lane mocks the Scotts' monthly payments.

The people of South River, N.J., have been making similar payments. Their plight sprang from an eventful day in June 1962. Prolonged drought was the main subject of conversation all around town as the day began. It worried farmers. But the weather was ideal for work on two new schools and a housing development at the edge of town. The usual crowd of onlookers watched machinery churning around the 45 acres completely cleared of vegetation. Clouds of dust added to the spectacle.

Then the rain came—4 inches in as many hours. Silt from the bulldozed earth poured like lava across St. Peter's Cemetery. It puddled and pooled among the gravestones. Onward it swept to the residential area along Prentice Avenue. Beds of mud layered the pavement of streets, gutters, and driveways. Storm drainage outlets disappeared beneath floes of sediment and debris.

By nightfall, South River had thousands of dollars in municipal damages and a Hobson's choice: Whether to devote the town budget to repairing results of the disaster or spend it on heading off another one. Whenever the next storm occurred, the 45 acres of recklessly developed soil hung over their heads like a sword. They bent to

391

the twin tasks of rehabilitation and prevention of further silt. They had, in fact, no choice.

The remorseless penalty exacted by misused soils hangs a pall over the Valentine subdivision, 35 miles from Chicago's Loop district. The building of a planned total of 72 homes on 80 upland acres came to a sudden halt a few years ago. The reason is not outwardly apparent. The development is rustically picturesque. Large lots lend a spacious look; the architecture is attractive; and nearby Lake Zurich is a pleasant town.

Since the Valentine subdivision was built on an unincorporated tract of land, however, the builder was able to proceed without reference to health authorities.

Some 20 units costing up to 25 thousand dollars each were erected before trouble was detected. The signal was a typical patch of feverish, tattle-tale green in each lawn. Beneath each such oasis was a septic sewage disposal system, which gave off both odor and effluent fertilizer to the sod. The uninvited lawn improvement was offensive. County health units, under extended authorization, stepped in. When soil percolation tests were made, grants for further construction were halted until a trunk sewage line could be installed.

Conservation methods had prevailed, but rather too late for the early Valentine settlers. For-sale signs bespoke their unhappy situation. The incident, though, served to put the Lake County Health Department squarely and properly in the field of soil science.

Also in Lake County, in a district several blocks from the Des Plaines River, a family bought a house that seemed to be a bargain. Houses like it in other developments cost more. The family moved into the new home on a fall day. Trouble came the following spring. Winter snow melted, spring rains came, and the soil soon absorbed all the water it could hold. Water then filled the stream, spilled over the banks, and flooded the bordering al-luvial soils on which the new development had been built. This family and many others in Lake County were reached by floodwaters. Structural damage to many dwellings exceeded a thousand dollars each; added to it was damage to personal property and lower resale value.

A family bought a house in Montgomery County, in Maryland, on the urban fringe of Washington, D.C. It had modern conveniences and cost more than 40 thousand dollars.

The family noticed a spot in the backyard soon after they moved in. It stayed wet even in dry weather, and it had an unpleasant smell, especially on warm days. Close inspection showed that raw sewage from the disposal field of the septic tank was seeping to the surface. When their well was tested, the water was found to be contaminated. The sanitary engineer they called for advice told them there was no practical solution to their problem that would conform with health regulations. The soil around their house was so impermeable to water that a septic tank just could not function properly. Waste from the septic tank system was polluting the well. Health authorities condemned the house.

A common thread runs through the problems of the Scotts in Virginia, the citizens of South River, the people of the Valentine subdivision, the flooded families of Lake County, and the owners of the condemned house in Maryland. All are problems of soil and water and man's failure to work with Nature as he develops his communities.

The soil and water realities of the suburban dweller are not unlike those faced by the American farmer as he manages his land. The problems differ only in intensity and viewpoint.

The successful farmer long ago learned the rationalism and skills of conservation of soil and water. He plans conservation in detail. He uses soil maps published by the Soil Conservation Service and the State agricultural experiment stations. He decides how each field on his farm will be used for crops or pasture or woodland according to its special characteristics and possibilities.

He determines the kind of treatment required for each type of soil. He provides for drainage systems on land that has too much water and for irrigating land too dry to grow crops. He protects sloping tracts with grass and trees. Where he raises row crops and cultivates intensively, he curves the rows around the slope and carries away the water from hard rains in terrace channels.

From time to time he puts back into the soil the fertilizer, lime, and organic material necessary to maintain good condition. Aware of the complexities of land management, he calls specialists to help him plan and carry out his farming operations. His county agent brings him the recommendations from the agricultural experiment station. Through his soil conservation district, he may get whatever technical help he needs.

THE SUBURBANITE can use the same skills and techniques, which vary in application only as the needs of intensive development vary from the requisites of growing crops. When conservation techniques are translated for him, the farmer's pasture becomes a lawn; his woodland, an ornamental planting. The farmer's drainage must dry the fields; the suburbanite's drainage must dry basements.

The farmer often can confine his soil and water troubles. Not so the suburbanite. His problems quickly infect entire neighborhoods. Thus municipalities become involved. They express their concern in official planning bodies, master plans, and in zoning ordinances.

Streams in suburbs create especially difficult situations. Besides the normal runoff from rain, they carry the stepped-up flow from roofs, streets, and storm sewers. An investigation by the Geological Survey in Detroit disclosed that the peak runoff in an urbanized watershed was three times greater than runoff in a similar rural land-and-water unit.

The situation in some suburbs is not unlike the one farmers faced a generation ago. Duststorms and floods ravaged entire river basins. They followed generations of reckless pillaging of soil and vegetation. They engendered the conservation programs of modern agriculture.

The urban and suburban exploitation of land brought on by a booming population has been even more devastating. Damages have occurred at blinding speed; only tardily have people realized how substantial they really are. Only moments ago—as it were—has it been widely understood that nonfarmland problems are first cousin to those out in the country.

Conservation in agriculture had a running start on suburbia. The gap of three decades is being closed. Planning the use of land and intelligent zoning have been gaining momentum. Enabling legislation based on a model act proposed by the Department of Commerce in 1928 has been adopted in all but a few States. State universities provide short courses and informational materials to help citizen planning boards. In Princeton, N.J., land use planning has been a popular course in a high school's night classes for adults.

Travelers on our miles of new highways can see many examples of the proper use of soils, the protective planting of slopes and banks and buffer strips, earth-handling techniques, selected plant materials, and structures. Motorists can see tremendous achievements in soil stabilization, erosion control, and landscape beauty. Highway engineers have used vegetative barriers to lessen noise and create good conditions for wildlife near rights-of-way.

Three thousand soil and water conservation districts, which embrace almost every acre of America with programs of land protection and improvement, are devoting more and more time to urban-related problems. Although districts were conceived to serve agriculture, their leadership has come to realize that "we are one people on one land." Whether plowland or playland, it is vital to conserve. Open space, pure water, soil firmly in place, and pleasant surroundings in which to work and play are necessary for everybody.

The districts have inherited the problems and opportunities of exploding suburbia. These units of State government were designed to aid farmers and ranchers. Their practices were aimed at shielding the earth from inroads of plow, ax, and hoof. For years, district help to townsfolk was informal, random, and—however friendly—limited by methods gaged to rural improvement.

Shifts and increases in population have altered burdens for many districts. A common experience has been the replacement of two or three problems of individual farmers by the soil and water ailments of thousands of new homeowners.

The newer activities of the districts include: Cooperating with highway commissions in selecting conservation plant materials and designing water-disposal structures to protect adjacent land; assisting public works officials in treating lands that are sources of municipal water supplies; aiding recreation interests in solving such problems as stabilizing ski slopes and conserving soil, water, plants, and wildlife to enhance shooting and fishing preserves; designing conservation controls for hazardous shifting of sands and soils in high-value lake- and river-front resort development; planning and applying conservation measures for campgrounds, forests, institutional sites, and wildlife areas used by educational organizations; recommending protective measures for industrial installations impaired by water and wind erosion; detailing of technicians to solve problems and provide for conservation needs on areas used for military purposes; furnishing soil survey data and specific interpretations to professional groups working in real estate, commerce, and industry.

Mrs. Robert Shepard is one of the few women serving as elected director of a soil conservation district. She is also active in other community affairs of Clayton Township, Mich. Seeking more orderly growth and development of her home area, Mrs. Shepard called upon Soil Conservation Service technicians to make an inventory of land resources. Section by section, SCS men mapped the different soils and topographic features. The results were presented to the township. A report showed the characteristics of each area and interpreted them as guides to development. For each area, the report spelled out its desirability for roads, buildings, parks, and agriculture. Special restrictions peculiar to each kind of land were noted.

The Extension Service made an inventory of occupancy of land and classification of buildings and analyzed the population and occupations. The studies were the bases for projections as to the future of the township to help it plan for business locations and home-sites. By January 1, 1963, township officials had made 38 changes in the zoning code based on the report.

Raritan Township, in Hunterdon County, N.J., looks to its soil conservation district for technical help in new housing developments. The township officials arranged for district supervisors to look over development proposals before they were approved. Conservation technicians pointed out the characteristics and special requirements of the soils, outlined major drainageways, estimated peak flows of water, and described the places that may be subject to flooding. Township officials used the information to perfect subdivision plans.

Some conservation problems, such as the development of a water-supply and flood-prevention measures, are too large for solution by a single municipality. Plans for a whole watershed are required in such instances. Watershed associations, like one on the Brandywine Creek of Pennsylvania and Delaware, are formed.

The Brandywine watershed includes farms, suburban communities, and cities, including Wilmington, Del., and Coatesville, Pa. The aim of the association is to protect homes and businesses from floods, to clean Brandywine Creek of debris and pollution, and to provide a stable supply of water.

Congressional action in 1962 authorized the Soil Conservation Service to provide technical and financial assistance through its small watershed program. Plans have been made to construct ten dams, to be used for recreation and flood prevention; two will provide municipal and industrial water.

Services of various kinds are available to homeowners, developers of subdivisions, and rural residents. Government publications pertain to aspects that should be considered in planning lots, reserves of open land, parks, the municipal wildlife developments, roads, sewage systems, and similar matters.

Workshops on soils have been conducted for town planners, consultants, businessmen, and industrialists to help them use available information and tailor it to fit their needs. County agricultural agents are available to conduct them.

But the actual conservation of soil and water rests with the individual suburbanite who owns the land. Whether his lot is big or small, he wants to manage it well in his own interest and his neighbors' interest.

CONSERVATION STARTS when a new home starts. A ground plan outdoors is as important as a floor plan inside. If the suburbanite builds his own home or has it built, he can arrange with his contractor for temporary measures to protect the land during construction. The contractor holds the key to much local soil saving. With simple techniques, he need cause only minor disturbance to neighborhood soils and waters. A leaflet, "Conservation Advice to Contractors," published by the Virginia State Soil Conservation Commission, outlines useful measures to control erosion.

Seedings of wheat, rye, or ryegrass will help hold roughly graded areas in place and prevent topsoil from moving.

In steeper places, diversion terraces can be used to convey excess water from the construction site. Straw scattered over the lot protects soil and lessens the nuisance of mud. The cost of these temporary measures is small.

Once construction is complete, the permanent conservation job begins. Although construction will have mixed or changed the soil, at least near the house, a published soil survey or unpublished field sheet is a guide to the way the soil will respond. In most soil and water conservation districts, technicians are available for consultation on soil problems. Groups of owners in a new development may arrange for an onsite examination of their soils.

Once the suburban conservationist has an understanding of his soils and knows what he wants to do, he is ready to make his plan. He decides on the use of each part of his lot and the treatments needed to support his selected use.

Lawns are placed on the level or gently sloping areas, where grass is easy to maintain and play space is important. Gardens go on the more fertile areas. Convenience in management and plant growth require good drainage. Steep banks are planted to trees or shrubs, which hold soil in place and require little maintenance.

The sketch on the next page shows the land use of a 2-acre suburban lot.

In this instance, the owner had a special interest in birds and has used the kind of planting needed to attract them. Shrub plantings are interspersed with cover-providing evergreens. A wet spot has been turned into a pond, into which extra water was brought. The lawn is arranged to give access to plantings. The total effect is an attractive landscape that takes into account soil and water requirements and serves the purposes of creating beauty and attracting songbirds.

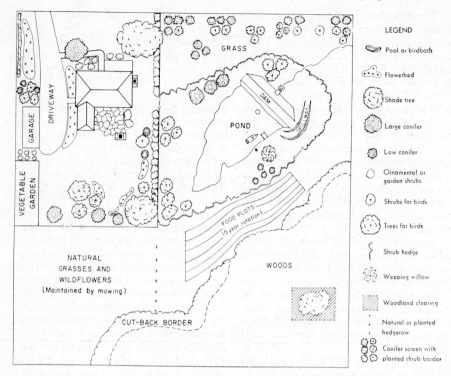

LEGEND

- Pool or birdbath
- Flowerbed
- Shade tree
- Large conifer
- Low conifer
- Ornamental or garden shrubs
- Shrubs for birds
- Trees for birds
- Shrub hedge
- Weeping willow
- Woodland clearing
- Natural or planted hedgerow
- Conifer screen with planted shrub border

A TWO-ACRE COUNTRY PLACE PLANNED FOR BIRD ATTRACTION

Attention to water starts near the house, where roofs, walks, and driveways present a special problem. Land must be graded away; otherwise, surface water may enter the basement. Downspouts are also piped away from the house. If the soil is well drained, they may be led into dry wells. From them the water can seep into the earth and in a small way recharge the ground water table. On less well-drained soils, spouts are outletted on the surface, where they will flow into natural or prepared drainageways. If the house is close to a paved street, they may be piped to the gutter. If not, spreader areas—flat, vegetated basins—may be used to disperse surplus moisture.

Rain and snowmelt off roofs and pavements aggravate water control problems and may do more damage in an hour than a whole year of random showers. Drainageways are necessary. If the lot is small, the entire area can be shaped and graded to encourage water to move off in an even sheet. On larger places, broad, shallow waterways are formed in low areas. A contour map will help to locate them. Lacking a map, a few sightings with a level will provide the clue. Keeping grass in waterways protects them from becoming gullies.

On steeper lands, diversion terraces may be needed. Like troughs on a roof, diversions intercept water. They carry it to a safe disposal place. Their grade is slight—the water moves gently so that channels will not erode. Diversions are particularly useful for gardens and steep banks.

Seepage water is a problem on some soils. Since deep ditches are usually

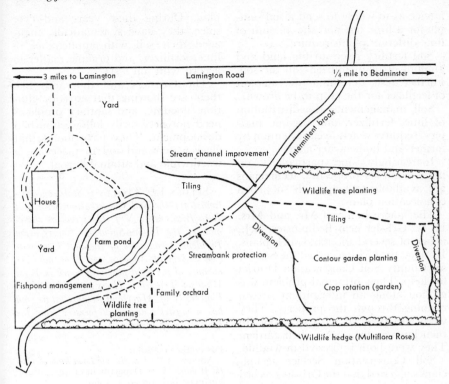

3 miles to Lamington ←   Lamington Road   ¼ mile to Bedminster →

Yard

Stream channel improvement

Intermittent brook

Tiling

Wildlife tree planting

House

Tiling

Diversion

Farm pond

Yard

Streambank protection

Contour garden planting

Diversion

Fishpond management

Crop rotation (garden)

Wildlife tree planting

Family orchard

Wildlife hedge (Multiflora Rose)

unwelcome in suburbs, underground drains are used. They may be short lengths of tile, laid end to end, or perforated pipe, placed below frostline. They intercept water as it moves through soil and carry it to a disposal point in a protected ditch or stream.

A MAJOR CONCERN of the suburbanite's conservation plan is the management of the soil. It must grow the kinds of plants he wants and needs. He therefore requires at least a rudimentary grasp of soil phenomena.

For example, soil structure refers to the arrangement of soil particles into small granules. When the structure is "good," the granules are more or less pea size; there is room for free movement of air and water between them. The "cement" that holds the particles together is mainly organic matter.

Thus the suburban conservation plan provides for mixing organic matter in the soil when lawns and gardens are established and adding to it from time to time. Peat moss, grass clippings, manure, leaves, compost, or practically any other type of organic material will improve soil structure.

The soil with good structure will drain better when it is wet, hold moisture better in dry times, and produce a more vigorous and erosion-resisting cover. All three conditions must be met.

Soil reaction means the relative degree of acidity or alkalinity in the soil. In humid sections, most soils are acid. Most plants prefer to grow where soil is neutral or only slightly acid. Lime is needed to reduce acidity and thus provide proper growing conditions.

County agricultural agents can give

advice as to where to send a soil sample for a lime test and the amount of lime different plants require.

Soil fertility refers to the kind and amount of plant nutrients in the soil. Further tests determine the amount of fertilizer for the crop to be grown.

Soil management—the distribution of lime, fertilizer, and organic matter—requires year-to-year attention by farmer and homeowner alike.

Increasingly, and particularly on large, complex properties, technicians are available to help with suburban conservation plans.

The 5-acre home of Mr. and Mrs. H. W. Grissler near Bedminster, N.J., is one of several thousand such plans. In 1955, the Grisslers asked the Somerset County Soil Conservation District for help. Their principal problem was erosion along an intermittent stream running through the property. They were also plagued with wet spots in their lawn and washes in their garden. They were both interested in wildlife.

Soil Conservation Service technicians suggested that the Grisslers record a conservation plan. It called for clearing out the stream channel, sloping its banks, and planting them with erosion-resisting vegetation. A tile line was indicated to intercept underground water causing the wet spots. Two diversion terraces were designed to protect the garden from surface water. Odd areas were planned for trees and shrubs. Bird-attracting multiflora rose was planned for a boundary fence.

DURING the next few years, the Grisslers progressively put their plan into operation. In 1956, they planted trees and shrubs and stocked their small pond with fish. In 1957, they straightened and deepened the stream and sloped its banks. The next spring, the banks were planted with erosionproof grasses and legumes. In the fall of 1958, they took advantage of dry weather to dig a trench and put in the planned tile line. In 1959, they built the two diversion terraces in the garden area and thus completed the initial plan. During these years and ever since, they have systematically managed their soil with applications of lime, fertilizer, and organic matter to accord with soil tests.

The Grisslers and thousands like them are showing that erosion, siltation, flooding, and sanitary problems need not necessarily follow suburban development. They have found that clear waters and soil in place are a worthwhile and attainable goal.

SELDEN LEE TINSLEY *is State conservationist for the Soil Conservation Service at New Brunswick, N.J. He serves as chairman of the Urban-Suburban Conservation Problems Committee of the Soil Conservation Society of America and is an advisory member of his local planning board in West Windsor Township. He is a graduate of the University of Maryland in agriculture and has a master's degree in forestry from the University of Idaho.*

For further reading:
Anderson, W. L., *Making Land Produce Useful Wildlife.* U.S. Department of Agriculture, Farmers' Bulletin 2035, 1960.
Beaumont, A. B., *Garden Soils, Their Use and Conservation.* Orange Judd Publishing Co., Inc., New York, 1948.
Bennett, Hugh H., *Elements of Soil Conservation,* 2nd edition. McGraw-Hill Book Co., Inc., New York, 1955.
Brune, G. M., *Sediment Is Your Problem: Wasted Soil and Water.* U.S. Department of Agriculture, Agriculture Information Bulletin 174, 1958.
Foster, A. B., *Approved Practices in Soil Conservation.* Interstate Printers & Publishers, Inc., Danville, Ill., 1955.
Higbee, Edward, *The Squeeze.* William Morrow & Co., New York, 1960.
Hubbard, A. H., *This Land of Ours: Community and Conservation Projects for Citizens.* The Macmillan Co., New York, 1960.
Kellogg, C. E., *Our Garden Soils.* The Macmillan Co., New York, 1952.
Osborn, Ben O., *Soil Conservation at Home—Tips for City and Suburban Dwellers.* U.S. Department of Agriculture, Agriculture Information Bulletin 244, 1962.
Terres, J. K., *Songbirds in Your Garden.* Thomas Y. Crowell Co., New York, 1953.
U.S. Department of Agriculture, *Know Your Soil.* Agriculture Information Bulletin 267, 1963.
——— *Soil,* the 1957 Yearbook of Agriculture. U.S. Government Printing Office, Washington, D.C.

A. A. KLINGEBIEL

LAND CLASSIFICATION
FOR USE IN PLANNING

THE sequence is familiar all over the country. The cover of trees or other vegetation is ripped from the land. Foundations are dug in soils not before used for building. Houses go up. Wells are dug, for there is no city water supply. Septic tanks are installed. Roads and curbs are placed. Parks and other public facilities are laid out. Acres of farmland or woodland are transformed in a short time into a new, treeless development.

It is another place where hundreds of families can see their dreams of modern houses, lawns, and gardens come true. Unhappily for many, the dream becomes a nightmare.

The septic tank does not function properly, and the water in the well is polluted. Floods menace houses in lowlands. Cracks appear in outside walls. Foundations slip. I can give scores of examples of these and other ruptured dreams and the loss and inconvenience that occur when poor sites are selected for homes.

Nor is the loss confined to private dwellings. In Fairfax County, Va., a site for a new school was obtained, and construction began. It was soon evident that the soil, high in content of unstable clay, would not keep the planned foundation from settling. A more substantial foundation added about a quarter of a million dollars to the cost of construction. Another place within the school property and only a few hundred feet away was well suited as a site for the building.

When foundations settle and crack, when new road pavements buckle and break, when septic tanks fail, or when floods drive people from their homes, the loss to the individual, the community, and the Nation normally is not the result of an unpredictable whim of Nature. It is the result of not knowing the soils on the landscape.

But how can a school board be expected to know that soils on a site they selected for a new school will not bear the load of the structure? Or how can they know that some soils swell when wet and shrink when dry and thus exert stresses that tear apart anything but an expensive, sturdy foundation?

How does a planning board, or zoning board, or county governing body

399

discover that one site is suited to septic tanks and another is not? How do they know which sites are subject to a high water table during winter, spring, and long wet spells?

Appearance at the surface may tell them nothing, yet they need to know about these things if they are to approve or disapprove an area when a developer or contractor requests permission to build.

Actually, it is no more reasonable to expect that these people will be able to tell good soils from poor soils than it would be to expect an untrained person to repair a watch or fly a jet airplane.

Many contrasting soils look alike at the surface, even to an expert. To find their worth for any particular purpose, we must dig into them. We must observe closely, and with understanding, the properties of each layer, and to think how these affect the intended use.

Many soil properties do not change, but their significance does, according to the intended use, whether it be digging a foundation, building a road, laying a waterline, planning a park, or simply selecting a plot for a garden.

That is the job of soil scientists, men who are trained in mapping, classifying, and interpreting soils. Since 1900, soil scientists have helped farmers, ranchers, foresters, and others who produce food and fiber. They have investigated the different kinds of soil in the United States and have prepared detailed soil maps for many counties and areas. Each year they map additional acres. About 55 million acres had been mapped in 1963.

Although civil engineers and soil scientists began to work together in 1925 or so, only during this recent time of rapid growth of the metropolitan fringe have urban planners and developers learned about soils. Now they have a new awareness that soil scientists can help them avoid costly failures and aid them in discovering savings in design and construction. With costly designs, houses and roads can be built on soils that are poorly

suited for that use. Unfortunate experiences on those sites, however, often lead to overdesign and extra costs on soils that are well suited for houses and roads.

Great losses still occur, but the trend is downward.

BUSINESSMEN in Atlantic, a city in Cass County, Iowa, had a soil scientist interpret soil maps before they selected a tract for a golf course. The scientist inspected the proposed sites with the builders. He described the soils on each site and assessed their suitability for greens, fairways, and roughs. Then each site was evaluated, and costs for construction and landscaping were estimated. Because they then could select a site that had no unfavorable soils, contracting costs were 30 thousand dollars less than on any of the other sites proposed. The cost of seeding and maintaining fairways also was less. The soil scientist found a suitable site for a pond on the course to store water. He located sand that could be used in establishing a proper mixture of silt and sand for the subgrade of the greens.

In the town of Wilton, Conn., an owner of 22 acres planned to develop a site for housing. The planning commission could not issue a permit because of the flood hazard from the Norwalk River. A community club, aware of a need for outdoor recreation, asked a soil scientist to determine the suitability of the tract as a recreation area. He showed the area to be suitable for a pond and a park. The people of the community bought the acreage and made an attractive sandy beach, which borders a spring-fed pond for swimming and skating.

In Stamford, Conn., a suggestion arose to convert a 30-acre swamp to a city dump. But property values nearby would be lowered. Study of a soil map showed the tract to be well suited for a recreational area. Some drainage was installed, and several ponds for wildlife were built. The people of the community now use this area for fishing, skating, hiking, and observing the wildlife attracted by the ponds.

These examples illustrate the advantages of using soil maps. Homeowners, farmers, engineers, real estate dealers, planners, and others benefit from information on soil maps in hundreds of ways. They help people in growing flowers, shrubs, grass, and trees; in growing corn, cotton, wheat, and truck crops; in building highways, schools, and homes.

To GET FULL advantage from the maps, however, we need to know more about the methods the soil scientist uses and about the kinds of maps he makes.

Most soil scientists are employed by Federal and State agencies. The Soil Conservation Service, an agency of the Department of Agriculture, employs approximately 1,500 soil scientists, who are stationed in all States.

Soil scientists prepare the maps and the descriptions that accompany them as part of a broad cooperative program, called the National Cooperative Soil Survey. The Soil Conservation Service is the agency that has primary Federal responsibility for making soil surveys. All of the work is cooperative with the State agricultural experiment stations and other Federal, State, and local agencies. This work includes field and laboratory investigations, classification of the soils according to a national system, and publication in a standard series by the Department of Agriculture.

Soil surveys have been published for many counties in the United States.

Preliminary reports and maps for many other areas can be seen in local offices of soil conservation districts or in the office of participating State and local agencies. The unpublished maps can be interpreted and used for planning purposes.

The soil scientist walks over the land, and studies the soils, vegetation, and features of the landscape. With his knowledge of soil genesis and soil behavior, he classifies the different kinds of soils and records their boundaries on a map.

He identifies the different soils by digging holes and examining the layers of soil, usually to a depth of 5 feet. He can make predictions, however, about the nature of the soil material below 5 feet for soils that derive from uniform parent materials.

He examines the thickness and arrangement of each layer; its color; the proportion of sand, silt, and clay; the shape, size, and consistence of the natural aggregates; the kind of parent material; the number of stones; acidity or alkalinity; and the content of organic matter. He evaluates other features that have importance to the use of soil.

Each of the many thousands of different kinds of soil in the United States are described in terms that have special meaning to soil scientists. The properties of each layer are studied and evaluated. The important properties are compared with those of similar soils that have been named in the national soil classification system. A soil that is unlike all others classified to date is given a new name.

We can transfer experience and information from one place to another when we have named and classified the soils. If we find that septic tanks do not work satisfactorily on some kinds of soil, for example, the results of such experience can be applied to other areas that have the same kinds of soil. Thus knowledge about the soils can be related to the problems and management of other areas of similar soils.

Then, from what the soil scientist has seen and determined by tests and from his knowledge of soil research and experience in the area, he draws inferences concerning the soil qualities that cannot be seen. This is the kind of information that can be useful to farmers, suburbanites, and others and can prevent costly mistakes.

He has observed, for example, grayish or bluish colors in the soil; from that he can infer poor drainage. Or by observing, molding in his hands, and perhaps obtaining laboratory tests on certain soil layers, he learns that it is of the kind that swells when wet and shrinks when dry. From this he infers undesirable stability and strong resistance to penetration of water.

When the qualities of the soil have been determined, the soil scientist can make predictions concerning its behavior. The soil with the bluish-colored layers may not be suitable for houses requiring septic tanks, but it may be suitable for agriculture, parks, recreation, or other uses.

Soils poorly suited for residential use may be well suited for growing agricultural crops. Some kinds of crops may be better adapted than others. By recording and assembling research data and experiences by kinds of soil, he can make predictions and suggest alternative uses. The soils can be rated or grouped into classes ranging from the best to the poorest for a specific use.

The soil scientist is impartial in his interpretations. He does not suggest what the use of any soil shall be. He predicts what its behavior will be under specified uses. The decision on use is left to the owner, buyer, or others concerned.

The soil scientist checks his predictions about soil behavior by studying the results of research and experience on known kinds of soils. He prefers data from research farms or plots, because on these the soils have been tested under controlled conditions, and the results have been tabulated. The Department of Agriculture and the State agricultural experiment stations have many research plots on identified kinds of soil.

Where such data are lacking or insufficient, the soil scientist depends more on his observation of crops in farmers' fields, of trees in woodlands, of plants on ranges, of highways on different kinds of soil, and so on. He examines areas where drainage, irrigation, or sewer systems have failed.

The next step is to design a map that will best serve all who can benefit from the information that has been recorded about each soil.

The detail of mapping depends on the location of the area, what investigation has shown to be the potential of the soils, what demands are now made of the soils, and what demands will probably be made in the future.

Soil maps are designed for use by farmers and those who work with them in planning the management for farms and fields. The increasing complexity of agriculture has created a demand for more and more detailed soil maps and more precise interpretations.

These modern soil maps, although designed mainly for agricultural use, can be interpreted for soil engineering, urban planning, and other purposes.

Soil maps are made at different intensities and scales, depending on the needs of the person who uses them. Two different levels of intensity commonly are made—general soil maps and detailed soil maps.

General soil maps show the soil resources for broad areas and their suitability for different uses. They are suited for the general planning of broad areas and usually cover a township, county, or several counties.

The general soil map is drawn on a small scale that covers an entire county or equivalent area and shows the different patterns, or associations, of major soils on the different kinds of landscape. A map of this kind may be made at a scale of a quarter of an inch to the mile and show as many as 10 different soil associations. Each soil association has its own pattern of soils.

By rating the soils according to their suitability for a particular use, one can determine the areas that are well suited or unsuited for that use. Such information is useful to those who are studying large areas for residential, industrial, or recreational development. It is also useful to farmers, food processors, and others who are searching for large areas that may be suitable for growing certain crops.

General soil maps give planning and zoning groups valuable clues to the location of broad areas suitable for various uses. Having found areas that are suitable for a particular use, they can then use the detailed map, at its larger scale, to achieve more precise selection of sites.

A DETAILED soil map, frequently at a scale of 4 inches to the mile, is made on an aerial mosaic that shows such features as natural drains, rock outcrops, lakes, ponds, levees, railroads, roads, powerlines, and buildings.

A detailed map provides the nearest practical approximation of the shape and extent of the areas of each kind of soil. Nevertheless, it is not feasible to show on a detailed map the exact boundaries of every area of each kind of soil, nor to delineate separately those areas of a given kind of soil that occupy 2 acres or less. Thus, an area delineated on the detailed map, and named for a given kind of soil, may contain up to 15 percent of another kind of soil. Also, soils of different kinds can occur in such intricate patterns that it is not practical to separate them at the scale ordinarily used for detailed soil maps. Boundaries are drawn around areas of such intricately mixed soils, and the soils within the boundaries are described and named as complexes.

In using a detailed map, therefore, one has to know that small areas of highly contrasting soils may lie within any area shown on it. The presence of contrasting soils in an area used to grow plants may not be of particular significance, but may be of critical importance in building a road, house, or swimming pool. It is therefore necessary to go to the site tentatively selected for a structure and examine it carefully. Preliminary inspection of the detailed map, however, shows which sites are definitely not suitable for the proposed structure; thus the number of the field examinations that otherwise would be needed is reduced.

The detailed soil map, properly interpreted, provides planning and zoning boards and other local government officials with the kind of information about soils that they need to approve or reject requests for development.

Before they can rule on an individual building application, however, they need to inspect the lot. Inspection of the detailed map shows whether a lot is subject to flooding, but it may not be precise enough to indicate tiny beds of peat, muck, or gravel that would seriously affect construction.

For example, a planning group receives a request for development of a subdivision beyond present sewerlines. The soil map shows that some of the soils in this area are slowly permeable, others have a high water table part of the year, and still others are less than 3 feet deep over rock. The local officials can point out these limitations and suggest changes to fit the soils or reject the request for development on the basis that the soils are not suited for residential use.

WHEN THE SOIL scientist has named, described, and mapped the soils in his area, he works out ways to present the information in a way convenient for people to use for their needs.

Interpretations can be made for the individual kinds of soil or they can be made by grouping the soils that respond similarly to use and management. More precise interpretations can be made for the individual kinds of soil, but soil groupings are helpful for some uses.

Soil groupings help introduce some map users to the more precise information on soil maps. For that reason, many groupings of soils have been worked out, each designed to serve specific users. The basic principle for each of these groups, whether for city planners, farmers, woodland managers, or ranchers, is that of placing together soils similar in the characteristics and qualities that affect the intended use.

Thus for many years groupings of soils have been primarily for farmers who grow cultivated crops; other groupings for those who produce trees; and yet other groupings of soils for those who manage rangelands. More recently, groupings have been made that show relative suitability for use for recreation and wildlife refuges and for septic tanks, roads, and other structures based on engineering tests.

Depending on the need, the soil scientist can prepare a number of different groupings and interpretations of soils, since he has recorded, in detail, the nature of each kind of soil in the area he has surveyed.

A FAMILIAR SYSTEM of grouping, one used by the Soil Conservation Service to help farmers develop conservation plans on their farms, is the land-capability classification. It provides information about soils at three levels of generalization—the capability unit, the capability subclass, and the capability class.

The capability unit, a group of soils similar in management needs and in response to that management, contains the most specific interpretations of the three. It is valuable in planning management of individual farms and fields.

The subclass is a grouping of capability units similar in kinds of limitations and hazards. Four general kinds of limitations or hazards are recognized: Erosion, wetness, root-zone limitations, and climate.

The third and broadest category places all the soils in eight capability classes. The risks of soil damage or the limitations in use increase as the class numbers increase from I to VIII. Soils in class I have few or no limitations when used for common cultivated crops, but those in class VIII will not justify inputs of management without major reclamation.

Soils are grouped into capability classifications primarily on the basis of their ability to produce common cultivated crops and pasture plants without soil deterioration over a long period of time. This soil grouping helps farmers to understand their soil and water conservation problems and to see which areas are best suited to cultivation and to permanent vegeta-

tion. The classification also shows them the hazards and limitations to use of the different soils on their farms.

Other groupings are more commonly used to express the suitability of soils for range and woodland. In like manner, soils are also grouped to show their suitability as sites for homes, public buildings, and similar structures. Many other special groupings can be made according to the need.

Community planners, local officials, developers, contractors, and prospective homeowners are not experienced in interpreting soil maps and cannot be expected to know all the characteristics and qualities of soils that are likely to affect their suitability for urban uses. Through the use of soil maps, however, they can learn about some of the major soil properties that influence the use of the soil.

PREDICTIONS can be made about the hazard of runoff and erosion.

The results of erosion can be seen in most urban-fringe areas. It is a serious problem on some kinds of soil, especially in places where contractors unnecessarily scalp the surface of all vegetation and leave the soil bare for long periods. The amount of soil that washes downhill depends on the kind of soil, the amount and intensity of rain that falls, and the cover on the surface.

Runoff water from heavy rains erodes the soil, and concentrated runoff cuts gullies in most soils. The sediment fills the basements of partly built houses, washes out streets, damages newly dug or filled areas, clogs up ditches and culverts along roads, and fills lakes with silt.

The developer has to clean up the area he owns and must try to regain his expenditure for this by increasing the price of his product in a competitive market. The community, and perhaps more than one community downstream, has to tolerate the damage done outside the development or take measures to remedy it.

By no means all of the erosion takes

place during the year or two that the soils are exposed during completion of the development.

When the homes, streets, and parking lots are all built, less area of soil is exposed to absorb water. Before the area of exposed soil was reduced by roofs and pavement, perhaps most of the gentle rains were absorbed. But in the same area, after much of it is under roof and concrete, a gentle rain can build runoff of destructive volume.

The water goes in one direction— downhill.

Suppose, then, that the lower end of a watershed has been developed and its storm sewers and water disposal systems have been installed. This older community may be suddenly confronted with a flow of water that its storm sewers cannot handle. It is water coming from the new development above—water that once soaked harmlessly into the soil.

This need not happen.

No one should be allowed to disturb a lot or tract of land for nonagricultural use without first obtaining a permit from the county or local officials. They should have a master plan for future expansion that is based on the potential needs of the area and on information from soil maps.

The maps will provide local authorities, the developers, contractors, and property owners with the location of the different soil areas and the predictions concerning the suitability of the soil for various uses. The master plan should show location of sewage disposal systems, water and sewer lines, roads, and parks. It should include a plan for controlling erosion, controlling sediment, and disposing of water. The plan should be for a watershed, and it should be based on the probable hazards when the watershed is fully developed.

The plan a contractor or developer presents should show where the lots, houses, and roads will be located; explain his plans for control of sediment and water; specify the size and location of waterways, storm sewers,

and diversion terraces; and indicate how he will use vegetation as a means of controlling erosion. The local officials then should approve this plan only if it meets requirements of the master plan.

Every effort should be made to acquaint developers, contractors, and others with the master plan. Soil maps, and their interpretations, should be available for reference. With the aid of a soil map, the developer should be able to plan for maximum utilization of the soils. Soils not suited for houses can be used for streets, parks, and other uses. Size and layout of building lots can be planned to fit the soils and topography of the area.

Shrinking and swelling of soil material is critical in selecting sites for structures, but that quality is not detected easily. Soils that contain unstable clays, even if nearly level, swell when wet and shrink when dry. Buildings placed on such soils shift and crack unless they have a sturdy foundation. Underground pipelines may break. Buildings placed on sloping soils of this kind may be damaged when the unstable soil slips downhill. If the shrink-swell properties of soils are known, it will not be necessary to overdesign structures built on soils that do not shrink or swell significantly.

Some soils tend to run when wet and fail to support foundations or other structures. Organic soils—peat and muck—are poor sites for construction because of their low ability to support loads. These organic deposits that the engineer wants to avoid may be sought by landscape supply businesses.

Wetness can seriously affect the suitability of a soil. A soil that is wet to the surface the year around is not a suitable site for construction. The soils that can cause serious trouble for the unsuspecting are those that are wet only part of the year, or that have a water table that moves up and down without reaching the surface, or that absorb water too slowly or too rapidly.

If the water table in a soil rises near the surface some time during the year, a septic tank filter field will not function properly during that time. Such a soil, furthermore, is not suitable for houses with basements, and foundations may be damaged.

Wet soils freeze in cold climates. If such soils are used under driveways or paved roads, ice may form under the pavement. Water keeps coming in by flow under the slab from higher ground or by capillary movement from the water table below. The deposits of ice grow until they heave up and break the pavement. If the hazard is discovered before construction, the contractor can raise the grade or add coarse-grained material to make a firm, well-drained subgrade.

DEPTH OF A SOIL critically affects many uses. The homeowner may envision tall shade trees around his new house, but he faces some real problems if he discovers that the soil on his lot is only a foot deep to hard rock. It is also difficult to dig a basement or pit for a septic tank in such a soil.

When the city of San Antonio, Tex., planned to install a 24-inch steel main along an owned right-of-way, the bids reflected the fact that the route was underlain by limestone. Through the use of a soil survey, a somewhat shorter route was found that was free of rock. The city saved a considerable amount in construction costs, even though easements for a new right-of-way had to be obtained.

Soil maps can be used also for design purposes. Through the use of the soil descriptions and interpretations that accompany the soil maps, it is possible to reduce the number of soil borings needed to determine the kinds of soil materials along the rights-of-way of highways.

The reaction of a soil—its acidity or alkalinity—affects metal pipes, cables, and concrete structures. The life of ordinary concrete may be greatly shortened if it is used in soils high in free sulfates or organic acids. It is possible in some places to guard against this damage by use of special,

more expensive materials in making the concrete. Studies made by the Bureau of Standards show close correlation between kinds of soil and susceptibility of pipe to corrosion. By knowing the kind of soil, one can predict the seriousness of corrosion and the need for different kinds of pipe and pipe coverings.

NEARLY ALL farmers require some direct technical assistance in developing a plan for their operations and for carrying out that plan.

Such technical assistance is based on a detailed soil map that indicates the alternative uses and combinations of practices for which the different kinds of soil are suited. The plan must be arranged to take advantage of the effects of the different practices on each kind of soil and among fields within the farm unit having different kinds of soil.

Some engineering assistance is needed to make maximum use of the water available and to take care of any excess without damage to crops or soils.

Many users prefer interpretations for single soils. Others prefer to have the soils grouped that are used alike and treated alike. The capability classification, which I mentioned earlier, is one of these groupings. Other, more highly specialized, groupings of soils can be made. For example, soils can be grouped according to their suitability for growing a single crop, such as corn, cotton, rice, wheat, cranberries, apples, or others.

Farmers who have woodlots may want to know what kinds of trees will grow on a given soil and how fast they will grow. Foresters and owners of large tracts of woodland need the same kind of information. Some soils now covered with slow-growing, unproductive trees and shrubs may be suited to fast-growing trees. Other soils are so unproductive of trees that the expenditure for improvement is not worth while.

Soil scientists and foresters determine the rate of growth of different species of trees on the major kinds of soil. With this information it is possible to predict the amount of wood crops that can be produced annually for each kind of soil.

Realtors, credit agencies, and appraisers find soils maps helpful in determining the value of land. The map shows the extent of each kind of soil, and the accompanying interpretations provide information about their capacity to produce. This information on productivity can then be appraised in terms of earning power of the soil considering location, size of unit, and similar factors. Then the size of loan and rate of repayment can be determined.

A prospective buyer of land should study the soil map and the interpretations. He should note the yields predicted for each kind of soil at different levels of management; the suitability of the soils for different crops; the response of the soils to management, including drainage and irrigation; presence of salts; and hazards of erosion. With such information, the prospective purchaser can decide whether he wants to buy and how much he should pay.

Tax assessors use the maps as a basis for valuing land. With appropriate interpretations, the maps can provide an objective basis for predicting the capacity of a soil to produce the major crops. The assessor can list the soils in decreasing order of yield and then assign ratings. The soils producing the most can be assigned a rating of 100; the soil producing the least, a rating of 10; the others get comparable ratings between. In urban and suburban areas, the suitability of the soil for building sites is a basis for arriving at land values for tax purposes.

Of course, kind of soil is not the only factor considered in determining land values and assessments. Buildings, roads, distance to market, and other factors that affect value need to be weighed in determining land values.

Manufacturers, canners, and proc-

essors have used soil maps to good advantage in locating their plants, in estimating the supply of raw material available for processing, and in appraising the marketing potential for finished products. Manufacturers of fertilizers, of farm supplies, and farm equipment are among those who profitably use soil maps to determine potential markets. Canners and processors use soil maps in locating their plants where soils and climate are best suited to growing of the crops they want to process. The map, with accompanying description, tells them the extent of the good soils and their probable yield.

More and more people are finding that soil maps are useful for many different purposes. The cost of making and publishing soil surveys is small in comparison to the benefits that can be derived from them. The savings in the construction of a mile of highway or pipeline, or school, or one small subdivision can more than pay the cost of a soil survey for an entire county.

A. A. KLINGEBIEL *is Director of Soil Survey Interpretation in the Soil Conservation Service, which he joined in 1937. He holds degrees in agronomy and soils from Iowa State University. He has done extensive research in soil physics and soil conservation and has studied soils throughout the United States and several other countries.*

For further reading:

Bartelli, L. J., "Use of Soils Information in Urban-Fringe Areas." *Journal of Soil and Water Conservation*, Vol. 17 (No. 3, 1962).

Bender, William H., *Soils Suitable for Septic Tank Filter Fields*. U.S. Department of Agriculture, Agriculture Information Bulletin 243.

Klingebiel, A. A, and Montgomery, P. H., *Land-Capability Classification*. U.S. Department of Agriculture, Agriculture Handbook 210.

Obenshain, S. S., Porter, H. C., and Devereux, R. E., *Soil Survey for Urban Planning and Other Uses*. Virginia Agricultural Experiment Station, Bulletin 538, 1962.

Osborn, Ben O., *Soil Conservation at Home*. U.S. Department of Agriculture, Agriculture Information Bulletin 244, 1962.

Ottoson, Howard W., Aandahl, Andrew R., and Kristjanson, L. Burbank, *Valuation of Farm Land for Tax Assessment*. University of Nebraska Experiment Station, Bulletin 427, 1954.

CARL B. BROWN

SMALL WATERSHEDS
AS UNITS FOR PLANNING

A WATERSHED is a drainage area on the earth's surface from which runoff resulting from precipitation flows past a single point into a larger stream, a lake, or the ocean. Thus the Mississippi River watershed comprises all the land and the streams and the lakes above New Orleans from which water comes to make up the flow of that great river. All watersheds can be divided into smaller and smaller subwatersheds. It is perfectly proper to speak of a 60-acre drainage area above the farm pond as its watershed.

We commonly refer to larger watersheds, such as that of the Mississippi or the Colorado or the Potomac, as river basins

The term "small watershed" has come to mean an area of fewer than 250 thousand acres, or about 390 square miles. There is actually no lower limit on the size of a small watershed, but in this chapter I use the term generally to mean a watershed that covers at least several thousand acres. Exceptions are mainly in and around the fringes of urban areas, where watersheds of fewer than a thousand acres may have such complexities of land use and water management that they constitute individual planning units.

The National Inventory of Soil and Water Conservation Needs, completed by the Department of Agriculture in 1961 to appraise the requirements for conservation and development of the land and water resources of rural America, divided the United States (exclusive of Alaska) into some 12,700 small watersheds. Each such watershed is a natural hydrologic unit suitable for planning the management of water and land.

Small watersheds are more suitable for certain types of planning than other units, such as a farm or ranch, a major river basin, a county, township, or a metropolis.

A watershed is generally the logical planning unit for water management, but not always. In some places, deep aquifers—porous formations through which ground water moves—may run crosswise of surface drainage; ground water therefore is not necessarily related to surface hydrologic areas. Desalting of sea or brackish water is another type of water management that may have no relation to small watersheds. Some other types of water use—the development of hydroelectric power, for example—are confined almost entirely to river basins. Navigation is rarely of concern in small watersheds.

On the other hand, most land problems are linked with water problems.

Nearly all of our surface water and most of the food and fiber we produce come from small watersheds. More than half of the flood damage in the United States occurs in small watersheds. A large percentage of the irrigated farmlands get their water from streams within small watersheds. Most of the drainage needs are confined to small watersheds. Thousands of towns and small cities use surface water supplies from small watersheds. The development of fishing, wildlife, and recreation must be accelerated on small watersheds if they are to be brought within reasonable distance and cost to most citizens. Many of the problems of erosion, as along watercourses, can be solved only by public action in small watersheds.

The place of small watersheds in the total scheme of national, regional, State, and local planning has become recognized widely only in the past few years. The Federal Government has been engaged in the planning and improvement of major rivers for navigation since 1824, in reclaiming arid lands in the West since 1902, and in helping farmers and ranchers conserve soil and water since 1933. Except for a few experimental areas, the first small watersheds on privately owned land were planned and treated under Federal programs in 1950.

It is not important here to trace the development of planning on small watersheds or to explain why it has lagged. Much more important is that it has made such rapid strides proportionally in the expanding field of conservation, development, and use of water and related land resources.

When they assist landowners and operators to plan and apply conservation practices, soil conservationists encounter many water problems that cannot be solved on single farms and ranches. Some examples: Frequent flooding of fertile bottom land makes it unusable for cultivated crops. Farmers, unable to control water runoff from other farms, are forced to plant sloping land that would be used better for grass or trees instead of the bottom lands that are not subject to erosion. Farmers often cannot obtain adequate drainage of their nearly flat fields because of lack of outlets through other and more distant farms. Irrigation commonly requires the storage and distribution of water to many adjacent farms. This can be best accomplished by watershed planning. Highway planners recognize that runoff from small watersheds is critical in the design of bridges and culverts; measures for flood protection and water management on small watersheds materially reduce the costs of constructing highways.

Urban planners realize that projects undertaken to control and manage water on small watersheds before building is done in suburbs mean savings for communities and building contractors. Some counties have planning staffs whose work has to do primarily with water management on watersheds that may affect their cities and suburbs. One is Fairfax County in Virginia, near Washington, D.C.

PLANNING and developing small watersheds once was an unfilled gap in the national effort to protect and develop our water and related land resources.

When public attention was drawn to the need through pioneering studies by the Department of Agriculture, dating from the thirties, appropriate political action was taken, as described in *Water* and *Land*, the Yearbooks of Agriculture for 1955 and 1958.

The work of the Department under the authority of the Flood Control Act of 1936 led to authorization in 1944 of programs in 11 large watersheds. The first measures were installed in 1947. The first sizable subwatershed projects were completed in 1952.

Those demonstrations that an adequate water- and land-management plan could be developed and carried out by landowners, aided by Federal, State, and local agencies, fostered action by the Congress in 1953 to establish a pilot demonstration program and to follow it in 1954 with permanent legislation, the Watershed Protection and Flood Prevention Act, Public Law 566 of the 83d Congress, to authorize a program for watershed treatment.

This act has been broadened several times since it was enacted. It is now a keystone for much of the Nation's total effort in meeting problems of the rural-urban complex.

THE SMALL WATERSHED program is carried out through projects sponsored by local units of government, which operate under authority vested in them by State legislation. They may include soil and water conservation districts, watershed districts, flood control districts, irrigation or drainage districts, counties, municipalities, or others.

Federal assistance is provided mainly by the Soil Conservation Service, but watershed protection work on public lands is carried out by land management agencies, such as the Forest Service, Bureau of Land Management, and Bureau of Indian Affairs. The Forest Service also has responsibilities with respect to management and improvement of privately owned woodlands.

Watershed projects may include measures for such purposes as flood prevention, including control of erosion, land stabilization, and reduction of floods and sediment damage; drainage; irrigation; fish and wildlife and recreational development; and municipal and industrial water supply.

Projects are limited to areas of 250 thousand acres or less. No single reservoir in a project may contain more than 25 thousand acre-feet of total capacity or more than 5 thousand acre-feet of flood prevention capacity. More than 50 percent of the land above each reservoir or floodwater-detention structure must be under agreement with the landowner to carry out a conservation plan on his farm or ranch.

The act requires that benefits must exceed costs. All structural improvements are evaluated with respect to each purpose, and only those are included that have annual net benefits in excess of annual costs. No economic evaluation is made of land-treatment practices, because the Congress has declared it to be public policy to provide for the prevention and control of soil erosion.

The process by which projects are selected, as required by law and policy of the Department of Agriculture, involves five items: Application by one or several qualified local organizations; approval and recommendation of priority for planning by a State government agency or the Governor; agreement of the local organizations and the Department of Agriculture on the plan; review of the plan by the Bureau of the Budget and its transmission to the Congress (except for very small projects); and approval by congressional committees.

Federal cost sharing in watershed improvements differs by purposes. Rates are established by law or Department policy.

Landowners must apply or install most of the conservation treatment on their own farms, but may obtain cost sharing from other sources, such as the Agricultural Conservation Program, for eligible practices.

For structural measures, local organizations are required, without regard to their purpose, to provide all land, easements, and rights-of-way, including replacements and relocations (except those required for recreational development), to guarantee operation and maintenance of these improvements, to bear the cost of contracting, and to provide water rights.

The Federal Government provides: Additional technical assistance for all land treatment measures and cost sharing (up to 80 percent) for vegetative planting on critical eroding areas, small erosion control structures, floodwater-retarding terraces, and (up to 50 percent) accelerated fire control;

All of the engineering services required except for municipal and industrial water supply;

100 percent of the construction cost for flood prevention structures (reservoirs, channels, floodways, levees, et cetera);

Up to 50 percent of the construction costs allocated to irrigation or drainage structures and fish and wildlife or recreational developments; and

Up to 50 percent of the costs of land, easements, and rights-of-way and minimum basic facilities for fish and wildlife or recreational development.

The Federal Government bears none of the cost of measures to improve municipal and industrial water supplies. Water supply for future use may be included in a reservoir, however, with repayment of the cost deferred for as long as ten years.

The act provides for Federal loans at a low interest rate computed each year by the Secretary of the Treasury (2.963 percent in 1963) for the local costs of any purpose included in the project. Repayment, which may extend over 50 years, must be guaranteed by charges to users for water and other services or local tax levees, either on the direct beneficiaries or ad valorem within a local unit of government. Loan provisions of the act are administered by the Farmers Home Administration.

The National Inventory of Soil and Water Conservation Needs listed the acreages and extent of the need for flood prevention, irrigation improvements, drainage, and other water-resource purposes that require action by local organizations rather than individual landowners.

The national totals disclosed a need for project-type action by public agencies on 8,288 small watersheds, or 65 percent of those delineated. These watersheds contain about a billion acres—55 percent of our land area exclusive of Alaska.

The inventory brought out that an estimated 61 million acres needed project action for flood protection, 15 million acres needed irrigation, and 43 million acres needed drainage.

Thus the dimensions of the watershed job ahead are large.

APPLICATIONS had been received to April 1, 1962, for Federal assistance under Public Law 566 on 1,867 watersheds containing more than 134 million acres. The total installation cost, Federal and non-Federal, for land treatment and structural measures on the first 450 watersheds authorized under the program was 668 million dollars—about 26 dollars an acre. Treatment costs on the 31 million acres in the 11 watersheds authorized in 1944 were about the same.

If 50 percent of the 8,288 watersheds classified as needing treatment prove economically feasible for the development of small watershed projects by the year 2000 and the cost is 30 dollars an acre, the total outlay would be 15 billion dollars. The estimated total local, State, and Federal outlay for watershed projects from 1947 through June 30, 1962, was about 525 million dollars. In the 1963 fiscal year, the total expenditure was estimated to be 141 million dollars.

The Department of Commerce, in a 1959 report, "Water Resource Developments—Capital Investment Values, 1900–1975," estimated that capital investment of 214 billion dollars would be needed over a 20-year period to meet existing deficiencies and to supply the increasing population. That included municipal and industrial water supply, sewage collection and waste treatment, pollution abatement, power, irrigation, navigation, flood control, fish and wildlife development, and recreation.

Of that amount, some 53 billion dollars represented the estimated needs for Federal expenditures if Federal responsibilities for cost sharing under existing authorized programs were continued. These projections include part (but not all) of the watershed program needs as estimated independently from the National Inventory of Soil and Water Conservation Needs. The watershed estimates may seem large, when they are considered independently, but the hypothesized 15 billion dollars required over nearly 40 years is only a small fraction of the total capital investment needed to improve water and related land resources.

SMALL WATERSHEDS have a significance as planning units that extend far beyond their immediate purpose of achieving the best possible management of resources.

They have also a social value as the focal point for a broader scope of comprehensive local (as contrasted with regional) planning throughout much of the United States. One reason is that project-type undertakings initiated and sponsored by local organizations generate a degree of public response beyond that inherent in Government programs providing assistance to individual citizens, on the one hand, or strictly Federal public works undertakings, on the other hand. The requirements for organization, educational campaigns, group and mass meetings, and so on generate cooperation and accomplishment that are a basic force in democratic societies.

The development of the Upper West Fork Cypress Bayou Watershed at Plain Dealing, La., illustrates this principle. The stores, streets, and many of the houses of this small city were flooded four times in 1957 and 1958. The 1,300 residents remember going to the post office in boats. Storekeepers shoveled silt from their stores. The oil and gas distributor recovered barrels of oil a mile downstream after the flood.

Moreover, the community needed more water for future growth. Youngsters had to go 25 miles away to swim.

The Lions Club asked a representative of the Soil Conservation Service to explain the new Public Law 566 pro-

gram. His analysis looked like the answer to the city's problems and those of farmers on the West Fork watershed. A citizen's group in Plain Dealing cooperated with the local soil conservation district in preparing an application for assistance. The application was approved by the State soil conservation committee, and on November 21, 1956, the Soil Conservation Service authorized planning of the watershed. SCS sent a planning team of specialists—an engineer, hydrologist, geologist, and economist—to work with the local SCS work unit staff in surveying the 5,500-acre watershed, its soils, runoff, flood history and damages, and water supply potential.

The city wanted flood protection, water supply, and recreational developments. Farmers wanted more productive farms. The planners, working with local committees and district supervisors, developed a plan for conservation treatment—terraces, pasture improvement, woodland management, and other practices on all the 4,680 acres of watershed lands outside of the city. They also planned three floodwater-retarding structures. They added storage for municipal water supply in one of these structures and for fish and wildlife (recreational) development in another structure.

The plan was completed, agreed to by local organizations and SCS, and authorized for operations on March 25, 1958. All of the reservoir structures were completed by March 1961, and 80 percent of the conservation practices have been applied on the farms.

Plain Dealing passed a bond issue of 42 thousand dollars to cover costs of land, easements and rights-of-way, municipal storage, and facilities for recreation with only one dissenting vote. The Louisiana Department of Public Works furnished engineering services valued at 11,250 dollars and contributed to the costs of construction. The estimated non-Federal cost for the project was 159,900 dollars; the Federal cost was 315,697 dollars. Citizens made various contributions.

Roads to the lakes were built and blacktopped by the Bossier Parish Police Jury across rights-of-way donated by local citizens. A local construction company donated the use of its work crews and equipment in clearing and leveling the lakeshore and picnic ground. Prisoners in the county jail cleared the underbrush and other debris from the recreational area. Boy Scouts piled the brush and planted grass. The Lions Club built a lifeguard tower. When a problem arose concerning an easement, seven Plain Dealing citizens went together and bought an 80-acre tract of land to clear it up.

Swings, slides, and a merry-go-round were built by two partners in an automobile agency at no cost to the town. The town council appropriated funds for a boat landing ramp, an enclosed swimming area, and a steel diving platform. Other businesses built picnic tables and benches.

The city in 1963 owned 60 acres, part of which is adjacent to the lakes and available for recreation. Women's clubs set up budgets for developments around the lakes. The American Legion shared the costs of a bathhouse.

As many as 3 thousand persons have used the lakes in one day for swimming, boating, picnicking, and fishing. In November 1962, a 5.5-pound bass was caught in Lake Plain Dealing, which was stocked by the Louisiana Fish and Wildlife Service.

The whole project has stimulated community spirit. The Plain Dealing Development Association was organized as an outgrowth of the watershed project. The association has made plans to construct a rest home for older persons which the availability of an additional supply of municipal water from one of the reservoirs has made feasible. The president of the association commented, "Every inquiry we get from prospective industries asks about recreational facilities for its employees."

A LARGE BODY of new State legislation (198 laws in 41 States since 1955) authorizing the formulation of local districts of several kinds for the conservation and development of land and water in small watersheds makes watershed projects the nucleus for planning for local economic development, community improvement, and rural areas development.

State agencies and committees have been established to review, approve, and recommend applications for assistance in watershed projects. A field force of Soil Conservation Service and other Federal agency and State technical specialists and administrative personnel has been developed. With some supplementation or adaptation, such a field force could rapidly expand the scope of planning and execution of more projects of even broader scope.

The further perfection of locally coordinated planning with Federal and State assistance is one of the challenges of our times. It may be a substitute for more centralized Federal or regional planning.

CARL B. BROWN *was Deputy Assistant Administrator for Watersheds, Soil Conservation Service, the Department of Agriculture. After serving with the Virginia Geological Survey, the United States Soil Survey, and the Geological Survey, he joined the Soil Conservation Service in 1934, in which he served until his death in 1963.*

For further reading:
Allan, Philip F., and McKeever, Ivan, "Multiple-Purpose Developments in Small Watersheds." *Transactions of the 27th North American Wildlife and Natural Resources Conference*, Wildlife Management Institute, Washington, D.C., 1962.
Economics of Watershed Planning, G. S. Tolley and F. E. Riggs, editors. The Iowa State University Press, Ames, 1961.
Kneese, Allen V., *Water Resources; Development and Use.* Federal Reserve Bank of Kansas City, December 1959.
U.S. Department of Agriculture, *Land and Water Resources. A Policy Guide.* Land and Water Policy Committee, 1962.
—— *Small Watershed Projects Under the Watershed Protection and Flood Prevention Act.* Program Aid 392, May 1959.
—— *Water*, the 1955 Yearbook of Agriculture, U.S. Government Printing Office, Washington, D.C.

FRANK T. BACHMURA

DEVELOPMENT COMMISSIONS
IN COMMUNITIES

EVERY community in the United States wishes to better itself economically. Development commissions help to do this. Through organized effort, community leaders can form a commission, which becomes whatever the group wishes to make of it: Something private or public, or both; something large or small. But whatever it does and however it operates, its overall purpose is to improve the economic well-being of the community.

The development commission may represent an entire State and be supported by public funds, as is the Arkansas Industrial Development Commission.

It may be organized for a specific purpose, like the encouragement of vocational training. It may be confined to one community, supported largely through private effort.

Local development commissions do a lot to improve the local economy. All too often, though, the commission may believe its mission is only to attract new industry. For many rural communities, such interpretation can lead only to frustration. More imaginative leadership will discover its role to assess and offset the many and varied economic and social costs to a community when people leave it to work in a city.

What are the costs?

First are the expenses of shoes, bluejeans, tricycles, hamburgers, crayons, books—a million items a family pays in bringing up the children and the costs that cannot be measured when the young people move to greater opportunities, the parents are deprived of the company and comfort of their children, and the children lose the guidance of their parents.

Then come the community's costs for education, recreation, health—the investments in children and people, which, when the economically productive years arrive, go to the place where the person takes up residence. The free movement of individuals is vital to us from political and economic points of view, of course, but when large proportions of the youths of rural communities leave for employment in cities, economic pressure rests on the local governmental unit.

The local government's costs derive from a narrowing of its tax base. As the number of people in a rural community drops, the basic costs of government per family go up (or its functions go down). The same principle applies to many community services: A drop in church membership places a greater obligation on the remaining members; a drop in the number of persons utilizing medical and hospital facilities has a like effect.

Private enterprises, too, are subject to influences from a decline of population. Even when the aggregate income does not decline but the number of buyers diminishes, the volume of sales of at least some local enterprises will fall, especially the commodities and services closely related to population— the number of haircuts, the number of movie admissions, the amount of money spent for food, and so on.

THE HELP a development commission can give depends on the commission itself, the local situation, and the permissive legislation of the State.

Basically, the function of a commission is to discover unfilled local economic potentialities and to bring them to the attention of entrepreneurs and business managers.

Often the potentials may be appropriate for public or private investment.

If the potentiality is most appropriate to public investment, the development commission can use its services to inform the local community and generally to publicize the usefulness of the specific public investment. Thus an adequate water system may permit new firms to buy fire insurance at economic rates as well as permit more advanced production processes. New water and sewage systems in Heber Springs, Ark., and Winder, Ga., indicate the fruition of such efforts. New port facilities in Saxman, Alaska, will permit that area to expand.

In the case of the private investment, the sources for potential economic development are so varied that most of the activity of the commission leads to understanding the needs of the new industry in the light of local needs and conditions. These examples will indicate something of this variety: A peat moss plant in Jonesport, Maine; a fish processing plant in Apalachicola, Fla.; a packing company in Greenfield, Ohio; an athletic equipment firm in Red River County, Tex.; a cedar fencing plant in Littlefork, Minn. All of these have been encouraged by local development groups in cooperation with the Area Redevelopment Administration.

The most universal of the underutilized resources in rural areas is that of underutilized human capacity.

Throughout broad reaches of American rural areas, the economic rewards to workers of equivalent skill is far less than the rewards to those located in urban centers, even if one allows for income in kind, such as homegrown food and fuel, and for the advantages of climate and scenery.

Considerable effort to equalize the incomes of farm and nonfarm people has been put into national farm programs for more than a generation, but it is evident that the widespread outmovement of population from agriculture stems from basic economic causes. The movements from rural areas are voluntary and are reversible. People are free to return, and many do. Some maintain ownership of their unutilized farmland in anticipation of cyclical changes in industrial employment. The overwhelming net balance of outmovement rather than inmovement is an indication of the economic superiority of urban employment. Free and independent actions of many individuals give us the surest appraisal of the economic worth of employment alternatives open to them.

The pattern of population mobility is clear enough. Single persons move more freely than married people and parents of young children. The costs of moving are less for unmarried people, as are the costs of misinformation about job opportunities. The younger person may be considered more adaptable by an employer. The older person may put greater strain upon the firm's retirement system, and seniority rules may keep him out of a job or may make the continuity of his work less certain. Education also generally is important. The high school graduate can expect more alternatives than the dropout.

Studies of employment attributes among rural people disclose that they do not have the educational opportunities readily available to urban people. Area vocational schools, organized under the National Defense Education Act, in such States as Louisiana, Minnesota, and North Carolina provide an unparalleled way of bringing greater opportunities within the reach of country people.

The Manpower Development and Training Act of 1962 recognized the need for training and education among rural youths and adults. The act provides for the education and training of rural persons, including allowances to them and their families while training. It permits subsistence payment for training while away from home.

The act no doubt will be an inducement to industry to relocate in the country, for it provides a way to develop specialized skills among adults and encourages development of adult education, in which our general educational system has had only a small part in comparison with the need.

Nevertheless, many businessmen are unaware of the number and capacity of workers available in rural sections. The manager of a factory, accustomed to utilizing unemployment data as an indication of the availability of labor, may be unaware of the availability of adequate labor force for industry in rural areas.

Rural women generally do not have the access to outside employment open to urban women, and in many places their potential contribution to the labor force remains untapped. In some communities that have attracted only apparel and textile industries, rather than a diversified and balanced industry, the participation of women in nonagricultural employment exceeds that of men, but nevertheless the general proposition that women have less opportunity for outside employment remains true. Development commissions may well direct their efforts therefore to expanding their industry mix so as to provide opportunities for both men and women.

THE DEVELOPMENT commission can make data on availability of workers known to potential employers. There comes to mind a leaflet issued periodically by the Employment Security Commission of North Carolina. It has a map that shows recruitable labor for industrial development by counties and a summary of the groups of actual and potential jobseekers. The commission offers to help local community groups and individual employers in making labor surveys.

Another type of service surveys employment aptitude. The United States Bureau of Employment Security and the Departments of Labor of Arkansas and Mississippi have made experimental surveys in those States. The results were useful to businessmen who were looking for new locations and workers. The Arkansas survey has led to promising development in the Gassville area.

Efforts of development commissions to measure the size and skills of the available labor force are useful to the Nation and the community. State participation in providing such information facilitates and expands the efforts of the commission, but a community can do it by itself. The filing of such information in the form of a registered community audit constitutes a positive first step. These audits, used by the Industrial Development Research Council, are filed with the development organizations of at least 25 States.

Development commissions must consider—in terms of costs—other productive inputs than that of the work force. Information about costs and cost advantages of a given location are crucial to the businessman's decision to relocate.

Roads, railroads, airlines, telephone, and telegraph connections are important. For example, if a trouble-shooting consultant is needed, a delay in his arrival may cost the firm a large sum. Transport schedules are important in the production or marketing process of a firm and industry. A firm that must be able to deliver its products to a distant point at the opening of the following day's business must be able to count on overnight transportation service.

A town with good communications and transportation has an advantage; one that lacks them should find ways to improve what it has. A reduction of the time-cost of transportation can provide many rural areas with production opportunities—for example, the production of baked goods and other commodities of everyday consumption, which can be produced in country towns for fast shipment to cities.

The transportation and communications costs associated with the plant site itself may be decisive to particular types of firms. Various production systems require a railroad siding; others, like paper production, may require a riverbank. The community that has a responsive development commission aware of the locational requirement of specific firms will find such land parcels and have them ready for an industry. Community leaders in Clarksville, Tenn., have encouraged development by an awareness of this need.

Frequently the consolidation of a number of small holdings into a larger parcel is indicated. It is possible for a development commission to survey likely parcels, obtain purchase options, and have all legal impediments removed in anticipation of a location decision by a firm. When the firm is ready to make such a decision, the avoidance of delays of any sort is in the interest of the community.

The availability of adequate and inexpensive local services is always a point in a community's favor—plenty of electric power, dependable water supplies, and perhaps water of a certain chemical composition for specific industries. The Tennessee Valley Authority area is an example.

The development commission will also be in a position to counsel the prospective firm on special legal matters that affect the traditional production method. For example, State restrictions on the employment of women for more than 8 hours a day present a particular problem for industries confronted with seasonal peaks of demand, particularly in the case of a perishable commodity. It may mean the hiring of a larger number of employees or it may entail the hiring of male employees. Usually the necessity of a shift either way adds to the firm's cost of doing business.

THE WHOLE QUESTION of the costs of nonlabor inputs comes to a consideration of capital availability and capital cost. This means that the availability of bank lending facilities in sizable amounts and at low rates of interest becomes important. Even more, the functioning of the capital markets for bonds and stocks and the prospective firm's access to these markets are important. The Louisville Industrial Foundation, organized in 1916, has functioned successfully by providing capital funds on a businesslike basis to new and expanding firms.

Because of the relative inability of both small and new firms to obtain risk capital, many States have enacted permissive legislation to offer special inducements to attract industry. Although it is conceivable that States might offer special inducements with respect to the cost of labor input, national minimum wage legislation tends to prevent it. Even without this influence, industrywide collective bargaining in many important industries establishes an effective minimum wage in these industries on a nationwide basis. To a certain extent, States with the so-called "right-to-work" laws sometimes do offer a limited special incentive. By and large, the relative inability of States to offer special labor cost opportunities directs the States' attention to the use of capital inducements of one form or another.

THIS HISTORY of local special inducements generally rests upon the enactment of permissive legislation which will enable local communities to incur debt, forgive taxes, or construct production facilities for private use, when these acts are in the general public interest. These activities modify the taxing and credit powers of the community in some way. One of the earliest of these is the Balance Agriculture With Industry plan in the State of Mississippi.

The community can also make efforts to construct facilities or to acquire land for a prospective firm. Sometimes these acquisitions may be made with the capital available to the community from general taxes, but mostly such funds are insufficient. The community may then wish to obligate its credit capacity, which is permissible in more than a dozen States. In some States, like Kentucky, the bonds may not obligate the general taxing powers of the community but will depend on the income received by rentals from the community-owned plant.

Still another inducement is the forgiveness, in whole or in part, directly or through rebate, of rents on a community industrial facility. At least nine States permit this. Frequently these facilities may be "shell" buildings suitable for adaptation to a wide variety of production processes. The incentive might take the form of financing a railroad spur or other utility extension. The construction of ordinary public facilities, such as streets and sewers, does not depend upon the enactment of permissive State legislation in most cases. In the region served by the Tennessee Valley Authority special opportunities appear in the form of cheaper electric power.

The history of special inducements to low income and other depressed areas has now been incorporated into Federal law with the Area Redevelopment Act. For agricultural areas more profoundly affected by technological progress than other areas, this is fortunate. The act provides for the lending of funds on a businesslike, yet advantageous, basis for public and private facilities. Moreover, outright grants may be made for the construction of public facilities. The Office of Rural Areas Development in the Department of Agriculture will take the initiative to help organize a local development commission and to formulate an overall economic development plan—necessary steps for obtaining a loan or a grant. However, the act applies only to designated areas.

The Small Business Administration makes advantageous loans to individual businesses in any community. Those communities not eligible under the Area Redevelopment Act thus have an added incentive to learn of the SBA's activities, particularly when local capital availability is a problem.

As a general proposition, loans for the purpose of relocating existing industry may not be obtained from Federal sources. Financing for this type of local development hinges upon local governmental or private sources.

DESPITE THE impressive array of governmental services available to the community, the development commission must ultimately depend upon its own sense of responsibility. Only the community can see the full panorama of local opportunities. Its initiative and imagination are the keys to the start of a vital development program. Once seen, these objectives can be realized only by hard and persevering effort by the community.

FRANK T. BACHMURA *heads the Rural Renewal and Development Investigations of the Economic Research Service, the Department of Agriculture.*

HOWARD L. HILL

PUBLIC RURAL RENEWAL
IN COMMUNITIES

MANY rural counties are not participating in the general economic growth and are in need of a broad program of development to improve farm incomes, provide employment, improve community services, and train people for better employment. This broad approach involves planning and financial and technical assistance and has been inaugurated in a number of States through local, State, and Federal cooperation.

More than 900 counties, of which more than 750 are rural, have been designated as redevelopment areas by the Area Redevelopment Administration, an agency established in the Department of Commerce.

Primary responsibility for assisting rural areas designated as redevelopment areas is with the Department of Agriculture. It carries out this responsibility through the Rural Areas Development program. Committees of local citizens have been organized in 1,700 counties to prepare programs for economic development in their communities and to plan specific projects. The aim is to use human and natural resources better and to bring new opportunities to rural communities.

The Food and Agriculture Act of 1962 provided new strength to rural development. It authorized the Department of Agriculture to give tech-

nical assistance and make loans to local public agencies designated by the Governor or State legislature to carry out rural renewal projects, so as to create conditions that attract investment and encourage individual as well as community enterprise.

Rural renewal gives the residents themselves an opportunity to take the lead in identifying and correcting the conditions that contribute to community deterioration, as reflected in the uneconomic use of land, inadequate community services, outmigration of young people, and high unemployment among people remaining in the community.

Some areas need broad programs of economic development. Others can concentrate on specific situations, such as community facilities, housing, enlarging family farms, shifting land from farming to other uses, or provid-

419

ing more jobs locally through industrial and business expansion. In all, attention can be given to improved education and vocational training, without which measures to improve job opportunities are likely to be ineffective and people from the area will be at a disadvantage in seeking employment elsewhere.

The Rural Areas Development program makes available to the community the technical assistance, credit, and cost-sharing assistance of agencies in the Department of Agriculture.

Locally, a rural areas development committee can draw on a Technical Action Panel, sometimes designated as TAP, whose members represent agencies of the Department.

A basic tool in planning for rural renewal and development is an inventory that provides information about the people, the organization of farms, and the use and capabilities of the land, housing, community facilities, local business and industry, and job opportunities in the area. Such an inventory makes possible an analysis of needs and potentials and the directions of economic development.

A CHRONIC condition in many low-income farm sections that is especially difficult to change is the small size of farms and the increase in idle land.

Although number of farms in most low-income areas has declined, the increase in the size of farms has been moderate.

Several factors bear on this situation. The shortage of capital among farmers in the low-income farm areas is great and would, in itself, prevent many of them from acquiring additional land and other farm resources. The rate at which changes in farm size occur also is influenced by the number of part-time, retirement, or residential farms. Farms in this category that are withdrawn from agriculture generally are small, but, if they are numerous, they can seriously hinder individual efforts to assemble tracts of farmland into farms of adequate size.

WHAT CAN be done through local efforts to bring about adjustments in farm size and land use?

It is important, first, to determine if existing credit and technical assistance services are adequate and if these services, in themselves, hold possibilities for bringing about the changes sought by the community.

But additional action, planned and carried out in the community, may be needed if any significant improvement is to be made. Several kinds of measures can be suggested. These could range from empowering public bodies to make direct changes in ownership and use of land to efforts by local groups to bring about changes in land use through voluntary cooperation of landowners and farm operators.

An example of direct action would be the purchase by a public body of idle or underutilized land to be consolidated into adequate farms and resold or leased to local farm families. Land not suited for farming could be acquired for conversion to forestry, public recreation areas, or other public uses, and retained in public ownership.

A major obstacle to this approach would be the large initial capital outlay for the purchase and development of land. Some of these costs could be recovered from sales and rentals of the land. Other land retained in public ownership would represent a substantial fixed investment, an important consideration in communities with rising expenditures for schools, roads, and other local services. Thus the financial burden alone could rule out land purchase as a device for rural renewal in many communities or may require that such a program be operated on a small scale unless supplemental financial assistance could be obtained from other sources.

A variation would be to empower a local public body to enter into long-term leases with owners of small holdings or other land. Landholdings acquired could be reorganized into adequate family farms or combined with existing farms and subleased to farm families. Land not suited for agriculture could be developed for public use. This approach would eliminate the financial burden of land purchase. Management responsibilities would be great, however, as landowners would want safeguards for property values and rentals in return for entering a long-term contract and agreeing to a sublease.

An approach of this type has been taken in western range areas. Cooperative grazing associations or other quasi-public groups have leased both public and private land, which then is operated for the benefit of members of the grazing association. Although the techniques are applicable mainly in range areas, the experience demonstrates how leasing can be used to make changes in land use without land buying.

Many communities will seek means that are less involved. One such avenue is to empower a committee to act as an intermediary between landowners and farm operators or others who would use the land and assist them in arriving at equitable and secure leasing arrangements or satisfactory purchase arrangements. Model contracts and leases that recognize the interests of both landowners and operators could be prepared and made available for use. This was done by TVA foresters and representatives of a forestry firm who prepared a model long-term forest management contract. The model contract takes account of the interests of the owner and the management firm, and gives both an incentive to manage the land as a long-term business enterprise.

Much the same approach, which involves working with landowners and others who might make use of the land, could be applied elsewhere.

New York, for example, has a program in which an organization of landowners, sportsmen, and county officials can enter into cooperative agreements for recreational use of private land. Agreements are made with owners of adjoining properties, which then are managed as one hunting area. For opening their land and following certain wildlife management practices,

landowners are provided technical services, planting stock, police protection, and other services.

Still another approach, which is used to control land use in urban areas and increasingly so in rural areas, involves the application of measures such as land use planning, zoning ordinances, acquisition of easements or special interests in land, and tax measures. Each of these measures offers a means of guiding changes in land use that is appropriate for certain conditions.

The foregoing examples are not offered as an exhaustive listing of measures that can be used to get changes in land use. Several considerations govern whether these or other measures would be appropriate and effective. Some of the most important considerations are the capacity of the community to make satisfactory adjustments, the potential for creating new economic opportunities on and off farms, the financial resources available for renewal and development, and the leadership and participation that residents will give.

ACTION to bring about areawide improvement in farm size and land use has economic and social implications for the whole community that warrant attention when plans for land use are being prepared.

A careful consideration should be given to those circumstances under which people own or occupy land and to the effect that particular measures will have on them.

Some rural districts have many retired farmers and part-time farmers. Many of them cannot participate very much in local development because of age, lack of special skills, or physical handicaps—often the very reasons why they do not move away. Local rural renewal programs affecting their holdings can create serious personal hardships for the occupants.

Additional measures are needed to aid them in their present situation or to minimize the personal difficulties of relocation. These steps might include improved housing and community facilities, training for nonfarm employment, assistance in relocating, compensation for improvements left, and related efforts to create new economic opportunities for people.

Local public rural renewal programs aimed at enlarging small farms, consolidating small landholdings, making changes in land use, controlling land use, or other measures to achieve more efficient use are long-term in nature. Such programs require a more formal type of organization with appropriate legal status, powers, sources of financing, and staff than the local committee type of organization possesses. However, a local committee can provide a valuable service by making a determination of the community's needs and recommending courses of action to be carried out by a local public body that possesses the power needed to plan and carry out programs.

Every State has authorized the formation of special-purpose districts that operate in some phase of resource use and management. These include official planning and zoning boards, and special-purpose bodies, such as soil conservation districts, small watershed districts, drainage districts, flood control districts, park and recreation districts, and many others that have been granted powers by the State legislature and authorized to carry out certain public projects. In total, their responsibilities cover a wide range, but as they now exist few could carry out comprehensive rural renewal programs involving land use planning, changing land ownership and use, and provide the services needed to support the broader aims of area development.

Few States have enacted legislation that is directed to renewal of rural areas. Ohio enacted laws in 1959 granting broad authority to county commissioners to carry out county renewal measures in areas outside the corporate limits of municipalities. County renewal projects may be undertaken to clear or prevent slums and for rehabilitation or conservation when in accordance with a county renewal plan

approved by the board of county commissioners. Among the powers granted to the county board for planning and carrying out renewal measures are the powers to acquire real estate and dispose of it by sale, lease, or transfer; enter into contracts; accept financial assistance; and borrow money.

Zoning powers are rather widely available to local governments, and in some rural areas this technique is being used to guide future land use. In several States, including California, Hawaii, Illinois, Indiana, Iowa, Kansas, North Dakota, Utah, and Pennsylvania, exclusive farm zoning districts have been established. These are areas restricted to agricultural purposes and related activities. They bar nonfarm residences and require minimum tracts ranging between 5 and 80 acres or more. Zoning is also being used in rural areas for conservation purposes, flood protection, preserving open-space areas, and encouraging recreation development.

Other means of guiding or changing overall land use and development in rural areas are not employed widely.

Much of the planning for rural areas has been concerned with production needs and adjustments and with community or regional resource management problems. With the exception of contractual restrictions employed by various land retirement programs, however, planning and land use control in rural areas have involved minimal restrictions on farm operations and land use.

The impact of urban and industrial growth on rural communities has focused attention on the need for land use planning in rural communities. Rural renewal can serve this purpose. It need not be limited to means of reorganizing farms and land use. It can be extended to a broad range of situations.

HOWARD L. HILL *is an agricultural economist in Land Tenure Investigations, Land and Water Branch, Resource Development Economics Division, Economic Research Service.*

C. B. GILLILAND

TECHNICAL SERVICES
IN PLANNING

HELP in the work of drafting plans for economic and social development is available in most of the 3 thousand rural counties in the United States. Immediate help can be had from a group of experts who compose the Technical Action Panel (TAP) of the Rural Areas Development (RAD) program of the Department of Agriculture. The local supervisor of the Farmers Home Administration is the chairman of the group, which includes representatives of the Soil Conservation Service, Agricultural Stabilization and Conservation Service, Forest Service, and other agencies of the Department.

They work with the county agricultural agent and the county planning commission (in counties that have them), and can furnish much of the technical services needed in developing an area plan, or Overall Economic Development Program (OEDP).

As the first step in an OEDP, the problems, ideas, and suggestions of all residents of the community are recorded. It need not at first be a perfect master plan, with which everyone agrees, but it is a manifest of the principle that everyone should participate in community improvement.

Attention is paid also to the phases of State and national policies and programs that apply to the community and region. In order to get help from outside the county or State, the planning must be consistent with State and Federal programs. It would not be wise, for example, to develop a plan that contains items contrary to the maintenance and improvement of family farms or contrary to established ideals of conservation.

The community committee very likely will include representatives of the county health department, the department of vocational education, chamber of commerce, labor organizations, and utilities and clergymen, lawyers, farmers, bankers, and others. Each of them has special knowledge, skills, and outlook that will insure a rounded, complete, and sensitive plan.

A valid core of a development program or plan is a trading center, a watershed, a small river basin—a unit of geography or economics small enough to handle, big enough to permit a range of projects, uniform in opportunities, homogeneous in loyalties.

GETTING OUTSIDE help is by no means the first order of business. Local initiative comes first. The people in the community or county or area have to make the first move. Thereafter various agencies of the Federal Government will be ready and willing to help.

The community can call also on the development and planning commission in its State, the land-grant university, farm organizations, and the State wildlife and conservation commission. Other groups may be able to furnish professional help also.

All States and territories have economic development agencies, which have such names as department of commerce, development commission, department of planning and development, department of conservation and economic development, and division of resources. Many States also had additional planning work in progress in 1963 under the publicity and parks commission, the State housing authority, and State university bureaus of business and public research.

Some States can give financial assistance for community or area development. In 1962 there were development credit corporations in 13 States and development authorities in 12 States. Twenty-two States had legislation allowing local government bodies to issue industrial building bonds.

About a thousand designated areas can get technical assistance in evaluating their problems and potentials for development from the Area Redevelopment Administration (ARA), of the Department of Commerce. This agency was created to administer the program authorized in 1961 by the Area Redevelopment Act, whose primary purpose is to assist designated areas by the creation of new jobs for people. The areas are designated primarily because of high unemployment [5(a)] or low farm income or underemployment [5(b)]. Requests for help under this act should go from the local or-

ganization through State RAD committee, the ARA representative, and the Governor's office. The latter forwards the requests to the Department of Commerce in Washington, D.C.

The Area Redevelopment Administration requires that a local organization submit for ARA approval an Overall Economic Development Program for an area, whether urban or rural, that wants to qualify for certain financial assistance under the congressional act that established ARA.

CITIES, TOWNS, and counties can obtain aid under the planning assistance program of the Urban Renewal Administration, Housing and Home Finance Agency. The program, sometimes called the "701 Program" because it is authorized by section 701 of the Housing Act of 1954, amended, offers aid in financing planning studies, including studies of economics and population, that are needed in preparing an OEDP.

The local or area group may find it necessary to employ a qualified individual or organization to assist in an analysis of the situation and point up the opportunities for development. Many qualified planners are available. Advice should be obtained from the chairmen of the State RAD committee and the TAP, or the head of the State planning commission, before contracting for assistance in planning. The needed work often can be done or the information obtained at little or no cost to the community. If a study or outside planning assistance is needed, however, qualified individuals should be engaged so that the community may move ahead with its development plan.

If local funds are available to pay for the services of professional consultants, the names of reliable individuals and firms may be obtained from the State university, State development and planning commission, and the National Planning Association in Washington, D.C.

A word of caution: A community should not buy a readymade plan, which purports to be adaptable to any community but which does not take into account the local resources, conditions, and characteristics of the people in the area. Outside assistance is good if it improves and extends community effort, but it should not make an outsiders' program out of what has to be a community's own OEDP.

A KNOWLEDGE of resources is important.

An evaluation of the characteristics of the population in comparison with State, regional, and national norms, changes by age and sex, and employment by industry and occupation, charts the potentials of the work force in the area.

Such information can be had from the State employment service and the Bureau of the Census, in the United States Department of Commerce. To determine employment potentials, local leaders should ask the State employment security office for available data and help in conducting an employment survey.

Information about agricultural resources, including the use of land, economic class and types of farms, the investment per farm, and distribution of farm sales by commodities and similar facts may be available from the Technical Action Panel.

Information about minerals, present and potential water supply, and scenic and recreational resources can be had from such agencies as the State geologist's office, the State development and planning commission, the Bureau of Mines of the Department of the Interior, the Forest Service, and the State conservation commission.

A list of industrial and commercial firms by type and number of employees will likely be available through the local chamber of commerce and the State department of commerce.

Bankers, chambers of commerce, and managers of utilities are among those who can suggest ways to develop further information that is needed to attract and develop commercial and industrial enterprises. The State development corporation and the State university may also be able to give helpful suggestions.

ABOUT COMMUNITY facilities, which should be planned to satisfy present and future needs, area planners may count on help from the local planning engineer, county and State health authorities, and the utilities commission. Other sources of assistance are community facilities services of the Housing and Home Finance Agency in the State or regional office, local health and welfare agencies, the school boards, State departments of education, and the Federal Department of Health, Education, and Welfare.

Advice on financial assistance, including loans, grants, bonding, and taxation, is available from many sources, notably local banks and other lending institutions. They can offer counsel on the need for financial help and perhaps can meet that need. If local financing is inadequate, the RAD committee and TAP can suggest kinds of assistance available to meet present and longtime requirements. If there are no rural area development or area redevelopment committees active in the area, requests for information about financing may be sent to the Department of Agriculture and Department of Commerce, respectively, in Washington.

The Small Business Administration (SBA) can help small business firms by lending money to small businessmen, directly or indirectly; helping small business get a fair share of Government contracts and surplus Government property; providing information and assistance regarding management and by sponsoring research into the management problems of small firms; developing and presenting helpful material in the foreign trade field; providing production and products assistance; and by providing informative publications on subjects of interest to small business.

An essential part of the SBA service is counseling by financial experts. Sometimes the specialist can show that it would be inadvisable or unnecessary to borrow money. If borrowing appears to be the answer to a firm's problem, the SBA may join with a bank or a cooperative in making a loan, or SBA may make a direct loan for the purchase of machinery, equipment, facilities, supplies, materials; working capital; and the construction, conversion, or expansion of a business.

The Small Business Administration provides guidance and advice on sources of technical information about small business management and research and development projects. SBA also provides 25-year loans for local development and plant construction, conversion or expansion (including acquisition of land) to assist a small business concern. Interest rates were 4 percent in 1962 in designated redevelopment areas and 5.5 percent in other areas.

The Area Redevelopment Administration is authorized to provide 4-percent loans up to 25 years, generally for land and construction or rehabilitation of industrial buildings in designated areas.

The Rural Electrification Administration, through its borrower cooperatives, makes loans for electrical equipment, including machinery, wiring, and plumbing, for persons in rural areas who receive electric services through an REA cooperative. The repayment period is usually 10 years, but not more than two-thirds the life of the equipment. The interest rate in 1962 was 4 percent.

LOANS AND TECHNICAL assistance may be obtained for improving farm operations and the development of collateral commercial enterprises.

The Farmers Home Administration has been authorized to make farm-ownership and improvement loans at 5 percent up to 7 years for equipment, livestock, feed, seed, fertilizer, other farm and home operating needs, and refinancing of chattel debts. The FHA provides 5 percent loans of up to 40

years' duration to enlarge, develop, and buy farms and refinance debts. FHA also makes emergency loans at 3 percent to farmers suffering losses due to natural causes in disaster areas.

The Farm Credit Administration provides low-interest loans of not less than 5 nor more than 40 years' duration to purchase and improve farms.

The Farmers Home Administration provides loans at 4 percent interest, of not more than 33 years' duration, for farmers and other rural residents to purchase or repair homes, farm buildings, and housing for farm labor.

The Housing and Home Finance Agency provides assistance to buy, improve, or rehabilitate homes or rental housing and nursing homes. These services are usually in communities of more than 2,500 population. In addition, they provide low-interest loans to build rental housing for the elderly.

The Veterans' Administration provides loans to qualified veterans to purchase, construct, or improve homes.

The Soil Conservation Service and the Forest Service of the Department of Agriculture give technical assistance in planning for conservation and certain recreation facilities.

The Geological Survey, the Fish and Wildlife Service, and the Bureau of Sport Fisheries and Wildlife, agencies of the Department of the Interior, assist in determining water and mineral resources and give technical assistance in developing and improving wildlife habitats.

Section 701 authorizes Federal grants to supplement State and local funds for studies and other planning work. The grants are made to State planning agencies and, under certain conditions, to a city, other municipality, or county in an urban redevelopment area. Although a local redevelopment area organization is not eligible to apply directly for section 701 planning grants, it can take the lead in obtaining the aid of an eligible official planning agency, or, where none exists, in getting one established.

The program encourages and assists

comprehensive planning for entire areas that have common or related urban development problems and for States and interstate areas. The planning work embraces the basic essentials of sound development. The essentials include economic and population studies; comprehensive planning of land use to guide residential, commercial, and industrial development; and planning the general location of transportation facilities.

Planning assistance grants under section 701 are made to the appropriate State planning agency to finance up to two-thirds of the cost of planning assistance to cities, other municipalities, and counties with a population of less than 50 thousand as well as neighboring rural communities, whose total population is less than 50 thousand. A request for assistance should be submitted to the State planning agency, which makes application to the regional office of the Housing and Home Finance Agency. In States that have no State planning agency, the grant may be made to an agency or instrumentality of State government designated by the Governor and acceptable to the Housing and Home Finance Agency as capable of carrying out the planning function.

Municipalities and counties with a population of 50 thousand or more that are in a designated rural redevelopment area must qualify as a metropolitan area to receive planning assistance under the 701 Program.

The Office of Rural Areas Development (ORAD), Department of Agriculture, may be consulted regarding kinds of technical assistance available to rural areas from the various Federal programs and from other national public and private technical planning services.

OCCUPATIONAL training and retraining needs are important in planning the OEDP. In the ARA-designated areas, funds are available for training or retraining to meet new employment opportunities that become available.

Under the 1962 Manpower Development and Training Act, the Department of Labor, working with the Department of Health, Education, and Welfare, is able to offer training and assistance to the unemployed.

Members of farm families with an annual net family income of less than 1,200 dollars are considered unemployed in the administration of the act. For farm families, it is a key provision of this training program.

Members of these farm families will have the same top priority as unemployed workers in selection for training. First, selections will be for training in skills needed in the labor market area where the farm family lives. Next comes training for skills that are needed in other sections of their State.

Members of these farm families are eligible for any of the training and skill development programs provided by the act. Training may be undertaken only for occupations where the Labor Department has found a need for workers—occupations in which there is "reasonable expectation of employment."

The training will be conducted in schools and on the job in facilities of cooperating organizations. Wherever possible, public education agencies and institutions will be used. However, arrangements may also be made to use private educational institutions.

On-the-job training programs may be set up by States, private or public agencies, employers, trade associations, labor organizations, and other industrial and community groups. The Secretary of Labor will encourage the development of such programs by those groups and set standards for the groups' participation under the act.

The local office of the State employment service interviews prospective trainees to determine their interests, suitability, and aptitudes for training and employment; refers them to a vocational training course or on-the-job program; keeps track of their progress; helps them find jobs related to the training they successfully complete; tells employers about people in training; and arranges interviews with prospective employers.

Career counseling and guidance for youth and adults are needed in most rural communities. The county agricultural agents and the local supervisors of the Farmers Home Administration are sources of assistance in this field. Vocational agriculture teachers and home economists are also available for advice, particularly to the youth. The State universities and the State employment services give assistance in career counseling.

A few of the problems in effectively utilizing technical assistance pertain to the youth on farms. These young people may not receive counsel from their parents on matters pertaining to occupations and education to the extent that urban young people do.

Rural people have a more limited understanding of employment trends, the relative chances youth from rural areas face in getting the best jobs of the future, what educational requirements are, and standards of performance.

A more striking and significant fact is that a relatively smaller proportion of farm youth will be needed and will have the opportunity to become farm operators of adequate family farms.

To insure that the problem of low production and income will not continue to be transmitted through the rural youth into future programs, area development planning should recognize that people not yet old enough for employment require adequate education and training.

Programs for area development need provisions that take into account the fact that youth who are not yet of employment age make up a large proportion of the population in these areas. Good educational opportunities should be a major part of a workable plan.

One problem in developing a plan for community improvement and getting action on such plan is in the attitude of complacency on the part of conservative individuals in the community who resist change.

How often have we heard someone say, "Who wants more dirty industrial plants?" "Who wants more paved roads and streets for reckless drivers to run over our children?" "Who wants more people here in our countryside diluting our rural environment? We like our quiet little community just the way it is!"

Rural renewal involves a complete plan. Just as cities can benefit from urban renewal projects financed in part with Federal assistance, so can rural areas take advantage of new knowledge of planning, new technology in construction and conservation, and progress in transportation and communication through rural renewal projects.

Under authority of the Food and Agriculture Act of 1962, the Department of Agriculture can provide technical assistance and loans to local public agencies designated by the Governor or the State legislature for rural renewal projects.

The loans can be used for forestry, soil and water conservation, flood prevention, and the reorganization of farm resources. Funds may also be used to install roads, parks, water supply and sewage systems, and community buildings related to conservation.

Another object of rural renewal projects is to create conditions that will help attract private industry to communities where incomes are low and unemployment and underemployment are high.

Through the use of technical assistance, rural and urban communities can help themselves.

C. B. GILLILAND, *Deputy Director, Office of Rural Areas Development, the Department of Agriculture, is an agricultural economist with special interest in the economic development of rural areas. He received his undergraduate training at the University of Arkansas and his graduate training at the University of Wisconsin. He has been associated with the Department of Agriculture since 1934 and has worked on programs designed to help rural people.*

ROBERT C. OTTE AND RAYMOND D. VLASIN

DISTRICTS THAT
MANAGE RESOURCES

RESOURCE districts, which are set up to handle enterprises beyond the reach of ordinary government, have been growing steadily in number since they began a century ago. Drainage is an historic example. Groups of farmers recognized that the only way to provide adequate drainage for their individual farms was to make ditches to carry off excess water from a large area having a common drainage problem. County governments had no authorization and usually no funds and staffs to build drainage systems. The places to be drained covered only parts of counties or extended over two or more counties. Laws in many States prevented counties from taxing only those who would benefit from drainage.

The next recourse was to the State legislatures. Local governments have no inherent powers; all are creatures of the State. Their powers and authorized functions are delegated to them by the State, either through the State constitution, by statute, or a combination of the two. The State legislatures could do one of two things. They could grant counties the additional authorities and powers needed to carry out drainage operations, or they could pass statutes enabling the creation of drainage districts. Most States have followed the latter course.

Legislatures often are limited by State constitutions or are hesitant to grant special authorities and powers to one or a few counties. People who op-

pose the giving of new authorities and powers can easily prevent legislation that will grant them to all counties of the State.

Much less opposition exists to enabling legislation for the creation of special districts. The law usually provides for petition to a court or county government for the creation of a district, after which a referendum is conducted among the people that will be affected directly. The legislature only makes it possible for a local group to vote themselves the new authorities and powers.

A legislature may have one other choice. If the State has no constitutional restriction, it may pass a statute creating one specific district. Two examples are the Bay Area Air Pollution

Control District in California and the Hartford County (Conn.) Metropolitan District, which provides a water and sewer system. Interstate districts have been created by special acts of the legislatures of the affected States.

A NUMBER of basic legal powers are required by special districts to carry out their authorized functions. They typically are granted power to hire and discharge employees, make contracts, sue and be sued, carry out works of improvement, levy taxes or special assessments, and borrow or issue bonds. Many have power of eminent domain.

Hundreds of general State laws permit the formation of special districts. New laws constantly are being added. (Many laws have been passed and lie unused on the statute books.)

The 1962 Census of Governments reported more than 18 thousand special districts, exclusive of school districts. About one-third of them are concerned directly with natural resources.

Soil conservation districts and drainage districts account for 25 percent of all special districts. Other single-function districts deal with urban water supply, irrigation and water conservation, sanitation, parks and recreation, and flood control. More than 300 districts are concerned with more than one major purpose, such as a combination of urban water supply and sanitation, irrigation, and flood control.

These districts include only those classed by the census of governments as independent. Many other districts, not reported by the census, are tied to State, county, or city governments and lack fiscal independence.

Some districts are not strictly local or designed for local problems. The 1957 census reported 15 interstate districts, including the Breaks Interstate Park Commission District in Kentucky and Virginia, the Lower Yellowstone Irrigation Districts Nos. 1 and 2 in Montana and North Dakota, the Mitchell Irrigation District in Nebraska and Wyoming, the Pathfinder Irrigation District in Nebraska and Wyoming, the Truckee Irrigation District in Nevada and California, and the El Paso Water Improvement District No. 1 in Texas and New Mexico.

DRAINAGE districts date from the early 19th century. Their major purpose is the construction and maintenance of works to remove excess water from land already in farms or to reclaim swampland. They have experienced several periods of major expansion stimulated by high prices for agricultural products, the latest such coming after the Second World War.

The 1962 Census of Governments reported 2,240 drainage districts in 33 States. The 1959 Census of Agriculture reported more than 4 thousand "legally organized public drains." In addition to districts, this included the drainage enterprises of State, county, and township governments. Another 4 thousand individual and cooperative enterprises were reported.

The 1959 census included only organized agricultural drainage operations of 500 acres or more. Of the 40 States considered "drainage States" by the census, 10 have county drainage enterprises, established and constructed as any other public work or local improvement and managed by officers who have charge of all agricultural drainage enterprises in the county. The remaining 30 have drainage districts, and their officers are elected or appointed by the court, county, or other authority that creates the district.

FLOOD CONTROL districts are of two general types. One provides for levees and dikes only. The other provides for all kinds of flood control devices, including dams.

The former, called levee districts, are commonest in the lower Mississippi area, where they originated about 1850. Some other States also provide for their formation, sometimes with drainage districts authorized under the same legislation. The levee districts were designed originally to build levees as a completely local undertaking. County authorities or local courts usually control the organization of levee districts.

The other flood control districts, which have a broader scope and have come into being mostly since 1930, have the predominant purpose of carrying out local responsibilities in Federal projects, usually in the urban areas. They provide rights-of-way and maintain and operate works after their completion. The organization of flood control districts is usually under State authority. The census of governments reported 500 levee and other flood control districts in 30 States.

IRRIGATION DISTRICTS appeared late in the 19th century. All Western States and several Eastern States have laws enabling their creation. Their primary function is to deliver irrigation water to farms, but many maintain drainage works and a few generate hydroelectric power, furnish municipal and industrial water, or provide for flood control.

They vary greatly in size. Some provide water for only a few farms. By contrast, the Imperial Irrigation District in California has more than a thousand full-time employees, an annual revenue of more than 14 million dollars, and an outstanding debt of more than 61 million dollars. There are at least five interstate irrigation districts.

Irrigation districts usually are created by petition of landowners to the county board or court. After public hearings, an election is held to vote on formation. Approval by a State water official or agency often is required. Financing is usually done by issuing bonds and levying special assessments on benefited lands to pay operating expenses and principal and interest on bonded indebtedness.

Most multifarm development of water supply and distribution works for irrigation in recent years has been by the Federal Government. A function of irrigation districts in such development is to enter into and carry out repayment contracts with the Government.

The 1959 Census of Irrigation reported more than 8,700 irrigation organizations in the 17 Western States and Louisiana. The organizations include districts, mutual companies, commercial companies, Federal agencies, and a few city and State agencies. The 557 districts that were reported served approximately 7 million acres, or 22 percent of the total of 31 million irrigated acres and 54 percent of the 12.8 million acres served by all organizations in those States.

SOIL CONSERVATION districts differ from other districts in several ways.

Every State has passed enabling legislation, and approximately 3 thousand districts have been created to cooperate with the Soil Conservation Service of the Department of Agriculture in a nationwide attack on soil erosion and other conservation problems.

The districts have responsibility for developing soil and water conservation programs and for assisting landowners and operators to plan, apply, and maintain conservation measures. Under agreements with the districts, the Soil Conservation Service makes available the services of trained conservationists and supplies facilities necessary for planning and applying conservation measures.

Soil conservation districts in only a few States have power to tax. Most carry out local responsibilities with modest grants from county and State governments. A number of districts have large investments in machinery for installing terraces, waterways, dams, and other conservation measures. Cooperators usually are charged for their use.

Most States authorize soil conservation districts to enact land use regulations by local referendum, but this power seldom has been used. Districts have preferred to use educational means, technical assistance, and voluntary programs to encourage conservation and adjustments in land use.

Since the passage of the Watershed Protection and Flood Prevention Act (Public Law 566) in 1954, many soil conservation districts have acquired new responsibilities as local sponsoring agencies for small watershed projects.

Legislatures of many States have broadened the authorities and powers of the districts to enable them to participate more effectively in watershed projects.

A significant development has been the provision by about one-third of the States for the creation of subdistricts of soil conservation districts to carry out small watershed projects that may cover only part of a district. Several of these States have authorized subdistricts to exercise power of eminent domain, levy taxes or special assessments, borrow, or issue bonds—powers that few States have granted their soil conservation districts.

MULTIPLE-PURPOSE resource districts exist in a number of States. These districts have authority to engage in a number of functions having to do with land and water.

Multiple-purpose districts are of two main types—those that have authority for several specific related functions and those that have broad authorities for development of land and water resources.

Examples of the first type are the water-storage districts in California, which may store and distribute water, drain irrigated land, and distribute electric power. Examples of the latter are the Kansas watershed districts, which may work on projects to conserve soil and water, retard floods, and develop water resources.

The first of the conservancy district enabling acts was the Ohio Conservancy Act, passed in 1914. Two of the Ohio conservancy districts are well known. The Miami, essentially a flood control project, provides protection primarily for Dayton, although flood control structures are located in rural areas.

The Muskingum Valley Conserv-

ancy District, which covers more than 8 thousand square miles, has 14 reservoirs constructed by the Federal Government. Four are single-purpose flood control reservoirs. The others have flood control capacities with storages for other uses, including recreation. More than 20 thousand acres of adjoining hill lands have been reforested by the district. The Corps of Engineers operates the reservoirs, and the district manages recreation facilities.

PARK DISTRICTS can be created in some States under general enabling laws. Some States have created park districts by special legislation. The 1957 Census of Governments reported 316 park and recreation districts in 18 States.

In Illinois they can be established by order of the county judge on petition of 100 voters; in North Dakota, by ordinance of a city or village; and in Washington, by a city council, either on its own initiative or upon petition by 15 percent of the city voters. Districts in Washington may include areas within the city and contiguous tracts.

After approval by referendum, park districts in Illinois may levy taxes and issue bonds. Districts in North Dakota may levy special benefit assessments or special ad valorem property taxes and may issue bonds. In Washington, such districts may levy a special ad valorem property tax and incur debt. They may levy special benefit assessments for improvements of a local nature.

New York, Minnesota, Ohio, California, and Oregon also have general park district laws.

A number of States provide for special districts to supply water for domestic and municipal use, sometimes as the sole enterprise and sometimes in conjunction with sewage disposal. Such districts usually are formed by petition or referendum and are empowered to levy general taxes, special-benefit assessments, service charges, or a combination of these. Ordinarily they are permitted to issue bonds of either the revenue or general obligation type.

A few States have water conservation districts. Such districts can be created in California by popular vote. They may levy special taxes. The Santa Clara Valley Water Conservation District, one example, covers 133 thousand acres. It has constructed storage reservoirs, water-spreading works, and a number of structures by which water is diverted to canals over gravel basins, where it percolates into the ground. Texas provides for water control and preservation districts to control salinity.

Districts that have reforestation as their primary purpose are authorized in Oregon. They can be established by county courts on petition by a majority of owners of logged-off or burned-over land. They may use county funds and may issue bonds after popular approval.

SUBURBANITES and other nonfarm people who move to previously rural sections may find themselves involved in the affairs of existing resource districts, on whose work may depend adequate drainage, the maintenance and improvement of sewage facilities, the solution of erosion problems, the suitability of sites for building, and the installation of septic tanks, and more.

In places in the West where subdivisions are replacing agriculture within irrigation districts, new residents find themselves concerned with questions of water rights, water allocations, and district operations in general. As one likely possibility, the district may supply their water. Irrigation organizations, including districts, in the Western States supplied about 1,450 million gallons a day to residential users in 1959. That was about 3 percent of all deliveries by such organizations. In some districts, water is delivered to city lots for irrigation of gardens, lawns, and trees. Some assess nonfarm property within the district, including business property, not for water delivered but rather to obtain some contribution from urban groups and others indirectly benefited by the irrigation project.

Residents of the urban fringe may discover that the existing government does not provide all the services they demand. The most prevalent deficiencies are in sewage disposal, sanitation, drainage, water supply, and recreation. To obtain such services, they often create special districts, either making use of existing enabling legislation or asking the State legislature for new authorities.

Rural and urban residents also are often involved in "land use districts," which have no separate governmental status and are established under zoning enabling statutes. Such zoning or use "districts" may reserve land for agriculture, residences, business, industry, forestry, or recreation.

Still other, newer land use zoning "districts" are designed to meet problems in floodways and flood plains, conservation of land resources, watershed protection, and reservation of open space.

The zoning "districts" are established and administered by the county, town, city, or village government responsible for enacting the zoning ordinances. These "districts" are areas reserved for certain land uses and should not be confused with the variety of special governmental arrangements we have discussed earlier.

Special districts have been formed to handle problems or achieve objectives that are neither strictly urban nor strictly rural. Some have been in existence many years. Others are new.

Some encompass a variety of problems and objectives, such as regulation of waterflow for boating, canoeing, fishing, mosquito control, and flood control; guidance of urban development; preservation of open space; resource conservation in rural-urban areas; forest restoration and preservation; multiple-use recreation development; protection of private land; and conservation and wildlife education. Others encompass one, two, or three of these and still other objectives.

A few examples of districts formed to deal with rural-urban problems will indicate their varied aims.

THE FOREST PRESERVE District of Cook County, Ill., is one of the oldest of the special districts formed to preserve forest lands in the path of urban expansion. It was authorized by the Illinois State Legislature in 1913 and was organized in 1915.

The Forest Preserve District commissioners can acquire and hold lands containing one or more natural forests or parts thereof for the purpose of protecting and preserving the flora, fauna, and scenic beauties within the district. They can restore, restock, and preserve the forests and lands in their natural state and condition for the education, pleasure, and recreation of the public.

The district is not a park, as that term is commonly used. Neither is it a group of parks. Instead, it is a naturalistic reservation and a forested sanctuary, with recreational facilities for picnicking and related forms of intensive use on the fringes. The natural interiors are accessible only by walking, bicycling, or by horseback riding over established trails. Location of intensive recreation facilities on the exterior and restrictions on mode of travel within the preserves enable the staff to maintain most of the holdings in a primitive state.

The Forest Preserve District is governed by 15 commissioners. Ten are elected at large from the city of Chicago, and five are elected at large from the area outside Chicago, including the cities, towns, villages, and unincorporated places. They are elected as county commissioners, but they also comprise the Board of Forest Preserve Commissioners.

Besides the board, the Forest Preserve District has a staff and an advisory committee, whose policies and plans are approved by the Board of Forest Preserve Commissioners and guide the district staff. The committee confines its activities to policy matters.

The district staff is organized into departments for such activities as engineering, finance, maintenance and operations, forestry, conservation, and real estate. Department heads are given full authority and responsibility and are permitted broad discretion in implementing district programs. The work of the staff is conducted at the general headquarters, garages and shops, and the nine division headquarters located on land held and managed by the district.

More than 47 thousand acres of district lands comprise many tracts of various sizes. They ring the city of Chicago on the north, west, and south and extend throughout the north-south length of Cook County.

Because of their location and the more than 200 miles of highway frontage, the preserves have become unique for their accessibility. Many of the preserves lie within the corporate limits of Chicago and a number of suburban towns. Many of the preserves can be reached by some form of public transportation as well as by auto. It is often said that none of Cook County's population of more than 5 million is more than a 30-minute drive from one of the forest preserves. Access between tracts is provided by the system of public roads that adjoin them and by the trails over bands of public lands that connect them. More than 185 miles of multiple-use trails wind through the natural landscape.

Because many preserve lands adjoin urban developments, private individuals and groups and public agencies have attempted to obtain them for their own uses. The Board of Forest Preserve Commissioners persistently has declined to sever any Forest Preserve properties from the established system for such uses as highways, municipal parks, schools, cemeteries, private lodges, housing developments, and commercial establishments.

Restoration and preservation of forests for public pleasure and recreation are not the only functions of the Forest Preserve District. It develops and maintains a variety of more or less intensive recreation facilities for county-wide use. It has an expanding, broad program of public education. It has a comprehensive wildlife management program. It cooperates with other government units in improving and developing water resources.

For countywide recreational use, it provides more than 115 major picnic centers and many smaller picnic areas on preserves throughout the county. Mostly it provides only the simplest of essential facilities—confined parking spaces, safe drinking water, sanitary conveniences, table and bench combinations, picnic stoves, and receptacles for trash and garbage. Some of the picnic areas have dance platforms and a shelter. All have open spaces, such as meadows, for play. Also for countywide use it provides more than 100 softball diamonds near the picnic grounds; a few large, well-drained playfields, each with several ball diamonds; some golf courses; outdoor swimming pools; places for fishing; a few minor winter sports centers; and a zoological park.

The district's public educational program is designed to teach adults and youths how to make better use of the preserves and obtain greatest enjoyment from them. The program also serves to inform the 15 million annual visitors of what there is to see and of their responsibility in preserving the available facilities.

Members of the staff often take part in television and radio programs to report activities and happenings in the preserves. They also provide films to Chicago television stations, give lectures to adult and youth groups, assist in the preparation of news releases for papers, publish weekly nature bulletins, and operate educational nature centers.

Each year they sponsor field trips and training workshops in conservation, forestry, and natural science for teachers; help train youth group leaders; conduct classroom field trips for hundreds of pupils from the elementary schools; help conduct day camps for more than 20 thousand children; and deliver school lectures to more than 100 thousand pupils of Chicago and Cook County schools.

The wildlife management program includes improvement of habitat for all forms of native wildlife; abatement of stream pollution; and improvement of the quantity and quality of fishing. New lakes have been created and stocked with fish to supplement other preserve waters open to public fishing.

In order to preserve forests and wildlife in their primitive state, hunting, trapping, and molesting wildlife are prohibited. No attempts have been made to remove surpluses, control diseases, or otherwise influence the cyclical fluctuations in any animal populations.

The water improvement and development program has other benefits besides increasing the quantity and quality of fishing. Through cooperative efforts with State and local agencies and the Federal Government, the district was able to construct a chain of lagoons and restraining dikes extending 3 miles through a 900-acre flood plain on the Skokie River. The reservoirs have helped to diminish flood damage to residential and school properties, prevent reversal in the flow of the Chicago River and its discharge into Lake Michigan, and maintain adequate populations of mosquito-destroying fish.

In its efforts to reduce pollution in the Des Plaines River and other streams in the preserves, the Forest Preserve District sponsored a Citizens' Clean Streams Committee. The committee has worked in cooperation with the Sanitary District of Chicago and other local and State agencies toward the elimination of the pollution.

The Forest Preserve District, in cooperation with the Division of Waterways of the Illinois Department of Public Works and Buildings, has engaged in a long-range plan for the improvement of low-flow, boating, canoeing, and fishing conditions in the Des Plaines River. Plans include the construction of several dams, some of which have been completed.

By acquisition of flood-plain lands along streams, the district has provided communities with flood protection. Preserves border along more than 88 miles of rivers and creeks that flow through Cook County. District staff members have reported that when preserve lands along streams are flooded, the damage is small.

Other forest preserve districts have been established in Illinois, although not on the scale of the Cook County Forest Preserve District. Du Page, Kane, and Wills Counties have districts that have acquired lands for forest preserves. A number of other resource districts in Illinois are neither strictly urban nor rural.

FISH AND WILDLIFE management districts in New York are examples of districts that include both rural and urban people. They were authorized by the New York Fish and Wildlife Management Act of 1957.

Previously, several related problems faced landowners, sportsmen, and State and local agencies. Hunting and fishing pressures on lands and waters were increasing. Posting of private lands was widespread. Some owners of unposted premises were unduly burdened. Concentrations of hunters in certain areas were endangering public safety. Relations between landowners and sportsmen were deteriorating rapidly.

The Fish and Wildlife Management Act established a legal framework and a broad State policy within which landowners, sportsmen, and State and local agencies could be brought together in a working partnership. Under the act, the Commissioner of Conservation is charged with establishing not more than 15 fish and wildlife management districts of one or more counties each. These districts include all counties of the State not entirely within cities.

A local landowner, a sportsmen's representative, and a local county supervisor represent each county on the district board and are appointed by the chairman of the county board of supervisors. Chairmen of the county soil conservation district and the local Forest Practice Act Board serve as advisory members without vote. Appointed representatives and advisory members constitute the district fish and wildlife management board. A district supervisor of fish and game, employed by the Conservation Department, assists the district board.

Each of the district boards annually elects from its membership a chairman, vice chairman, and representatives to the State Fish and Wildlife Management Board. The State board consists of two representatives from each of the district boards, at least one of whom is a landowner. Also on the State board are several nonvoting advisory members—the Commissioner of Conservation; the Commissioner of Agriculture and Markets; representatives of other interested State agencies; representatives of farmer, sportsman, and conservation organizations; and heads of educational institutions.

Each district board is authorized to study local wildlife management needs, access requirements for hunting and fishing, and local landowner-sportsman conflicts. It formulates programs of fish and wildlife management practices, which are submitted for approval to the State board and the Commissioner of Conservation. The district board adopts the statement of approved practices and encourages landowners, lessees, and sportsmen within the district to carry out the practices.

To implement the district practices, the act provides for cooperative agreements between landowners and the State Conservation Department. The act also permits great flexibility in agreements that can be made to meet specific local needs.

Agreements have been made with several adjoining owners of relatively small properties which then are managed as one hunting area. In some areas, hunter density is tightly controlled by a permit system. In others, less stringent controls are used. Agreements are made also with scattered individual landowners. Thousands of acres of land have been made available for hunting and fishing by agreements with the owners. For opening land and following certain fish and wildlife practices, landowners are provided technical services, planting stock, a subscription to the magazine, New York State Conservationist, safety zone posting, and police protection.

The fish and wildlife management districts and the Conservation Department also have obtained agreements with owners of large tracts.

One agreement, for example, was made with a paper manufacturer to open company lands to hunting and trout fishing. The agreement also allowed improved access to large areas of State-owned land. An agreement with another paper company provided for cooperative policing, game and timber management, and forestry and wildlife research on the company's extensive timber holdings.

Agreements with the Army opened about 65 thousand acres of the Camp Drum military area to public use.

An agreement with the Forest Service established district fish and wildlife management policies on more than 13 thousand acres of Federal lands. Some New York State forest lands also have been opened to district fish and wildlife management.

Other States—among them Pennsylvania, Connecticut, Delaware, New Hampshire, New Jersey, and Vermont—have programs to open posted lands and improve sportsman-landowner relations.

THE TOWN CONSERVATION commissions in Massachusetts are official agencies of cities and towns. They facilitate local participation and financing of conservation and development of recreation facilities.

A town conservation commission makes inventories of land resources, recommends programs for use and management, coordinates community conservation matters, and prepares informational materials.

A commission may receive gifts of real and personal property in the name of the city or town. It may acquire land

and water rights in fee. It may acquire such lesser interests as development rights, easements, and contractual rights necessary for conservation and utilization of open spaces and other land and water areas within its city or town. It has responsibility for managing the properties.

Members of a commission are appointed by the selectmen, the town or city manager, or the mayor. To finance a commission and its activities, a city or town may appropriate a sum not exceeding one-twentieth of 1 percent of the assessed valuation and not exceeding 15 thousand dollars in any one year. The money may be accumulated in a conservation fund and may be used for planning, land acquisition, and development of resources.

To assist communities to establish conservation commissions, the Massachusetts Department of Natural Resources provides information and guidance on organization and the use of resources and may reimburse a city or town up to 50 percent of the cost of each project that relates to planning and acquisition of land.

Rhode Island and Connecticut have passed legislation to create similar commissions.

THE WESTERN PENNSYLVANIA Conservancy is another of the districts that include rural and urban people. It is not a special governmental unit; it is not attached to a governmental unit; and it does not have access to public funds. Instead, it includes more than 3,200 public-minded citizens of Allegheny County and the nearby counties of Butler, Lawrence, Fayette, Westmoreland, Mercer, and Beaver, who have devoted their time, effort, and money to the conservation and preservation of resources and development of recreation.

The organization has taken a major part in the development of two State parks.

One is McConnells Mill State Park, which preserves the spectacular gorge of Slippery Rock Creek and its wooded hillsides of more than 2 thousand acres.

The second is a State park in Butler County of approximately 14 thousand acres, including a lake of 3 thousand acres. This area, shaped by a glacier 14 thousand years ago, is expected to be the largest recreation-conservation complex in the developing Pennsylvania system. The conservancy has acquired and sold to the State at less than cost more than 2 thousand acres for the park.

The Western Pennsylvania Conservancy also has assembled land for a third State park in the Ohiopyle area of Fayette County. It has obtained options to purchase about 5,400 acres.

Among its other functions, the conservancy has an expanding conservation education program. It has undertaken a study of natural areas in western Pennsylvania to determine which should be preserved.

SEVERAL POINTS need emphasis.

Special districts are not a cure-all for problems of resource management.

They tend to fragment government. If too many special districts are superimposed on the general governments, jurisdictions and functions are duplicated and public awareness of governmental activity becomes difficult. If a district is small, it may not be able to maintain a competent staff or finance necessary improvements.

Taxation and expenditure by one special government for one or a few isolated purposes does not permit the weighing of a number of possible public expenditures one against the other.

Special districts have definite advantages, however. They can be created to provide a service not available from existing governments. They permit decentralization of State authority and State management of natural resources. They can concentrate on a specific undertaking. They can be created to encompass a problem area that does not coincide with the boundaries of existing governmental units. They can be terminated when their job is completed.

Their flexibility and adaptability are demonstrated in the examples we have presented—autonomous units of government, subordinate agencies, quasi-governmental organizations, and private groups operating in cooperation with local and State governments. In this flexibility lies their great potential in meeting new and emerging problems of management of resources.

ROBERT C. OTTE, *Assistant Chief, Land and Water Branch, Resource Development Economics Division, Economic Research Service, is a native of Nebraska. He holds the bachelor of science and master of arts degrees from the University of Nebraska and the doctor's degree from the University of Wisconsin.*

RAYMOND D. VLASIN *is Leader, Resource Institutions Investigations, Land and Water Branch, Resource Development Economics Division, Economic Research Service.*

For further reading:

Bollens, J.C., *Special District Governments in the United States.* University of California Press, Berkeley, 1958.

Ellis, H. H., "Regulation of Water Use in Local Areas by State or Local Governments and Districts." *Water Law and Policy in the Southeast,* University of Georgia School of Law, Athens, 1961.

Economics of Watershed Planning, G. S. Tolley and F. E. Riggs, editors. Iowa State University Press, Ames, 1961.

Frost, S. L., *Ohio's Conservancy Districts.* Ohio Forestry Association, Columbus, 1956.

Kelley, W. R., "Water Conservancy Districts." *Rocky Mountain Law Review,* Vol. 22.

Manual for Town Conservation Commissions. Massachusetts Department of Natural Resources, Boston, 1960.

Smith, R. L., "Districts Affecting Water Use and Control." *Iowa Law Review,* 1956.

Smith, S. C., "Problems in the Use of the Public District for Ground-Water Management." *Land Economics* (August 1956).

U.S. Department of Commerce, "Drainage of Agricultural Lands." *1959 Census of Agriculture,* Vol. IV.

——— "Governmental Organization." *1962 Census of Governments,* Vol. I.

——— "Irrigation of Agricultural Lands." *1959 Census of Agriculture,* Vol. III.

Vlasin, Raymond D., and others, "Facilitating Recreation Development—Part IV." *Potential New Sites for Outdoor Recreation in the Northeast.* ORRRC Study Report 8, U.S. Government Printing Office, Washington, D.C., 1962.

FRED A. CLARENBACH

THE USE OF RESOURCES
AND PROPERTY RIGHTS

IN ANY field of action, a decision to do something is best taken in the light of the means available for the task. The *what* and the *how* are only provisionally separable from one another in the practical affairs of everyday living. When public action is needed to influence development or use of land and water resources, often a decision is delayed overlong because fair and appropriate means for the job do not seem to be available.

There may be general agreement about what is wrong in an existing situation and also a consensus about a more desirable state of affairs, but no sufficient knowledge of instrumentalities and devices for getting from the one situation to the other.

In recent decades, several varieties of new or newly adapted implements of public purpose, for land and water, have come into wider and more effective use by State and local governments and by the National Government. These tools are geared into underlying constitutional powers: The taxing power, the broad spending power, the police (regulatory) power, and the power of eminent domain (to take private property for public purposes with just compensation).

While innovation and adaptation are going on continually, the working instruments need to be chosen carefully and used in appropriate combinations to achieve the goals of public policy under given local or regional circumstances. Effective action with fairness is needed, without too much delay.

This chapter is concerned chiefly with methods of obtaining limited public rights and interests in lands that are to be used for public and private purposes concurrently. The public purposes to be served include land conservation; protection of water supplies; control of water pollution; prevention or reduction of flood damages; preservation of wildlife and fish habitat; provision of access to and protection of areas having special scenic, historic, or scientific value; provision for public access to land and water for various types of outdoor recreation; and (in urban areas especially) to provide open space as a basic "structural" element or as a buffer area or as a firebreak.

Another kind of public purpose in acquiring limited rights may be to forestall development in a given area until broader decisions as to land use plans can be made. Still another might be to get for the public treasury a major increment in land—development—values attributable perhaps to nearby public works.

THE SAME LAND SPACE in or near a metropolitan region often may be used concurrently for several different purposes by different persons. Such multiple use may be not only practically inevitable but also productive of far greater benefits than would accrue from any single use. A farm-forest-marsh-stream-lake-road complex can serve primarily as an agricultural establishment and at the same time can contribute other important values.

It may provide wildlife and fish habitat and thus hunting and fishing opportunities for the farmer and others. A nature trail or a hikers' path might cross a wooded tract. A pleasant landscape or beautiful vista would give enjoyment to the passing motorist.

Conservational management of the land can enhance the contribution of a watershed to downstream water supplies and can minimize siltation of streams and lakes and reduce the chances for floods.

This example of multiple use and varieties of benefits could be expanded, and other illustrations could be elaborated. A more important exercise here, however, is the inquiry into how arrangements can be made to accommodate all the most valuable public and private purposes or as many of them as can be sensibly provided for.

Not everything can be done at the same time on any single piece of land. Some uses are complementary and harmonious, but others may conflict so seriously that there is no possibility of "working things out together." The idea of multiple use provides no universal solution, and very often some uses incompatible with others must be wholly ruled off. Ordinarily such pro-

hibited uses must be allowed on some other land appropriately located.

How to decide what uses are to be located where? Private owners make most of these decisions, of course, but they are made within a system of property law and a framework of regulations designed to protect other private persons as well as various public interests. Moreover, in many areas—urban, rural, or mixed—community and regional land use plans are more and more frequently made and accepted by citizens and by officials as basic guides and aids for public decisions on land use questions.

The broad utility of a carefully prepared and democratically accepted general plan for land use has been demonstrated widely. Some such plan, embodying policy but not a detailed or rigid blueprint, is essential for intelligent public action to influence or control the actual use of land. Uninhibited private action typically does not properly protect public interests, but ill-considered public action may yield other results as bad or worse. Intelligent local and regional planning and effective implementation of plans can yield handsome private and community dividends, tangible and intangible, year after year.

A REASONABLE GENERAL PLAN for land use having been made, the next step is to begin to put it into effect.

The particular devices and techniques for exerting public influence upon or directing the use of land resources are numerous. Differential taxation may be employed in many forms and variations; graduated rates, exemptions, deferment, alternative severance taxes, and similar schemes can operate either to promote or to discourage certain uses of land. Government aid (cash, materials, services) may be given to private landowners to establish, for example, soil-conserving practices or to build water conservation structures. Zoning regulations, subdivision controls, official map procedures (to indicate locations of future streets and roads in order to forestall development in such strips), and other measures may be taken under the police power—which is the power of government to regulate in the interest of public health, morals, safety, or the general welfare. Or a government may hold and manage land in its full ownership, acquired by gift or by purchase from a voluntary seller, or by condemnation with just compensation under the power of eminent domain, or by conquest, cession, escheat, or reversion for nonpayment of taxes.

These ways through which public authorities can influence or control the uses of land—subsidies, zoning and related direct regulations, and public management after purchase or condemnation—are generally known and familiar to most people.

As indicated earlier, however, the chief concern here is with methods of obtaining limited public (property) rights and interests in lands that are to be used for public and private purposes concurrently. An exploration of possible legal devices of this sort must be prefaced by a brief consideration of the nature of property in land.

Property in the legal sense is not a physical thing, and property in land is not the actual land itself. Rather, it is a *bundle of rights* or interests. The bundle comprises a person's rights to possess the land and to exclude others who might want to trespass; powers to sell or otherwise dispose (by gift, lease, mortgage, will, and so on) of whatever rights or interests one may hold; and privileges to use the "owned" land as the "owner" pleases—but subject always to the rights of others who have a legal interest in the land, and subject to "police power" regulation by government, and subject also to the common law of nuisance.

The person who holds the basic "fee simple" title is ordinarily called the "owner," but sometimes his "ownership" may be only nominal because so many rights and interests are held by others. The fee owner may dispose of many different "sticks" from the

"bundle" of rights, and then each holder of a stick has a kind of "share in the property." Thus "property" may be almost infinitely divisible, and the fee owner may transfer especially all sorts of "privileges to use" to many different persons.

A UNIT OF GOVERNMENT (as a legal "person") may acquire certain limited rights of *use*, from private owners, in order to serve important public purposes and needs. This device may prove to be, in some circumstances, a significant alternative to full public ownership or zoning regulation or the "bribe-in-aid," and at times it may be used in conjunction with these other measures.

A leading expert in property law, Norman Williams, Jr., reporting to the Outdoor Recreation Resources Review Commission in 1962, recommended that new State enabling legislation be designed specifically to provide a sound legal basis for a program of joint public-private ownership of open-space land for some purposes.

Mr. Williams proposed: "The statute should authorize three different, and alternative, methods of splitting up the various rights as between public and private ownership:

"1. Conveyance of certain stated rights by the private owner to a public agency, with the private owner retaining the fee; i.e., the typical situation of public acquisition of an 'easement.'

"2. Public acquisition of the fee and lease-back to a private owner of certain stated rights over the land or, alternatively, public issuance of a special use permit for the same purpose.

"3. Public acquisition of the fee and reconveyance to the former private owner of a new type of legal interest in land, consisting of whatever rights are specifically reconveyed. This interest should specifically be made assignable and devisable; i.e., it can both be sold and inherited."

While Mr. Williams thinks that all three methods should be tried out, he suggests that experience may bring out many advantages in the third method.

Under this alternative, the public agency would hold the residual rights, while the reoccupant ordinarily would have all the rights he had ever used. The net cost to the public should be substantially less than that of acquiring and holding the "full bundle" of rights (or the limited right device probably should not be used). In some instances, subsequent conveyance of publicly held rights to private persons could yield substantial gains for the public treasury. Moreover, Mr. Williams points out, "the existence of a sales price at reconveyance will help solve another difficult and important problem—the valuation of the privately held rights for local tax purposes."

WHAT TO CALL the limited publicly held rights is a matter of considerable legal and practical significance.

Mr. Williams strongly advises that the word "easement," widely used by others, be avoided. As he says, the term can correctly be applied only to the first of the three alternatives above. He is much concerned, moreover, with the danger that troublesome and inappropriate common law rules of interpretation will be applied by courts, even though the potentially more bothersome of such rules of easement interpretation can be explicitly disclaimed in the statute.

"Once the door is opened on common law easements," he says, "there is simply no way of knowing when the language in some reported case will be applied to the public detriment. Moreover, there is something a little ridiculous in labeling a grant an easement and then laboriously setting out to disclaim the application of the principal rules of easement law."

He believes that these rights should therefore be referred to by some other term, as "conservation rights and interests" or "statutory rights and interests, as herein defined." Another possibility is to call them simply "public rights" in the property. Whatever the name, there can be no full guarantee that

conservative jurists—or some judges who may mistakenly feel themselves to be truly conservative—will always steer clear of the old ruts of easement law.

In any event, public bodies for centuries have been acquiring and holding rights in land short of the entire "bundle," so that both the general principle and practice are well established.

In a system of private property in land, the public ownership of only limited rights, sufficient to protect and promote recognized community interests, is a conservative instrument of public purpose. Typically, those parts of the "bundle" of rights that account for most of the current market value would remain with or be reconveyed to private owners, and these parts would thus remain taxable as real property on the local tax rolls. This is a great advantage. Private persons remain in possession and regular use of the land, subject to the carefully spelled-out public rights in the property which are important, too. Disturbance to the local economy and fiscal system is held to a minimum. In fact, through intelligent planning and relating of private and public uses, both the private and the public benefits can be enhanced substantially.

Realistic opportunities for such an outcome, of course, do not offer themselves in every square mile of territory on the map. The private-public splitting of property rights is undoubtedly simply an irrelevant device in many areas, where no important purpose needs to be served through it.

Often direct zoning and other land use regulations will meet the public needs, if any, in a better way. In other cases, such as public parks in both urban and open country regions, outright public ownership is almost always the appropriate arrangement. Nevertheless, the potential usefulness of the less-than-fee-simple public holding device is great enough to warrant broad experimentation with it by Federal, State, local, and regional agencies.

Adaptations of the tool should be tried in various combinations with other measures, in different settings and jurisdictions, and for a considerable number of different specific purposes. The power to condemn limited property rights should, of course, be given to selected public agencies along with the power to acquire from willing sellers and donors.

SOME EXPERIENCE has already accumulated, and some of it does not seem to be very favorable for some applications of the easement principle. The National Park Service, for example, reports multiple difficulties in the administration of scenic easements on some of its parkways, and in some localities this type of easement has not effectually served the intended purpose. New private purchasers of land may not be informed about the easement and cut protected trees. Other owners, who do know about and do understand the easement, cut anyway. Still other farmers have quarreled with Uncle Sam and gone to court to settle "whether specified trees and shrubs are mature or immature, straight or crooked, sightly or unsightly, and which thickets can be cleared."

Such experience with scenic easements along parkways in some regions, however, is not at all conclusive as to their possible value elsewhere, nor does this experience have any direct bearing on the question of the usefulness of other types of easements.

The experience of several other Federal agencies with other sorts of easements, in fact, has been considerably more favorable.

The Fish and Wildlife Service has sometimes acquired easements (and at other times fee simple) in pothole regions of the Dakotas and Minnesota in order to preserve such areas for use by ducks and other migratory waterfowl, particularly as breeding places. These wetland easements mean in effect that the owner-farmer gives up his right to drain or to fill the potholes and his right to burn the marsh vegetation. But he retains his right to farm the land by ordinary methods whenever the pothole is naturally dried out. The private owner also sells the Government a right of entry, in addition to the other easement rights. Apparently no major difficulties have arisen from this splitting of pothole rights between farmer and Government, and Mr. Williams found no litigation in connection with these easements.

The Corps of Engineers has a long-established policy of acquiring flowage easements from private owners of land in the emergency spillways that are part of the flood control system in the lower Mississippi River Valley. This type of interest provides a public legal right to flood the lands in the spillways, in emergencies, in order to reduce pressure on levees and generally to lessen the danger of flood disaster in cities and in populated rural territories. The corps often acquires also, on the same spillway lands, a negative easement, which gives the agency a right to prevent residential construction and a right of review over proposed nonresidential structures.

These several limited public rights, ordinarily purchased for substantially less than the cost of fee simple title, are sufficient to achieve particular public purposes in a system for control of floodwaters and reduction of flood damage. The basic rights of ownership that permit agricultural use, subject to emergency floodway use, are left in private hands. The legal basis of public flowage interests is well established, and careful use of such easements evidently does not generate major practical difficulties.

Another use of easements by the Corps of Engineers for some years after 1953 did, however, lead to considerable controversy. Many large reservoirs used for flood control and other purposes, including recreation, have fluctuating water levels and shorelines.

The corps' policy from 1953 to 1962 was to obtain fee title to (*a*) the lands to be permanently flooded; (*b*) additional areas subject to flooding at least once in 5 years (or, alternatively, a strip 300 feet wide measured horizontally from the edge of the permanent pool); and (c) parts of some parcels which, if not wholly acquired, would leave just remnants with the owner.

In practice, when the 5-year flood frequency rule was followed at places where reservoir banks were steep, a narrow strip of publicly owned land afforded little or no space for usable public recreation developments; and the less often used 300-foot rule would usually not yield satisfactory public recreation space.

When flowage easements were taken on other land, somewhat higher and flooded less frequently, the average cost was about three-fourths of the cost of getting the same land in fee simple, but the flowage easement as such did not include a right of public use for recreation purposes. The flowage easement price was high, and the public paid it, but the right of recreation and other uses remained with the private owner of the fee.

A new policy statement approved in February 1962 provides: "Insofar as permitted by law, it is the policy of the Departments of the Interior and of the Army to acquire, as a part of reservoir project construction, adequate interests in lands necessary . . . to assure full realization of optimum present and future outdoor recreation and fish and wildlife potentials of each reservoir." This could mean that less reliance is to be put on flowage easements and fee title obtained oftener in situations where significant public recreational use may be expected.

Examples of the use by Federal agencies of easements for purposes other than conservation are many.

Limited property rights often are acquired in the vicinity of airports to insure enough unobstructed airspace for arriving and departing planes. Clearance easements are also obtained around missile sites to keep out structures that would interfere with radar, among other purposes. Safety easements in zones around missile-launching sites and ammunition storage facilities prevent construction of residences, gatherings of more than 25 persons, or other specified land uses not considered appropriate for such areas. Other special types of easements—trajectory, electronic, avigation—are employed to accomplish particular objectives effectively and at costs lower than the costs of alternative ways of meeting the need.

STATE AND LOCAL governments have long used "limited property" devices to achieve various public purposes, including some of the same objectives sought by Federal agencies in their uses of these tools.

Since 1959 a surge of interest in preservation of open space resulted in new legislation authorizing public acquisition, for recreation and other uses, in California, New York, Maryland, Massachusetts, Connecticut, New Jersey, Wisconsin, and other States.

The California law of 1959 specifically authorized counties and cities to acquire "the fee or any lesser interest or right in real property in order to preserve, through limitation of their future use, open spaces and areas for public use and enjoyment."

Other States have since put similar provisions into their statutes, sometimes specifically extending the broad acquisition authority to units of local government other than counties and cities.

WISCONSIN IN 1961 took a major step in the development of its historic policies in conservation and outdoor recreation. The legislature authorized what is now known as the Outdoor Recreation Act Program (ORAP) to be financed by an additional tax of 1 cent on each pack of cigarettes sold. The authorized program is to be carried out in 10 years at an estimated cost of 50 million dollars.

Because of the broad scope and variety of its provisions, and especially because of its considerable emphasis on public easements and similar limited property rights, the Wisconsin program may appropriately be examined more extensively. It is a promising example of a multiple-lined attack on the problems of preserving open space and providing public recreation facilities.

While the central concern in this discussion is with less-than-fee public interests in land, it is quite important to see how the acquisition of such interests may be fitted into more comprehensive programs.

The Wisconsin act created a State Recreation Committee and gave it the duty to develop and disseminate a long-range plan for the fullest utilization of all the recreational assets of the State and to coordinate related plans of State agencies for acquisition and capital improvement of areas necessary for a statewide system of recreational facilities. The committee must also recommend to each successive legislature the appropriations necessary to accomplish the priorities established for the following biennium. Thus the fundamental idea is that the parts should be made to fit into a sensible long-term whole as this is evolved in detail, period by period.

The Wisconsin Legislature divided the authorized expenditure of 50 million dollars approximately as follows: State park and forest recreation areas, 33 million dollars; fish and game habitat, 9 million; youth conservation camps, 2.5 million; protection of scenic resources along highways, 2 million; new lakes (with Federal watershed program), 1.5 million; State aids for acquiring rural lands for metropolitan recreation and recreational facilities in county forests, 1.5 million; and tourist information centers and planning and surveys, 712 thousand.

By far the largest part of the funds to be spent for acquiring property rights in land will be used for outright, fee simple purchase. This is the strong backbone of the acquisition program. Governor Gaylord Nelson proposed, however, that a substantial share be spent for easements. Over the 10-year period, the Governor suggested, about 7.5 million dollars could wisely be put into easements in these categories:

Park and forest recreation areas, 3.3 million dollars; fish and game habitat, 2.4 million; and highway scenic resources, 2 million.

Governor Nelson said: "I am convinced that this 7.5 million dollars will assure the public permanent preservation of outdoor assets that would cost Wisconsin between 15 and 20 million dollars if we had to rely solely on outright purchase."

His list of kinds of easements to be acquired included "scenic easements . . . access rights, public hunting and fishing rights, use and alteration rights of headwaters and springheads, wetlands drainage rights, scenic overlook rights, fence-row rights for the protection of game cover, platting rights along trout streams, subdivision and timber-cutting rights along lake shorelines, and development rights to protect lands adjacent to state parks and campgrounds from the clutter of billboards, taverns and concessions."

The right or combination of rights to be purchased would be determined case by case, but in each case the State would pay only the difference between the market value of the land with and without the rights sought by the State.

BEFORE THE INITIATION of ORAP in 1961, Wisconsin had had substantial experience in acquiring limited rights.

Since 1952 the State, through its highway commission, had been acquiring scenic easements along the Great River Road, anticipating the day when scenic parkways might be established on both sides of the Mississippi from the Gulf of Mexico into Canada. These easements usually covered a minimum distance of 350 feet on both sides of the highway and were acquired (1952–1961) on about 55 miles, at an average cost per mile of about 650 dollars.

The standard "development restriction right" (easement) prohibited commercial and industrial uses of land, erection of buildings for such uses, removal of trees and shrubs (except when incidental to permitted general farming), dumping, billboards, and fur farming. It may be significant that for wooded areas fee title was acquired in order to prevent more effectively cutting or destruction of the trees. The scenic easements in no way gave the general public the right to enter the covered area for any purpose.

In 1961 the highway commission had plans for acquiring an additional 61 miles of scenic easements along the Great River Road, at average costs higher than those of 1952–1961.

The Wisconsin Conservation Commission since 1927 had had the power to acquire lands for conservation purposes in fee simple and also the power to purchase or condemn any limited interest in such lands. Since 1950 the commission had leased from private owners several hundred thousand acres for public hunting grounds and had also leased much land along trout streams on a "20-year plus 20-year" arrangement. In addition, the agency had had some considerable experience since 1935 with several types of perpetual easements for forest protection in county forests.

Other important and interesting limited public interests in some lands have been retained under a 1911 law still in force (as amended slightly in 1951). This law requires for all land sold by the State not only a reservation of the mineral rights but also a reservation to the people of "the right of access to such lands and to any meandered or nonmeandered stream, river, pond or lake navigable in fact for any purpose whatsoever, bordered by such lands and all rights necessary to the full enjoyment of such waters. . . ."

The Director of the Wisconsin Conservation Department, L. P. Voigt, commented on the situation that developed from the 1911 law: ". . . Here we have perpetual easements . . . for public use on many parcels of land, but we don't know where they are and no one has been given the responsibility of enforcing or managing the public rights here preserved. I am advised that the State Land Commission has been including this deed reserva-

tion on all their public land sales and no doubt the properties still could be located. However, as these rights never have been publicized, enforced, or used by the public, such action today may come as a shock to present owners."

Again we have the oft-repeated story of poor or nonexistent stewardship of public properties. The obvious remedy is not abandonment of the public rights, but greater initiative and vigilance on the part of public servants.

Soon after the Wisconsin Outdoor Recreation Act Program was established in 1961, the Conservation Department prepared and adopted five basic conservation easement forms for use in obtaining flowage, wetland, fishing and hunting, right-of-way (for trails, roads, access ways), and scenic easements.

Recognizing that it would be necessary from time to time to modify or redraft these basic forms to meet specific problems, the department also prepared a series of 32 further covenant clauses to be added or substituted when applicable or desirable in particular sets of circumstances.

The legal staff subsequently developed additional clauses to fit individual cases. The rights obtained are in perpetuity and continue with the land, regardless of change in ownership of fee. Easement rights to be acquired are appraised as the difference between the full market value of the land and the market value of the land without such rights. The assessed valuation for property tax purposes may be reduced (just as if the grantor had sold some of his land with fee title), but that is a matter for the local officials.

Important public purposes to be served through acquiring the various sorts of conservation rights under the Wisconsin program are these:

To preserve esthetic features of the natural landscape along roads, parkways, streams, and lakes, and in other places with rare geologic formations or exceptional natural beauty.

To obtain rights of public use on hiking trails, canoe portages, access ways, and parking areas.

To protect entrances to State parks and other public areas where undesirable development on private lands could destroy esthetic values.

To preserve fish spawning places in wetland and flood plain areas.

To preserve the natural habitat for fish and wildlife in wetlands and waters (by, for example, maintaining the quantity and quality of the waters).

To preserve wildlife habitat elsewhere (as on fence rows and copses), even in the absence of public hunting rights.

To facilitate streambank improvement and beneficial management, control, and diversion of waters (as in flowages).

To preserve springheads and small headwater streams.

To obtain rights of public access and use of shorelines and water areas for fishing and other recreational activities.

To obtain public hunting and habitat development rights, especially on properties near publicly owned areas.

In the year following September 1, 1961, when Wisconsin's ORAP was activated, the Conservation Commission (with ORAP funds) made 411 acquisitions, of which 348 were fee simple and 63 were easements. The 411 parcels covered 36 thousand acres at a cost of 3 million dollars, and more than 132 miles of frontage on lakes and streams (plus 3,600 acres of private ponds) were thus acquired or brought under easement rights. Special attention in the new program was given to acquisition of wetlands for wildlife habitat and related uses and to acquisition of remnant fish spawning grounds. The 63 conservation easements covered 1,800 acres with a water frontage of 54 miles, at a cost of 59 thousand dollars. All but one of the conservation easements involving water frontages were perpetual easements along the shores of important trout streams.

IT IS TOO EARLY to judge with much assurance how successful the easement parts of Wisconsin's conservation and recreation space programs are likely to be in the long run. But the effort in acquisition of limited rights has been moving into high gear, along with other parts of the program.

Among the questions that have been posed (by the director of the Conservation Department and others) and that have not yet been fully answered are:

When is it best to purchase conservation easements instead of land in fee simple, in view of prospective long-term needs and possible future management considerations?

In what kinds of situations should an option to buy in fee simple be taken at the same time an easement is acquired?

Should conservation easements be written in a way that will make them transferable and negotiable? Under what conditions might transfer from State ownership be desirable?

Under what circumstances should a public agency buy the land and then return to the previous owner specified rights which the agency does not want to keep? Would this policy effectively preserve for the public some important rights which at the time of acquisition may not even be recognized as potentially valuable?

In what circumstances and to what extent should condemnation be used for acquiring conservation easements and other limited interests in private lands?

Probably only experimentation and experience can yield good answers to these and other large questions of policy and procedures. In matters of this nature, no answer is ever likely to be quite final.

But the unfolding experience in Wisconsin and elsewhere must be studied diligently if the better answers being evolved in some places are to become more widely understood and creatively adapted to the needs of other peoples and places.

The tiresome formulas of the lawyers

are necessary channels through which a fuller enjoyment of the good earth may come to be shared more equitably among men.

FRED A. CLARENBACH *is professor of urban and regional planning at the University of Wisconsin, Madison. He has held other university appointments in departments of economics, agricultural economics, and political science, and has served with the United States Department of Agriculture, the Department of the Interior, and the Public Health Service, and as a consultant for the Food and Agriculture Organization of the United Nations and for the Wisconsin State Department of Resource Development.*

For further reading:

Beuscher, Jacob H., "Conservation Easements and the Law." *Conservation Easements and Open Space Conference* (proceedings of conference sponsored by the Wisconsin Department of Resource Development and the State Recreation Committee, Madison, Dec. 13–14, 1961).

Northeastern Illinois Metropolitan Area Planning Commission, *Open Space in Northeastern Illinois.* Technical Report 2, Chicago, 1962.

Siegel, Shirley A., *The Law of Open Space.* New York Regional Plan Association, Inc., New York, 1960.

Solberg, Erling D., "Open Space Control." *Urban Research*, Highway Research Board, Bulletin 256, Washington, D.C., 1960.

Whyte, William H., *Open Space Action.* ORRRC Study Report 15, U.S. Government Printing Office, Washington, D.C., 1962.

Williams, Norman, Jr., *Land Acquisition for Outdoor Recreation—Analysis of Selected Legal Problems.* ORRRC Study Report 16, U.S. Government Printing Office, Washington, D.C., 1962.

MAURICE K. GODDARD

LAND ACQUISITION
BY PUBLIC AGENCIES

No POWER of government, except taxation, is more apt to inspire dispute than the power of eminent domain, the right of government to act on behalf of the people in acquiring land for public use. Yet, in coping with a land-hungry urban civilization eating its way across the rural landscape, no instrument of public policy is more crucial.

The sprawling modern metropolitan environment requires that lands for such urgent present and future public needs as alinements for new highways, sites for new airports, reservoirs for water supply and flood control, parks, and open space be obtained immediately before they are lost irretrievably or before costs for acquiring them climb so high that public acquisition is impossible.

As the urgency of the problem has grown, there has been increasing interest in finding new and less costly techniques than outright acquisition to use land for public purposes.

Zoning, easements, and purchase of development rights are three methods now being tested. Each unquestionably will have its place in the box of tools available to public bodies for the acquisition of land, but each, in my view, has serious limitations.

Employment of the police power, as in zoning, on any large scale does not conform, it seems to me, to our notions of the right of individual property owners to realize the economic benefits which they might realize by developing their land. There is no alternative to zoning in a dense urban community, but I see great difficulties in applying it, for example, on the land in any wholesale manner to preserve watersheds or general recreational areas. Besides, zoning is vulnerable to a steady erosion of exceptions and variances, which any zoning agency hardly can resist.

By paying a property owner to give up the development potential in his land, we resort, of course, to other than the police powers of the State to achieve our aims. But we have let ourselves in for another set of problems. Most of the value in a property in any growing metropolitan area is in its potential for urban development.

449

The closer in to the metropolitan area, the higher this increment of value will be. Thus, if a public agency pays for the full development rights on the property, it may be putting up a sum approaching that of acquiring the land in fee—particularly if the payments are spread over time, as, say, in granting tax benefits to the owner.

Easements are useful, but there is the risk that if the public agency decides to give up its interest in a long-held easement, there is no way to recoup the public outlay made over many years. Moreover, problems of public access and use crop up frequently.

As a matter of practical necessity, therefore, I have found that there is little or no substitute for outright public ownership where a clearly defined public need must be satisfied.

Yet in a private market economy such as our own, any public official responsible for land acquisition bears a heavy burden. He must meet rigorous standards that do not apply in government-directed economies. With the high premium we place on private property "rights," the public official who infringes on these rights by condemning them must be prepared to defend his decision with an ironclad argument on the economics of the project he proposes. He must also compensate the landowner in accordance with the rules of the marketplace. Both of these requirements bear examination.

Given the nature of our system, public acquisition of a property must have a clearly demonstrable beneficial impact upon the commonweal. The easiest way to measure the benefits is to quantify them in economic terms.

Fortunately, the powers of eminent domain normally are employed in the United States for purposes generally easy to quantify or to relate to some agreed upon public need, such as defense. These include land for transportation facilities, military installations, public institutions, recreational areas, forest preserves, water projects, urban and industrial redevelopment projects, and land reserves.

Most citizens would agree in principle with the necessity for government to provide for the public welfare and preserve the common defense, and each of the uses of public land in this list meets these requirements.

Inevitably, however, the people who are concerned with the encroachment of governmental authority on our free market raise a variety of objections to the specific ways in which the powers of eminent domain are employed. The powers come into play notably in the public ownership of forest lands or in the construction of a public project for hydroelectric power or water supply.

In such instances, the line that separates the proper role for public ownership and private capital is a hazy one. It is possible, nevertheless, to agree upon some general principles.

As to forest lands, for example, the case for public ownership must rest ultimately on its protection of amorphous values difficult to measure, such as the protection of a watershed or of open space in a metropolitan area. We cannot justifiably expect private enterprise to manage timberlands for purposes so diffuse in benefit that a profit cannot be realized. When the multiple use of forest lands is of vital concern, such as on the headwaters of a major river system, therefore, public ownership is clearly justified.

The same kind of yardstick can be applied to construction of a reservoir. Only a few water uses can generate profits for private capital. No profit is to be gained by a corporation in the fields of flood control, or low flow augmentation, or pollution abatement, yet it is absolutely essential for the economic success of a community that such needs be looked after just as effectively as water supply or power.

With the rapidly growing pressures in society for the total benefits that a river basin program can provide, the problem gets more difficult. The number of good multiple-purpose reservoir sites on any stream is limited. Taking one for limited use rules out other essential benefits. Generally speaking, a multiple-purpose site should be developed by public interests in order to maximize benefits.

Note, however, that the premise upon which such a guideline rests must be the economic contribution that public development can make. The official who follows such guidelines must be able to make a case for this.

The charge leveled oftenest against public ownership is that it lays a heavy hand on the surrounding economy by ruling out private development and by not contributing its fair share to the local tax base.

If either objection applies to a project, it is a case of bad management. The purpose of public investment in the United States is to reinforce the private economy by providing opportunities for private investment and by protecting land and resource values.

These benefits can be measured through the increased tax revenues, higher land values, new economic growth, or increased resource supplies engendered by the project.

A report in 1962 of the Outdoor Recreation Resources Review Commission, "Outdoor Recreation for America," documented the economic impact of seven reservoirs in Texas, Arkansas, Oklahoma, and Missouri:

"In the 10-year period, ending in 1960, all counties in the study lost population, but the 17 reservoir counties lost only 8.5 percent in contrast with the 25.1 percent loss in the non-reservoir counties. From 1949 to 1959, annual per capita income of the reservoir counties in Arkansas increased from $669 to $1,053, or 57 percent, in contrast to an increase of $349 to $431, or only 23 percent, in the non-reservoir counties.

"The gain in bank deposits also favored reservoir counties. [Bank deposits in 17 reservoir counties rose from 82.6 million dollars in 1949 to 130 million dollars in 1958. Bank deposits in 8 non-reservoir counties were 15.1 million dollars in 1949 and 21.2 million dollars in 1958.]

"The growth of local tax collections points up the value of business generated by reservoir recreation. From 1945 to 1956, 10 Oklahoma reservoir county tax levies increased nearly 64 percent. Two selected Oklahoma non-reservoir county collections were up only 3.8 percent for the same period. In that period, school taxes were up 296 percent in the reservoir counties compared with 190 percent in the non-reservoir counties.

"Another aspect of the effect of reservoir recreation has been the steady annual increase of investment in overnight accommodations from an initial investment in 1945 of $1.4 million to the 1959 total of $20.8 million in the 14 reservoir counties for which data are available. These capital expenditures are, of course, in addition to income generated by visiting recreation seekers."

Payments by the Army Engineers to counties around Lake Texoma in Texas and Oklahoma for leases adjoining the reservoir have exceeded the tax revenues the counties would have earned over the same period had the project not been built.

IT IS NOT difficult to pinpoint the benefits from airfields, highways, or reservoirs. It is also easy to identify the beneficial impact of industrial and urban redevelopment projects.

A good example is the 7 million dollars spent by the Commonwealth of Pennsylvania in clearing 36 acres of commercial and industrial slum at the tip of Pittsburgh's Golden Triangle. The new park created gave Pittsburgh a very presentable "front door," which made possible the private redevelopment project called Gateway Center. This center, which includes a new hotel and office buildings, increased the taxables in downtown Pittsburgh by 100 million dollars—an excellent return on the public investment.

In protecting open space in urban areas, it will be difficult to identify

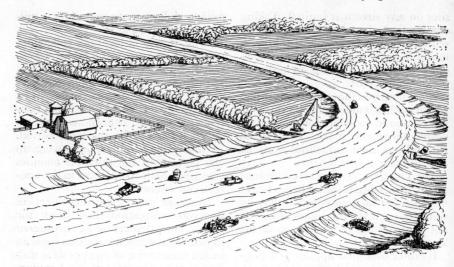

benefits clearly, but it seems plain that the community is bound to suffer if the livability of the urban periphery is destroyed without regard for the amenities of landscape and recreation. Suburban and rural residents affected by new open-space programs in several urban States should recognize that their own land values and livability will benefit. Builders and developers will find that prices for homes in an area offering the amenities suburbanites seek are several thousand dollars more than those that could otherwise be expected.

Public forest holdings are subject to more criticism than any other form of public ownership.

In my own State of Pennsylvania, for example, local and industrial interests frequently argue that the Commonwealth should surrender large portions of its 2 million acres of State forest to "stimulate" the local economy.

First acquired when they lay overcut, burned over, and delinquent on the tax rolls, these forests have been converted into a rich resource. When first acquired, they had been destructively exploited by private capital. Now that their value has been restored, private capital wants them back. I doubt whether the taxpayer

would like to give up his investment.

It is true the State pays only 10 cents per acre in lieu of taxes to the counties in which the forest holdings are located, but it is also true that no schoolchildren live on them, and the State is responsible for roads and fire protection. Since no local services are required, it would be difficult to defend any substantial payment to the community.

The economic benefits can be and are more far reaching. The forests have had an important place in establishing a strong locational advantage in northern Pennsylvania for wood-using industries. Two new plants alone, being established in the area in 1963, are expected to create 2 thousand jobs. The indirect benefits to the entire State in watershed protection and recreation must also be taken into account.

Having said this much, I do feel, however, that great regard for local interests is implicit in any land-acquisition program. It is no longer appropriate for Federal agencies to carry on large development programs, particularly for water, without regard for State interests. State agencies must not disrupt local plans with their own acquisition efforts. Highways, parks, reservoirs—all must be established in close consultation with the agencies and people affected. There is no substitute for full information and close cooperation. A highway department that condemns all properties along an alinement and then negotiates with property owners is obsolete.

Too often officials are oblivious also of the impact that acquisition and construction may have upon the local real estate market. The more quickly an acquisition program can be carried out, the better.

MY OWN AGENCY—the Pennsylvania Department of Forests and Waters—has been experimenting with means for speeding up acquisition and construction and for improving public knowledge of our intentions.

Generally, the following rules apply:

The project is announced in general terms to apprise the public of our intentions and to solicit the necessary legislation and funds.

A public meeting is scheduled as soon as planning and design have reached a stage sufficiently conclusive to enable us to provide local property owners with considerable detail on our intentions. Affected landowners only are invited to the meeting, and no information is released beforehand, so that they are protected from unprincipled speculators. Two weeks before the date of the public meeting, registered letters of invitation are sent to the owners of record of each of the properties located within the boundaries of the project. The letters advise the property owners as to the date, time, and place of the public meeting and of the fact that detailed and pertinent information will be made available at that time.

Preferably within the week before the public meeting, informal consultations are held with various official groups having specific jurisdiction over all or part of the project area for the purpose of acquainting them with the general details of the project.

The public meeting is held in an appropriate building, preferably located within the project area.

Available for distribution to the public are maps showing main project features, appropriate streams, highways, and the proposed project boundary; leaflets outlining the steps to be followed in the land acquisition procedure; information about the primary purpose and anticipated secondary benefits of project; the cost of project and the method of financing; the land-acquisition schedule (in this phase, it is of almost vital importance that land acquisition work be initiated immediately after the public meeting and that it be continued, as it is only in this manner that the inevitable rumors can be kept to a minimum and undesirable land speculation kept down); the project construction schedule; a large map of project showing the proposed boundary, roads within the boundary properly oriented to nearby communities and local landmarks, streams, property lines within the project boundary (the names of the property owners are not included on this map), and physical features, such as buildings, reservoirs, and highways.

PUBLICLY OWNED lands take up but a small fraction of the Nation's land surface. Yet the vital services performed thereon may determine the economic well-being and security of our country.

Rural residents will have to become reconciled, particularly in urbanizing areas, to an upswing in public land acquisition as the demands on land and water intensify in metropolitan regions. Generally, most of these new developments will greatly benefit landowners in the area and add new life to the local economy. Public officials must see that the painfulness of acquisition is minimized and that close coordination with local interests is observed.

MAURICE K. GODDARD *is Secretary of Forests and Waters for the Commonwealth of Pennsylvania. A former director of the School of Forestry at The Pennsylvania State University, he is a member of the Federal Water Pollution Advisory Board and many other State, regional, and national resource agencies.*

CHESTER W. BAIN

THE ANNEXATION OF

FRINGE TERRITORY

A RECURRING dilemma for all municipalities is the peopling of the areas just beyond their boundaries. It arises from the legal definition of city boundaries. Walls once were built to protect a city against attack, and the neighborhood and residents outside the walls usually were not considered a part of the city. Cities no longer are defined by walls, but often the legal boundaries are almost as restrictive, for they are established by law, and the city's jurisdiction does not extend beyond them.

Since the boundaries can be changed only through established legal procedures, cities do not expand automatically to accommodate the development that takes place beyond their limits, although the fringes are economically and sociologically a part of the city around which they have grown, and the entire area constitutes a unit with many common problems.

Yet as long as a city's legal and actual boundaries are not made to coincide, there are actually a central city and adjacent tracts of semiurban or urban development under one or more different units of local government.

A basic—and obvious—element in the development of communities just outside city limits is growth in population. Another factor is a tendency for people to concentrate in the 212 places that we call standard metropolitan

statistical areas. A third is that rapid urbanization requires more space.

The result is that suburban fringes have developed faster than the central cities. Despite annexations by some cities, the satellites grew almost five times faster than the central cities.

Prof. Victor Jones, of the University of California, reported in *The Municipal Year Book, 1961*, that "If there had been no annexation, the fringe would have grown 41 times as fast as central cities."

Two-thirds of the increase in the population of the United States between 1950 and 1960 occurred in the outlying parts of the standard metropolitan statistical areas.

Sooner or later, available land within a city's legal boundaries is used up, and land must be sought elsewhere. As land becomes scarcer and more

454

expensive, those who are unable or unwilling to pay the market price for it turn to land beyond the city's boundaries. Besides, there has developed what appears to be the great American desire for the advantages of both cities and suburbia, without the disadvantages of either, and for owning one's own home. Dreams of a freer, fuller life have become realities for many, but the dreams failed to include the difficulties that arise when a city's actual and legal boundaries do not jibe.

You may ask: What difference does it make whether or not a city's legal boundaries coincide with its sociological or economic boundaries?—after all, the entire area is under some type of government, and that should be sufficient for the situation. Why should a city and the surrounding developments be placed under one governmental unit?

The answers to these questions are not simple.

THE DISADVANTAGES to the central city as fringe areas develop around it are fairly obvious.

All too often the older residential and business sections within the city fall into general disrepair as residents and business firms seek larger and better sites farther out. Then real estate values decline, and part of the city's tax base is lost. Stores and businesses transfer their locations outside the taxing jurisdiction of the central city. As the city loses these various sources of revenue, the per capita share of government may increase, and capital outlays for various items may fall more heavily on those who remain within the city's taxing jurisdiction.

Equally important, the growth of the fringes often deprives the city of strong civic and political leaders and denies the suburbanite a voice in the management of the affairs of the city of which he really is a part and from which his livelihood is drawn.

The effects of fringe developments on the central city would not necessarily mean much if it were not for some other factors.

Foremost among them is the extent to which the central city is expected to provide services and functions for the suburbanite when he is in the city—streets and traffic control to get him in and out of the city, police and fire protection, water supply, and sewage disposal. They cost money, yet the suburbanite, being outside the city's taxing jurisdiction, does not help pay for them. The central cities consequently take the position that the fringe areas and the central city have a community of interest and therefore should be merged into a single political unit.

But that is not all. It is a truism that new needs arise as people concentrate in an area. Many services that are not urgent or are even unnecessary in the country become critical when population becomes congested. Indeed, the need for them is the very factor that has led to the creation of municipal corporations.

Thus, while a person may settle in what appears to be a semirural environment just outside the corporate limits, the continuing flow of people into that area soon places it beyond the point that the individual can safely do without or make personal provision for many functions required by urban populations. At that point, it no longer is a question of what the individual desires but what is actually required for the existing conditions.

The situation is summarized in a 1941 decision of the Virginia Supreme Court of Appeals:

"A county resident may be willing to take a chance on police, fire and health protection, and even tolerate the inadequacy of sewerage, water and garbage service. As long as he lives in an isolated situation his desire for lesser services and cheaper government may be acquiesced in with complacency, but when the movement of population has made him a part of a compact urban community, his individual preferences can no longer be permitted to prevail. It is not so much that *he* needs the city government as it is that the area in which he lives needs it."

While counties can and do provide many of the services required by places that are approaching urban concentration, they frequently are unable or unwilling to provide additional services to the residents of suburbs.

Since community effort, through governmental organization, is required in many functions, the residents of developed areas must look to other sources when the county does not provide the needed services.

If the adjacent city can be prevailed upon to furnish these services, this arrangement may suffice. But cities often are unwilling—and oftener are unable—to furnish such services. As I noted, cities may take the position that the people in the fringes who want a municipal type of services and functions should come into the city and share in the financial burden.

If the city does not supply services outside its boundaries, the only recourse left to the suburb is to incorporate as a separate municipality or be taken into the city.

FOR MANY years the problem of growth on the edges was handled by extending the boundaries of the city so as to absorb this growth, a legal process known as annexation.

Annexation worked quite well until the late years of the 19th century, and many of our large cities thereby gained many square miles of land.

No uniform procedure was followed. Actions were completed through such means as a referendum, a special act of the legislature, general legislative acts that applied to a special class of cities, and a combined vote of the city and of the area to be annexed. Regardless of the method, annexations generally met only token opposition.

Beginning about 1900, however, people's attitudes toward annexation began to change, and many States adopted provisions that made annexation more difficult.

A typical example was the provision included in the Virginia Constitution of 1902 that "The General Assembly shall provide by general laws for the extension and contraction, from time to time, of the corporate limits of cities and towns; and no special act for such purposes shall be valid."

Rhode Island still has a statutory provision that city and town boundaries shall remain "as now fixed."

Annexation, when it was permitted, often was made complicated and difficult. In many States, the residents or the voters in a community were given final say as to whether their community should be annexed. For reasons I cited, the people responsible for the rapid suburbanization usually rejected annexation. Annexations consequently were rather infrequent and were limited mostly to small, unincorporated areas just outside the city's boundaries.

A resurgence in the annexation movement started in 1945 or so. The postwar period saw a tremendous spurt in suburban development. As the accompanying needs and problems became too great to be ignored, more and more attention has been given to the search for a solution that would accommodate the conflicting interests and views reflected in the issue.

Because of a shift in attitudes, today each of the States has constitutional and statutory provisions on annexation. The provisions vary considerably.

I provide only a general review of the major elements of the different types of procedures. Readers interested in complete details should consult the State's constitution, statutes, judicial proceedings, and literature.

SOME STATES—for example, Delaware, Maine, Massachusetts, and Maryland—have no general law provisions on annexation. The cities in those States must depend on the legislature to pass a special act annexing suburban territory to the city. When this procedure is followed, a bill providing for the annexation of fringe territory to a particular city is introduced by a representative and is considered in the regular procedure for enacting a law, unless special actions for this type of bill have been provided.

Annexation proceedings determined through the legislative process are subject to all the parliamentary maneuverings and the special-interest lobbying normally associated with the legislative process. Annexation then can become a political gambit, in which the outcome may rest on grounds other than the merits of the case. This method often is criticized by both the advocates of a more liberal annexation policy and people who would like to make annexation more difficult or impossible.

THE AVERAGE citizen favors the method of annexation that vests the final decision in the voters.

Many believe that in a democracy each registered voter should have a voice in determining changes in the form of government under which he lives and that annexation proceedings should be determined by a popular referendum. That this view has strong popular support is attested by the number of States in which annexation is determined by a referendum.

The combinations of steps in annexation referendums are legion.

A special legislative act authorizing the referendum may be enacted first, or general statutory provisions may be in existence. A variety of ways are used also for initiating the specific proceedings. The action must be initiated by the city in some instances; in others, the residents of the suburban territory must initiate action. Sometimes either method may be used.

The nature of the final vote also varies. In some jurisdictions, the majority of the total vote cast by voters of the city and the area to be annexed determines the outcome. In other jurisdictions, annexation is permitted only if the question receives an affirmative majority in both the city and the area to be annexed; thereby a veto is given to the voters of the area to be annexed.

In a few jurisdictions, participation in the referendum is restricted to voters residing in the area to be annexed.

As I suggested, the determination of annexation proceedings by referendum is considered by many to be the only procedure consistent with democracy.

Others are just as strong in their objections. Their view is that a popular referendum usually obscures the merits of the case and that the final decision turns on appeals to the emotions. While neither position is followed consistently, the frequency with which annexation referendums are defeated has caused many to look for different methods of deciding when a city's boundaries should be extended to include the developments beyond its boundaries.

THE SEARCH for a method to determine annexation proceedings other than by popular referendum has led to the use of the State's courts. In a few instances, the function of the court is to determine whether certain standards laid down by the legislature in the statutes have been met. If these conditions are found to exist, the court enters an order annexing the territory to the adjacent city.

This approach assumes that general standards for annexation can be established in advance by the legislature and that there is merely the need for an agency to determine whether these conditions have been met. As courts are regarded traditionally as impartial tribunals, the determination is left in their hands.

A different situation exists when the court must determine whether to grant or deny annexation, rather than merely determining whether statutory provisions have been met.

Under the Virginia annexation system, annexations are determined in a suit at law between a municipality and the county in which territory sought to be annexed is located. Proceedings may be initiated by a municipality, by 51 percent of the voters of an area who desire to be annexed, by the governing body of the county, or by the governing body of a town desiring to be annexed by a city.

Irrespective of how proceedings are initiated, the action is filed with the circuit court of the county in which the territory to be annexed is located. Contested proceedings are then heard by a specially constituted annexation court, consisting of the judge from the judicial circuit hearing the case and two judges of judicial circuits remote from the area, who are designated by the Chief Justice of the Virginia Supreme Court of Appeals.

The annexation court must determine the annexation proceedings in the light of a statutory guide, which reads: "The court shall determine the necessity for and expediency of annexation, considering the best interests of the county and the city or town, the best interests, services to be rendered and needs of the area proposed to be annexed, and the best interests of the remaining portion of the county." Even after a number of court decisions, the exact meaning of this legislative guide still escapes many laymen and some lawyers.

In addition to determining whether all, part, or none of the territory involved shall be annexed, the annexation court must determine the terms and conditions upon which annexation is to be granted.

These determinations include: The metes and bounds of the territory to be annexed, the "just proportion" of any "existing debt" of the county to be assumed by the city, the amount the city is to compensate the county for any public improvements annexed to the city, the program of public improvements to be provided by the city in the area annexed, and how much the city shall compensate the county for its loss of tax revenues due to the annexation.

Appeals from the decisions of the local court are taken to the Virginia Supreme Court of Appeals.

The Virginia system of annexation has been roundly praised and roundly condemned. Those who favor the procedure believe that the most important element is the determination of annexation proceedings on grounds other than the narrow, selfish interests of the residents of the territory to be annexed. This position, however, is exactly what many people do not like about the judicial proceeding—it denies to the residents of the territory a vote in the annexation proceeding. That these people individually or collectively have a right to appear in court and defend their interest is not a satisfactory substitute for many.

FRINGE TERRITORY in some States may be annexed through an ordinance passed by the adjacent city.

For example, in Texas a city of more than 5 thousand by a majority vote may adopt a home-rule charter, which includes provisions for annexing fringe territory. Most of the Texas home-rule cities permit the city to annex contiguous unincorporated territory by simple ordinance of council, with no action whatsoever necessary in the territory to be annexed, but some charters also require approval by the voters in the territory to be annexed.

North Carolina in 1959 adopted a statute that authorizes cities of at least 5 thousand to annex by council ordinance when certain legislatively formulated standards are met and when certain required services can be provided to the areas.

The procedure in North Carolina, which has been sustained by the State's highest court, differs from Texas in that the North Carolina Legislature has established the conditions that must be met, whereas in Texas no legislative standards guide the action.

The North Carolina statute requires that the area be contiguous to the city's boundary for at least one-eighth of the total external boundary of the area to be annexed, in order to prevent strip annexation, and that the area not include part of another incorporated area. Although no popular referendum is provided, many believe that the State standards adequately protect the interests of the residents of the area to be annexed. The entire proceedings may be reviewed in the State's superior court.

California has a procedure under which either the city council or the property owners in the outlying areas may start annexation proceedings. No referendum is necessary, and the action of the council of the annexing city determines the outcome.

MANY PERSONS, searching for a fair method of determining annexation proceedings, have urged the use of a board or a commission for such decisions.

Although used in England just after the Second World War, the idea was tried in the United States only recently.

Provision for a local boundary commission was included in the constitution Alaska adopted in 1956. The commission considers all proposed local government boundary changes. All approved changes are presented to the legislature during the first 10 days of any regular session. The proposed change becomes effective 45 days after presentation—or at the end of the session, whichever is earlier—unless disapproved by a resolution concurred in by a majority of the members of each house.

Washington has established a review board to determine the feasibility of all proposed annexations to cities. The board consists of the mayor of the annexing city, the chairman of the county board of commissioners, the director of the State department of commerce and economic development, the chairman of the board of school directors of any or all school districts in the area to be annexed, and a local resident and property owner, who is selected by the others.

The Washington review board must determine within 3 months whether a proposed annexation would be in the public interest. The board studies the future population of the area, the present and anticipated need of the city to expand geographically, the past

and future needs for city services in the area to be annexed, and the ability of the area to provide public services. Proposed annexations of very small areas are exempt from these review proceedings if the mayor, county board chairman, and county superintendent of schools agree to dispense with them.

Wisconsin requires a discretionary review by the director of regional planning.

Minnesota has a municipal commission of three members appointed by the Governor, who are joined in some instances by two county officials. Annexation proceedings approved by the commission are not final, however, until local voters sanction them.

IN SUM, DESPITE many changes in procedures, the issue of annexation is charged with individual emotions and value judgments. In such a climate, attempts to solve the growing pains of many cities will be unpleasant but maybe not fatal.

CHESTER W. BAIN *is professor and head of the Department of Political Science at the University of South Carolina. He formerly served as associate professor of political science and assistant director of the Bureau of Public Administration at the University of Virginia, of which he is a graduate.*

For further reading:
Bollens, John C., *The States and the Metropolitan Problem*. Public Administration Service, Chicago, 1956.
Government Affairs Foundation, Inc., *Metropolitan Communities: A Bibliography*. Public Administration Service, Chicago, 1956.
International City Managers' Association, *Municipal Year Book*. International City Managers' Association, Chicago, published annually.
Jones, Victor, "Local Government Organization in Metropolitan Areas," in Coleman Woodbury, editor, *The Future of Cities and Urban Development*. University of Chicago Press, Chicago, 1953.
Tableman, Betty, *Governmental Organization in Metropolitan Areas*. University of Michigan Press, Ann Arbor, 1951.
Whyte, William H., and others, *The Exploding Metropolis*. Doubleday & Co., Inc., New York, 1958.
Wood, Robert C., *Suburbia*. Houghton Mifflin Co., Boston, 1959.

ROBERT E. COUGHLIN

PROGRAMING PUBLIC FACILITIES
TO SHAPE COMMUNITY GROWTH

ONCE built, public facilities exert a long-lasting influence on communities, an influence that often is felt after the facilities themselves have disappeared. The streets that were laid out when America was settled almost invariably still exist, repaved and widened; the early public buildings usually have been outgrown, but their past influence on the surrounding concentration of commercial and public activities is evident. In some towns, they have become museums; in other towns, they have been torn down to make room for the commercial growth they helped nurture.

The public development of transportation systems and the provision of sewage and water utilities have been key factors in determining the extent and types of private building in all communities. Basic decisions on the development of port or railroad terminals have had major effects on the amount and nature of economic activity and on the social aspect and physical layout of many cities. In most cities, these decisions have involved local government cooperation; in many, direct government investment as well.

The decisions made in the 18th century and early in the 19th century to acquire and maintain land as a town green have set the character of many towns in New England and Ohio. Late in the 19th century, as they grew from good-sized cities to spreading metropolitan areas, Boston, New York, Philadelphia, and Chicago decided to acquire large tracts for use as major parks. To the decisions to provide these public places one can attribute much of the amenity these cities now have.

In our generation, suburban towns have grown up where farmers farmed. Quiet villages have become the nuclei of mushrooming cities. Asphalt has been laid down. Bricks and steel have been built up. Some areas also have been preserved in their natural state. The decisions to build, not to build, and where to build will shape the economic and social functioning and the amenities of the communities for generations to come.

In the next 10 years, local governments in districts that are now rural will build roads, schools, sewage systems, water facilities, public buildings, parking areas, libraries, health centers, and rubbish disposal plants in unprecedented numbers. They will acquire land for recreation, flood control, and nature preservation. They will buy and prepare land to be sold for industrial and commercial development. Their actions will set the form and aspect of their communities for decades or even centuries.

This chapter is concerned with programing such actions—the scheduling of the undertaking of public improvements and the payment for them. But it cannot avoid being concerned also with the plan itself, for what is done first will determine to a large extent what can be done next; unless a consistent set of steps is taken, an originally agreed on plan cannot be achieved. Worse than that, the later steps may contradict the earlier ones, and the contradiction will bring financial loss and social dislocation.

As THE GROWTH of our cities has speeded up and their problems have grown increasingly complex, governing bodies have come to realize the need for more comprehensive and continuously updated knowledge on which to base decisions.

The more forward-looking local governments have systematized that knowledge about the trends, forces, and problems of their communities and have prescribed the measures they should take to reach their goals. Such is the long-range plan. It sets down, usually in a series of maps, the proposed locations of major streets and rail lines, commercial centers, manufacturing areas, residential neighborhoods, ports and airports, parks, and playgrounds. It shows also the proposed locations of future schools, libraries, health centers, fire and police stations, and public buildings and delineates the main elements of the water and sewer system. Such a plan is indispensable for a community that wants to be sure that as it develops it will develop well.

Although the plan is long range, its only purpose is to guide decisions that are about to be made. The 20-year plan made in 1963 is made in order to bring all available knowledge and community aspirations to bear upon decisions to build in 1963, not to guide decisions to be made in 1983. By that time a new—and perhaps quite different—plan will be guiding development decisions, and it will be drawn up with a year such as 2003 in view. The plan must be brought into reality one step at a time, but the plan itself does not usually delineate those steps. The major governmental device for deciding on the steps to be taken is the capital program and budget.

Regulatory devices, such as a zoning law or building and housing codes, can prevent actions that are not in the public interest. By themselves, they cannot bring about the positive steps that are most important for the community's development. If a community draws up these regulatory codes and enforces them in a manner consistent with the long-range plan and with the capital program, which provides the public impetus to good development, however, that community has powerful implements with which to make its future development healthful, economical, and, if some care is taken, beautiful.

In communities where the capital program is used most fully, the administrative branch of the government, usually with the advice of a planning commission or department, forwards to the legislative branch its intended list or program of facilities to be constructed or acquired during the coming 5 or 6 years. After advice and comment by citizen groups, the legislative branch makes a number of amendments and then gives formal but general approval to the program as a whole, and specific approval to each of the projects and to the money appropriated to them in the first or budget year of the program. Every year the program is reevaluated, a new year is added, and an adjusted program is enacted. The community in this way always has an officially enacted statement of its building plans for the coming program period.

In other communities where the programing process is less fully developed, the capital program may have no statutory force, but may exist solely as a staff document prepared for the advice of the administration.

Between these two extremes, the capital program and budget can take on many characteristics that reflect the local way of doing things. The program may be formulated by the chief executive's office, by the planning commission, or by a specially formed "public improvements committee." The total amount of money to be spent may be set by the administrative or the legislative branch. Referral of proposed amendments back to the planning commission may or may not be required. The length of the program may vary. Some are for 2 or 4 years. A few cover more than 10 years.

Despite variations in procedure, the act of programing always strengthens rational, democratic decisionmaking.

It enables a community to consider its financial resources and the demands that will be made on them. In this way it can plan both its complement of services and the resulting tax rate.

It enables the community to consider the cost and desirability of each project as compared with all other projects.

It lets everyone know what is going on—the administrator, the elected representative, the citizen, and the nonresident businessman and industrialist.

It provides a vehicle by which all members of the community may debate issues of community development. The community thus can focus on the question of what kind of a physical environment it wants in the future: What it wants, where it wants it, and when it wants it.

BUILDING a town is different from building a building. A building is completed in a matter of months. A town is built and rebuilt over generations.

All elements of the plan for a building are known and set forth in blueprints. The owner has control over the smallest detail of the building through his architect and contractor. The question of what to build first is dictated only by the law of gravitation and the rules of construction efficiency. In building a town, however, the government itself builds only a small part. Most of the town is built by many private entrepreneurs, who act individually and over whom the government has but partial control.

The town government cannot carry out a plan simply by its own actions. Its tactics must be to locate and construct the critical elements, which will create the structure of the town and to which private investors will find it desirable to relate all the other elements that make up a town. Private and public facilities thus will be arranged in a consistent way and will be most useful for their intended purposes. Public and private improvements will complement each other rather than weaken and waste each other. Private facilities, such as houses and shops, will locate in such a way that schools and roads will be used to capacity. Public facilities will be located and built in such places and at such times that they will serve a maximum number of people and will make the environment more convenient for people living, doing business, or seeking entertainment in the town.

If this balance between private and public development decisions is not attained, some public facilities will go unused, while the demands of private development elsewhere in the town will force the building of duplicate facilities and services. Similarly, public facilities may be located in such places or built at such times that they are not convenient to the people they were intended to serve.

URBAN GROWTH in rural areas can occur in myriad situations and for a variety of reasons, but rapid growth is associated almost invariably with the coming of people and investment into the area.

Setting the stage for decisions of people or industries to move into a rural area may be the provision of major public facilities, such as transportation routes and terminals, major water supply systems, and major sewage systems. These facilities can shape the growth of the entire metropolitan region. Usually the decisions to construct them are made by metropolitan, State, or Federal bodies. The local community is not in full control.

Because growth usually is due to forces beyond the control of a community, the question facing it is not: "Do we want to grow or to remain just as we are?" Rather: "Within rather small limits, how much growth and what kinds of growth do we want?" "Where should the various types of urban activities be located?"

If the community is to act intelligently, it must first determine whether growth is unlikely, probable, or inevitable. If it is convinced of the inevitability or even the probability of development, it should accept that as fact and strive to make sure that the development is good development.

If large growth is expected, the community should make a clean break and build public facilities at the scale necessary for the new development. It should avoid the temptation to make do by patching on. To accommodate large growth usually requires laying out and constructing an entirely new road pattern.

Failure to realize this necessity is apparent in many of our towns and cities, where streets of once handsome houses have been destroyed by the noise and smells of heavy traffic and the commercialism that has followed in its wake. If the old and desirable parts of our communities are to endure and enrich the newer developments by linking them with a traditional past, they must be allowed to exist in the scale for which they were intended. Otherwise, traffic and the pressure for commercial real estate development

will wipe them out. A town center or a residential street can be expected to maintain something of its amenity and character if it is called on to serve a community that doubles in size. It cannot be expected to survive as the sole center and maintain any of its original character if the community grows tenfold.

To SEE the types of choices a community may have, let us consider a hypothetical community in which the pressure for major suburban development is building up rapidly.

The rural town we have in mind has concluded that urban growth is inevitable, has estimated its amount, and has prepared a general plan for the community of the future. The plan calls for areas of medium-density housing and some open and unbuilt areas, in contrast with the lower density scatter of house lots over the entire town, which would occur if no regulations were imposed on growth.

In order to channel residential development into the areas designated for higher density development, trunk sewers and water mains must be constructed there before suburbanization occurs. Because the housebuilder will realize a higher return on his investment in land when he builds at higher densities, one can expect residential construction to occur in the places where trunk sewers are available rather than in areas where the builder must install individual septic tanks or package sewage systems.

Between 1950 and 1960, two counties suburban to Philadelphia grew almost equally in population. But in one, the new population used up four times as much land as in the other. A major reason that one county developed in a compact, efficient, and economical pattern is that trunk sewers were ready when the growth began. In the county where the growth scattered out, sewers were not available.

If a medium-density residential growth is to occur, the community has no choice but to provide local water and sewer lines. In addition, residential streets must be provided. In many localities, a major part of the cost of these facilities is borne by the builder or by the new residents, but usually a considerable cost must be borne by general taxes. In effect, the decision to grant the developer a permit to build forces these direct costs on the community at large. Once that decision is made, the provision of the facilities is no longer a programing question; it becomes a program necessity.

Although the private decision to build houses must be accompanied by the public decision to build local streets and water and sewer lines, the prior construction of these utilities by government will not necessarily lead private entrepreneurs to build houses. In fact, because the utilities may limit the variety of layout possible on a tract, their existence may turn away prospective developers. The failure of such public facilities to induce growth was a hard-learned lesson for many towns that in the twenties and thirties constructed streets and waterlines in the absence of demand for new housing. These premature subdivisions sterilized thousands of acres that were neither built on nor fit for rural uses.

Once building permits have been granted for a sizable number of new dwellings, the programing of funds for new school buildings becomes virtually imperative. But the school, like the trunk sewer, is a strategic facility, which will attract a concentration of new dwellings in its vicinity—a schoolbus program notwithstanding.

If no area has a trunk sewer and if the zoning ordinance calls for uniform residential densities, an elementary school may be the facility with the greatest effect on directing growth within our town. In the metropolitan competition for socially responsible and economically secure families, an outstanding school plant and program is a strong attraction.

Water, sewers, streets, and schools are closely related—if a town gets new residents, it will necessarily provide them at some level of quality and in some spatial arrangement. They are immediate and direct requirements of development and must be programed for immediate construction.

But what of other facilities that have a greater effect on the overall structure of our hypothetical community? The arterial street system and the system of major open spaces are among the more important.

The arterial street system will create the sites suitable for commerce, industry, schools, and churches; by removing through traffic from the local street system, it can create quiet and safe residential areas. A new arterial street will change the accessibility of an area. The developer will interpret this as a change in its possibilities for development. Therefore, unlike a new local street, which simply capitalizes on the existing convenience of the location of a tract, the new arterial street is likely to change the development trend of a town.

The creation of the arterial system will not follow settlement inevitably, as will the construction of local streets, sewers, waterlines, and schools. Every resident has interest in the adequacy of the arterial street system, but few are seriously enough concerned to make a major political issue of its improvement and expansion, particularly at a time when its improvement could be accomplished at moderate total cost. Often by the time that these inadequacies are generally and acutely felt, adequate arterials can be constructed only after tearing down many new houses.

A realistic policy is to program the acquisition of rights-of-way for all planned arterials as early as possible, but to program the actual construction of arterial streets over a longer period and to coordinate their construction with that of other public facilities and with the demand for developable acreage for private building.

A system of major public open spaces,

in which building will be prohibited, will define the areas where it will be permitted and so will give variety and form to the town. It will provide places for outdoor games and recreation, conservation of wildlife and plants, and the natural drainage system and will maintain a pleasant setting.

Interest groups readily come forward in behalf of playgrounds—in fact, subdividers often are required to dedicate land for the purpose. But preservation of the larger open spaces, which would serve several neighborhoods and over the years would be of major importance to the biologic and social functioning of the town, is far from an inevitable accompaniment of urbanization. Development rapidly removes natural areas from the possibility of preservation, and the community typically becomes concerned only when open land becomes scarce and can be acquired only at very high prices.

But urban development is irreversible. Once land is built on, the economic and social costs of reclaiming much of it for public open space are impossibly high. The political feasibility of such action is correspondingly slight. Even with the generous powers of redevelopment, it is feasible to clear only limited areas to create public open space and these areas must be of formal design and for intensive use—clearance to create large, natural areas for low-intensity use is unthinkable. The relatively few people now living in the richly endowed surroundings of the natural countryside have a great responsibility to preserve a structure of open spaces so that the many more people who will live in the same location in the future will be able to live in an environment fit for man.

The act which should be given high priority in capital programs is the preservation of designated natural areas in their undeveloped state. The actual development of park and recreation facilities in these areas is better put off until the preservation of all the proposed public open spaces is assured. Preservation is normally accomplished by acquisition of the land in fee simple. In some situations, if scenic and ecological values of the land are to be preserved but it is not necessary to allow public access to the land for recreation, the community may be able to acquire a lesser right in the land—for example, only the right to develop the land may be purchased from the owner. The owner could then continue to live on his land but would not have the right to build on it or otherwise destroy its natural character.

A TOWN IS MORE than a collection of houses, shops, factories, churches, and schools, even though they are rationally connected by a system of arterial streets and articulated with major and minor open spaces. To be comprehensible as a place, it must have a center. Acre for acre, the center is the most important part of town—the scene of intense activity. If it is located well, developed fully, and designed compactly, it will save hours and miles for those who frequent its shops, institutions, and government offices. The center can develop as a place of character, fitting for the public life of the community's residents, or it can be shoddy and formless: The town will be judged accordingly.

But, with the exception of the municipal government building, a library, and perhaps a courthouse or public health building, the town center is built primarily by private commercial entrepreneurs and by institutions. The local government must place these few public buildings at times and locations where they will have the most beneficial effect on shaping private development in the town center, but if it restricts itself to this endeavor it is not likely to create the kind of center called for in its plan.

If it is to be successful, the strategy of creating the town center must deal with a more widespread set of facilities. Roads and transit lines must be designed and brought into being so that they have one preeminent confluence —the intended location of the center.

Until the growth of the center gains momentum from its own development, transportation improvements should be programed to discourage the emergence of any other points of high accessibility, which could compete for the role of town center.

However, by themselves, the public buildings and transportation facilities could not be expected to bring about the development of a single economically viable, efficient, and architecturally pleasing center. The programing of public facilities must be combined with other tools.

A zoning ordinance and map, economically sound and resolutely backed, is essential. It can prevent commercial scatter elsewhere in the town and keep it within the bounds of the center.

Within the center itself, subdivision regulations and building controls can be used effectively, but only if there is a clear idea of what the center should be and only if careful design has established where the major public buildings should be, where the commercial buildings should be, and where the major movement channels should be. A most important function of planning is to set up these movement channels— the roads and transit lines by which people come to the center, the parking and terminal areas through which they enter and leave, and the ways and malls through which pedestrians pass.

A design plan that defines these ordered spaces and relationships but allows the private builder freedom as long as he respects the basic structure they create is the image that can capture the understanding and support of residents and investors and can form the basis of defensible public policy. Just as the general master plan is the image and policy for the town as a whole, the design plan is the guide for the future of its important center.

THE FOREGOING example of a growing suburban area highlights the influences that decisions to build public facilities can have on private building decisions. Though strong, these influences can be weakened and even be eliminated by contradictory public policies.

Zoning, the most important of these, can strengthen or dissipate the influence of public facilities on development. It is possible that an available trunk sewer would not attract a concentration of development around it if the zoning in its vicinity called for lots of 2 or 3 acres, while zoning in another part of town allowed lots of one-half or 1 acre. The construction of a school may not attract discriminating prospective homeowners to settle near it if the zoning ordinance allowed industrial areas in the nearby residential neighborhoods. Carefully timed construction of a good road system may fail to bring about the commercial development of sites if, for example, many other sites also were zoned for commercial use. In particular, even though an excellent transportation system were provided, the town itself may not develop as planned if zoning permits commercial activities in many other sites with less accessibility but with much lower land costs to the developer. Even the beneficial effects of an excellent park system can be dissipated if the zoning pattern allows an industrial band to separate it from residential areas.

Other controls are important for harmonious growth. A public facilities program consistent with zoning policy could lead to shoddy development if subdivision or building regulations are poorly conceived or not vigorously and imaginatively enforced. The provision of local government services, too, is important. Failure to provide adequate operating programs for sanitation, public health, and police and fire protection can vitiate efforts to create good development through the proper provision of public facilities and sound zoning controls. Good school buildings will fail to have their desired effect if they house poor education programs; so will good arterial streets with poor traffic control.

The emerging structure of a community's public facilities systems will have its most significant effects on the development of residential and commercial areas. Its effects are perhaps less on the location of new areas for manufacturing, for which ties to distant markets and supply sources may be more important than the intimate relation with local activities. Defense and other Federal Government installations share this quality.

In order to achieve development of manufacturing areas in harmony with the rest of the town, major reliance must be put on zoning regulations, but they will fail unless they reflect the real economic values of the land, which grow out of the locations of related economic activities and of transport.

Despite the efforts of the local government, some major industrial, State, or Federal decisions may be made that are not in accordance with the locations or sizes called for in the town plan. They may so alter basic functional relationships that the plan and the public facilities program must be altered drastically.

Some development problems are beyond the control of any single local jurisdiction. Problems of air pollution, pollution of major streams, flood control, and water supply can influence strongly the physical development of a town. So can the location of major interurban transportation routes and of Federal Government installations, which need not obey local zoning regulations. Such problems must be attacked through cooperation of local government units among themselves and with other levels of government.

The programing of public facilities, then, has important effects on community development, but the prospect of success in shaping the community is great only if all the policies of the town are consistent among themselves and with the physical structure that is actually coming into being.

IN THE EXAMPLE of the programing of urban development and public facilities, I tried to identify facilities whose provision is almost inevitable with an increment in growth and to identify the facilities whose timing and location are more subject to community choice and therefore should be the object of much greater scrutiny in the programing process. The latter facilities are strategic in that they induce broader effects on the development of the community as a whole.

Alternatively, one may find it useful to characterize facilities as city building or city serving. Police and fire stations, for example, may be classed as city serving, because, once minimum service levels are met, the timing and location of their construction would not be expected to have an important influence on the amount or locations of other development. In formulating a program, most care should be given to the city-building facilities—roads, open spaces, community centers.

More formal methods may be introduced to help evaluate the great variety of desirable facilities that are encompassed in a plan and to choose from them those few that can be constructed in a given program period.

Within any one class of facilities, such as libraries or playgrounds, a comparison of expected benefits in number of people served with estimated costs often can identify quickly the facilities that would provide the greatest service for a given budget outlay. Such analysis can also be extended to segments of the arterial road system if their interrelatedness is considered.

Programed outlays for each of the different facility groups as a whole can be compared with the totals called for by the long-range plan.

Preparation and study of such financial profiles for the program and the long-range plan are of great use in helping a community decide how to allocate its resources in a program period and enable it to answer fundamental but elusive questions, such as "Which sets of facilities are we now acquiring at a faster and which at a slower rate than the average rate implied by our long-run plan?"

With such knowledge, the community can decide more intelligently which sets of facilities it should be acquiring at a faster rate and which at a slower than average rate in the next program period. Such formal methods of program analysis and evaluation become increasingly necessary as communities grow larger and more complex.

The community can be provided with procedural and analytic tools for formulating the most effective capital program, but it cannot be provided with readymade programs.

No readymade answers could take into account the city's plans and aspirations, its existing pattern of public facilities and private development, the opportunities for development presented by its unbuilt sites and by those in nearby communities, and the concurrent public and private development decisions in surrounding communities. Yet all these things are relevant in determining at any particular time what public facilities in what locations will most strongly structure the pattern of land development.

Although public facilities can be separated roughly into types—those that can be expected to play a strategic role in timing and structuring development and those that will have little effect—the same facilities in different circumstances can have very different effects.

To BE EFFECTIVE in dealing with the forces of urbanization, governmental institutions must be strong yet flexible. Governments in districts that are now rural must acquire strength and foresight if they are to guide the physical development of their communities.

Two weaknesses are endemic.

In most rural areas, no one governmental unit is charged with providing enough services so that it could program the variety of facilities needed for and necessary to shape urban development. Although this chapter has concentrated on public facilities and the effect they might have on other physical development if they were programed in a comprehensive manner with a plan for the community in mind, there are few governmental units with the powers necessary to carry out such a comprehensive programing.

Typically, the State is responsible for most major roads, the county for others, and the local municipality for still others. A school commission is responsible for schools. A sanitation commission is responsible for sewerage and perhaps the water supply, a park board for parks and major recreation areas, the county for jails and hospitals, the municipality for an occasional public building or other facility, and special commissions for airport or port development. Ways must be found of integrating the governmental structure before it can act effectively.

Second, the now-rural jurisdictions lack the financial resources necessary to provide facilities and reserve land in advance of growth. One of the great dilemmas of urbanization is this: It can be accomplished most efficiently and harmoniously if the key public facilities are created early and shape rather than accommodate themselves to growth, but the tax base necessary to pay for the facilities is not available until after the growth has occurred. One way out of the dilemma is an expanded program of State and Federal grants for those facilities and for the reservation of open-space areas that are most critical for communities.

The greatest successes of planning and programing have been in correcting the mistakes of earlier development. Prevention of mistakes in present and future development is a higher and more worthy role. If governmental responsibilities can be consolidated and financial resources assembled, we can look forward to many examples of creative programing. Capital programing can become not merely a fiscal device but an important democratic procedure for creating humane and efficient communities.

ROBERT E. COUGHLIN *is a research associate at the Regional Science Research Institute, Philadelphia.*

MAX S. WEHRLY

CLUSTER SUBDIVISIONS AND ZONING

SINCE 1916 we have been attempting to bring order into urban growth and development by applying zoning and subdivision regulations that specify—mostly in a negative way—the location and manner in which land could be cut up into individual lots and parcels for row houses, apartments, and one-family homes. To a discouraging degree our efforts in this direction have produced results that are not attractive, economical, or efficient.

The legal stipulations of uniformity within any one zoning district have produced a repetitive pattern of sterility and monotony.

Large-lot zoning and arbitrary "standard" engineering requirements for roadway widths, underground utilities, and grading usually designed for more intensive usage have resulted in costly and stereotyped development.

Acreage zoning, mistakenly applied to create "open development" or to prevent low-cost homes, has absorbed land at accelerated rates without producing increased amenity, desirable living, economy of layout, convenience of access, or preservation of rapidly diminishing open space.

The resulting pattern of urban sprawl is wasteful of land, utilities, and services and is costly to administer.

The pressure of urban growth and rapid absorption of suitable land in relatively restricted areas of the country, notably along the eastern seaboard, the Great Lakes, and the west coast, make the need for more efficient methods of developing new urban residential land areas progressively more urgent.

Thus the major objectives in the search for better methods should include reductions in the mounting costs of providing and maintaining streets, utilities, and services; more variety and amenity; the creation of permanent open space; and flexibility in planning, which will release residential development from its present straitjacket of subdivision and zoning regulations based on rigid specifications for the individual lot.

The cluster method of planning for residential development has been advanced as satisfying most of those objectives.

469

The cluster principle contemplates the arrangement of dwellings in groups, courts, or clusters on smaller sites than those required by conventional subdivision planning or zoning specifications. The resulting differential in lot areas is then consolidated into open space for conservation and recreational uses for the common benefit of the adjacent residents with the overall density—that is, the total number of families to the acre in the development—remaining substantially the same as in a conventional layout.

The principal advantages include flexibility in arranging building and open-space areas to fit the physical characteristics of the site; variety and diversity of site and architectural grouping; preservation of natural and topographic features; economy in the length of streets and utilities; and freedom from through traffic.

Obviously, if this type of development is to be realized in areas where regulations of public land use are in effect, provisions permitting cluster planning must be present in zoning and subdivision codes.

Most regulations are still based on individual lot specifications for minimum width, depth, and area, which are then applied in a blanket fashion to the entire development. Conversely, the cluster concept seeks to realize the objectives by grouping homes within and around common open space, with greater economy in streets and utilities and with substantial increase in the attractiveness and livability of the entire development. Thus, the zoning code needs to be based essentially on density—maximum number of families on an acre of development, rather than minimum dimensions or size of the single lot.

The density approach requires a project of some size, either in terms of area or number of families, or both.

For example, a project area of 25 acres developed for 5 homes per gross acre would accommodate 125 families on a conventional street and lot pat-

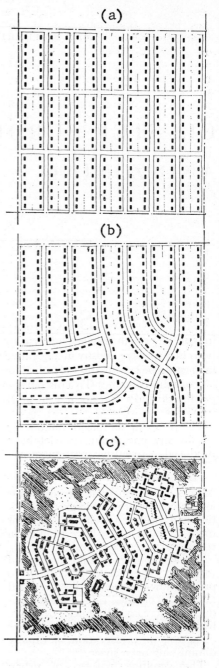

The diagrams illustrate three treatments of a site of approximately 70 acres: (a) Traditional "gridiron"; (b) curvilinear or "contour"; and (c) cluster, with surrounding common areas. The same number of families is maintained in each layout.

tern. By increasing the density in a part of the tract most suitable for building to six, consolidated common open space of about 4 acres (16 percent of the project area) would result, with no increase in overall family density. Commensurate savings in street and utilities, not required to service this open space, should result in enhanced attractiveness and livability. The size of the development and density ratios could vary as densities were increased or diminished. Open-space areas of less than 2 to 2.5 acres are of doubtful value except for playgrounds for preschool children.

A number of communities are experimenting with zoning code provisions that will permit so-called integrated, community, or planned-unit development. While details vary, all have the common objectives of providing flexibility in layout, design, and usage within a specific project by permitting departures from conventional lot-by-lot development, while retaining comparable densities of population within any given area.

A higher degree of competency in land planning and architectural design obviously is required for this type of development than is customarily found in the conventional lot and block pattern.

The creation and preservation of open space has been stressed as a major objective of cluster planning.

Several questions then arise: Once the open area is created, by whom and how will it be used? Is it adequate for the purposes intended? Who will administer and maintain it? What is its legal status? What is the assurance of its permanence as a continuing asset to the community?

Open space is an important and at the same time an uncertain element in the cluster concept.

The consideration of use must be determined, of course—at least broadly, as part of the original planning. Proposed and actual uses of common areas range from open meadows for grazing the riding horses owned by the residents of a rural estate development to natural woodlands, water areas, golf courses, parks, playgrounds, swimming pools, and tot lots in progressively more urban and higher density developments. Obviously, the size, location, and type of maintenance and operation of such areas will vary considerably among these facilities.

The questions of ownership, administration, and maintenance of common areas in many respects are more critical considerations in the cluster concept than are the technical aspects of design and engineering, for upon them rests the question of continued success or failure.

Two major alternatives exist. One is the dedication of common areas by the developer to the community as public open space. The second is assignment of the areas to an organization composed of the homeowners in the development.

Other, less common, approaches include the establishment of private clubs and the retention of title by the developer, who makes the areas available to the residents through fees, lease arrangements, or other methods.

Dedication of the open space to the community places it entirely within the administrative discretion of the city, town, or county as the property of the public.

This approach has a number of disadvantages. Control over future use and maintenance policy would pass to the municipality. The common areas would be open to the public at large, although an integral part of the cluster plan is that it is designed primarily for the use and enjoyment of the adjoining residents. The municipality is often unwilling to accept dedication or later is unable adequately to maintain, operate, and police the areas or continue the type of use for which the areas were intended. A few States permit the creation of recreation districts under the control of the adjoining residents, a procedure that avoids most of these objections.

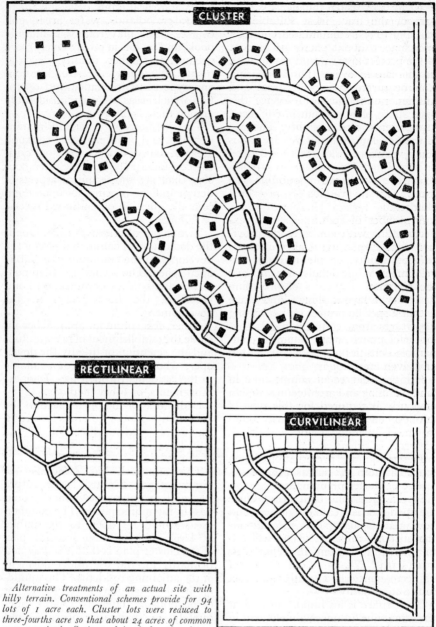

Alternative treatments of an actual site with hilly terrain. Conventional schemes provide for 94 lots of 1 acre each. Cluster lots were reduced to three-fourths acre so that about 24 acres of common area remained. Savings claimed for the cluster plan include 6 thousand lineal feet of street and improved circulation and storm drainage, compared to 12 thousand lineal feet and 11,600 lineal feet for the rectilinear and curvilinear schemes, respectively.

Retention of the open areas by membership associations composed of the property owners appears to be a satisfactory way to assure the successful operation of common areas created by the cluster design. The associations can be incorporated with powers of assessment for raising the necessary operating revenues, and can retain ownership and control over policy and operation for the exclusive benefit of their members.

A STUDY of homes associations has been made by the Urban Land Institute for the Federal Housing Administration with the cosponsorship of the National Association of Home Builders, Office of Civil Defense, Public Health Service, Urban Renewal Administration, and the Veterans' Administration.

The procedure for organizing homes associations is: Before selling any of the subdivided land, the land developer incorporates the homes association and files in the public land records the legal agreements that apply to all of the land and run with it. The land agreements empower the association to collect assessments from every property owner for the maintenance of common areas. The land agreements also define other powers, rights, and obligations—such as voting rights—of the association and the property owner.

The association is an incorporated nonprofit organization, usually created by the developer, initially operated by him, and then taken over by the residents at a later stage of development or after the development itself has been completed.

In the study, the experiences of several hundred homes associations were analyzed through questionnaires, field investigations, conferences with association officers and homeowners, and legal research with relation to the administration of common properties and facilities. The study identified about 500 subdivisions having properties maintained by homes associations or other private organizations.

The study revealed the ability of properly established homes associations to own, regulate, and maintain the common open spaces and facilities in cluster subdivisions and similar types of residential development. It furnished guidelines for planning common properties and establishing effective associations under agreements running with the land.

The homes association has proved to be a successful approach to the problem, provided that legal agreements are recorded to establish a firm foundation for its creation and operation prior to subdividing the land and provided that the common properties are designed for the use and enjoyment of the residents involved.

Homes associations can help to satisfy the growing demand for open space in the urban community and the part the cluster and similar land planning ideas can have in creating a better environment.

Additional studies in new concepts in land development have been undertaken in a program sponsored by the Urban Land Institute and the National Association of Home Builders.

MAX S. WEHRLY *is executive director of the Urban Land Institute, an independent, nonprofit research and educational organization, which specializes in land economics and urban planning and development. A graduate of the University of Pennsylvania and the Harvard School of City Planning, Mr. Wehrly has served on several committees of the Federal Government in connection with housing, community facilities, urban renewal, and the census. He is a member of the Building Research Advisory Board and former chairman of the National Capital Regional Planning Council.*

For further reading:
"Cluster Plan Cuts His Costs by One-third." *The NAHB Journal of Homebuilding* (May 1962), pp. 74–76.
New Approaches to Residential Land Development, A Study of Concepts and Innovations. Urban Land Institute, Technical Bulletin 40, January 1961.

WILBUR H. SIMONSON

SAFE, FUNCTIONAL,
AND BEAUTIFUL ROADS

FOUR million miles of roads and streets in the United States are traversed daily by 96 million automobiles and 13 million trucks and buses. They are a part of the assembly line of industry, the conveyor belt of agriculture, the distribution chain of business, and the fabric of our daily lives.

As the population grows and becomes more urbanized, our highway needs will be concentrated more and more in cities and their suburbs and the main intercity routes. The highway network in cities particularly must be planned in relation to other modes of transportation and to needs of cities.

The need is not alone for more of them. Roadsides and rights-of-way need planning and continued attention to control erosion, insure greater safety and comfort and an attractive appearance, and protect the investment in the thoroughfares.

The Bureau of Public Roads and the State highway departments embarked in 1956 on a program of building the National System of Interstate and Defense Highways, a freeway network of 41 thousand miles that links and serves all our larger cities and many smaller towns. For this network alone, an estimated 1 billion dollars of the total

cost of 41 billion dollars have been earmarked for erosion control on roadsides and planting of the rights-of-way—a manifest of the importance attached to the roadsides.

The conservation and development of an appropriate highway environment for the motorist and for the community are among the objectives set forth as a statement of policy for the National System that the American Association of State Highway Officials adopted in 1961. The statement called for careful consideration of the visual aspects of highway location and design from the standpoint of the users of the highways and of the people through whose communities the highways pass.

People have come to value the economic and esthetic values of roadside improvements since 1933, when the Bureau of Public Roads encouraged each State highway department to include such work in its program— eliminating construction scars, flattening and rounding slopes, seeding, sodding, planting, and so on.

The Bureau of Public Roads, an agency of the Department of Commerce, and the Soil Conservation Service in 1936 began studies of soil erosion along highways in more than 20 States to evaluate methods, practices, and plantings under varying conditions of slope, soil type, and climate.

All such demonstration work before the Second World War was carried out as a separate operation after a highway was built. During the war, because of shortages of manpower, money, and materials, the planting of roadsides was omitted, and the basic erosion-control work was included with grading and drainage operations as a part of the construction of access roads to the mines, forests, and factories. After the war, the Bureau encouraged the States to provide basic roadside improvement work as a regular part of the construction plans for projects of the Federal-aid highway system.

The need for highway landscape development was emphasized by the Bureau of Public Roads in 1939 in a report to Congress, "Toll Roads and Free Roads." A subsequent report, "Interregional Highways," submitted to Congress in 1944, recognized that highway design rests on a balanced agreement of landscape principles and engineering principles, which can be combined in consistency with utilitarian functions.

THE FEDERAL-AID Highway Act of 1956 set in motion an expanded, long-range program that called for close collaboration of all available talent in every State, imagination, and foresight in planning and designing highways.

Improved design standards for the National System of Interstate and Defense Highways were adopted by the American Association of State Highway Officials in July 1956 and approved by the Commissioner of Public Roads for use on Federal-aid projects.

All known features of safety and utility are incorporated, including those that take advantage of terrain and other conditions for safe and comfortable driving, economy, and pleasing appearance.

Efforts to reduce disturbance and possible damage to streams, trees, and other natural features by adjustments in alinement, profile, and cross section produce curves that fit the terrain, instead of long tangents in alinement. Thereby reductions are possible in the areas of cut and fill slopes, the cost of erosion control measures, and annual maintenance.

Sometimes a stream can be retained in the median strip that separates two one-way roadways of a divided highway, and the roadways can be designed independently, one on either side, with flowing, graceful lines to take full advantage of every natural feature of the landscape.

If a highway is to run on the side of a hill or a gentle cross slope, the cost of construction usually can be lowered by building the separate roadways at different levels. Motorists on each roadway then can have a good view of the countryside.

Even on flat terrain, a slight variation of the curves of the two roadways can alter the width of the median and relieve the monotony of long parallel lines, with little effect on the total requirement of the width of the right-of-way. Such variations in the lines and grades of the two roadways relieve monotony, which may cause driver fatigue and drowsiness, and reduce the hazards of headlight glare in night driving and the possibility of head-on collisions by vehicles leaving the roadway in emergency and crossing the median.

For the enduring investment in the Interstate System, there can be no sparing of thought and care to place the roadways in locations of utmost fitness from every point of view. This includes the fullest practicable development of scenic possibilities, consistent with the primary requirements of traffic service.

Unless engineering requirements and the objectives of landscape archi-

DIVIDED HIGHWAY TRENDS

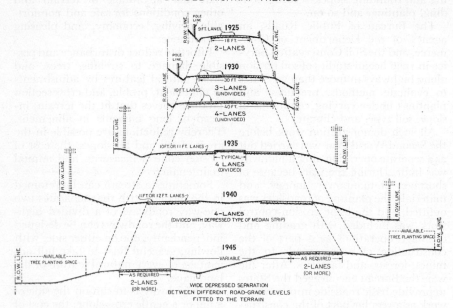

The modern controlled-access highway is the result of a long evolution in highway development—wider traffic lanes, wider separations of opposing traffic streams, and wider rights-of-way.

tecture are coordinated in the early stages of location and design, the opportunity is lost for the effective and economical development of the natural features of landscape.

As in the location and construction of the routes, design for utility and economy goes hand in hand with sound landscape design in producing a complete highway facility that is easy to maintain. Flattening of roadside slopes favors growth of vegetation, prevents erosion, and thus removes the cause of much troublesome clogging of drainageways. The flatter slopes can be moved by machine instead of by hand methods. The streamlined rounding of cut slopes reduces drifting of snow and facilitates machine methods of snow removal.

THE PLANNING of clearing operations provides for conservation of desirable trees and other existing vegetation, the removal of unpleasant and view-obstructing growth, and the saving of topsoil where practicable. Streamlined grading provides the flattened cut and fill slopes and rounded contours that are essential to mold the highway into its surroundings.

Row planting of trees at regular intervals is out of place on rural roadsides. The aim is to preserve or re-create a natural environment on the right-of-way in harmony with the distant view and in keeping with the character of nearby land use.

To that end, it is advantageous to save existing well-placed and beautiful trees wherever feasible at the time roadway locations are being made and adjustments in slope grading are possible.

Trees are planted as necessary to supplement existing growth, to highlight the natural beauty of the view, and to screen unsightly or distracting objects or activity. Trees adapted to the environment are best suited for these purposes.

IN CITIES and the rural-urban fringe, the interstate highways carry heavy traffic. Although roadside space for functional planting is limited, adequately planted borders lessen the sense of crowding of buildings against the right-of-way and insulate adjacent residential and business properties from the noise and fumes of traffic.

A width of 60 feet of right-of-way on the outer roadside borders of each roadway is desirable to provide adequate space for a shoulder reserve for use by vehicles in emergencies, a wide gutter or drainageway safe for vehicles to negotiate in time of trouble, and buffer planting. A mixed planting of trees and shrubs can screen roadways from a paralleling railroad, adjacent freight yard, industrial siding, or other unsightly or objectionable roadside conditions.

Trees in formal arrangement in the cityscape may be desirable when set against the straight lines of frontage roads and local streets paralleling the highway. Such planting helps to insulate bordering residential property from the restless movement of traffic on urban expressways. The overall objective is to avoid monotony and tiresome sameness in such plantings. Visual variation is afforded between roadside cuts and fills and between urban and rural sections of highway improvement by providing appropriate transitions in grading and planting for erosion control and other purposes.

Other functions of planting are:

To protect cut and fill slopes against erosion, to eliminate siltation and clogging of roadside ditches and culverts, to control stream or wave erosion on embankments, and to prevent drifting of snow or sand upon the highway.

To eliminate unnecessary mowing of areas difficult to maintain in grass.

To frame desirable views as seen by motorists.

To provide effective barriers for control of headlight glare.

To provide advance warning to traffic along approaches to bridges and other structures.

To guide traffic by indicating need for turning movements of vehicles, as around curves and at intersections and interchanges.

Planting in medians has important functions for safety and economy, such as:

Providing crash barriers in front of concrete or stone piers at grade separation structures (underpasses), and in advance of hazardous openings in medians between narrowly separated bridges (overpasses and waterway crossings).

Reducing headlight glare across the medians from vehicles in opposing traffic streams.

Providing living barriers to prevent vehicles from crossing medians into opposing lanes.

Providing ground cover to eliminate mowing and reduce cost of maintenance.

Supplementing existing trees and other desirable growth saved in wide medians to improve appearance.

In addition to these purposes of planting in highway medians and in the outer borders of roadside areas, planting has special functions within the widened areas of rights-of-way at traffic interchanges and safety rest areas. These include:

Providing advance warning to motorists to supplement traffic signs along roadway approaches to interchanges and safety rest areas.

Guiding traffic in turning movements at the ramp intersections and around curving ramps.

Reducing the extent of areas that require repeated mowing.

Providing shade at scenic overlooks and safety rest areas.

Providing buffer protection against trespass by pedestrians along right-of-way boundaries in lieu of or supplemental to regular fencing.

Supplementing existing trees and

other growth retained within interchanges and safety rest areas to improve the appearance of the areas.

Plantings of small flowering trees and
ground cover may be appropriately
placed in the wider median or lateral
areas and on the side slopes of depressed roadway sections and ramps of
interchanges. Retaining walls at crossing structures and against local frontage roads offer opportunities for attractive groupings of small trees and
low-growing plants in suitable relation.

The wide median and right-of-way
can form a much needed green, open,
parklike space to give relief to the
confining sameness of the walled urban
complex. Adequate widths of outer
roadside borders, medians, and interchanges are essential for effective and
pleasing results. The right-of-way
should include sufficient space for
required planting clearances from the
edges of pavements, in addition to
the space required for the actual
planting itself, with due allowance for
ultimate growth at maturity.

The intensity and scope of roadside
planting on rural and urban highways,
and the design of planting are, of
course, affected and influenced by
different climatic conditions and traffic
requirements. Nevertheless, it is desirable to emphasize that landscape
planning and functional planting have
a threefold basic purpose in engineering for conservation and development
of the highway landscape:

To counteract the attention-lulling
ease of fast travel on modern pavements and the unrelieved monotony
of the standardized width of paved
roadways stretching out before the
eyes of the motorist.

To promote the safety of traffic
through variations in flowing, graceful alinements and feasible adjustments in streamlined profiles and cross
sections to save trees and other landscape features and protect rural and
urban property values.

To simplify and increase the effectiveness of maintenance operations and
lower the cost of upkeep.

All these things may be done in
complete consistency with the utilitarian functions of the highway system.

WILBUR H. SIMONSON *is Chief of the
Roadside Branch, Highway Standards and
Design Division, Office of Engineering,
Bureau of Public Roads, the Department of
Commerce. He has served in the Bureau
since the development of the Mount Vernon
Memorial Highway in 1929, the first project
in our national roadside program.*

For further reading:
American Association of State Highway
Officials, *The AASHO Manual for Signing
and Pavement Marking of the National System
of Interstate and Defense Highways.* 1961.

———— *A Policy on Arterial Highways in Urban
Areas.* 1957.

———— *A Policy on Geometric Design of Rural
Highways.* 1954.

———— Committee on Planning and Design
Policies, *Geometric Design Standards for Highways Other Than Freeways.* 1962.

———— Committee on Planning and Design
Policies, *A Policy on Safety Rest Areas for the
National System of Interstate and Defense High-
ways.* 1958.

———— Operating Committee on Roadside Development, *A Policy on Landscape
Development for the National System of Interstate
and Defense Highways.* 1961.

———— Special Committee on Nomenclature, *AASHO Highway Definitions.* 1962.

The Highway and The Landscape, W. Brewster
Snow, editor. Rutgers University Press,
New Brunswick, N.J., 1959.

Highway Research Board, *Report of Committee on Roadside Development.* 41st Annual
Meeting, 1962.

———— *Roadside Development, A Selected
Bibliography (Annotated).* Bibliography 26,
1960.

Kanwit, Edmond L., and Todd, Thomas
R., *Recent Population Trends and Their Highway Implications.* U.S. Department of Commerce, Bureau of Public Roads, January
1961.

*Report of the Hershey Conference on Freeways
in the Urban Setting.* Sponsored by U.S. Bureau
of Public Roads, U.S. Housing and Home
Finance Agency, and Automotive Safety
Foundation, Hershey, Pa., June 1962.

*Twenty-first Short Course on Roadside Develop-
ment.* Ohio State University, Department of
Landscape Architecture, and The Ohio
Department of Highways, Columbus, October 1962.

Wells, Nelson M., "Landscaping," Section
28, in Kenneth B. Woods, editor, *Highway
Engineering Handbook,* 1st edition. McGraw-
Hill Book Co., Inc., New York, 1960.

RAYMOND D. VLASIN

HIGHWAYS AND
ADJUSTMENTS IN FARMS

ONE estimate is that 1.5 million acres of land will be acquired for 41 thousand miles of interstate highways authorized by the Federal-Aid Highway Act of 1956. Almost 1 million acres will be in farms at the time of acquisition. Only a small acreage of needed right-of-way will come from land in urban areas. Approximately 75 thousand farms will give up some of their acreage for rights-of-way.

Requirements for rights-of-way for new State primary roads of a design similar to interstate highways will affect additional thousands of farms.

Most interstate roads will be four-lane divided highways and six and eight lanes in and near large cities. Two-lane roads built in sparsely settled areas will be expanded to four lanes when traffic requires it.

Most interstate highways will be on strips of new, fairly straight rights-of-way. Frequently they will run on the bias, instead of paralleling existing property boundaries or roads. Strips will average 250 to 300 feet in width. Some will be twice as wide.

A 300-foot right-of-way takes 37 acres a mile. To that must be added other land for interchanges—sometimes as much as 40 acres—and land for overpasses, underpasses, and feeder roads. Together, these requirements will probably approach 50 acres a mile in many rural areas. For example, a segment of Interstate 35 in Minnesota took 47 acres a mile. Another segment in Iowa required 55 acres a mile. A section of Interstate 70 in Kansas took 57 acres.

Access to the highways will be strictly controlled. Users can enter and leave them only at interchange points. Grade crossings will be eliminated by interchanges, overpasses, and underpasses. Those structures, 1, 2, and 3 miles apart, are the only points at which landowners and farm operators and others can cross the highways.

Benefits from the new high-speed roads will be numerous and large. The Bureau of Public Roads expects that their safety factor will save 4 thousand lives a year. Traveltime and costs of operation of vehicles will be reduced greatly. Studies of freeways similar to

479

the interstate highways show that their cost is balanced out by savings in vehicle operating expenses in less than 10 years.

The high-speed roads can reduce producers' transportation costs to distant markets for farm supplies and products. They can make city jobs more accessible to farmers and other rural residents. They can open regions for development. They can bring recreation areas closer to rural and city people.

Some of these benefits will be reflected in rises in land values. Even greater rises in value will accrue to lands so situated that they can be used for residential, commercial, or industrial development.

SUBSTANTIAL immediate effects on farms and other properties result from design features, which are a boon to through travelers.

The broad, straight, or gently curving highways with their access control reduce the size of some rural properties and occasionally take entire farms. They impose erratic shapes on farms. They leave some lands inaccessible to their owners and operators or accessible only by several miles of travel.

Highways also can disrupt school routes, milk routes, and mail routes. They can isolate one part of a community from certain services, such as fire protection, that are provided in another part. They can change the kind, rate, and direction of urban and commercial development in a rural community.

In short, the superhighways require substantial adjustments by the rural property owners, farmers, and rural communities through which they pass.

How EASY and satisfactory those adjustments will be depends on at least two conditions: How great they are and how well highway agencies assist owners and operators in making them.

A common ground for both conditions are the procedures employed by highway agencies.

The magnitude of the adjustments is affected by the procedures used in routing the highway, holding public hearings, obtaining information useful to engineers, and designing and locating interchanges, overpasses, underpasses, drainage facilities, and service roads.

The ease of adjustments is affected by the procedures used in informing property owners and operators about the land a highway will take, appraising properties, purchasing and condemning rights-of-way, purchasing land remnants, paying owners, and taking possession.

The procedures have been a source of dissatisfaction in some States, as expressed at public hearings, at meetings of landowners, and also in letters to newspapers.

Concern regarding the adequacy of eminent domain procedures and laws for all public projects led to the creation of a Select Subcommittee on Real Property Acquisition by the Public Works Committee of the United States House of Representatives.

The subcommittee has begun to evaluate both procedures and compensation techniques used in acquiring lands for Federal programs and federally assisted State programs. It has solicited information from Government agencies, professional groups, and landowners and tenants regarding adequacy of eminent domain procedures and law. Land acquisition for highway rights-of-way has been one part of the broad field to be analyzed.

States also have started to review their laws of eminent domain and procedures and have suggested changes in both.

A detailed analysis was made in Wisconsin. Representatives of State agencies, property owners, attorneys, judges, appraisers, and researchers worked cooperatively in a yearlong study. They developed recommendations for modifying the law. A new law based on the recommendations was passed by the legislature. The new law and the procedures adopted by State agencies to implement it I discuss later.

Other States are making broader use of powers authorized under existing laws.

In Iowa, for example, the purchase and resale of excess land has aided farmers in reorganizing units crossed by a highway.

It will be helpful to review some of the immediate effects of a superhighway in Iowa in detail and then consider adjustments farm owners and operators made and how they were assisted by highway agencies.

AN ANALYSIS was made of changes over a 3-year period in 80 farms crossed by a 33-mile segment of Interstate Route 35 south of Des Moines.

The segment disrupted all or part of six sets of farm buildings. The right-of-way requirements averaged 19 acres a farm, just under 7 percent of the farmland in the farms the highway crosses.

Had no adjustments been made, 40 farms would have been left with an average of 66 acres separated from the farmstead. They would have had 43 separated parcels, of which 27 would have been accessible to the operator by road; the other tracts would have been landlocked by the highway. Because access to the highway is limited, the parcels that could be reached were actually separated from the farmstead by an additional road distance that ranged from one-half mile to more than 5 miles.

These adverse effects would have been even greater if engineers had not mapped the new highway to follow property lines and avoid farm buildings.

At the time right-of-way was acquired for Interstate 35, the Iowa Highway Commission was authorized to buy and sell property in addition to land needed for rights-of-way and to rent out property acquired but not needed.

The commission purchased buildings in the right-of-way or allowed farmers to move them. It purchased small separated parcels and remnants and entire units or large parcels from owners whose farms were badly cut up or who wanted to dispose of their lands and retire. Most of these excess lands were purchased along with the right-of-way. They were voluntary transactions between the commission and property owners. Amounts offered for the excess were based on the commission's appraisals of the property. Owners who sold excess land to the commission transferred to it the risk, time, and expense involved in selling isolated or landlocked parcels to the one or few persons who could use them.

The commission sold or rented most of the excess parcels to other farmers, some of whom were operators who had lost land and wished to reorganize their operating units. The transactions were made both during the period in which rights-of-way were being acquired and later. Owners of property adjacent to the parcels being sold were given first opportunity to buy or rent the land.

Five farms near an interchange would have been cut up badly if the Iowa Highway Commission had purchased only the needed right-of-way.

The commission arranged a number of almost simultaneous transactions. They made possible the reorganization of four of the units and the voluntary sale and reapportionment of the fifth. More than 500 acres of land worth nearly 200 thousand dollars changed hands. The transfers saved the commission more than 9 thousand dollars in construction costs.

The benefits of the procedure in facilitating adjustment of ownership and operating units are apparent, but negotiating such a series of trades takes time, and the commission assumed the risk and expense of holding excess land.

It may be required to prepare elaborate documentation to explain its involvement in the land market. Factors like those may keep authorities from such negotiations, even though fully authorized to do so.

As one measure of the actual change in the 80 farms crossed by Interstate

35, the purchase of right-of-way and the simultaneous purchase and disposition of excess land caused an immediate average reduction in farm size of about 10 percent.

Not all of the 80 farms remained in existence, however. From 1956, the crop year preceding the acquisition of right-of-way, until 1959, 11 of the 80 farms went out of existence—that is, the farm buildings had ceased to serve as headquarters of the farm operating unit, and the land had been absorbed by other units. Most had one of two distinguishing features: The farms were operated by persons nearing retirement, or taking the right-of-way caused serious interference with farm operations. Both features occurred on a few farms.

Five of the farmers whose units went out of existence took advantage of the opportunity to sell excess land to the highway commission. Three of them sold their units to the commission.

The farmers confronted with the loss of some or all of their buildings moved part of them from the right-of-way and sold the rest to the commission, or sold all buildings in the right-of-way and constructed additional buildings on their land to replace those lost, or sold the buildings to the commission but did not replace them.

Of the 69 farms that remained in existence in 1959, 41 had made a total of 83 real estate transactions since 1956—more than twice as many as other farms in the area that were not crossed by the highway. The commission was a party to 32 transactions—other than purchase of needed right-of-way—and involved one-third of the farms that remained in existence.

The commission bought 1,121 acres of excess lands along the 33 miles so as to transfer them back to farms that lost land and to others in the area. It bought separated parcels from approximately one-half of the owners who had tracts separated from the farmstead by the highway and mostly inaccessible by road.

Despite efforts of the commission to

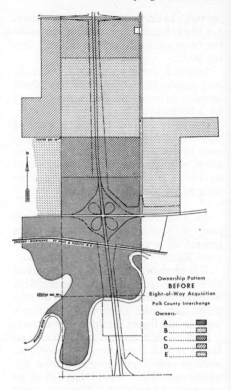

Ownership Pattern
BEFORE
Right-of-Way Acquisition
Polk County Interchange

Owners:
A ....
B ....
C ....
D ....
E ....

facilitate farm adjustment, the impact of the highway on some farms was large and persistent.

Seven-tenths of the farms crossed were smaller in 1959 than in 1956, the year before land was acquired. Most of them were operating with a reduction in acreage of 10 percent or more. Half of the farms with separate parcels did not dispose of them. The continued use of the separated parcels presented difficulties in many instances.

The farms crossed by the highway showed a greater dispersion in their tracts in 1959 than did other farms in the area. They operated more noncontiguous tracts, they had more acres separated from the farmstead and land adjoining it, and they had a larger percent of land located one or more miles from the farmstead. Operators of farms crossed by the highway reported other effects, such as problems of drainage and erosion.

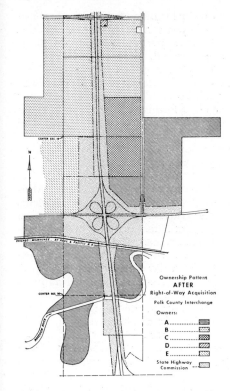

Ownership Pattern
AFTER
Right-of-Way Acquisition
Polk County Interchange

Owners:

A ....
B ....
C ....
D ....
E ....

State Highway
Commission ....

An analysis of costs of the project and benefits to the users is not intended to give complete consideration to all possible beneficial and disruptive effects of the highway. For example, little consideration may be given to the cost of providing community services because of the location of the highway or to the cost of adjustment by farmers or by the community. Even if the engineers attempt to analyze effects well beyond those estimated in costs of rights-of-way, the data necessary for the analyses may not be available.

If the engineers are to reduce the adverse effects, they should have additional facts about farms and the possible effects on them of alternative highway locations.

The details needed for each possible location include the amount and kind of agricultural land and buildings taken, value of properties, number of farmownership tracts and operating units bisected, and number and acreage of properties landlocked. Also needed are details of severance damages to farms that can be reduced by adjustments in the routing of the alternate highways and in the placement of related structures.

PLANNING EXPERIENCES in Iowa, Wisconsin, and other States furnish other examples of ways to reduce the initial disruptive effects and make farm adjustment an integral part of the highway program.

Two reasons why planners should try to reduce the magnitude of disruptive effects when they plan highways are that a reduction in expenditures by a highway department may result and some of the adverse effects for which no compensation is made may be minimized.

Planning engineers in Iowa and Wisconsin carefully consider factors necessary in making an accurate comparison of benefits to road users with project costs. They determine the cost of right-of-way, construction, maintenance, and operation. They consider economic benefits to road users through reduced vehicle operating costs and savings in time.

Facts about communities that would be helpful to planning engineers include details about the amount of farm-to-market travel and other rural traffic disrupted by each alternate location and its overpasses and interchanges; school, milk, mail, or other routes that may be disrupted; the extent of rerouting in passenger-miles or in cost of rerouting; soil conservation, irrigation, drainage, fire protection, and other districts that will be severed; and the extent to which any serious effects of such severance can be overcome by adjustments in the routing of the alternate highways and in placement of related structures.

Planning engineers should try also to determine whether the routing they choose and the position and design of related structures are consistent with county or town plans. If development is likely to occur at an interchange or in a nearby town, they should determine if the county or town government is equipped to plan and guide orderly changes in land use in that area.

If the county or town has neither the planning staff nor the necessary ordinances to guide orderly changes in land use, highway workers may need to assist local communities in formulating and implementing plans. Such cooperation benefits the community and provides some measure of control over the traffic generated by the urban or commercial development.

THE IDEA that engineers can reduce disruptive effects of highways by considering additional farm and community effects is not new. A thesis for a doctor's degree at Cornell University in 1951 on "The Severance of Farms by Limited Access Highways" showed how disruptive effects can be minimized. The author, R. B. Costello, who was trained in civil engineering and economics, analyzed actual farm situations along the New York State Thruway.

Severance damages to farms were large. The land made inaccessible entailed the greatest damage and the greatest resentment among farmers, rather than the few acres actually taken for limited-access highways.

The highway agency had no agricultural consultants to aid highway engineers in determining where the less productive lands were located. Property maps were not available to indicate the location of property lines. The engineers therefore had difficulty in routing highways through subnormal areas or along property lines two stated planning policies of their agency.

Dr. Costello recommended that engineers use data on soil productivity and property boundaries to minimize highway severance damages, obtain the assistance of county agricultural agents and county highway officials, and ask farmers and property owners for information about their farms. He demonstrated that sometimes a shift in highway location of a few hundred feet may bypass most of the productive soils in a particular group of farms being crossed.

He also described experiences by a second highway agency, a parkway commission. The commission adjusted its plans for highway location to avoid better land. It also acquired needed rights-of-way well in advance of construction, thereby allowing farmers more time to adjust their units.

A STUDY at the University of Minnesota in 1960 of farm adjustments along Interstate 35 in southeastern Minnesota disclosed the highway acquired 9 percent of the total acreage of 28 farms along one segment. Award payments, however, equaled 52 percent of the estimated market value of the land and buildings. One of the larger costs in the total was payment for buildings condemned and taken to make way for the highway.

Farms also were damaged by loss of nonbuilding improvements, such as fences, wells, and windbreaks; lower efficiency in scale of operation; changes in the crop and livestock systems; changes in the size or shape of fields; and loss of direct access to surrounding areas.

To reduce total payments to property owners, the Minnesota study recommended that economic and geographical data be included with more standard considerations of engineering and design. The Minnesota Highway Department has added workers trained in economics and geography to its staff to assist in making necessary studies of land use.

County conservation and agricultural specialists and other local officials can be helpful in the work of planning and designing highways. Employees of the Soil Conservation Service, Agricultural Extension Service, and Agricultural Stabilization and Conservation Service can provide information on the location and productivity of different soils; boundaries of farmownerships and operating units; irrigation, conservation, and drainage arrangements and problems; existing and proposed structures, facilities, and land treatments on individual farms; and boundaries of special-purpose districts.

Other local officials and groups can provide information helpful to highway planners. School officials have information on school routes and the location and composition of school districts. Postal officials can supply information on mail routes. County and town officials can give information on plans for police and fire protection. County agents and other agricultural officials can assist in delineating farm-to-market traffic patterns and otherwise supplement studies of origin and destination of traffic. County and town engineers and planners, local governing boards, and the county attorney can furnish data on community plans and the laws and procedures available to execute those plans. Owners and operators of land abutting proposed highways also can be important sources of helpful information.

Highway engineers in Iowa proved the value of such information. In planning and designing the segment of Interstate 35 south of Des Moines in 1956 and 1957, Iowa highway planners consulted school and postal officials in an effort to keep disruption of cross-traffic patterns to a minimum. The planners found the information helpful in spacing crossing points. In the same project, however, there was little contact between highway planners and owners of abutting land or local conservation and agricultural technicians.

A short time later, the Iowa Highway Commission made an effort to coordinate more completely the location, elevation, and design of highway drainage structures and conservation and drainage on abutting lands. Commission engineers enlisted the help of a Soil Conservation Service technician for one project.

They visited owners and operators of abutting lands and located tile systems and planned ways to preserve them. They also considered changes in the design and height of culverts to be placed under the highway and other related structures to insure proper drainage and control of erosion. The result was substantial control of erosion, better drainage, and savings in construction costs.

Engineers of the Wisconsin Highway Commission also have received helpful information from farmers.

In northeastern Wisconsin, a district engineer met with farmers who had or expected to have drainage problems because of a new highway. Each situation was explored, and adjustments accordingly were made later in existing structures.

A district engineer in western Wisconsin gave the residents information about the proposed location of an overpass near their small town. Farmers and businessmen suggested changes in its location on the basis of their knowledge of marketing, school transportation, and fire protection. The suggestions were made before the highway plans were final, and the suggested changes were reviewed and adopted by the Wisconsin commission.

Highway engineers in central Wisconsin found most helpful the facts and recommendations presented by local farmers for routing a new section of Highway 51 near Westfield. The farmers had used questionnaires to gather information on two possible routings. They determined probable loss of property, inefficiency imposed on farm operations, reduction in farm income, and loss of tax revenues from the alternate routings. They got the help of agricultural leaders in the county and members of the College of Agriculture and Extension Service in obtaining and analyzing the information.

The engineers analyzed the facts and the recommendations for routing made by farmers and decided that the recommended routing could be included advantageously within their overall proposals for relocating the highway.

For many farm and nonfarm people, local public hearings are the chief source of information about the location of new highways and a way in which people can express their views to the highway departments.

In some States, engineers do not present the alternative routes they consider, but limit discussion to approval or disapproval of the route the highway department has decided on. Other States disclose alternative routes for a proposed highway so as to get as much useful information as possible at a public hearing.

Hearings that are designed to provide information to the public and to elicit information and facts, as recommended by the Bureau of Public Roads, put engineers in touch with groups that have useful information and dispel the uncertainty by many people regarding new highways.

A STUDY in Wisconsin in 1959, "Property Owners' Problems and Legal Information They Need in Land Acquisition for Highways," disclosed that owners and operators can avoid difficult and costly problems if they are fully informed about acquisition of land. It recommended that a bulletin be prepared for owners and operators to explain rights of property owners, rights and procedures of the highway department, possibilities of adjustments available to owners and operators under procedures of the highway department, tax requirements on funds received, and the latitude of reinvestment permitted under the laws.

The Wisconsin study pointed out that State bar associations, university extension divisions, and highway departments might cooperate in preparing and distributing comprehensive informational bulletins. It suggested that bulletins be available to those attending public hearings and given to owners when they are informed that their lands will be acquired.

Plat maps, which show the exact amount and location of property needed from an owner, help owners and operators to determine the effects the right-of-way may have and to

plan adjustments before the actual taking. In Wisconsin, where the highway commission provided plat maps to owners who requested them, maps also indicated such details as access control on side and main roads near the property and limited highway easements to be acquired from abutting owners that would influence the adjustments they could make.

APPRAISAL PROCEDURES also can be carried out in a way that will assist farm adjustments.

Careful appraisals insure full compensation without overpayment to property owners. The appraisals should take into account all facts that influence values before and after the right-of-way is taken—the location of tile fields and mains, waterlines, sewage systems, and springs that may be affected; farm lanes that will need to be moved; new in-farm travel patterns required; and crop rotations and grazing arrangements that no longer will be possible. Such details could be overlooked or not fully considered.

If owners and operators are to be of help to appraisers, they must have prior notice of the appraisal. Appraisers often overlook this step, to the detriment of themselves and the landowners. Even worse, they may not call back to review facts with the owner or operator.

Wisconsin in 1960 revised its statutes on eminent domain to require that appraisers for highway agencies confer with an owner or his representative if reasonably possible. To be of help, obviously, the owners need advance information about the right-of-way and the acreage required.

The buyer's review of the appraisal with the owner provides a check on the completeness and the accuracy of the appraisal. To achieve a thorough review, the buyer may disclose the individual items in the appraisals and the importance the appraiser placed on each.

An inquiry by the highway-laws project at the Law School of the University of Wisconsin in 1958 found that some States disclosed appraisals on which offers were based, some disclosed only part of the appraisal data, and some disclosed none to the owner. The 1960 statutes in Wisconsin provided that the owner be allowed to inspect the appraisal or one of the appraisals of the property—if more than one is made—on which the offer of the highway commission is based.

Even though property owners may be offered alternative ways to make a settlement, such as the right to retain and move or dispose of buildings, sell some excess land, or sell all land and buildings, they may have difficulty in deciding among the alternatives. To facilitate their adjustment, owners need to be informed not only of the alternatives but also of the legal advantages and responsibilities that go with each settlement.

THE TIME of taking possession and payment are important factors.

If owners and operators are to adjust without costly interruptions in farm operations or elimination of entire enterprises, they need a reasonable time and enough money to finance their adjustment. The interval between the beginning of negotiations by the highway department and taking possession of the property sometimes is 3 months or less.

That may not be enough time. A city person may be able to find a new home in 2 or 3 months, but a farmer may need much more time to locate another farm or a set of farm buildings to rent or buy; move buildings, feed, machinery, livestock, and fences; construct new improvements back from the right-of-way; or harvest crops growing in the right-of-way.

To help overcome adjustment difficulties, some highway departments allow 6 months between notification to the property owner of the date of the taking and the actual taking.

A few use a technique called advanced acquisition, by which land is purchased a year or more in advance of construction. Highway departments thereby reduce their costs, especially in developing areas where buildings may otherwise be built on land to be used for highways. Advanced acquisition gives property owners more time for negotiating and for planning and making adjustments.

Owners and operators need adequate funds with which to finance adjustments. A bad situation may arise when property owners do not get paid until about the time they vacate— some cannot vacate until they acquire other suitable property and cannot acquire other property until they are paid for their present property.

Some States have provisions for making a partial payment before title is taken to provide early financial assistance to property owners. Some of the States limit the partial payment to the amount needed for moving buildings and fences or for other expenses incurred by owners before conveyance.

Some others, including Wisconsin, make payments promptly so that compensation is in the hands of owners before they are required to give up possession of the property.

Another procedure would be to allow property owners to sell their property to the highway agency and receive payment for it but continue to occupy the property, subject to certain leasing requirements, while they are trying to acquire other suitable property.

Payment for additional costs not covered by compensation for property acquired also would aid property owners and operators to adjust their units. It seems only fair to reimburse the owner for such costs as those of rearranging or moving personal property and refinancing the replacement property. Payment of these costs, however, probably would require permissive State legislation.

Wisconsin amended its eminent domain law in 1961 to expand the items for which highway agencies could make compensation. It divided compensable items into those that could be determined by appraisers before the acquisition of rights-of-way and those that could best be determined later.

In the appraisal before acquisition, the highway agency appraisers have included as compensable the land, improvements, and fixtures actually taken; existing access taken or restricted (this does not restrict the highway commission's police powers to regulate access); loss of air rights; loss of legal nonconforming use; damage resulting from severance of improvements or fixtures and proximity damage to remaining property from the location of the improvement; damages to property abutting on a highway right-of-way because of change of grade when there is a taking of land; and the cost of fencing reasonably necessary to separate land taken from the remainder of owner's land when the improvement does not include fencing of the right-of-way.

The 1961 Wisconsin law also authorized special claim procedures and payment for items of damage that can best be determined after the acquisition of land: Rearrangement of personal property on the same site; removal of the personal property to some other site; refinancing costs for the purchase of replacement property under certain conditions; net rental loss resulting from vacancies during the year preceding the taking of the property; and the expense of plans that are made unusable. The owner must show that damages exist, and he must apply to the highway agency for payment. Owners or tenants have a right to contest in court claims that are denied by a highway agency.

The Federal-Aid Highway Act of 1962 provided for relocation assistance to families and businesses. The Secretary of Commerce can approve as a part of the cost of construction on any of the Federal-aid highway systems relocation payments made by a State highway department to eligible persons. Payments may not exceed 200 dollars in the case of an individual or family, or 3 thousand dollars in the

case of a business concern (including the operation of a farm) or a nonprofit organization. Expenses for transportation for distances less than 50 miles are allowed. The Secretary cannot require a State to make relocation payments if the payment is not authorized by State law.

One final point needs to be reemphasized. New superhighways have a substantial impact on farms and rural communities in their path. The amount of farm disruption can be reduced, the required adjustments by farmers can be eased, and some savings can accrue to farmers and other taxpayers by modifications in procedures used by highway departments in planning highways and acquiring lands. In certain instances adjustments in procedures are possible only by passing new State laws.

RAYMOND D. VLASIN *is Leader, Resource Institutions Investigations, Land and Water Branch, Resource Development Economics Division, Economic Research Service. He was born in Nebraska and attended the University of Nebraska, where he earned the bachelor's and master's degrees. He received a doctorate from the University of Wisconsin. Dr. Vlasin has served as an economic consultant to the Select Subcommittee on Real Property Acquisition of the Committee on Public Works of the House of Representatives.*

For further reading:

Frey, J. C., Dansereau, H. K., Pashek, R. D., and Markham, J. W., *The Economic and Social Impact of Highways.* Pennsylvania State University, Agricultural Experiment Station Progress Report 219, University Park, 1960.

Gustafson, D., and Smith, E. G., Jr., *A Highway Change in Changing Faribault.* University of Minnesota, Minneapolis, 1959.

Heaney, D., *Valuation of Property for Highways Under Eminent Domain.* Automotive Safety Foundation, Washington, D.C., 1960.

Pine, W. H., and Hovey, R. M., *Impacts of Interstate Highway 70 on Farmers in Trego County, Kansas.* Kansas State University, Agricultural Economics Report 100, Manhattan, November 1961.

Vlasin, Raymond D., "Property Owners' Problems and Legal Information They Need in Land Acquisition for Highways." *Wisconsin Law Review* (No. 4, July 1959).

EXAMPLES

STATE the problem, define its terms, solve it: The tide of urbanization formed residential islands in agricultural communities in Los Angeles County; Dairy Valley was incorporated to protect a way of life threatened by political and economic events. Hawaii has a narrow-based economy; State-level zoning established land use districts within which county governments may plan and zone. Alaska needs to develop its land while protecting its amenities; the new State embarked on a comprehensive land management program. In Canada, which needs plans for a broadening spectrum of resource uses, farm and city folk are beginning to see themselves as parts of a whole. Japan has limited space for a large population; care and energy and a feeling for beauty make it possible for many Japanese to enjoy the benefits of the rural scene. Britain has had an abrupt rise in the pressure on land; new towns, green belts, planning, and Government action have helped. Western Europe turns to river basin planning and rural development to cure ills of the land. For some of our problems, garden clubs and centers and Rural Areas Development projects have an answer.

489

WINSTON W. CROUCH AND ROBERT N. GIORDANO

THE EXAMPLE
OF DAIRY VALLEY

LOS ANGELES was still one of the main agricultural counties of California in dollar value of its farm products in 1963, but urbanization has cut heavily into the acreage devoted to agricultural activities. The outward thrust of core cities is a steadily advancing tide, which forms residential islands in the midst of agricultural communities.

Twenty-nine new cities were incorporated in the Los Angeles County area between 1954 and 1963. One of the incentives to incorporate has been to keep old cities from annexing nearby tracts. Because annexation law in California favors local municipal expansionists, groups in suburban fringes often are inspired to use the remarkably permissive incorporation laws as a countermeasure.

A tremendous growth in population is a central factor in the drives to annex and incorporate. The Los Angeles Regional Planning Commission estimated that the population of the county reached 6,370,976 on April 1, 1962, an increase of one-third million persons since the 1960 census was taken. The rate of increase was 45.9 percent between 1950 and 1960.

As density of population increases and open areas disappear, municipal leaders have sought new means by which to gain advantage over their municipal rivals. By annexation they seek room for development. Often they try to block competing cities by annexing small strips of land, so as to annex small parcels later; the opposition groups are divided among local residents to insure favorable majorities in annexation referendums on specific parcels.

A city may annex "uninhabited" contiguous territory without the consent of its residents. A territory is deemed uninhabited if fewer than 12 registered voters reside within it at the time proceedings are instituted.

Some cities have tended to be quite uninhibited at times in their anxiety to annex surrounding territory. Others, more subtle, have employed carefully designated moves that skillfully excluded opponents so that an unincorporated community can be absorbed bit by bit. At times the only practical

491

defense against a divide-and-conquer annexation drive of an aggressive municipality has been incorporation as a separate city. Defensive activity to preserve the identity of a community has been one of the important causes of incorporation.

Other issues run parallel to the threat of annexation. A community may desire to maintain control of the use of its land to preserve a unique quality or character. Indeed, diversity has rated high among the values held by urban groups in Los Angeles County.

Some cities, such as Rolling Hills and Hidden Hills, have incorporated to keep intact a community of large, estate-type properties. Other communities wish to maintain a smalltown or village atmosphere. Three of the newly incorporated cities were organized to protect industrial developments and to keep residential and agricultural land use to a minimum.

ONE CITY—Dairy Valley—has been fighting to preserve an industry and a way of life that has existed in a corner of Los Angeles County for many years.

Steadily increasing population pressure threatened a valuable concentration of dairies, and long-established farms faced the prospect of being abated as a health menace to newly arrived subdivision dwellers. Control of planning and zoning became the key to preserving the existing mode of life.

The threat of annexation and eventual control of land use have made citizens of many communities want a grassroots administration. They have felt the county government had become too large and too far away to give adequate local service and representation and that local home rule would mean they could elect their own administration.

The social-economic makeup of many of these cities differs sharply from that of the traditional city, which usually is pictured as a composite of a central business district, manufacturing areas, and residences. The mercantile and manufacturing sections, because of their high value, strengthen the tax base and assist in supporting municipal services.

In California, a city receives a pro rata share of the State-collected municipal sales tax based on mercantile and local retailing businesses. The sales tax revenue in many instances comprises a major portion of the city's income.

The traditional city usually has a city hall, police and fire departments, and an array of departments that provide municipal services. The new cities often are not like that at all. Many have little or no business districts.

Some have industrial firms but relatively little residential development, and they want to remain that way. The communities that have little commercial enterprise must exist without the revenue commerce usually provides, and their income comes only from property taxes, license fees, and State subventions from State taxes, such as the automobile in-lieu tax, and taxes on gasoline and liquor. Most State subventions are apportioned on the basis of population.

Fees for liquor licenses are returned to the city of their origin, and revenue is available from fines and forfeitures imposed by law after arrest within the city. Some of the new municipalities have relied chiefly on the sales tax and State subventions and have levied no city property tax. School districts, which are separate from the municipal governments, continue to levy property taxes.

Much of the incorporation activity would not have been feasible or would have been difficult to achieve if it were not for the concept of county contract services. Many of the cities have established only a minimum of the traditional city facilities and depend on Los Angeles County to supply police protection, road maintenance, planning jail facilities, building inspection, health facilities, fire protection, library service, and other services, in accordance with county-city contracts.

The county-city contract system operates in several ways. For one, a city may contract with the county for a specific function, such as police protection, and pay the estimated cost of a unit of service such as a patrol car maintained for a specified number of hours a day. Again, the city may contract for a service, such as tax assessment, which the county performs for its own purposes. No variation in level of service is made in contracting for this type of service.

Under a general service agreement, a city may request a variety of services, such as engineering services and checking of plans, as need arises. For them, the city pays the cost of the work, plus a percentage for overhead costs of county administration. Finally, a city may obtain county fire protection and county library service by electing to remain within the appropriate special district and paying the district taxes. The county fire system and the library program are financed by special district taxes, the districts comprising cities as well as unincorporated areas.

In essence, when a city adopts the county-city contract system it substitutes county personnel and administration for city departments and city personnel. The sheriff becomes the city police chief. The county engineer becomes the city engineer. The county road commissioner becomes the street superintendent.

The city of Dairy Valley, incorporated in 1956, is one of the new cities formed to protect a way of life that was being threatened by economic and political events. It has elected to have its governmental services performed by the county under contract. It is unique in that it is devoted entirely to the dairy industry. Whatever commercial activity exists in the community is related to dairying. All residences are occupied by dairy owners and their employees.

The dairy industry in Los Angeles County operates quite differently from dairying in New York and Pennsylvania, for example. Most dairymen in New York and many in Pennsylvania try to grow on their own farms all the hay necessary to feed their cows and a substantial share of the grain. In those and other States where the market for fresh milk is excellent, good pasture and grass-legume silage are stressed.

Dairy farmers in Los Angeles County raise almost none of the feed for their cows. They keep herds of moderate size on small acreages and import feed from other localities. Farmland in Los Angeles County has become extremely valuable. The extent of dairy land has diminished, but the market for milk has increased. Dairies have been reduced to an average of 10 or 15 acres. An operator may keep as many as 300 milking cows on 15 acres. Most dairymen buy all grain and hay. Pastures have become feeding pens. Land has become too valuable to be used for producing feed.

The dairy industry was widely dispersed throughout Los Angeles County during the thirties. Pomona, El Monte, and the southeastern section of the county—Artesia, Norwalk, Downey, Bellflower, and Compton—were important producing areas. Less important ones were in Venice, Gardena, San Fernando Valley, and Long Beach.

The growth in population has increased the economic pressure on the dairy lands since 1930 and has intensified a demand for new dwellings. Subdividers brought about an exodus of dairymen from several farming areas, particularly the El Monte-Pomona and the southwestern sections of the county. It is estimated that urban encroachments on dairy land produced an average loss of one dairy a week between 1948 and 1950. In 1963 the boundaries of the city of Dairy Valley marked one of the main areas of dairy concentration in Los Angeles County.

BEFORE IT WAS incorporated, Dairy Valley was considered a part of the Artesia dairy community. From the midforties, dairymen were besieged by land speculators and subdividers, but they succeeded in thwarting attempts

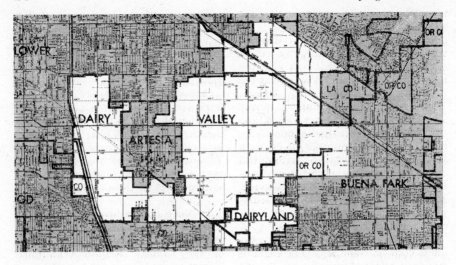

to urbanize the section. As the Los Angeles metropolitan complex developed, the value of land in the Artesia-Dairy Valley community increased from 1,500 dollars to more than 10 thousand dollars. Farmers throughout the southeastern part sold their land for large sums and relocated elsewhere.

Although the Los Angeles County Regional Planning Commission had zoned the area A–2–5 (heavy agriculture, with a minimum lot area of 5 acres), the dairymen felt that economic pressure would eventually force the commission to rezone. Developers had already begun to make inroads into the agricultural zone. Several acres which had previously been zoned A–2–5 were rezoned by the commission for residential use.

When this rezoning took place, the dairymen believed that dairying would be compelled to relocate elsewhere in California. Accordingly, some farms were allowed to deteriorate for a time. Broken equipment got only makeshift repairs. The dairymen ceased to invest more capital and reinvest profits to improve and maintain the farms that the cities would engulf in time. The community was divided as to the question, to sell out or fight.

It was not the subdividers who made the initial overtures to the dairymen concerning their land, however. A number of influential citizens in the central Artesia community formulated plans to incorporate the entire Artesia dairying complex into the city of Artesia. The Artesia Chamber of Commerce invited a group of dairymen to a meeting to discuss the problems of urban encroachment in the community. The incorporation plan was broached then, and suggestions were made for intensive development of the central Artesia business and residential district.

The dairymen studied the report of the chamber of commerce. They discovered what they considered to be a flaw in the incorporation plan—it contained no provision for improving the outlying area and protecting dairy interests. The dairymen believed their total input of property taxes, sales taxes, and license fees would be greater in the long run than the benefits they would derive from being part of the proposed city of Artesia.

To them, the only benefit of incorporation was a slightly longer life expectancy for the industry; between Los Angeles County and Artesia it was a matter of six of one and a half-dozen of the other. If their dairy industry was to be preserved, the most effective action would be to incorporate the part of the community that was devoted only to agriculture. Above all else, the one act that sparked the incorporation of Dairy Valley was the possibility of incorporating Artesia.

The idea of establishing a purely agricultural city with strict zoning laws to protect the farms had enough support to arouse a number of citizens. It was believed that an agricultural city would provide a stable environment in which dairying could survive. Many dairymen reevaluated the situation and decided to stay and rehabilitate their farms.

Meanwhile, another group was seeking to come into the area. The Cerritos Junior College District was in the process of acquiring 90 acres of choice dairy land adjacent to the Artesia business center. County authorities did not seem to be too concerned about rezoning the land to accommodate the new college, which was to serve a wide area.

The proposed city of Artesia viewed the construction, the new students, and staff as a potential source of income. The dairymen believed the most effective way to fight the acquisition of land by the junior college district was to incorporate.

Not all landowners in the proposed city of Dairy Valley favored the formation of an agricultural city with strict zoning laws. To many of the opponents, some of whom were foreign-born, naturalized citizens, incorporation was a new concept that implied many added responsibilities and changes in customs. Opponents of incorporation included operators and absentee landowners, who did not want to restrict the land to dairying because incorporation as an agricultural community would halt all urban development. All land bought by speculators could only be sold for agricultural purposes or left barren in hope that the city would someday change its zoning laws. A vigorous campaign was organized to defeat the movement.

The Board of Supervisors of Los Angeles County held hearings, as required by law, and thereafter modified the proposed boundaries and voted to submit the issue to the people at a general election.

Out of a total number of 1,080 registered voters, 865 voted—442 for incorporation and 396 against. Five councilmen were elected. A charter providing for a city manager system was adopted. The city was incorporated on April 24, 1956, and had a total area of 8.45 square miles.

To KEEP control over land use, the new council adopted as an interim zoning ordinance the A–2–5 ordinance of the County Regional Planning Commission. Heavy agricultural zoning provided a measure of security against urban encroachments, but dairymen saw a flaw in the land use pattern—a property on the southern boundary of the community that before the incorporation had been zoned for residential use and had been subdivided and placed on the market.

The incorporation movement was gathering momentum at the time the houses in the subdivision were offered for sale. The dairymen believed that people buying the homes would join with the opponents of incorporation, and the leaders of the incorporation movement therefore had made downpayments on many of the houses to control the occupancy of the tract, at least until after the election.

After incorporation was approved, two alternatives were open to the dairymen. They could retain the houses and rent them to persons who had an interest in the dairy industry or try to exclude the part of the city that was incompatible with an agricultural community. Under the existing exclusion statute, an area could not be excluded from an incorporated city without the consent of the residents of the affected area. Although dairymen owned many of the houses in the tract, an even larger number of individuals not connected with the dairy industry had purchased in the subdivision. A vote in favor of exclusion therefore was unlikely.

The total area of the tract is 0.064 square mile. Because of the low density of population in Dairy Valley, a tract that small can have enough voters to tip the balance of political power in the newly formed city away from the dairy group. The latter believed that the situation had to be corrected before the postincorporation election for council members came in 1958 to keep an antidairy group from electing members to the council.

In the 1957 legislative session, the Dairy Valley city attorney and council sought and obtained an amendment to the State's general city law to permit a city, within 5 years after incorporation, to exclude a portion of the city by vote of a majority of those voting in the city at large. Armed with this new legal formula, the city excluded the subdivided tract, leaving the balance of the city zoned for heavy agriculture uses.

At the same time, increasing the accessibility of Dairy Valley from all parts of Los Angeles and Orange Counties increases the desirability of the section for residential development. By the time this State freeway system is completed, Dairy Valley will be one of the few remaining large tracts of open space in the southeast portion of Los Angeles County. Assuming that the population pressure continues and that the demand for land for development as residential and commercial property continues in approximately the same intensity as that experienced since 1956, Dairy Valley will be in an advantageous position to shift from agricultural to residential use. Demand for housing and the cost of land will combine to make multiunit apartments feasible. By organizing a city to control land use, the dairy operators have maximized their investment in land and have offset the efforts to force sales before they reach the most advantageous price.

Single-purpose cities are fairly common in Los Angeles County. Unlike the city of Dairy Valley, most of them fit into the urban environment that dominates the metropolitan region. Some are exclusively residential. Some are largely industrial. Dairy Valley is different. Although it has pretty well excluded other land uses than dairying, it cannot exist in isolation from the surrounding area.

By establishing a city form of government, the dominant political group has determined the level of government services and controlled the tax demands made upon the economy of the community. They have been able also to protect the dairy operations from those who seek to oust them because of flies and odors.

They cannot control the costs of all governmental services, however. The area must participate in school programs that are largely metropolitan in character and standards. As valuations of dairy property rise, the Dairy Valley farmers have to pay more school taxes. This increases their costs and reduces their profits. Yet, as they approach that point, where it is not profitable to continue dairy operations, they can sell their property under favorable conditions.

The decision to incorporate as an agricultural city was probably the most rational choice the dairy owners could have made in 1956. California law gave them no protection against annexation by surrounding cities. The dairymen were able to take the initiative in incorporation and to propose city boundaries that included a majority of persons favorable to dairying. The law did not require any particular density of population to form a city.

Although the county supervisors altered the proposed city boundaries before calling an election, it could not prevent the proposed city of Dairy Valley from becoming a reality. After the city was organized, the controlling group of dairymen followed a rational policy by excluding residential tracts. They achieved a political unit in which there was a minimum number of conflicting interests. Although city government gave the dairymen the opportunity to have more governmental services than they needed or desired, it gave them the most effective method to protect their preferred land use that California law could provide.

The receipts obtained through restricted funds are derived from State-collected motor vehicle license fees, county aid to cities, the State gasoline taxes, fines and forfeitures, storm drainage refunds, and county allocations for highways-through-cities. The estimated total amount available for the 1962–1963 fiscal year was 149,951 dollars. Restricted funds may be used only to pay for specific functions performed; for example, vehicle license fees and gasoline tax receipts may be used only to maintain and build roads. The total funds estimated to be available from all sources for the 1962–1963 fiscal year amounted to 406,026 dollars. Thus the municipal transactions are of no small consequence, even though the city has an estimated population of 3,500 and an area of a little more than 8.5 square miles.

The budget for 1962–1963 allocated 112,905 dollars for general city functions, which included salaries and wages for the city manager, clerk, attorney, auditor, and receptionist; general city expenses (telephone, printing, public relations, travel); maintenance of the city hall; public safety; and engineering expenditures. The building and maintenance of streets and highways had an allocation of 154,700 dollars.

The estimated expenditure in 1962–1963 was 267,605 dollars, compared to 152,022 dollars the previous year. The costs of government have gone up, although the city has kept services as low as possible. It has employed a minimum of local staff and purchased the services from the county to gain the economies of a large-scale operation. The rise in costs of municipal services has forced Dairy Valley, like many other cities, to seek other sources of revenue.

Dairymen dislike taxes on real estate and personal property. The city council has not considered levying them. Because the city's population may remain stable, the possibility of increased State subventions, which are apportioned according to population, is scant. The only remaining possibility of raising additional revenue seemed to be to increase the city sales tax base.

The city obtained 55 thousand dollars in 1962 from commercial enterprises, chiefly gasoline stations, feed and grain distributors, a hardware store, fertilizer and cattle sales, and a few other franchises.

To increase the sales tax receipts and provide a greater variety of retail outlets, the city rezoned three areas on the major thoroughfares, two for retail stores and one for light manufacturing.

DURING the years since its incorporation, Dairy Valley has been able to sustain itself economically and agriculturally. But economic pressure has increased on dairymen to sell their farms and on the city council to open the city to residential and commercial development.

The environs of Dairy Valley have been subdivided, and the value of the remaining open acreage has increased rapidly. Land a short distance beyond the borders of Dairy Valley sold for 17 thousand dollars an acre in 1963.

Dairymen have said that economic pressure need not force the city government to rezone the municipality. Nowhere else in the State, they say, is the margin of profit on dairy products as high as in Dairy Valley; it is well located for dairying because of favorable climate and convenience to the large market of Los Angeles.

If a dairy farmer did sell his land, the only area in which it would be economically feasible to relocate and yet remain relatively close to the Los Angeles market is Chino, 60 miles eastward, in San Bernardino County. Land in Chino is less expensive, but operating costs there are greater and cows produce less milk because of the higher temperatures.

The farmers also point out that a dairy operator in Chino transporting 10 thousand pounds of milk a day to Los Angeles would pay 2,853 dollars more a year in shipping costs than would a dairyman in Dairy Valley. Furthermore, the high assessed valuation of land, lower cost of milk production, the established and comparatively close market, and the relatively high return on initial input encourage bankers to lend money to Dairy Valley farmers.

Taxes are an important consideration. Taxes imposed by the city, county, metropolitan water district, cemetery district, and mosquito abatement district are negligible. A more substantial tax claim is that of the five school districts within which Dairy Valley is located—Cerritos Junior College District, Excelsior High School District, and three elementary school districts. In each of the school districts, voters in Dairy Valley are combined with those in surrounding cities and unincorporated areas and thereby lack the voting influence that they exercise within the city. A typical dairyman who owns 15 acres in Dairy Valley paid approximately 4 thousand dollars in school taxes in 1963.

Several farmers in Dairy Valley own and operate farms in other sections of the State. We do not know whether they bought the other farms in anticipation of a move elsewhere, but men who do not own land outside the community have said they will retire from dairying if they have to move from their present locations.

PRESSURES from other than taxes and land speculators have started.

One is a division of political aline-ment in the city council. In the city election in 1962, two farmers who ran for the council said they would seek a change in the agricultural zoning laws to allow residential development. Other residents have expressed the view that if they wish to sell their property, they should not be held to a price determined by its value as dairy property; if it were sold to a developer, it would bring almost twice as much.

Another factor that may affect the ultimate status of Dairy Valley is the plan of the State highway commission to build two freeways through the many farms in the city. Many valuable acres will be taken out of production.

The superhighways and the conditions they bring are bound to upset the delicate balance among the various factors that determine the economic feasibility of maintaining the dairy industry.

Traffic on streets near the freeways will increase greatly and very likely will make inadequate the present law-enforcement supervision. More patrol cars may be needed. More traffic on the roads will mean increased road maintenance.

NEW SOURCES of revenue will have to be found to compensate the county for increased services to the city. The most logical method of acquiring the needed revenue would be to provide additional consumer services for those having access to the city via the streets and freeways. This would add to the city sales tax receipts. Naturally, more land would have to be rezoned to provide these services. The problem here lies in the fact that enough commercially oriented people may be integrated into the population to upset the balance of power held by the dairymen, although the balance of power would shift only if these people were resident voters.

WINSTON W. CROUCH *is professor of political science in the University of California at Los Angeles. He was director of its Bureau of Governmental Research from 1948 to 1962. He has served as commissioner of the Los Angeles County Civil Service Commission.*

ROBERT N. GIORDANO, *a graduate student in public administration in the University of California in 1962, formerly was a research assistant in the Bureau of Governmental Research and an administrative intern in the Los Angeles County Road Department.*

FREDERICK K. NUNNS

PLANNING AND
ZONING IN HAWAII

STATE-LEVEL zoning, with features widely sought but never before realized, was initiated in Hawaii in 1961. The features, all in one statutory package, include State-established land use districts within which county governments may plan and zone; areas reserved exclusively for agricultural or rural land uses; and a directive that tax assessments on real property be commensurate henceforth with authorized land uses.

The people's appreciation of the need for a new approach to the planning of land use and zoning was hastened by the problems of a narrow-based and rather unusual economy.

Federal expenditures, tourism, and agriculture comprise most of Hawaii's economic base. More than half of the State's support comes from expenditures of the Armed Forces and civilian Federal agencies. Tourist expenditures in 1962 were less than income from agriculture, although tourism has grown to major proportions.

These nonagricultural items are valuable parts of the economy, but the State needs to reduce its dependence on them. Military and tourist spending are markedly vulnerable to political changes and business recessions. Agriculture is still the most stable segment of the economic base, and as such merits protection plus any ex-

pansion that can be managed. The point is strengthened by the fact that Hawaii lacks the essentials for heavy industry, such as cheap power and high-value minerals.

Agriculture itself needs increased diversification, although some specialization is unavoidable. Sugarcane and pineapples, for good reason, occupy most of the arable acreage. Long-distance shipping and increasingly sharp competition from foreign and domestic producers demand high-value crops and ever-increasing efficiencies in production. Most of Hawaii's crops must be exportable, because a shift to self-sufficient production of staple foods would require an acreage equivalent to less than 4 percent of the area used by sugarcane alone.

New exportable crops, large-scale production, and conservation of the

499

best farmlands are needed therefore to keep our agricultural producers and dependent processing industries in a profitable position.

Progressive mechanization of the production of sugarcane and pineapples has brought increasing employment and business problems to the islands other than Oahu, because their economies have been almost wholly geared to oldtime plantation agriculture. A steady stream of population has moved to Oahu, because job opportunities have centered around Honolulu's expanded military facilities and tourist business. Eighty percent of the State's population lived on Oahu in 1963.

The continuous siphoning of population from the Neighbor Islands to Oahu has created a need for developing new jobs and business opportunities on the islands removed from Honolulu's metropolitan area. A larger portion of the State's tourist business would be helpful, but the greater longterm opportunities for the Neighbor Islands lie in the full development of the use potentials of the more than 3 million acres of nonarable lands. Foresters have estimated that an intensive forestry program could make a million acres of this land productive of exportable tropical hardwoods, which are prized but are not producible on the mainland.

Additional employment and business would be generated by increased development of needed outdoor recreational facilities, parks, scenic sites, and various attractions conducive to extension of tourist visits. Furthermore, planners believe that some of these nonarable lands could provide satisfactory space for urban expansion in lieu of prime croplands on all islands, including Oahu.

The migration of Neighbor Island population to Honolulu's environs intensified the urban boom that followed the Korean conflict and increased the pressures of new subdivisions on Oahu's choice farmlands, which comprise onehalf of the State's best agricultural acreage. Farmed tracts near rumored or scheduled subdivisions became harder and harder to buy, lease, and pay taxes on because even the most unrealistic speculative values often came to be accepted as plausible.

The impact of these speculative asking prices, whether for fee simple purchase or lease, undoubtedly encouraged premature retirement of land from agriculture. Very likely these inflated prices also have discouraged capital investments from outside sources.

Thus the need for comprehensive zoning of rural and urban land uses became clear.

TRADITIONAL PLANNING and zoning started in Hawaii at the county level when the city and county of Honolulu (Oahu's only local governing unit) initiated some rudimentary city zoning ordinances during the early 1900's. This type of local planning was complemented then and later by the limitedpurpose planning of several State-level (then Territorial) organizations for such needs as highway, airport, deepwater harbor, and homesteading programs.

A territorial planning board existed from 1937 to 1941, but its short life and public concentration on the Second World War precluded any far-reaching influence on long-range planning.

A new and persistent surge toward organized public planning developed when the Territorial Legislature of 1957 enacted three statutes (Acts 234, 35, and 150), which prepared the way for Hawaii's planning-zoning program.

Act 234 authorized all counties (the only form of local government) to plan and zone rural as well as urban land uses. Another section of the act directed the Territorial forestry office to assess the capabilities of the forest reserve areas and zone the land uses accordingly.

Act 35 established a Land Study Bureau at the University of Hawaii.

It directed the bureau to develop studies that classified, mapped, and rated all lands according to their capabilities in present and potential uses and to supply the Governor, the legislature, and other public agencies with factual information on land use.

The bureau thereupon collected, added to, and adapted available data on land resources for its program needs. The data provided information essential to the State and county planning that followed.

STATE-LEVEL PLANNING of land uses in an integrated and comprehensive manner was initiated by passage of Act 150. The resultant program became the forerunner of Hawaii's State zoning program and is the planning component of the State's planning-zoning program. As such, the planning program bears a heavy responsibility for facilitating long-range decisions.

Act 150 created a Department of Planning and Research to perform a program of unusual scope, influence, and coordinating functions. The act required that the agency be headed by a professional planner. In 1963 its duties were transferred to the Department of Economic Development.

THE CONTENT of the planning program is indicated by the department's statutory responsibilities:

Preparation and periodic updating of a generalized statewide plan of land use, transportation, and economic development to guide and assist the legislature, county planning units, and other governmental agencies.

Review of capital improvement programs and capital budgets submitted by other State departments and the four counties to determine whether the proposed expenditures are in accordance with the substance and priorities of the State's general plan of physical and economic development. Recommendations thereto are submitted each year to the Governor and the Hawaii Legislature.

Review of all State-financed planning projects, related research, and expenditures to determine whether they further the State's general plan. The Governor may suspend expenditures of affected projects upon receipt of adverse recommendations by the department.

Provision of technical advice and general assistance to county planning agencies. In this connection, Federal funds available for such purposes may be allocated to counties for approved planning studies.

Performance of special research, planning studies, and submission of recommendations respecting State-financed public facilities, capital improvements, and development projects.

The key assignment of the Department of Planning and Research was to prepare the State's initial long-range plan for economic development and beneficial patterns of rural and urban land uses.

HAWAII'S GENERAL PLAN, a 20-year projection of the use of land and economic development, was the department's first and most important creation. Its many aspects required the collaboration of many State, county, and Federal agencies.

I list a few of the contributions to indicate the varied information needed to develop the first version of the plan. The United States census provided data on population trends. The Armed Forces and other Federal agencies indicated future needs for space. The Hawaiian Departments of Social Services and Education estimated future needs and locations for public facilities. The Department of Land and Natural Resources indicated development plans for its State-owned acreages. The Department of Transportation projected its plans for future land, sea, and air facilities. The Department of Economic Development indicated localities where there was need and possibilities for commercial and industrial development. The four counties provided indicators of local planning goals through their respective master plans, which were in varying stages of progress.

The university's Land Study Bureau contributed statewide, generalized classifications that rated and mapped the lands according to their physical suitability for intensive agriculture. The land classification maps became major points of reference for developers of the general plan when various areas were allocated to rural and urban land uses.

The general plan was developed by the Department of Planning and Research from the contributions I mentioned and from its own supplementary studies.

Basic features of the plan included maps that plotted proposed locations of lands reserved exclusively for agricultural purposes; areas reserved for urban development, including residential subdivisions, resorts, and industrial and commercial centers; areas reserved for forestry, miscellaneous open space, and multipurpose needs; sites for institutional, educational, and park facilities and for airports and deepwater harbors; military and other Federal areas; and major highways needed to service the economy.

The plan was completed after 3 years of work. The legislature in 1961 adopted it by resolution as Hawaii's long-range guide toward balanced and coordinated economic development in all parts of the State; conservation of the best farmlands and other areas for uses vital to the State's interest; greater expansion and diversification of the overall economy; more profitable utilization of large, underdeveloped acreages; and well-placed expenditures for capital improvement.

A STATE ZONING statute was proposed to the legislature as the logical vehicle for implementing the general plan.

Emphasizing that the plan would have little value unless effective implementation followed its adoption, proponents submitted a bill that would have the State classify and zone all lands into major categories of use. Within this framework, the county governments would continue to zone and regulate specific uses of land.

Members of the legislature were by no means unanimously in favor of enacting such a far-reaching and un-

precedented statute. The State was experiencing a rousing boom in real estate, and believers in unrestricted speculative development and latecomers to the subdivision business had an understandable lack of enthusiasm for new zoning legislation.

Hawaii's history of strong centralized government was undoubtedly helpful to proponents of comprehensive State-level zoning. Important matters such as tax assessment, the collection and disbursement of revenue, major programs for capital improvement, and public education always have been administered firmly from the State or Territorial level.

The unusual simplicity of Hawaii's governmental structure was another factor that minimized resistance to State-directed zoning. Hawaii had never known more than one level of local government, the consolidated city and county unit. Separate municipalities and special purpose districts never existed. Thus few factions were inclined to resist restriction of prior privileges.

In any event, the bill to establish State zoning of major land uses was passed with support from both political parties, and Hawaii's State zoning law became Act 187 (SLH 1961). Governor William F. Quinn's signature made the act effective from July 11, 1961.

THE "FINDINGS and declaration of purpose" of the State zoning law were so perceptively expressed that they merit quotation:

"Inadequate controls have caused many of Hawaii's limited and valuable lands to be used for purposes that may have a short-term gain to a few but result in a long-term loss to the income and the growth potential of our economy. Inadequate bases for assessing lands according to their value in those uses that can best serve both the well-being of the owner and the well-being of the public have resulted in inequities in the tax burden, contributing to the forcing of land resources into uses that do not best serve the welfare of the state. Scattered subdivisions with expensive, yet reduced public services; the shifting of prime agricultural lands into nonrevenue producing residential uses when other lands are available that could serve adequately the urban needs; failure to utilize fully multiple-purpose lands; these are evidences of the need for public concern and action.

"Therefore the Legislature finds that in order to preserve, protect and encourage the development of the lands in the state for those uses to which they are best suited for the public welfare and to create a complementary assessment basis according to the contribution of the lands in those uses to which they are best suited, the power to zone should be exercised by the state and the methods of real property assessment should encourage rather than penalize those who would develop these uses."

A COMMISSION of nine members was created by Act 187 to administer the State zoning program. Seven commissioners selected by the Governor are nonsalaried. One serves at large. Six represent their respective senatorial districts. Two commissioners are ex officio voting members. One is the Director of the Department of Planning and Research. The other is the Director of the Department of Land and Natural Resources.

The commission is associated administratively with the Department of Planning and Research but is not controlled by it. An executive officer, experienced in planning and zoning, is employed by the commission to direct the zoning.

Unusual statutory powers permit the commission to bolster its operations by drafting data, facilities, and personal services from various departments of the State.

Four major land use districts constitute the framework of the zoning program. The commission must zone all lands of the State for four major types of uses—urban, agricultural, conservation, and rural.

Urban districts are to include existing urban areas, plus reserve areas sufficient for foreseeable urban growth. Boundaries are to remain unaltered until there is shown to be substantial need and justification for change.

Agricultural districts are to be reserved for farming, ranching, forestry, and other rural purposes determined to be compatible with agricultural activities. The commission's zoning is to give the greatest possible protection to tracts that have superior capabilities for intensive cultivation.

Conservation districts include (but are not limited to) lands that were set aside earlier for watershed purposes. Conservation of soil and water is an important objective. Other permissible uses include forestry in commercial and in noncommercial forms, public parks and other places for outdoor recreation, historic and scenic areas, wilderness areas, and other compatible activities.

Rural areas are primarily small farms intermixed with low-density residential areas.

Zoning responsibilities of the commission cease with the creation of the three major districts of land use. Within those districts, the four counties plan and zone permissible land uses within the urban and agricultural districts. The Department of Land and Natural Resources plans and zones the uses within the conservation districts, a responsibility that continues the department's earlier legislative mandate (Act 234) to plan and zone land uses within the State's forest and water-reserve areas.

Prompt creation of the major land use districts was regarded by the legislature as a matter of major importance to minimize "closing hour" additions of premature or unfortunately located urban developments legalized on a *fait accompli* basis before the district boundaries were established.

The commission therefore was directed to establish the boundaries of the major land use districts in two stages. The first stage involved the speedy creation of temporary or interim districts so as to hold the line until more deliberate studies of the second stage could develop boundaries of greater refinement.

TEMPORARY district boundaries and interim definition of permissive uses within urban, agricultural, and conservation districts were required of the commission on a statewide basis by or before 9 months of the effective date of the act.

The statute was explicit: ". . . Boundaries shall be determined and shown on interim use classification maps. These temporary districts shall be determined so far as practicable and reasonable to maintain existing uses and only permit changes in use that are already in progress. . . ."

Permanent district boundaries and use regulations were required of the commission within 24 months of the effective date of the act. Classification maps showing the proposed district boundaries in each county were required within 18 months. So was completion of proposed regulations as to the use of land.

Public hearings on proposed district boundaries and land use regulations were required of the commission during both stages of development. One or more hearings were necessary in the county concerned before the adoption of either item. All interested parties and governmental units were given opportunity to review the commission's proposals before the hearings. Protests or recommendations could be filed up to 15 days after a hearing.

The commission's decision on boundary locations and regulations had to be made within 90 days of the final hearing. The commission was also obliged to provide each county with copies of classification maps showing the district boundaries in final form.

Amendments of district boundaries or use regulations may be made at any time, subject to prescribed statutory procedures that permit reasonable speed of action when need and justification are clear but provide safeguards against pressured decisions when justification is subject to question.

A mandatory statewide review of district boundaries and land use regulations is required of the commission every 5 years from the date of their adoption, irrespective of adjustments that may have been made in the meantime. The intent of this provision is to insure that the district zoning keeps pace with changing needs.

The periodic reviews are to be made jointly with the counties and agencies concerned. Any changes made by the commission are to be effected under procedures required for adoption of district boundaries.

Any landowner, lessee, or public agency may submit a petition to the commission for amendment of a district boundary or land use regulation.

The commission itself may initiate a proposed change, subject to this procedure: The petition is delivered to the county planning unit in which the land is situated. The county is allowed 120 days to append its recommendations before submitting the petition to the commission. Within 120 days after receipt of the petition, the commission must advertise a public hearing on the island concerned. The public hearing is held 15 or more days after its notice, and the commission must arrive at a decision within 90 days but not earlier than 45 days after the date of the hearing.

Final action on a petitioned change thus could take as much as 12 months or as few as 10 weeks.

The petitioner must show reasonable proof that the land involved is needed for the currently disapproved use, that the area is unsuitable for the use prescribed by the district in which it lies, or that existing use regulations are unreasonable.

Favorable action on the petition requires affirmative votes from six of the nine commission members.

Special permits may be granted by the commission for certain unusual uses that are determined to be compatible with (but different from) those for which the district is classified.

Decisions on petitions must be preceded by a public hearing in the county affected within 120 days but not earlier than 30 days after the request is received.

Nonconforming uses may be continued by an owner or lessee if such uses were lawful before the commission's land use regulations were adopted. However, the commission may adopt regulations for elimination of nonconforming uses upon a change in ownership, lessee, or land use.

Appeals from any final order of the commission may be submitted to the appropriate circuit court.

TAX ASSESSMENTS and zoning entered a new era of coordination when State-level zoning was enacted.

Before 1961, the tax assessor relied principally on personal judgment to guide his valuation of rural lands presumed to be destined next for urban development. Now he receives a measure of guidance from the urban, agricultural, and conservation districts zoned by the commission.

The commission, upon adoption of district boundaries and land use regulations, must furnish certified copies of the district maps and use regulations to the Department of Taxation. "Thereafter the Department of Taxation shall, when making assessments of property within a district, give consideration to the use or uses that may be made thereof as well as the uses to which it is then devoted."

The statutory provision that land can be dedicated (set aside for a declared purpose) to a specific agricultural use added another aspect to the relationship between tax assessments and use of land.

Responsibility for this section of the zoning law may be attributed principally to livestock ranchers in Hawaii. Many ranchers had experienced sharp increases in tax valuation of grazing lands near speculative urban developments. Other cattlemen had fears of losing particularly valuable tracts be-

cause of urban development and changes in land use zoning.

The dedication of land gives limited protection to grazing lands against transfer to other uses and generally insures a relatively low level of tax valuation. Persons who want to engage in an agricultural enterprise whose use is higher than grazing have little reason to be interested in the dedication of land.

Owners and lessees of land within agricultural and conservation districts may dedicate all or part of such lands to specific agricultural uses for successive 10-year periods and thereby obtain tax assessments at values corresponding to such uses. Lessees were included in the provision, because payment of real property taxes generally is their responsibility in Hawaii.

Petitions for land dedication must be submitted to the Department of Taxation. Petitioning lessees must submit evidence of a lease that remains active for 10 years or more from the date of the petition unless the owner cosigns the request.

When the petition is received, the Department of Taxation must refer it to the Department of Planning and Research for a ruling as to whether the proposed land use conforms to the State's general plan of land use and economic development. The petition must be referred also to the Land Study Bureau for a classification of the tract as to agricultural productivity and a ruling as to reasonable suitability of the tract for the proposed use.

If both rulings are favorable, the Director of Taxation must approve the petition for land dedication and apply tax assessments for the ensuing year that conform to productivity of the tract in its dedicated use. Disapproved petitions may be appealed in the manner available for contesting other tax assessments.

Dedications are automatically renewable for successive 10-year periods. If the land is rezoned to an urban district, the dedication may be canceled within 60 days of the change, provided there is mutual agreement between the petitioner and the Director of Taxation.

Violations of the dedication cancel the special tax assessment privileges retroactively to the date of the petition, and "all differences in the amount of taxes that were paid and those that would have been due from assessment in the higher use shall be payable with a five per cent per annum penalty. . . ."

ENFORCEMENT of district zoning and land use regulations adopted by the Land Use Commission is assigned to the county planning units. Violations are to be reported to the commission.

Penalties for violation of district zoning are a fine of not more than 1 thousand dollars or imprisonment for not more than one year, or both.

A THOROUGH ANALYSIS of the strengths and weaknesses of the zoning program can be made only after it has been in operation for some time.

I should like to mention, however, several points based on my observation of the program after its first few months.

A well-developed general plan, adjusted periodically to changing conditions, is virtually indispensable to a comprehensive State zoning program, because it is a framework of reference for establishing and revising the location of major land use districts.

Readily available data directly applicable to planning and zoning are helpful. The Land Study Bureau has been able to provide maps of uniform scale and statewide coverage that show current land uses, major ownerships, and classifications of land according to levels of crop productivity. Soil and forest surveys made by the United States Department of Agriculture are of great value.

Minor changes of certain provisions in the State zoning law might have simplified the application of the program and facilitated its acceptance by the public at the outset.

There might have been a practical

advantage in substituting the name "rural district" for "agricultural district." The agricultural districts, as defined by statute, must also encompass certain residual rural uses that are compatible with agriculture but are not agricultural in nature. Pavementlike lava expanses, for instance, have no discernible need for conservation and little tangible use unless they happen to be where urban development is feasible.

The Department of Planning and Research might have had greater influence in the implementation of the master plan if the law had required that the commission use the department's professional services for most routine and special work projects. Such a change, however, would have been followed probably by the removal of the director of the department from the commission.

Had the language of the State zoning law emphasized that the State Land Use Commission would seek suggestions and active assistance from the county planning units in the course of establishing district boundaries and land use regulations, some of the initial fears that the counties would be ignored might have been lessened.

Effective implementation of the State zoning program will depend in part on widespread public familiarity with the provisions and objectives of the law. Citizens should be encouraged to review plans and be heard at public hearings, where they would counter the influence of proposals that are contrary to the public interest. Much educational work should be done along this line by appropriate public agencies.

Our Department of Taxation has expressed some concern about the impact of the State zoning law on tax revenues from real property. The statute provides that the department must consider removal of any increments of urban value from valuations of farmed lands within agricultural districts.

Now that certain lands within urban

districts are earmarked for urban development, it behooves the tax officials to assess them boldly at urban values, at levels in keeping with the estimated imminency of development. Guidance in this task can be obtained from county planning officials and county development plans. Thus the county can help to guide urban developments into desired channels by exercising some warranted influence on tax assessment levels, and the tax officials will have improved bases for defending their assessments.

Taxation of real property and resource development might be linked further and to mutual advantage by greater use of another device that has been used in Pittsburgh, New Zealand, parts of Australia, and elsewhere. It is the policy of taxing site values heavily and improvements lightly. Uniform application of this assessment procedure would tend to force certain areas into urban development that now stand virtually idle, economize on the total acreage taken for urban development, and make it unprofitable to maintain deteriorated areas in choice central locations. This approach, however, would also require judicious application to guard against premature forcing of higher land uses.

The State Land Use Commission is confronted with a delicate problem of balance in its task of delineating urban districts with sufficient reserve area for foreseeable urban growth.

The areas zoned at any time for urban expansion should not be minimized to the extent that long-range planning by private and public developers is hampered by scarcity of approved acreage.

Underzoning of reserve urban areas increases the need for frequent changes in district boundaries, and constant boundary changes add needless uncertainty to the planning of urban developers. Furthermore, skimpy reserve areas tend to place public planning and zoning in the position of following rather than guiding the development of land resources.

Overzoning of reserve urban areas, on the other hand, encourages an equally upsetting series of events. Rural land uses that would otherwise continue tend to be forced into premature and often unnecessary retirement by markedly higher taxes and uncertain tenure induced by the anticipation of urban development. In turn, the combination of overzoning and higher land costs frequently forces premature and marginal urban developments that are failure prone and susceptible to rapid deterioration.

Possible applications on the mainland of Hawaii's planning-zoning program vary according to the need of other States for comprehensive zoning of land uses, the simplicity of governmental structure, and established precedents in distribution of zoning powers.

It would be unrealistic, for instance, to consider that the prairie State of North Dakota has need for a replica of Hawaii's zoning system, which conspicuously protects choice farmland against urban sprawl.

Hawaii's ability to institute State-level planning and zoning was considerably strengthened by its tradition of strongly centralized government.

City and county government have never been divided. State-level dominance in finances, education, and resource development has never been challenged seriously.

The inhabitants of many other States are inclined to retain their traditionally strong powers of local government. Whereas Hawaii has two levels of government, they commonly have four or more—sometimes many, and usually overlapping. Furthermore, some mainland States lack active county or other local planning agencies, whereas Hawaii's counties all pursue an active planning-zoning program.

Nevertheless, the more densely populated mainland States have a growing realization that steps must be taken toward imposition of centralized zoning power if land resources are to be conserved, capital improvement expenditures are to be better utilized, and new urban developments are not to be endangered by rapid deterioration because of unfortunate location.

Hawaii's framework of comprehensive State-level zoning, within which local government is guided in its planning and zoning of specific uses, has logic that is difficult to refute. It seems likely that the essence of the Hawaiian system is most applicable on the mainland at the regional level, which commonly includes city and rural localities within one or more counties related in development.

THE RESULTS of zoning and planning in Hawaii will depend partly on wholehearted liaison between county planning officials and the work of the State Land Use Commission, which in 1963 was made part of the Department of Economic Development. Counties became its junior partners in considering petitions for special land use permits.

Despite the problems that are inevitable when rural land uses are zoned for the first time together with urban uses, a number of beneficial results may be expected with *effective* administration of the State zoning law.

I list some benefits that can materialize from the program:

District zoning, by virtue of being coordinated with the State's master plan of land use and economic development, should promote fuller development of all land resources and help to balance the State's economic development according to the needs and capacities of the various counties.

Farmers should have more assurance that good farmland within agricultural districts will be protected generally against urban absorption and be taxed at levels commensurate with agricultural values.

Premature and unnecessary retirement of good revenue-producing farmland for urban purposes should be lessened.

The requirement in the law that prime cropland be reserved for agricultural uses should encourage more urban development in localities where lands are marginal or unsuited for cultivation. Thus more productive use should be obtained from some lands that heretofore have yielded little income or tax revenue.

Land values should assume a more logical pattern upon the establishment of major land use districts. Sale and lease prices of most land within an agricultural district should tend toward approximated agricultural values, because the areas of speculative urban development are reduced. Longterm leases should be easier for farmers to obtain within an agricultural district.

Taxation of real property in rural areas should become simpler and more equitable. Tax assessors, by referring to the maps of major land use districts, will know where they should add or refrain from adding increments of urban value to their assessments.

Land developers, by operating within districts officially designated for urban usage, should have increased protection for their investments, because the likelihood of wildcat speculative subdivisions is reduced.

By reserving logical locations for urban development, and assuming responsibility for providing and maintaining urban-level services, the State and the counties should reduce their problems of delivering timely and economical services at costs that correspond to taxes paid.

FREDERICK K. NUNNS *became Director, Land Study Bureau, the University of Hawaii, at the close of 1957. Formerly he was an agricultural economist in the Land and Water Branch of the Farm Economics Division, Economic Research Service, the Department of Agriculture. In the midfifties he spent 3 years in the Middle East, where he was a professional consultant to the Turkish and Jordanian Governments on land development and utilization. Prior years of professional service were divided principally between Montana State University and the Bureau of Reclamation.*

SALVATORE DELEONARDIS AND HERBERT C. LANG

PLANNING FOR
ALASKA'S RESOURCES

THIS is the challenge in Alaska: To resolve the clash of two opposing forces. One is the need for more and faster development of the land and its resources. The other is the need to retain the qualities of wild country, grand scenery, and a hunting and fishing paradise that are cherished by all.

The challenge is a homegrown symptom of general national trends, such as the extension of concrete and asphalt, but it is unique in that in Alaska we are starting with a relatively undeveloped area and not with a complicated and historical pattern of settlement and development of land.

The admission of Alaska into the Union on January 3, 1959, signaled a major change in the pattern of landownership in the new State. Alaska was transformed overnight from a Territory with little land to a State with major important landholdings and responsibilities of management.

The State became the owner of an estimated 64 million acres of tidelands, and submerged lands along a coastline of some 30 thousand miles, longer than the coastline of the continental United States and Hawaii combined.

Title to the tidelands, the area between mean high and mean low tides, had been held in trust by the United States Government during Territorial days.

Submerged lands, from mean low seaward to the 3-mile limit, together with historic bays and the bottoms of inland navigable waters automatically became State property at statehood under the terms of the Submerged Lands Act of May 22, 1953 (Public Law 31).

School lands, sections 16 and 36 in each surveyed township, held in trust by the Federal Government, immediately reverted to State ownership. Section 33 in each surveyed township in the Tanana Valley, reserved for support of the University of Alaska, also became State property. Prior land grants to the Territory included an additional grant of 100 thousand acres for support of the university and one of 1 million acres for support of a mental health program.

509

The Alaska Statehood Act of July 7, 1958 (Public Law 85–508) confirmed and continued the previous quantity grants for the university and the mental health program, but canceled the school and university in-place section grants on any lands surveyed after statehood. The State, however, was authorized to select about 103.5 million additional acres from the public domain to compensate for the loss of the school section grant and for the general support of the new State.

About 365 million acres of land were added to the public domain of the United States when Alaska was purchased from Russia in 1867. By the time of statehood, the public domain had shrunk to fewer than 300 million acres, primarily because of large Federal land withdrawals for various official purposes. Public lands of the Federal Government that are not withdrawn or used for official Government purposes constitute the public domain.

The State and Federal Governments are now the major landholders in Alaska, with the State assuming an ever-increasing share of the land while progressing toward completion of its land selection program. Both will continue to be major landholders for many years. Policies concerning the management of land and resources followed by the State and Federal Governments will govern the direction, speed, and type of future developments in Alaska.

Even if Alaska selects all the land it is entitled to select, the Federal Government will still retain ownership to more than 250 million surface acres, or more than two-thirds of the entire land area in the State.

A considerable acreage of the lands in Federal ownership was withdrawn by 1963 for wildlife ranges, national parks and monuments, national forests, Indian reserves, and military reservations. Most of these areas, except several military installations, were largely undeveloped.

The timber resource in the national forests was brought into partial utilization by 1963 with the construction of two pulp mills in the southeastern part of the State. Of the three major park and monument areas, only Mount McKinley Park was developed to any extent. Mount Katmai and Glacier Bay National Monuments, accessible only by air or boat, were practically undeveloped.

Wildlife ranges and refuges, which cover huge parts of the State, were all undeveloped, except the Kenai National Moose Range.

Located within the most populous area of Alaska, the Kenai Moose Range is accessible by highway and plane. The only producing oilfield in the State was within its boundaries. The exploration, discovery, and production of oil has created a development boom and influx of population in the area near the range. The first oil refinery was under construction in 1963 on a site that the State sold to a refining company.

The Federal Government has been quick to withdraw large tracts of public lands. Their development or relinquishment has been slow. Private individuals cannot gain title to any of the withdrawn lands for any purpose. Mining and mineral extraction were allowed on a few of the withdrawn lands under special conditions, as in the case of the Kenai Moose Range, but sometimes the restrictions were so severe as to preclude any mining activity. In none of the reserves was mineral exploration encouraged in 1962.

Public land remaining outside of the withdrawn areas, the public domain, was subject to unrestricted settlement under the settlement laws, mineral leasing, and appropriation under the mining laws of the Federal Government.

It is a paradox that the Federal Government in Alaska, on the one hand, managed withdrawn land under the most stringent controls and, on the other, exercised virtually no control on the public domain.

Until 1949, the only way title to Federal public domain in Alaska could be obtained was through land settlement or development. Lands could not be purchased and title could not be acquired except through compliance with the settlement laws. The upshot often was improper, costly, and uneconomic land development, merely to enable individuals to obtain title to the land.

By the time Alaska became the 49th State in 1959, less than 1 percent of the surface area had passed into private ownership as a result of appropriation and development under one of the land settlement laws.

MOST OF THE LAND in private ownership in 1963 was located in and around the larger communities, scattered along the length of the relatively few access routes, and concentrated around former mining areas. Of the total homesteaded land in private ownership, less than 10 percent was used for agriculture in 1962. The rest lay unused.

Indiscriminate settlement under these laws has caused problems and hardships among citizens and to the local, State, and Federal Governments.

The residence requirements of the settlement laws were unrealistic and created hardships. Because many of the claims were remote, people on them lived far from areas of potential employment and normal community facilities, such as schools, hospitals, and public utilities.

Individuals had to complete required developments whether economically feasible or not and regardless of whether the land itself could support the type of development required by the particular settlement act. Although Alaska has a limited supply of lands suitable for the production of agricultural crops, homesteading remained the most popular way of obtaining title to Federal public lands. The homestead laws required settlement and cultivation and planting of part of the area, regardless of the agricultural capabilities of the soil or the marketability of the products.

Generally speaking, what settlement had taken place had been strung out along any available access route. The resulting low population density per unit of area created financial problems for State and local governments in building and maintaining roads and providing school services, power, and other utilities.

THE BASIC provisions of the Federal settlement laws were developed a century ago and were based on the economics and standards of living of that period. It is imperative that they be modified to reflect more nearly our modern economic and social standards and to prevent the flagrant waste of manpower and land resources they encourage.

Furthermore, some discretionary authority for classification of lands to highest and best use should be exercised on the public domain to encourage their proper use.

The lack of any control over the public domain has helped to discourage any attempt at developing a substantial timber industry, because adequate future supplies could not be guaranteed. Tracts opened by logging roads would soon be blanketed by homestead filings and the area lost for any future timber production. The State thus has been forced to select lands in desirable areas to protect itself and its citizens from the evils of indiscriminate settlement, destruction of resources, and impossible burdens of public services.

The application of basic tools of land management may do much to prevent the creation of rural slums on the public domain. Some assurance of future availability of resources encourages the development of resource-based industries and stabilizes the communities that naturally grow in their support.

State and local governments to a large extent may be relieved of the costs of furnishing a variety of governmental services to areas destined to return shortly to the natural condition because of premature development or because the land is physically incapable of supporting the development attempted.

It is relatively easy to sit back and

criticize someone else's land management program. It is altogether different to produce an alternate program that will satisfy all the criticisms and still remain effective.

Statehood gave Alaska an immediate land management responsibility and the chance to produce its own program, tailored to local economic and social conditions and the peculiar conditions of soil and climate. Alaska quickly accepted this challenge by enacting its land law in the first legislative session.

A difficult responsibility is the selection of lands to satisfy the grant of 103.5 million acres. All must be selected before 1984. This is how big the task is: The area that Alaska is entitled to select approximately equals the total area of California; if all the land is to be selected before 1984, an area the size of Rhode Island must be selected every 60 days for 25 years.

About 10 percent of the job had been completed by 1963, when some 12 million acres were selected from the public domain. The freedom of choice in selecting State land is an acute departure from virtually all of the previous land grants to new States, which generally included only certain numbered sections within each surveyed township. They often are referred to as in-place grants.

LAND SELECTION by Alaska therefore is a deliberate action and involves many policy decisions.

One is the determination of whether the State should select all or only part of the land it is entitled to select. One element of pressure was the limitation that lands under Federal mineral lease had to be selected before January 3, 1964. Some 19 million acres of public domain were under mineral lease in 1962.

It costs money to select lands: Direct costs in making selections and for future management, such as for fire protection, and indirect costs caused by the loss of Federal highway matching funds, which are based on the extent of Federal landownership within the State.

Against those costs must be balanced the utility of the land for State purposes, potential revenues from sale or lease of the land and the land resources, and the potential advantages of local control to encourage development. If the lands do not offer any of these advantages, they will eventually become a financial and management burden to the State.

Selections must be made in blocks of not less than 5,760 acres (nine sections), unless the lands selected are isolated from other public domain by withdrawn, patented, or entered lands. In any given block of minimum acreage size, some unproductive lands generally exist. They must also be included within the selection area.

It is all the more imperative therefore that selected lands have some potential for future development. It is not easy to predict which lands will have the greatest potential in the near and distant future, particularly because of the lack of any solid surveys of resources over much of the State.

Nor is land selection a job only for the State. The Federal Government, through the Bureau of Land Management, must process each application for selection and adjudicate each parcel where land conflicts exist. Once the status of the land has been cleared, the boundaries of the selected areas must be surveyed by the Bureau of Land Management before title can be issued to the State.

Before statehood, less than 1 percent of the surface area (some 2.7 million acres) of the State had been surveyed into townships and sections. Most of it has since passed into private ownership. Alaska selected approximately 12.5 million acres between 1959 and 1963. This selection represented about five times the total number of acres that have been processed, surveyed, and patented by the Federal Government in all the years since Alaska was purchased from Russia.

Land selection, therefore, is a major

task of both the State and the Federal Governments, for even with the use of the latest and more efficient aerial photography and electronic measuring devices, the surveying of selected areas looms as a major continuing project for the Federal Government.

THE PROPER MANAGEMENT of lands and resources in State ownership is, of course, one of the keys to rapid and lasting development. Alaska has been in a position to profit by examining both the successes and failures of land and resource management programs of the Federal and the other State Governments.

The Federal program and other State programs have been reviewed. Two pitfalls have become apparent: Land management in other States has been complicated because of the widely scattered pattern of lands in State ownership; many States also sold off lands and resources at nominal prices, often without regard for land capability. Those States have come to realize the error of such a policy, often to the sorrow of the taxpayer who must eventually shoulder the burden.

The first pitfall can be avoided by choosing large blocks of land, as Alaska has been required to do by law. A proper disposal program should insure that solid blocks of land are retained in State ownership rather than isolated parcels.

The second involves the entire policy and philosophy of land and resource management in Alaska, the goals we are attempting to achieve, and how this policy is operating.

The constitution of Alaska compels the application of the multiple-use concept in the management of land and resources. That concept requires that land be used for a variety of purposes if the uses are compatible with the primary or most important use.

The Alaska Land Act of 1959 (Chapter 169, Session Laws of Alaska 1959) established the Division of Lands within the Department of Natural Resources as the organization to select and manage State lands. The act also provided the basic tools for management and some of the policy guidelines.

The act provided that title could be issued to tidelands that were occupied before statehood, thus for the first time giving legal status to previous occupants. Before statehood, occupants of tidelands were in technical legal trespass. The Territory had no legal jurisdiction over those lands, and the Federal Government, while holding them in trust, did not exercise jurisdiction. Tidelands were occupied whenever and wherever there was need.

Sometimes the occupation was covered by the dubious authority of a special land use permit issued by the Federal Bureau of Land Management. This document merely permitted usage of the area, was revocable at any time, and did not allow the permittee to place any permanent improvements on the land. Permanent canneries, docks, wharves, and other developments nevertheless were placed on the tidelands, the only serious check being that the Corps of Engineers could prevent any development which was a hazard to, or interfered with, navigation.

It is hard to believe that no greater control was exercised in an area that has such a long coastline, depends to a large extent on waterborne transportation, and has salmon fishing as a major industry.

A substantial number of tideland tracts have been patented to the preference right occupants. More than a hundred others were being processed toward patent in 1963. This action by the State will help clear up what for years has been a complicated and confusing legal entanglement and a bar to financing of improvements. In addition, 31 municipalities located adjacent to tidelands (and in some cases partly on the tidelands) were eligible to receive title to the tidelands seaward of their boundaries. These involve some of the most highly developed and valuable tidelands in the State. Seven cities have received title; 14 others were being processed in 1963.

ALL MINERAL rights are reserved to the State, even if the surface is eventually leased or sold.

Minerals, whether hardrock, placer, or other, may be removed only under a lease arrangement or mining claim location. Hardrock or placer minerals are subject to location or to exploration under a prospecting site permit. Before actual mining, a lease must be obtained or the claim must be properly located and recorded.

A major departure from Federal mining law in regard to hardrock and placer minerals is that the State does not allow title to the minerals to pass into private ownership, regardless of the amount of assessment work performed on the mining location. A second departure is that no extralateral rights are recognized by the State. The third lies in a system of permits for prospecting sites that grant exclusive prediscovery rights for 2 years to permit the use of modern prospecting techniques.

Leasable minerals, defined by law as coal, phosphates, oil shale, sodium, sulfur, potassium, oil, and gas, may be leased competitively or noncompetitively, depending on certain criteria, as outlined in law. These leases must be issued competitively if the area is known to contain commercial quantities of the mineral or if it is located on tidelands and submerged lands or on lands that have been obtained by the State for support of the general schools, university, or mental health programs.

Prospecting permits and competitive and noncompetitive mineral leases had been issued by 1963 on more than 1 million acres of upland, tideland, and submerged lands. Bonus payments have been in the tens of millions of dollars, but, more important, the State is assured of a multimillion dollar yearly investment for exploration of these properties and ultimate substantial income from royalties on production from the leases.

DISPOSAL of State lands and resources is controlled rigidly by law.

Uplands may be leased or sold only after being classified as suitable for agriculture, residential, commercial, or private recreational use. If they are to be sold, the lands must first be offered for sale at public auction; the minimum acceptable price is the fair market value as determined by an appraisal. Lands not sold at the auction are available for purchase over the counter at fair market value on a first-come, first-served basis.

Tidelands, with the exceptions we noted, may be leased only. Upland and tideland leases may be issued for varying periods up to 55 years. Leases issued for any period up to 5 years and for an annual rental of less than 250 dollars may be negotiated. All other leases must be awarded at public auction after due advertising. The minimum acceptable rental is the fair market rental as determined by an appraisal. Rentals are adjustable at 5-year intervals, based on fair market rental at that time. Leases not issued at auction are also available over the counter at fair market rental on a first-come, first-served basis.

The State by 1963 had sold or leased more than 500 tracts totaling 45 thousand acres and valued at 3.25 million dollars. Many substantial economic developments were started on these lands.

Timberlands may not be sold, but sales of timber and such materials as gravel, sand, stone, and clay must be by public auction when the value exceeds 2,500 dollars. Sales involving lesser values may be negotiated.

Requirements as to advertising and the basing of all sales and leases on the appraised fair market value or fair market rental should insure that disposals are fair and that the State receives a reasonable return for the lands and resources utilized.

Provisions also were included in the Alaska Land Act of 1959 to allow homesteading on State lands. To implement the homestead provision of the act, regulations were developed by the Division of Lands after a series of pub-

ings according to a set schedule. The credits allowed are fixed by regulation and may or may not cover actual costs.

This credit system, however, does allow the person who actually intends to farm the land to use his funds for actual development and write off part or all of the remaining purchase price. If the land is not developed, the purchaser must pay the annual installments according to the terms of his contract.

ECONOMIC CONDITIONS will dictate to a large extent which lands will be developed.

The State homesteading program provides some incentive for developing the lands for agricultural purposes and was specifically designed for this. It is a flexible program and leaves the decision of when and how much to develop entirely up to the individual purchaser. The State does not recognize any land settlement claim or so-called squatter's rights.

Two sales of homesteads have been held on one concentrated area of the Kenai Peninsula, the first in the summer of 1961. Even in its first year, the program seemed to be working. Most purchasers made their second payments. Several applied for and received credits for development. A few purchasers assigned their interests to others. Some defaulted in their payments, and the land was made available for other sales.

The main management tool that has been given to the Division of Lands is the authority to classify lands to the highest and best use and to develop area plans for land use. A provision for reclassification, when necessary, permits a desirable flexibility to allow for shifts in development and population, new industries, and other changes that may occur. When the areas are within or adjacent to a community, the proposed plan for land use must be reviewed by the local planning agency or informed citizens. This provision prevents arbitrary decisions by government officials and encour-

lic hearings. Thus it was possible to develop a unique homesteading program tailored to the economic and social conditions in the State. The program is a synthesis of many recommendations and suggestions made at the hearings, including many from individuals who had obtained homesteads from the Federal Government. Alaska homesteading bears little resemblance to the Federal program.

Classification of the lands as potentially suitable for the production of agricultural crops is the first necessary step. Secondly, the area must be designated as a homestead area by the Director of the Division of Lands. Once these conditions have been met, the land is offered for sale at public auction, the minimum acceptable price being the appraised fair market value.

The purchaser must pay 10 percent of the total purchase price of the homestead unit at the auction. The balance is payable in nine annual installments. Interest at 5 percent is charged on the unpaid balance. The payments may be made in cash or may be worked off in whole or in part by developing the land. Neither development nor residence is mandatory.

Credits are offered for land clearing, fencing, wells, homes, and other build-

ages the active participation of the community in planning for future uses of lands.

Regulations require that lands be classified as to their highest and best use before any disposal action. The classification itself determines what disposal actions are permissible and whether the land must be made available for sale or lease or must be held in State ownership for a particular purpose. Good judgment is needed, for at this point the decision is made which will have lasting effects.

TEN GENERAL land classifications were in use in 1963:

Agricultural—lands that have the physical and climatic features to make them usable primarily for the production of agricultural crops. They may be disposed of by lease, sale, or homesteading.

Commercial-Industrial—lands that because of location, physical features, or adjacent developments may best be utilized for manufacturing or business. They may be sold or leased.

Grazing—lands that have the physical and climatic features that make them useful primarily for pasturing livestock. They may not be sold but may be leased.

Material—lands that are chiefly valuable for material, including the common varieties of sand, gravel, stone, pumice, pumicite, cinders, and clay. They may not be leased or sold.

Mineral—lands that are chiefly valuable for minerals, including coal, phosphate, oil shale, sodium, sulfur, potassium, wherever it seems likely that the surface use for the extraction of such minerals would preclude other utilization. These lands may not be sold but may be leased.

Public Recreation—lands that because of location, physical features, or adjacent development may be utilized best by the public for parks, scenic overlooks, campgrounds, historical sites, and fishing-hunting access sites. These lands may not be leased, sold, or otherwise disposed of.

Private Recreation—lands that because of their location, physical features, or adjacent development are chiefly valuable for noncommercial development as sites for private summer cabins and camps. They may be sold or leased.

Reserved Use—lands that have been transferred, assigned, or designated for present or future use by a governmental agency or for townsite development. They may not be leased, sold, or otherwise disposed of except to a qualified governmental agency.

Residential—lands whose location, physical features, or adjacent development are such that they may be utilized best for single- or multiple-unit dwellings. They may be leased or sold.

Timber—lands that are useful primarily for production of forest products or watershed protection. They may not be disposed of by sale or lease. Management and timber disposal are under a sustained-yield program.

ALASKANS are giving special attention to the growing need for provisions of open space for outdoor recreation. The new State, a land of incomparable scenic and wildlife resources, is starting out with a relatively clean slate. Proper planning can assure a system of parks and recreation areas second to none.

The State recreation program has been concentrated heavily on public campground and wayside scenic and rest stops and water access points for the use and enjoyment of the motoring public.

Sixty-three campgrounds and 12 scenic and rest areas in use in 1962 had more than 500 thousand visits. Hundreds of potential park areas are held in public ownership through the use of suitable land classifications. The authority to classify lands is an indispensable management device and can insure that the financial burdens faced by the other States in acquiring recreation and access sites will be prevented.

Subdivisions planned by the State include areas for parks development. When the tracts are near bodies of water, public access sites are reserved for use by the public. Alaska has such a limited road network that any water bodies accessible by road are subject to intensive public use, and it is imperative that all water bodies which are suitable for water-oriented recreation be serviced by public access sites.

Several subdivisions for both residential and private recreation purposes have been designed and offered for lease or sale. The subdivisions included tracts reserved for parks or public access.

Private recreation sites are made available for summer cabin sites and are usually located on shores of lakes or in other good recreation areas.

Public recreation and hunting and fishing access sites are reserved by suitable classification wherever required on State-owned lands, regardless of the grant under which the land was obtained. It is agreed that this policy is entirely justified and in the long run will prove of financial benefit to the State, notwithstanding an apparent loss of some immediate revenue.

Timberland (and potential timberland) is protected by classification. With proper forest management, these tracts can become the backbone of a stable forest products industry. Under the multiple-use concept of land management, they will be of great importance also for recreation, hunting, fishing, camping, and so on.

The authority for the Division of Lands to classify lands is a rough and preliminary zoning implement, effective only as long as the land remains in State ownership. Once patented, land may be utilized for any purpose in the absence of local zoning laws. The State is not authorized or equipped to establish and administer a statewide zoning system, and it is believed that it is not in the best interest of the State to undertake such a program.

PLANNING AND ZONING properly are local functions, and the authority for implementing planning and zoning regulations should remain at the local or intermediate level of government.

The State government assists and encourages local governments in these activities.

First-class cities in Alaska have assumed planning and zoning functions within their incorporated limits. Most communities have established building codes and regulate subdivision planning. The Division of Lands has cooperated with communities in planning and zoning State-owned lands within the community boundaries. The communities also have participated in advising the State on land classification in the areas surrounding the communities that are of importance for the support, growth, and expansion of the community.

Outside of the communities, there was no effective control on planning or zoning of privately owned lands in 1962. Building codes and subdivision regulations are nonexistent. These are local problems and are best handled by local government.

State law has established the framework for a borough system of local government somewhat analogous to the county system of government found in most other States.

Three degrees of boroughs may be established—first class, second class, and unorganized. The unorganized borough will be all of the lands within the State that are not incorporated into boroughs of the first or second class by July 1, 1963. The unorganized borough will be governed directly by the State and will not have any formal government or local power. First- and second-class boroughs are established by petition and general election.

First-class boroughs will have their own governing bodies. They are empowered to levy taxes. They must establish an area school system and assume planning and zoning jurisdiction within the borough area. They also will have the power to provide area services such as power, telephone, water, sewer, streets, police and fire protection.

Boroughs of the second class will have their own governing bodies with the authority to levy taxes and establish a school system. They will be responsible for planning and zoning. They also will have powers that the petition for incorporation specifically provides.

By the end of 1962, one second-class borough had been formed.

Preliminary discussions were held for the formation of a number of other boroughs throughout the State.

The active participation of the borough governments in land use planning and zoning of State lands within the boroughs is anticipated because it is in fact essential for orderly development. The costs of providing governmental services can be reduced a great deal by concentrating and grouping settlement units and other developments when possible. Lands can be and are reserved for potential community townsites, for the expansion of existing communities, or for the development of new communities. The local needs for schools and other public facilities can be met on these reserved areas.

ALASKA, owner of some 64 million acres of tideland and submerged land and potential owner of about 105 million acres of upland, must encourage rapid, orderly, and proper development of its land and resources with a minimum of delay and redtape. Failure to do so could place an impossible tax burden on its citizens to even carry on the minimum essentials of government.

The State government can go only so far, however, without usurping local governmental responsibilities, for which the people of Alaska have no desire. They have, in fact, insured that such a situation will not come to pass, by insisting on public hearings, public sales, and auctions and requiring the participation of local government in area land use planning. Zoning regulations and their enforcement have been left to local government, with the State participating only by land classification in broad general terms.

The Division of Lands has been chosen as the arm of State government to manage Alaska's lands and resources. It has been given a good, workable land law and the essential means to do an effective job of land management with the active participation of private citizens and local governments. We feel strongly that this is the only way that the job can be done properly.

Alaska is only in the infant stage of a land management program, designed to meet the challenge of insuring orderly and proper development of its land and resources. Only time will tell if this challenge has been met.

SALVATORE DeLEONARDIS *is Classification and Appraisal Officer, Division of Lands, in the Alaska Department of Natural Resources. He is stationed in Anchorage. After taking a bachelor's degree in forestry at Syracuse University and a master's degree in wildlife management at the University of Alaska, he became a range conservationist in the Bureau of Indian Affairs at Kotzebue in 1955 and later was Land Selection Officer in the Division of Lands.*

HERBERT C. LANG *is Lands Officer in the Division of Lands, Department of Natural Resources. He has degrees from the University of Alaska and the University of Pennsylvania. He was agricultural loan agent of the Territorial Department of Agriculture during 1955–1958 and Land Disposal Officer in the Division of Lands during 1958–1961.*

For further reading:
The Alaska Book. J. G. Ferguson Publishing Co., Chicago, 1960.
Colby, Merle E., *A Guide to Alaska, Last American Frontier.* The Macmillan Co., New York, 1940.
Gruening, Ernest, *The State of Alaska.* Random House, Inc., New York, 1954.
Hulley, Clarence C., *Alaska, Past and Present.* Binfords & Mort, Portland, Oreg., 1958.
Murie, Adolph, *A Naturalist in Alaska.* Devin-Adair Co., New York, 1961.
Potter, Jean, *Flying Frontiersmen.* The Macmillan Co., New York, 1956.
Rogers, George W., *Alaska in Transition; the Southeast Region.* The Johns Hopkins Press, Baltimore, 1960.
——*The Future of Alaska; Economic Consequences of Statehood.* The Johns Hopkins Press, Baltimore, 1962.

BALDUR H. KRISTJANSON

DEVELOPMENT OF RESOURCES IN CANADA

CANADA, like the United States, is facing difficult problems of resource management. Some have been with us since the early days of settlement, but the rapid growth of cities has brought new challenges. Some people may wonder that Canadians have such problems, for Canada is larger in area than the United States and has only about one-tenth as many people. It is important to remember, however, that Canada has only 100 million acres of improved farmland in production and that her population is concentrated.

Two-thirds of the people live in a narrow corridor of 700 miles from Quebec City to the city of Windsor in Ontario. More than one-half of the people in British Columbia reside in the extreme southwestern corner of that Province.

Despite a relatively small population of 20 million, the regional distribution and concentration of inhabitants is such that in areas like the St. Lawrence Lowlands and the Lower Fraser Valley, which are focal points of industrialization, urban areas are making critical demands on available land.

Besides the increasing pressures from urban dwellers for more use of the countryside, Canada must pay particular attention to the management and harvest of her resources for the export market. We may not wish to remain hewers of wood and drawers of water, but the fact is that the harvest of our natural resources is vital to our economy. The problem then becomes one of promoting efficient exploitation of our natural resources while accommodating at the same time a marked pressure from the city dweller for more freedom of action in the countryside.

To meet these twin objectives, planning is required. An approach to planning that gives proper recognition to the city as the dominant actor in the development process also is needed.

The question is: How does a country proceed to plan for this broadening spectrum of resource uses?

Canada is approaching this in various ways.

One interesting action was a Resources for Tomorrow Conference in Montreal in 1961. It was a nationwide, free, and open discussion of emerging problems in resource development. A good deal of attention was paid to regional planning. For Canadians, the conference turned the spotlight on a method by which the public can come to grips with its development problems in a thoroughly constructive and democratic way.

This is important, because if we need more public planning we also need more public participation in the planning process. If we can no longer afford to drift in an unplanned way, we can afford no less to leave the planning entirely to bureaucrats and experts.

There is in fact a discouraging tendency in this day and age for the average citizen to throw up his hands in despair where public issues are concerned. Things have become so complicated—or so it is said.

But have they? No. The issues remain fairly simple if we remember that the public in a democracy must set the goals. The goals in turn can be no more complicated than the public makes them. For example, the public probably wants full employment, clean water, adequate recreation areas, and so on. These are not complicated. The problems arise in finding ways of getting these things. It is here that the expert enters the picture to give the public a clear understanding of alternatives that can be pursued in reaching the various goals.

The Resources for Tomorrow Conference was based on this philosophy— the need for public clarification of goals, coupled with expert views of various ways by which the goals can be achieved.

The background documents on which conference discussions were based and the proceedings of the conference are available in print. They represent the thinking of more than 700 persons from all parts of Canada and all walks of life and were supported by 3 years of intensive preparation.

Conference publications include two volumes of background papers in the fields of agriculture, water, regional development, forestry, wildlife, recreation, and fisheries; a volume on the proceedings of the conference; and a guide to benefit-cost analysis.

I said the conference paid a good deal of attention to regional planning. This was so for two reasons.

First, to involve the public in a meaningful way, problems must be seen in the first instance in terms of the environment familiar to the people involved. Therefore the study of problems needs to begin within the various regions of a national economy.

Second, we could, for purposes of discussion, draw on a limited but growing experience in Canada with regional planning.

The Province of Ontario, for example, has become involved extensively in regional planning through its Conservation Authorities Act. The important sections of the act were described at the Resources for Tomorrow Conference, as follows:

Authorities are formed only at the request of the municipalities in a watershed. In other words, the people must take the initiative.

An authority is a form of commission—that is, a body corporate, and appoints its own officers and hires its own staff.

It must initiate its own schemes concerning flood control, land use, forestry, wildlife, parks, and so forth, within the framework of the Conservation Authorities Act.

It has power to expropriate land.

It engages its own engineers or other specialists.

It requests and receives the assistance of other departments of the Government, particularly Agriculture and Lands and Forests, for assistance in carrying out its schemes.

It raises its own funds from the taxes of the member municipalities and receives grants, mostly from the Ontario Government, and in special instances from the Federal Government.

Thirty authorities in Ontario in

1961 covered an area of 19,535 square miles and comprised 438 municipalities. Municipalities are represented in their respective authorities on a population basis. The authorities vary from 86 square miles to 2,614 square miles and from 8 member municipalities to 78 member municipalities.

THE PLANNING EXPERIENCE of the city of London, on the Thames River in southern Ontario, is typical of the activity under the Conservation Authorities Act.

Four pieces of planning legislation were applied to the Thames Valley region at London—the Conservation Authorities Act, the Planning Act, the Water Resources Commission Act, and the Highway Needs Program.

The Upper Thames Conservation Authority was initiated by a survey in 1945 under the Authorities Act. A further, more complete survey was made in 1950. A summary volume of the report of these surveys, with photographs, maps, charts, text, and a special section of recommendations was published. It is considered by the authority as its blueprint for action. The summary volume has been distributed through the municipalities and service clubs, and special efforts were made to insure that teachers received it. This attention to the information needs of community opinionmakers has had a profound effect on the acceptance of the program by residents of the valley.

Teachers who took geography courses at the University of Western Ontario were given instruction in the use of the report in teaching conservation in Ontario. The Ontario Department of Education advised teachers to present conservation material whenever the course of studies permitted its presentation in a proper scholarly and meaningful way. The teachers of the Thames Valley have directed attention to regional problems described in the report and so have made young people in schools and their parents keenly aware of the needs and possibilities.

Fanshawe Dam, near the city of Lon-don, is the largest construction project so far undertaken by the authority. Costs were shared by three levels of government, the Government of Canada contributing 37.5 percent; the government of Ontario, a like amount; and the authority, the remaining 25 percent.

The Upper Thames Conservation Authority has undertaken a fair number of projects of smaller magnitude. A lake formed by Fanshawe Dam has been turned into a recreation area; water-storage and recreation projects have been combined in other locations; stream channel improvement work has been done; and reforestation projects carried out. Hundreds of farm ponds have been planned and either built outright by the authority or subsidized by it. Scores of well-devised conservation education programs were carried out.

The Federal Government has announced its intention of participating with the Province and the authority in a complete watershed program involving flood control, farm ponds, storage dams, reforestation, management of wetlands, recreational use of lands, research investigations, and management programs.

The Federal and Provincial contributions are related to the engineering aspects of the watershed program, but the authority has always believed that the various aspects of river valley development are inseparable. Participation by the senior governments (Federal and Provincial) must be integral with the whole development.

PROF. E. G. PLEVA, in a background paper, "The Thames River Valley, Ontario," for the Resources for Tomorrow Conference, pointed out that the experience of the Upper Thames Conservation Authority suggests the following steps:

"1. Prepare as complete a survey and plan as your resources permit.

"2. Place the report in the hands of persons who are most concerned specifically with the future, namely the elected and appointed officials, the teachers in the elementary and secondary schools, and the residents of the area. The findings of the report should be presented to the general population through newspaper articles, radio scripts and television presentations, and the educational programs of the authority through fairs, youth groups, and service clubs.

"3. Be certain that your staging of projects is realistic. It is impossible to get public acceptance for a complete program immediately. The first project should aim at a partial solution of the major regional problem and at the same time create side effects of a beneficial nature. . . .

"4. Research and practice will modify the long-range plan as the program is developed. The fact that the original plan of area development has been modified is an evidence of strength in the procedure. It is inevitable that continuing research will indicate necessary modifications to the policy planners."

UNDER THE Provincial Planning Act, London became a regional city with control over the entire urban fringe.

The Ontario Water Resources Commission Act was passed in 1957 to enable the Province to cooperate with local municipalities in matters related to water supply and sewage disposal.

Under the Highway Needs Program, the Ontario Government prepared a 20-year program for highway construction, which planning officials in the London community have studied for implications that may affect plans of the conservation authority.

The use of the Planning Act and Conservation Authorities Act depends on the initiative of the municipalities and is adaptive in nature. Municipalities already firmly established in local government joined together in joint planning and operational devices for the purposes of regional or area urban development and for the conservation projects and programs.

London uses the Water Resources Commission Act to enter into agreements with the Province to finance, construct, and operate water-supply systems and sewage plants. Finally, London relates its program of street and road construction and maintenance to the Provincial highway program, and is aided in doing so by a Provincial grants system suited to such aims. This could be described as planning-sensitive legislation.

A FURTHER EXAMPLE of planning-sensitive legislation for a city-centered region exists in the Province of Alberta. The capital, Edmonton, has made considerable progress in planning within this framework.

The Edmonton District (Regional) Planning Commission covers 5 thousand square miles. Its boundaries, measured from the central city, run some 60 miles to the west and 24 miles to the north. Nineteen councils are members. The commission includes representation from the Departments of Agriculture, Education, and Highways, and representatives of the councils.

Within the boundaries of the commission live 29 percent of Alberta's population. It is diverse. It comprises rural, town, and city elements. The various elements have a sense of identity related to the complex interdependence existing between central city, district towns, and rural areas for a wide range of economic, social, and recreational activities.

Since 1951, the area has absorbed 32 to 58 percent of the annual increase of the Provincial population. This rapid growth has brought the whole area within the influence of the major urban center. This can be seen in relation to the rapid change in land use, the intensity of land use, traffic movement, utility extensions from the central city, and decentralization of certain major uses, such as airports, recreational facilities, institutions, and power stations.

The North Saskatchewan River, whose flow in 10 years varied between 106,600 c.f.s. (cubic feet per second) and 430 c.f.s., is a key factor in the Edmonton environment.

The Brazeau Dam, on a major foot-hills tributary stream, was completed in 1962. Its total cost was 24 million dollars, exclusive of power installations. It will eventually impound some 324 thousand acre-feet of water and will enable the flow of the North Saskatchewan to be stabilized at 1,500 c.f.s.

Ground water supplies have proved inadequate in most cases, and the district towns have begun to use the North Saskatchewan water supply. Thus they depend on the city treatment plant. Lines radiate up to 20 miles.

As an agriculture-based city, Edmonton had a growth potential of 2 thousand to 3 thousand persons a year. In the years since 1951 its average growth has been 16 thousand a year. The population of metropolitan Edmonton was 337 thousand in 1961.

Between 1951 and 1962, general urban, industrial, and related development in the Edmonton district used up agricultural land at the rate of about 2,200 acres a year. Financial implications have led the municipalities to consider the direction, sequence, and extent of this growth in terms of urban costs. Low residential densities of new developments have raised similar questions. Scattered development could double or triple the agricultural land affected and immeasurably influence urban costs and the quality of the environment.

A comment by D. Haskell, printed in the Edmonton Journal, is applicable to many cities:

"Modern traffic, like a many-bedded river, has torn wide gashes through today's central cities and has carried beyond the city large chunks of urban enterprise which now will never return to the center. . . . In some cities traffic takes up twice as much land as is given to all other forms of human occupancy. . . . This ratio, as high as it is, is still not high enough—it must increase."

THE LOCATION of a highway or an airport has wide repercussions. Thus governments at three levels—Federal,

Provincial, and municipal—must be involved in planning.

The Alberta Town and Rural Planning Act provides for Provincial, regional, and municipal planning agencies. The Edmonton and, indeed, the Alberta situation is unique in Canada because of the positive duty that the legislature imposes on local planning commissions to prepare a district plan and because of the extensive jurisdiction of each commission. The Edmonton Commission in 1961 had a staff of 11.

PROGRESS OF THE commission in achieving its goals was outlined at the Resources for Tomorrow Conference as follows:

"A regional preliminary plan is in effect; all development within the ambit of the plan is under control. The detailed metropolitan section of the plan is complete. It covers 400 square miles, of which some 70 square miles represent the area of the Edmonton urban municipalities, and it provides for estimated metropolitan land needs for 15 years. . . . The plan for Edmonton's metropolitan area is a section of the regional plan formulated by representatives of the total region and not by the metropolitan area urban councils alone. The highways section of the plan is completed and in force; all highway development is under strict control.

"The district and new towns section and the parks and recreation section are also far advanced; agreement has been reached on annexations; utility extensions, and sewage disposal (which involve regional towns some distance out); and a number of other studies have been undertaken. The regional water supply has been examined with regard to future needs. The long-term use of the Saskatchewan River Valley through the region is controlled through the plan, which also includes measures with regard to air and water pollution. The survey work for all lakes in the region, except the area of a newly admitted member, has been completed for the park and recreation section. Industrial and other urban growth has been encouraged and directed to regional towns with success."

A STATUTE known as the New Towns Act was adopted by the Provincial legislature in 1956 to insure rational siting and orderly development of new communities. Among the requirements of this act is that economic planning studies of land use within the townsite will accompany an application for incorporation. The governing body of a new town is, under the act, directly responsible to the Provincial Planning and Advisory Board. The new town of St. Albert, a few miles northwest of Edmonton, was established under the act.

The Province and member municipalities share equally the expenses of the commission, which must carry out certain definite studies and surveys on a district basis and prepare a district plan.

The adoption of the plan requires a two-thirds majority vote in favor by member municipalities and final approval by the Provincial Planning Advisory Board. Once the plan is adopted, no member municipality may permit a land use at variance with it.

The commission is also a land subdivision authority. It provides technical assistance to municipalities that do not have their own planning staff. The commission began in 1950 as an advisory body but has now come to assume much direct responsibility for regional planning.

IN A BACKGROUND paper for the Resources for Tomorrow Conference, F. Marlyn and H. N. Lash commented: "The commission has laid great stress on detailed studies and surveys, and . . . has completed studies on such matters as: the economic base, population projections, district water supply, district lake surveys, district towns, rural community structure and land use, metropolitan land use, land use along highways, smallholding and

country estate development, and the journey to work. A district transportation study has been planned.

"The principles and policies which have guided the commission touch on many diverse aspects of land use. These policies are by and large neither startlingly new nor unusual; their significance lies in the fact they are being applied on a regional basis, that they have been adapted to the area, and that they have gained municipal acceptance and are being implemented."

THESE EXAMPLES may suffice to indicate the interest Canadians have in coming to grips with the problems of urbanization and the kinds of action that are being taken.

To some extent at least we have tried to see the problem in the perspective of the whole economy and of the national development trends taking place. But we are still very much in the experimental stage, and much pioneering work remains to be done in achieving harmony between the environment and its people. The encouraging fact is that farm and city folk are beginning to see themselves as parts of a whole— parts that need to be fused together in a plan for living.

BALDUR H. KRISTJANSON *is Acting Assistant Deputy Minister, Canada Department of Agriculture, Ottawa. He was secretary of the Resources for Tomorrow Conference and formerly was employed in the Department of Northern Affairs and National Resources, Ottawa.*

For further reading:
Resources for Tomorrow Conference Secretariat, *Guide to Benefit-Cost Analysis.* Queen's Printer, Ottawa, Canada, 1962.
——— *Resources for Tomorrow*, Vol. 1. Background papers on agriculture, water and regional development. Queen's Printer, Ottawa, Canada, 1961.
——— *Resources for Tomorrow*, Vol. 2. Background papers on forestry, wildlife, recreation and fisheries. Queen's Printer, Ottawa, Canada, 1961.
——— *Resources for Tomorrow*, Vol. 3. Proceedings of the Resources for Tomorrow Conference. Queen's Printer, Ottawa, Canada, 1962.

JOHN L. CREECH

JAPAN—
LIKE A NATIONAL PARK

MANY travelers have experienced the beauty of rural Japan, the neat fields, villages framed by evergreens, wooded mountains, and the myriad islands close at hand. The Japanese cherish these national treasures. They are among the most Nature-minded people in the world. So many of them tour their island kingdom each year, it is as if the whole chain of islands were a national park, centered on majestic Fuji-no-yama.

The Japanese have preserved and improved their natural resources without interruption during a long and dramatic history. Now they demonstrate an ability to cope with an abrupt involvement in the modern world without losing sight of traditional ways of life and, in the midst of rapid industrial transition, a remarkable degree of self-discipline in preserving their resources and maintaining the social character of the country.

The crowding of many people on little land is conspicuous in Japan.

Some 93 million people inhabit 148 thousand square miles of mountain-festooned islands, approximately the size of California, most of which have been sifted through the fingers of preceding generations for more than 1,500 years.

Although less than one-sixth of the total land area is cultivated, more than 40 percent of the Japanese engage in agriculture. Now, as for centuries, they carefully employ the practices of terracing, irrigation, conservation of water, reclamation of peat lands, and many unique cultural methods. Their intense regard for countless details requires a far greater input of labor than would be economically feasible by American standards.

These ways of doing things, handed down from generation to generation, have resulted in high yields of crops. The yields of rice per acre, as an example, are among the highest in the world.

Anyone who has traveled in Japan is aware of the tremendous energy and time put into farming and can understand why the Japanese have become a nation of successful farmers—and also why Japan, through this same ability, has become a leader in industries such as shipbuilding, radio and optical equipment, and many kinds of consumer goods.

BUT MORE remarkable is the fact that the Japanese are able to devote similar energy and interest toward partaking of the natural and scenic beauties of their homeland. Leaders of government and industry, small shopkeepers, teachers—everybody takes excursions into the countryside—some to view the cherryblossoms or wild azaleas, others to climb the mountains and enjoy the hot springs. Most of these ventures are undertaken as group activities of business or social organizations, or children with their teachers, for travel is by bus or train. Even if there were sufficient private cars, the roads could never accommodate the numbers of people who travel to the parks of Japan.

Other enjoyments include many flower shows and exhibits of plants staged throughout the villages, according to the season of the year. One cannot miss the autumn chrysanthemum shows, for example, for many of the displays are arranged on the railway platforms, where the greatest number of people may see them.

Schoolchildren, too, are given every opportunity to enjoy Nature and to see the famous landscapes of the country. I have visited almost every mountain region of Japan and have always encountered schoolchildren, with their teachers, climbing the hills and exploring the natural wonders.

In the homes and around farms too small for a lawn, men and women create miniature gardens with stone lanterns and tiny pools, carefully train plants in pots, and plant flowers for cutting and arranging.

No more than 19 percent of the total area of Japan, predominantly a mountainous country, can ever be expected to be cultivated. Forests cover 66 percent of the area. Because of a high rainfall throughout the year, the forests are luxuriant, possibly the richest in woody species of any comparable part of the

world. The swift, short rivers that flow down from the mountains are also an important natural resource.

These two resources, the forests and the rivers, have been important in the development of Japan, not only from an economic standpoint but also in maintaining the rural character of the country.

Water for irrigation is essential to the rice culture, and since each small subdivision of land held by the farm family requires its share of irrigation water, a community plans the irrigation canals, dams, tunnels, and other means of distributing equally the benefits of this abundance of water.

The Japanese place great value on the esthetic qualities of the forests and rivers. Eleven percent of the land area is in parks and restricted forests, where felling of trees generally is prohibited, wildlife is protected, and visitors are encouraged. Japan has 19 national and 20 quasi-national parks, which are established on a basis similar to that of Europe, rather than the United States and Canada, where public and private lands can be designated as national park land. This system assures the protection of the beauty spots that the Japanese have prized for centuries.

A strict system of zoning is enforced in the parks. Some parts are kept under natural conditions for scientific study. Others are developed with lodges, parking facilities, and gardens for public enjoyment. In one year, 90 million visitors enjoy the parks, a total that almost equals the entire population.

A major reason for this intense interest in natural things stems from the rural origin of modern Japan.

Because more than 40 percent of the people live on farms and Japan is still a country of villages, most of the people who have entered into the tremendously dynamic life of the large cities still recall a rural background. Their attitude toward encroachment on the areas of natural beauty consequently is governed by an ingrained respect for their natural surroundings.

Thomas C. Smith, in his book, *The Agrarian Origins of Modern Japan,* pointed out that the tradition of village life is one of the factors that have perpetuated Japanese social character despite industrialization. In most countries, industry has broken up the peasant village, dispersed the population, and weakened its solidarity by creating deep class divisions. These developments did not make the same inroads into Japanese life. Today the Japanese village is predominantly a community of small farmers faced with the same problems of small-scale cultivation and marketing as their ancestors.

While the arrival of the modern suburban development in rural areas in the United States is not grounded in the same heritage as the Japanese village, it appears to have a somewhat similar social character—many people with similar circumstances of living, a lessening of class divisions, and an opportunity to enjoy equally the benefits of the rural scene, if we protect and expand the natural areas surrounding our new suburban communities. If the planners of our new communities will allow for natural parks and ponds and develop plans to beautify streets and

residential districts, an interest in their maintenance, use, and expansion will come naturally to citizens.

SINCE THE VILLAGE is a fundamental social institution of Japan, you may be interested in some aspects of the village structure.

As a horticulturist, I consider it particularly appropriate to illustrate the planned use of trees and shrubs on a communitywide basis. Some Japanese call it a residential forest.

Anyone who travels north or west of Tokyo across the Kanto plain sees small clusters of trees scattered about the cultivated fields. This area is called Musachi-no and was given over to intensive agriculture about 360 years ago, when numerous farms and villages were laid out.

The Kanto plain is characterized during the winter dry period by strong winds, which raised clouds of dust. The small forests were developed partly to curtail such wind erosion. Where the farmhouses were isolated, the so-called forest consisted of densely grown cryptomeria trees, broad-leaved evergreen hedges, and bamboo plots laid out to give the harmonious composition so typical of Japanese farm homes.

In some instances the villages were more precisely planned and the farm dwellings were grouped.

The village of Kurume-machi, not far from Tokyo, was developed in this fashion about 350 years ago. Each farmer initially was allotted 4.94 acres of forest and 7.41 acres of arable land. The farmhouses of Kurume-machi stand in a row along the main road for about a mile. Each house is surrounded by a belt of trees of similar species, giving the aspect of a single large forest. The main trees are located so as to produce a shelterbelt. In addition, these small forests are homes for birds, a device for conserving water, a source of firewood and timber, which is selectively cut, and a means of climate control, since the temperature inside the residential forest is cooler in summer and warmer in winter.

THE SPECIES in this particular forest are common Japanese trees, which, incidentally, are useful for landscape purposes in the United States. They include two conifers, Japanese cryptomeria (*Cryptomeria japonica*) and Sawara cypress (*Chamaecyparis pisifera*), and a number of broad-leaved trees—Japanese zelkova (*Zelkova serrata*), sweet olive (*Osmanthus fragrans*), Japanese cinnamon (*Cinnamomum japonicum*), sasanqua camellia (*Camellia sasanqua*), a kind of holly (*Ilex integra*), sweetbay (*Laurus nobilis*), sweet viburnum (*Viburnum odoratissimum*), Japanese hornbeam (*Carpinus*), and an evergreen oak (*Quercus acuta*). All, except zelkova and hornbeam, are evergreen.

These choice plants provide a pleasant setting to the farmhouse on which the forest is centered. Besides them, a small grove of bamboo provides poles and edible shoots. It should be noted that these residential forests, established more than 300 years ago, are still intact as a result of the careful selective cutting and replacement program followed by the residents.

In regions with a low water table, villagers, who previously had to walk 2 to 5 miles for water, found that once the residential forests had become established it was possible to drill wells locally.

The use of the residential forest has been successful not only in the plains but also in the mountainous regions of western Japan, where the forest plots are somewhat larger in size, up to 25 acres. Here, again, the permanency of the planting is emphasized. The conifers are cut on a selective basis, and the other trees are used for fuelwood after 14 or 15 years of growth. The dominant conifer species for these mountain dwellings is Japanese red pine (*Pinus densiflora*). An edible mushroom, shiitake (*Lentinus edodes*) is cultivated on logs on the forest floor. Additional species used include Japanese camellia (*Camellia japonica*), Japanese bayberry (*Myrica rubra*), and Japanese eurya (*Eurya japonica*)—all evergreen shrubs.

WHERE THE VILLAGES are subject to floods, as on the Hinokawa plain, the farmhouses are surrounded by earth mounds, on top of which the trees are planted. Japanese black pine (*Pinus thunbergii*) and bamboo appear most frequently in the flood plain plantings, which usually are held down to some 21 feet to 25 feet in height by topping. Seen from passing trains, the houses seem to be surrounded by tall hedges.

Where lower branches have been removed, shrubby specimens of Japanese euonymus (*Euonymus japonica*) are interplanted to maintain a compact unit. The farmhouse is thus surrounded by evergreen trees and hedge plantings, which protect against flood, wind, and dust; provide a source of small fuelwood and timber for farm repairs; bamboo, with so many essential uses in Japan; and an attractive setting for the farm home.

JOHN L. CREECH, *Assistant Chief, New Crops Research Branch, Crops Research Division, Agricultural Research Service, was trained as a horticulturist. Dr. Creech has undertaken three plant explorations to Japan in search of ornamental and economic plants.*

G. P. WIBBERLEY

BRITISH EXPERIENCE
IN LAND USE PLANNING

IN MOST societies, at least during their periods of settled growth, there have been various schools of thought as to the type of physical setting most conducive to the full life for an individual. Those who have extolled the virtue of the so-called simple rural life have had periods of dominance, whilst at other times, and amongst other groups, the cultural advantages of the city have been stressed.

Sentimentality, escapism, and different sets of personal values are all mixed up in the attitudes of individuals and groups about the worthwhileness of scattered as against nucleated settlement. The stress on actual and supposed urban values led to the development of much of the form and activities of cities and towns like 18th century London, Bath, and later Tunbridge Wells and Cheltenham in England and the dominance of Paris in French society.

The alleged benefits of the individual family farm and of rural society in general have been strong operative factors in the extensive and relatively rapid reclamation and agricultural development of the United States and Canada. Affection for the amenities of farmed countryside, woodland, and hill areas is also a potent and continuing force behind the preservation of much of rural Britain and even rural Europe.

Attitudes such as these, held and developed by influential individuals and by groups of like-minded individuals, are difficult to appraise systematically, but it is unwise, even foolish, to ignore them, as they are vital to any discussions and action by mature societies in relation to rural and urban land use.

The abrupt rise in the use of the surface of the land of Britain which modern-day urbanisation has involved is evident in the graph overleaf.

Whereas both population and the area under urban uses increased in roughly similar proportions between 1900 and 1925, the urban area has since soared above population in its rate of increase. Thus the area of urban land in England and Wales, which was 5.4 percent of the total in 1900, had

The Proportionate Increase in Population and Urban Land in England and Wales Since 1900–1901

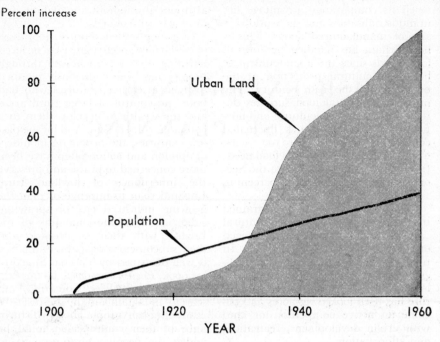

Percent increase

Urban Land

Population

YEAR

risen to only 6.2 percent by 1925, whereas in the next 25 years it rose to 9.7 percent. This illustrates the argument that a basic reason for urban growth is not so much population growth but the increasingly extensive use of land, both public and private, by individuals and society in general.

The important Anglo-American difference in this general picture is that of relative shortage of land. Of cultivable land, the United States has about 6 acres per person, whereas the United Kingdom has just over half an acre per person. (Total land per capita is 14 acres for the United States and 1 acre for the United Kingdom.)

THE AMOUNT of land needed to feed one person varies tremendously, and the assessment of the area required is a highly complex problem, because it involves consideration of the diet which people are prepared to accept, personal incomes, the relative prices for food,

other necessities and luxuries, political circumstances, the fertility and flexibility of use of cultivated land, and the availability of food from other areas or countries.

Yet with Western standards of diet, incomes, and yield levels of crops and livestock, the ratio of 1 acre of food-producing land or its food import equivalent to each inhabitant is certainly a minimum ratio. During the Second World War, the area of land needed for food for a person in the beleaguered United Kingdom was pushed down to 1.15 acres in 1943–1944, the tightest year of the war in relation to food supplies. Even on a basis as severe as this, Britain has obviously too little land to feed herself without fundamental changes in diet and crop and stock yields, whereas the United States can cope handsomely with the food needs of her people and yet neglect much of her land surface for food production.

A nation with too little land to feed itself easily can handle this problem through imports of food, especially when its comparative advantage lies in industrialisation and the worldwide sale of manufactured goods. This is how Britain has handled her overall food needs since the abandonment of home agricultural protection at the beginning of the 19th century. The proportion of total food supplies derived from home agricultural and horticultural production has fluctuated considerably in the past 100 years, from 48 percent or less of all food needs (by money value) just before the Second World War to about 55 percent in 1963.

This situation became so ingrained that at periods of home agricultural depression, considerable areas moved out of crop use into a derelict state. In times of agricultural prosperity, however, and especially immediately following the two World Wars, agriculture has itself looked for acres and become an active competitor for land with urban development, recreation, and afforestation.

Much of the expansion in home food supplies during 1939–1945 came from intensive cultivation of land nominally in agriculture but actually lying derelict or semiderelict within farm boundaries. It was only after this kind of reclamation had been completed that an actual expansion of the land being farmed became really important to the food production campaign and brought agriculture and urban growth into opposition.

But the important aspect of a country actually or potentially short of cultivable land is the type of thinking and emotional reaction of its inhabitants, particularly if its food supplies have been in obvious danger during the lifetime of the existing population. Land becomes something sacrosanct, and loss of it becomes a potential threat to one's personal security. A person's protest may become muted if the financial gain to him of the change in land use is considerable, but the background of potential land scarcity is enough to give an impetus to preservationist societies and preservationist attitudes throughout the nation and in its various councils.

In a long-settled country, too, most of the farmed countryside is an ordered harmony that has mellowed through time or has been consciously planned by men in earlier centuries who had both the control of large rural areas and the wealth to develop them to a conscious rural design. And for the past few centuries, the articulate moulders of opinion and action often have been more concerned to praise and preserve the inheritance of lowland rural England than to improve or plan the growing industrial city or sprawling suburbia. The emotional link of the English with their countryside and their subconscious rejection of the city is well described by Thomas Sharp in his book, *English Panorama*. To this emphasis on actual or potential land scarcity in Britain and the sensitivity of many English people to the disturbance of their countryside should be added the peculiar circumstances of the years 1940 to 1950. It was a time of considerable social and political discussion and action, much of it designed to rebuild a country after the end of the war which would be better to live in in all sorts of ways than it was in the years of the 1930's.

THREE REPORTS of special commissions appeared during the early part of this decade, and these reports were vital to the British experiment in the democratic control of land use. Each report left its mark on the thinking of responsible citizens and on legal and administrative arrangements made by the Government in the years towards the close of this decade.

These three reports were those of the Royal Commission on the Distribution of the Industrial Population (the Barlow report), 1940, Cmd. 6153; the Committee on Land Utilisation in Rural Areas (the Scott report), 1942, Cmd. 6378; and the Committee on

Compensation and Betterment (the Uthwatt report), 1942, Cmd. 6386.

The Barlow Committee considered what social, economic, and strategic disadvantages arose from the concentration of industry in certain areas and cities. The report recommended the redevelopment of congested urban areas and the dispersal of industries and associated population from such areas in order to give a more balanced scatter of employment throughout the country.

This strong recommendation for the control and planned dispersal of industry led to the Distribution of Industry Act of 1945, which gave financial and other powers to the Board of Trade to promote industrial development in the main problem industrial areas in Britain, which, in the past, have been peculiarly liable to severe unemployment in times of depression because of their dependence for employment and prosperity on a few basic industries.

The recommendations of the Scott Committee on the use of land in rural areas were in line with those of Barlow in relation to the need for a central planning body. The Scott report examined the effects upon agriculture of urban encroachment and was insistent that most of them were deleterious. The Committee stressed the necessity for maintaining the country's supply of good agricultural land and safeguarding natural amenities and asked that these factors should be an integral part of land planning decisions. This attractively written report, with its sharp division of opinion between a majority and a minority, had a considerable impact on private and official thinking.

All administrative and legal arrangements made in Britain in land planning since the time of this report have had built into them an emphasis on the safeguarding of good agricultural land.

The Uthwatt Committee also favoured the creation of a central land planning authority and suggested increased control of development, with greater power of compulsory purchase by local authorities and a drastic revision of the laws of compensation and betterment.

This last is a fundamental element in any control of land uses. The financial value of different land uses shows great variations, as between, for example, the value of a level piece of lowland Britain for agricultural use (450 dollars per acre), for residential use (ranging between 3 thousand to 15 thousand dollars per acre), with higher values still for industrial and commercial uses. The key point here is that much of this difference in financial value is not due to differences in the management ability of the owners of the different sites, but results fortuitously because of the action of other individuals and social groups.

A classic example of this is the case of a farmer owner-occupier whose land has rocketed in value because of intense urban growth in the neighbourhood. The farmer will probably have done nothing to bring about this urban growth, and his original purchase of the farm probably was related entirely to its farming capabilities. Yet the passage of time and the work and thought of other people have combined to give this owner of open land a windfall, which he has done nothing to earn directly. This financial gain is known as betterment.

On the other hand, the owners of some land can have the potential uses, and so the potential financial value, reduced through the lack of development in the area, through planning restrictions. This depreciation in the value of land can result from activities and decisions of people and groups outside the influence of the landowner. This type of financial loss has a prima facie case to some sort of compensation by the community at large. It was the complicated but fundamental interactions of this betterment and compensation problem in relation to land planning that were investigated by the Uthwatt Committee.

The powerful impact of these major

independent reports on public opinion and the fact that legal and administrative action was taken on many of their recommendations were due to the receptive state of the Nation to ideas of planning and reconstruction. The Coalition Government of the war and the Labour Government which followed it were politically in favour of this emphasis on land use controls, following the experience and success of much wartime planning and the urgent need for reconstruction in the bombed areas of cities and the drive to renew the expansion of residential areas as soon as hostilities had ceased.

IT IS ONLY DURING the past 50 years that recognition has grown in Britain that in such a densely populated country some form of coordination and control over the use of land is essential. Laissez faire liberalism was dominant during the 19th century as the accepted way toward national and individual prosperity, and most extensions of Government control or activity were resisted.

This produced, at least as far as the development of land was concerned, a situation in which buildings of all sorts were erected where sites were cheapest and most convenient. Building restrictions and preservation of general amenities were minimal.

The effect of this kind of development was part good and part bad. Both national and personal incomes rose, but these were accompanied by heavy congestion in those towns and cities that were most advantageously sited for industry. Large areas of the older parts of these expanding towns rapidly became unfit for human habitation, as judged by modern standards, and the towns became surrounded by a rash of suburban development, which sometimes used up land of great value for either mineral development, food production, or natural beauty.

Legislation began with town planning rather than town and country planning, and within towns it began with sanitation. The Housing & Town Planning Act of 1909 enabled local authorities to prepare planning schemes for land being developed or likely to be used for building purposes. Even so, most of the schemes concentrated only on the provision of proper sanitary arrangements.

The principle of compulsory town planning was introduced in Acts passed in 1919, strengthened somewhat in 1923 and 1925, and planning powers were given to the larger local authorities, known as County Councils.

The most important land planning legislation prior to the Second World War occurred in 1932, when a Town & Country Planning Act was passed. It provided for the preparation of land plans for the whole country, whether urban, potentially urban, or distinctly rural. Together with clauses designed to preserve buildings of special interest and woodlands of high amenity value, this Act made it possible for a man to be asked to pull down without compensation any property he had erected without planning permission if, later on, it was found to conflict with the planning provisions of the local authority.

Special legislation was enacted in 1935 to prevent building out along the sides of main highways. This Act came into being rather late because a good deal of this type of "ribbon" development had already occurred by this time.

Until the outbreak of the Second World War, however, the legislation and administration of land planning in the city and in the countryside had a number of serious faults.

The main one was that it was permissive in character—this emphasised its negative nature. Plans, usually of private persons, could be amended or rejected, but little constructive planning or creation of new development could be made by a local planning authority. Planning was still very much a local effort, and in many areas development plans were poorly prepared or not prepared at all. All plans, too, were weak and poorly used in practice because of the problem of liability to compensation if planning permission were refused for a proposed piece of development. The principle had been generally accepted throughout the country by this time that the property of a private individual could and should be subject to restrictions in the public interest, provided adequate compensation were paid for any private loss caused by such restrictions.

If, however, local planning authorities refused the application from a private individual to change his land into higher value use as being contrary to the best land use for the neighbourhood, they were faced with potentially heavy claims for compensation. On the other hand, the power to collect betterment from owners of property whose land had had its value increased as a result of planned development was not available or it proved impossible to collect in practice. This meant that few local planning authorities were able to meet any heavy claims for compensation. Consequently, planning schemes were drawn up in a very loose form with few practical restrictions on the permitted use of any area of land and little real control of the density of building development.

DURING THE WAR YEARS certain steps were taken to prepare the country for a more systematic and complete approach to land use planning. Following the recommendation of the three wartime committees mentioned previously, a new Government office, termed the Ministry of Town & Country Planning, was set up in 1943 to take over planning powers operated by the old Ministry of Health.

The new Ministry was charged with the task of "securing consistency and continuity in the framing and execution of a national policy with respect to the use and development of land." Emergency planning decisions relating to the restart of building development were covered in Acts passed in 1943, 1944, and 1945.

The most radical and comprehensive legislation, however, was passed in the Town & Country Planning Act of 1947. This repealed or consolidated previous planning legislation and set up a comprehensive planning system for the whole of England and Wales (with a special Act in the same year providing for a similar system for Scotland).

The main purposes of this Act were to:

(1) Secure the preparation of so-called Development Plans, which were based on careful surveys of the land and other resources of each major local authority area and would lay out in cartographic and written form the desirable range, place, and time of future development against which day-to-day proposals to develop could be judged as to their desirability.

(2) All development (that is, major changes in use), with certain exceptions, was brought under the planning control of either a local authority or of a central Government Department.

(3) The powers of local authorities to acquire and develop land themselves were strengthened with increased grant aid made to them from central Government funds for this purpose.

(4) Powers to handle special problems of amenity were strengthened, such as the preservation of trees of special beauty or importance and buildings of special historic or architectural interest and the control of advertisements.

(5) Some new arrangements were made to institute a nationwide collection of betterment as regards land that received unearned increments of financial value following general community development and payment of compensation to land that suffered a deterioration in its financial value as a result of planning decisions.

The main elements of these revolutionary financial provisions were:

(a) no development could be made without previous planning permission;

(b) this permitted development could not be carried out until the land concerned had been assessed for betterment (the "development charge," as it was called) and this sum paid;

(c) payment of compensation would be made (out of a fund of 300 million pounds) to anyone who could show that the Act had materially depreciated the value of his land as on July 1, 1948; no compensation would, however, be paid subsequently if and when planning permission were refused; and

(d) the price at which land could be bought compulsorily was to be its current market value in its existing use.

THE AIM OF THIS Financial Section was to achieve a balance between the money paid out in compensation and that received as betterment. This, it was hoped, would mean that major changes in land use could be made without consideration of changes in financial values and without fears for legal action and heavy bills for compensation to aggrieved owners.

As will be seen later, serious practical difficulties arose in the working of these provisions of the Act, and later Town & Country Planning Acts (those of 1953, 1954, and 1959) involved mainly changes in the financial provisions of the 1947 Act relating to compensation and betterment.

Other postwar British legislative enactments relating to land planning matters included the New Towns Acts of 1946, 1952, 1953, and 1955, which, following a careful report on the desirability of creating new towns in Britain, gave statutory and financial powers to the Minister of Town and Country Planning to designate areas for, the building of new towns by special public development corporations. Up to 1961, 15 new towns had been built or started under the provision of these Acts.

The National Parks & Access to the Countryside Act, 1949, set up a National Parks Commission to designate and control areas of outstanding national beauty as National Parks or required local planning authorities to survey existing public footpaths in the countryside and to improve public access to unfenced countryside.

THE PRACTICE of British Land Use Planning can be described in either of two ways, the first being a recital of the machinery involved, the second attempting to trace the course of action by an individual wishing to build a house on a piece of land.

The second method of description has been chosen because the skeleton of the planning machinery should be clear from the earlier description of postwar planning legislation.

The plot of land on which it is intended to build the house may already be owned by the intending builder or occupier. If it is not, its purchase from the existing owner will usually be made subject to planning permission being given for the housing development. This stipulation is made as there is such a difference in the financial value of a plot of land in different uses. In 1963 in southern England, for example, a plot of a quarter of an acre worth, say, 120 dollars in agricultural use will immediately increase in value to about 3,000 dollars if planning permission has been given for the erection of a house on it.

Planning permission for minor matters, such as the building of one or a few houses, is dealt with by the local administrative authority of the area, such as a Rural or Urban District Council. These local units operate their planning powers through delegation from the larger and main planning authorities—previously the County Councils—although larger towns and cities of county borough status are their own planning authorities.

In deciding whether or not to grant planning permission to the use for housing of the particular plot of land, the local planning authority will be guided by whether or not a Town Map has been prepared for the general locality. This Town Map, prepared by full planning committees for all major settlements in their area or county, especially for those areas where considerable major changes in land use are expected, have been a major task under the 1947 Town & Country Planning Act.

Present and expected population and its demographic structure, the age and condition of existing buildings, the structure of local employment and expected changes in it, the geographic character of the land of the area (for example, its agricultural qualities, mineral content, and topographical problems), parts of the area or building structure that have unusual scenic, historic, or architectural value—these are some of the analyses made prior to the drawing up both of development plans and of specific Town Maps.

These plans are prepared in a draft form at the outset and made available to the public for information and for them to exercise their democratic right to disagree with the proposals. Disagreements can be formalised by complaint about the proposed plan to the central Government office responsible for land planning—at this time (1963) the Ministry of Housing and Local Government. The disagreements are heard and resolved at public enquiries organised by this central department, and at them its planning inspectors hear the case made by the local planning committee in support of its draft plan and also the reasons why individuals, who are likely to be affected by the plan, disagree with it.

These nonjudicial appeals are reported on by the presiding inspector to the Minister responsible for land planning in the central Government, and the Minister either confirms the plan outright or with modifications designed to meet the objections that he thinks have been shown to be valid.

If a Town Map has been made and approved, the local authority will be able to decide, by examination of the plans, on the merits of the case for allowing residential accommodation to be constructed on the site in question. If the area concerned is zoned for residential use at densities of the order of that proposed by the applicant, general planning approval will be given to the proposed change of use, subject usually to further consideration of the detailed design and layout of the proposed house.

If a Town Map has not been made or approved for the area in question, this specific application will be considered as a special *ad hoc* case and decided on its planning merits.

Factors taken into consideration include the presence, absence, or nature of existing development in the proximity of the proposed house; the likely effect of the proposal on road problems, traffic, existing or proposed services, such as piped water, grid electricity, sewerage; and so on.

The local planning authority may turn down the application to build this particular house on this particular plot. If so, the prospective developer has the right to appeal against the decision in the same way as individuals affected can appeal against the proposals shown in draft development plans; the Minister of Housing & Local Government makes the final decision on the report of one of his inspectors.

It should be noted that the bulk of applications to develop by private individuals or groups are given planning permission. A study by Daniel R. Mandelker shows it to be some 85 percent of the total number of applications in an average county.

Larger and more complicated types of proposed development, such as large-scale building development, the siting of a new factory or major extensions to an existing one, and the commercial working of surface minerals, receive more involved consideration by the local and county planning authorities.

Considerable modifications may have to be made to the original plans before planning permission is finally given. In relation to major developments carried out by Government Departments themselves, consultation is necessary with local planning committees, and any major disputes are settled at the highest level—that is, in the Cabinet. In areas that have been designated as National Parks or as Nature Reserves, the local planning authorities are careful to evaluate the likely effects of any proposed development on the character and amenities of the area. For example, in some National Parks where the typical farm buildings and farmhouses are built in local stone, any new building development must use the same kind of stone unless there are special difficulties.

WHAT IS THE RELEVANCE of this experience to conditions in North America?

The British town and country planning machinery is complete in that all the country is covered by it, rather than only a few areas. This is in contrast to the United States, where the work done on land planning is very patchy. Again, this complete planning machinery in Britain works in practice.

Building development, both simple and complicated, takes place, and the basic planning machinery has remained practically unchanged since the 1947 Acts. This is probably due to the fact that, in operation, British town and country planning is very flexible. There are a minima of planning standards or dicta laid down and a maximum of local decisions.

This emphasis on the *ad hoc* method of handling land planning problems is both a strength and a weakness of the British way of doing things. It certainly allows for flexibility but maybe at the expense of general policy. It means that considerable differences in interpretation and decision exist from one part of the country to another. It also means that national planning policy is not carefully thought out and does not receive constant and critical examination and change. The British system can indeed be criticised in that the legal and administrative arrangements for planning have received more attention than the policies for planning committees.

Basic matters, such as standards to use relating to residential densities, land classification, decentralisation of

factories, service industries and office employment, traffic densities and probabilities, and cost and benefit analysis of large-scale proposals, have had to be discussed during the time when development plans were being made or had been made. For example, many discussions and important pieces of research on problems of land use have been carried out in Britain in the late fifties *after* planning authorities had taken arbitrary decisions in the development plans prepared during the early fifties.

In the public mind, land planning in Britain is associated with restrictions on the individual. This is so even though the large majority of applications for planning permission are allowed. There is, therefore, an acceptance of the need for land planning but no enthusiasm for it. (This acceptance is general and by the three major political parties, Conservative, Labour, and Liberal.) The probable major reason for this poor public image has been the emphasis on restricting private plans by the planning authorities with little spur to new development.

THE ONLY MAJOR constructive planning, in most people's minds, has been the creation of the new towns.

Probably, however, this defensive image of land planning would be hard to avoid in a long-settled, crowded country like England. There are so many competing claims for land and so many things done with land over the past centuries which have been attractive and interesting and for which an argument for preservation against change can be made. Therefore, the restrictive aspects of land planning are bound to be considerable, certainly much more than in North America, where there are relatively few legacies from the past in terms of building development and much land is in indifferent or low-value uses. Land planning on that Continent should be able to balance its restrictive aspects more easily with an emphasis on initiating desirable new building development and commercial growth in places where it is needed.

The deliberate creation of new towns has been the constructive part of British land planning which has created most interest and drawn most visitors, at least from outside Great Britain.

It is rather sad how well these towns are known abroad and relatively how little known they are by the domestic British. Maybe this is because they were started in the period of the Labour Government and their early stages ran into fair or foul criticism from the Conservative opposition. Only a few new towns have been started since 1951, but those already in existence continued to develop under a relatively disinterested Conservative Government. Three new ones were designated in 1962, but out of the 15 already in existence, 8 are ringed around London, 1 borders South Wales, another is in the East Midlands, 2 are in Durham, and 3 are in the central valley of Scotland.

These new towns, planned as a whole from the start with residential accommodation, local employment, commercial, shopping, and cultural facilities being provided as required, are now sufficiently far advanced to be judged by what there is to see and the reactions of the people working and living in them. Though there is nothing grand about them as towns, they are distinctive and provide very pleasant working and living conditions with a minimum of travel.

They also provide these conditions with an apparent plenitude of public open space even though, on analysis, the density of urban development is surprisingly high. Most of them are already a success economically. Some are a success esthetically. It is too early still to assess their success on social grounds.

THE GREEN BELT is another part of British planning policy that is quite impressive in concept and in practice.

It is a belt of open land around major cities where, except in exceptional

circumstances, relatively little building development is allowed. The land is used for agriculture and public and private open spaces, such as golf courses, playing fields, and common land.

The idea has been in operation for most of this century, and the results, particularly the retention of an attractive area of wooded and farmed land surrounding London, are obvious to the eye. It is a type of restriction that has an understandably dramatic effect on the spread of land values. Residential property already existing within the green belt, or on its inner or outer edge, is highly priced because of its favourable position.

Farmland within the green belt is valued above its agricultural worth but nowhere near the value of farmland with planning permission or likely permission. The fact that this land is protected from urban development means, therefore, a damming up of land values on the inner edge and a spread of rising land values in and around the settlements outside the green belt that have been zoned for some increase in population. Recent experience has shown that permanent or immovable green belts can only be preserved around growing cities if ample land and good transport facilities are available for urban use in the areas outside the green belt.

Has the green belt any value for North American conditions?

The fringes of American cities are strange to a European visitor. They appear to be rural deserts in that agriculture has so often retreated from the countryside. Between the time when commercial agriculture ceases to use this land and the time when active residential subdivision takes place much of the land goes derelict— back, slowly or quickly, to its natural vegetation, seemingly resting whilst its financial value rises towards the level it will reach in the market when subdivision actually takes place.

If, in certain selected areas, fringe land was conserved for nonresidential uses in a form of statutory green belt, would this be sufficient to maintain the agricultural use of it? It would probably do so if the authorities responsible for local tax assessment were sufficiently convinced of the permanence of the green belt to assess taxes due according to the existing use of the land rather than any prospective higher value use.

It has been suggested by Dr. Mandelker, who has a good knowledge of both American and British planning legislation and practice, that the concept of the English green belt would have value under American conditions if it became a creeping zone or else a narrow, rigid belt. In the latter case, planning restrictions can be strict and public purchase of part can be contemplated, if necessary, for public open space. In the case of the creeping green belt, this would involve only temporary restriction of use and so avoid the more serious of compensation problems. It would, however, be a valuable check on intermittent residential sprawl and yet allow the major movements of urban growth to find a natural outlet through time.

My PERSONAL view is that the narrow restrictive green belt is clearcut and can be made to work. This is partly be-cause the general public finds the idea of a green belt easy to grasp and its advantages to them in terms of an open lung into the countryside are appreciated. It is hard, however, to distinguish the creeping green belt from general planning restrictions in rural areas. It would be doubtful if agricultural land use would be improved in a creeping green belt in America as compared with the effect of strong action against scattered development based on carefully thought out and constructive regional plans whose findings have been well publicised.

WHAT, IF ANYTHING, can Americans gain from British experience of the vexed compensation and betterment problem? It should interest the country that produced the writer Henry George, with his ideas on the leading role of land in the taxation structure of a progressive country.

The British record shows the difficulties that arise in practice in a capitalistic society when attempts are made to compensate private individuals against deleterious effects on their property by the action of the general community from funds secured by the special taxation of unearned increments on land that has appreciated in value as a result of community action.

The history of the development charge, imposed between 1947 and 1951, shows the weakness of a system that attempts to cream off 100 percent of betterment. Since the abolition, in 1951, of any attempt to collect this type of unearned increment, the British land planning system has tried to operate under a land market free of practically any restrictions on values and one in which gains from capital appreciation on land have been excluded from general taxation.

IT SEEMS UNLIKELY that any special compensation and betterment legislation will be passed in Britain in the near future. It is much more likely that the problem will be handled by the introduction and extension of a general capital gains tax on private individuals.

This means that Britain will be following the example of United States in this kind of taxation.

THE SAME EXPLOSIVE FORCES are operating in North America as in Britain to disintegrate the old pattern of cities, towns, villages, and open countryside.

Though America is not worried by an absolute shortage of land resources, this disintegration is causing a wide and expensive scattering of physical services of all kinds—road networks, electricity, water and gas supplies, sewerage, commercial and educational establishments.

This scattering of heavy investment, together with the visual and social problems associated with it, are forcing Americans to consider the advisability of more land planning and less complete reliance on the untrammeled forces of private enterprise. But the British experience shows that any undue emphasis on the restrictive aspects of land planning soon leads to public apathy and criticism of planning.

It also shows the vital role of the planning official with the consequent need for well-trained men in the social and physical aspects of land development and salary scales high enough to prevent the entry of bribery and corruption into planning decisions. And if a system of land planning can be used in America to create more beautiful and more varied towns and cities and less neglected countryside than now exists there, then at least one European, the writer, would be glad to see the system put into operation.

G. P. WIBBERLEY *is reader and head of the Department of Agricultural Economics at Wye College in the University of London, England. He has worked closely with the agencies for land use planning in that country for many years, advising them on the agricultural aspects of their problems. Dr. Wibberley was visiting professor in land economics at the University of Illinois in 1961–1962 and is the author of* Agriculture and Urban Growth.

For further reading:

Best, Robin H., *The Major Land Uses of Great Britain*. Wye College, University of London, Report No. 4, 1959.

Crowe, Sylvia, *Tomorrow's Landscape*. Architectural Press, London, 1956.

Cullingworth, J. B., *Housing Needs and Planning Policy*. Routledge & Kegan Paul, London, 1960.

Heap, Desmond, *Outline of Planning Law*, 3d ed. Sweet & Maxwell, London, 1960.

Keeble, Lewis, *Principles and Practice of Town and Country Planning*, 2d edition. Estates Gazette, London, 1959.

Lichfield, Nathaniel, *Economics of Planned Development*. Estates Gazette, London, 1956.

Mandelker, Daniel R., *Green Belts and Urban Growth; English Town and Country Planning in Action*. University of Wisconsin Press, 1962.

Self, Peter, *Cities in Flood; the Problems of Urban Growth*. Faber & Faber, London, 1957.

Sharp, Thomas, *English Panorama*. Architectural Press, 1950.

Stamp, L. Dudley, *The Land of Britain; Its Use and Misuse*, 2d edition. Longmans, Green & Co., New York, 1950.

Wibberley, G. P., *Agriculture and Urban Growth. A Study of the Competition for Rural Land*. M. Joseph, London, 1959.

Acts of Parliament published by Her Majesty's Stationery Office, London: Town & Country Planning Act, 1932; Minister of Town & Country Planning Act, 1943; Town & Country Planning Act, 1944; New Towns Act, 1946; Town & Country Planning Act, 1947; Town & Country Planning (Scotland) Act, 1947; National Parks and Access to the Countryside Act, 1949; Town & Country Planning (Amendment) Act, 1951; Mineral Working's Act, 1951; Town Development Act, 1952; Town & Country Planning Act, 1954; Town & Country Planning (Scotland) Act, 1954; New Towns Act, 1955; Housing & Town Development (Scotland) Act, 1957; New Towns Act, 1958; Town & Country Planning Act, 1959; Town & Country Planning (Scotland) Act, 1959; New Towns Act, 1959, and Caravan Sites and Control of Development Act, 1960.

Official Reports published by Her Majesty's Stationery Office, London: Distribution of the Industrial Population (Barlow Report), Command 6153, 1940; Land Utilisation in Rural Areas (Scott Report), Command 6378, 1942; Compensation and Betterment (Uthwatt Report), Command 6386, 1942; Control of Land Use, Command 6537, 1944; Footpaths and Access to the Countryside, Command 7207, 1946; New Towns—Final Report, Command 6876, 1946; Report of the Committee on National Parks, Command 7121, 1947; Schuster Report on the Qualification of Planners, Command 8059, 1950; and Density of Residential Areas—Ministry of Town and Country Planning, 1952.

CARL B. BROWN, DONALD R. BURNETT, LUDWIG L.
KELLY, KARL S. LANDSTROM, AND WARREN T. MURPHY

RIVER BASIN PLANNING
IN WESTERN EUROPE

THE Food and Agriculture Organization of the United Nations sponsored a seminar on watershed management and study tour of six Western European countries in 1962. Forty men and women from 22 countries spent about a week each in the Netherlands, West Germany, Austria, Switzerland, France, and Italy. The five representatives from the United States wrote this chapter.

The seminar was designed to develop a better understanding of the physical, economic, and social aspects of the use of land and water in relation to the well-being of people.

It covered a wide scope of enterprises—sea reclamation in the Netherlands; improvement of river navigation and control of pollution on the Rhine and Rhone Rivers; reforestation and the control of erosion in West Germany, Switzerland, Austria, France, and Italy; rural redevelopment in Switzerland and France; land consolidation in the Netherlands, Switzerland, and Italy; protection of small watersheds in West Germany and Italy; avalanche control in Austria and Switzerland; multipurpose power, irrigation, and flood control in southern France; and other aspects of the use of land and water.

Each of the six countries we visited developed a program of lectures and field inspections to illustrate the phases of land and water development that have received particular attention in that country.

We Americans were impressed by the spectacular advances in some spheres of activity and the lag behind the United States in others. Of the many that we saw and studied to our great profit, we here describe a few to illustrate how the efficient use of land and water is creating in the old countries of Europe a new and better environment for its peoples.

SOME OF THE concepts of runoff and control of sediment have a long history in Western Europe. Much of the forest area had been cleared by the end of the Middle Ages. Clear-cutting, culti-

541

vation of oversteep slopes, excessive grazing, and litter raking brought the usual results of destructive floods, avalanches, and flows of debris. As early as the 13th century, several forest-covered areas in Switzerland were declared to be "banned forests." The cutting of living trees and detrimental secondary utilization were outlawed.

Germany, Austria, France, Switzerland, and Italy have developed progressively more intensive programs of forest management and reforestation and structural measures to control associated torrents and debris since the beginning of the 19th century. Major water projects, such as the correction works on the Rhine and other great rivers of Europe for navigation, local flood protection, and the development of hydroelectric power and the Zuider Zee reclamation in the Netherlands, were planned or underway before 1900. The timing in many ways parallels experience in the United States.

Western European countries are just now, however, beginning to enter an era of multipurpose development of watersheds and river basins. Concepts of small watershed projects that began to crystallize in this country in the thirties and have been progressively maturing from the late forties to date have taken root in Europe only since the midfifties.

THE PARLIAMENT of the Federal Republic of Germany in 1957 enacted what is known as the Water Household Law to provide for the general planning of the subwatersheds of the main rivers, such as the Rhine. The law provides for the development of plans to assure needed improvements in management of water and land for immediate purposes and for the next 30 years.

The Federal Government establishes the standards and undertakes the coordination of water planning, but the actual planning is carried out by the German Länder—States—under the direction of the State ministries of agriculture and forestry. One State, Hesse,

has underway or has completed 10 watershed management plans, comprising 76 percent of its total area of 8,147 square miles. The watersheds covered by the plans range from 52 to 2,682 square miles.

All but four are within the size limits authorized for Public Law 566 projects in the United States—namely, 250 thousand acres.

The plans are truly comprehensive. They include the present and future needs (up to 30 years) for flood control, use of surface and ground waters for domestic and industrial supply, irrigation, improvement and maintenance of water quality, recreation, and other purposes.

The planning takes into account the potential of planned economic development of the region. It also evaluates the potential downstream effects of whatever measures may be proposed in the watershed on navigation, hydropower, and control of water quality. The planning process is aimed at establishing a balance between demand and supply of water. The plans include suggestions for administrative procedures and data on admissible maximum water extraction from ground water and for granting of water rights to the use of surface water.

Benefit-cost analysis as it is practiced in the United States does not provide the framework for German water resource developments. Decisions are based on whether a project is needed to maintain or develop the resource. Projects decided upon are designed to last forever, insofar as technical knowledge permits. The rate of undertaking projects is dependent on National and State budgetary considerations.

The watershed plans of Hesse are worked out by planning groups comprised mainly of experts of the Water Management Department of the Ministry of Agriculture and Forestry. A special working group or committee of consultants is established also for each plan as a body to look after the interests of the respective municipalities, the chambers of agriculture and forestry, the chambers of industry and commerce, various economic associations, navigation authorities, and so on.

The planning is administratively in the Department of Water Management of the Hessian Ministry of Agriculture and Forestry. Other ministries cooperate. The Water Management Department works closely with the Federal authorities who have responsibility for seeing that the uniform national procedures are followed and also assists in coordination where the watersheds extend into other States, as is often the case.

Watershed projects corresponding rather closely to Public Law 566 projects have been started. One is the Weschnitz River watershed project, of 102,500 acres, in the south end of Hesse. It extends into Baden-Württemberg. The Weschnitz, an eastern tributary of the Rhine River, enters the Rhine just north of the old town of Worms, which is on the west bank. The principal town within the watershed is Weinheim, some 10 miles north of Heidelberg.

Flood control has been an unsolved problem in the Weschnitz area for centuries. Inundations are recorded since the Roman era. Attempts have been made since the 15th century again and again to reduce the flood dangers. About 24,700 acres, mainly agricultural land, are still subject to flooding. Damage to agriculture from inundation and waterlogging during the fifties averaged about 75 thousand dollars annually.

The plan of improvement includes a total of 11 small upstream floodwater-retarding structures and one floodwater-detention basin on the flood plain near Lorsch. Six of the retarding structures are upstream from Weinheim and have an aggregate capacity of 648 acre-feet. The capacity of five retarding structures on tributaries below Weinheim is 624 acre-feet; they control 18,532 acres, or 46 percent of the 42-thousand-acre drainage area above Weinheim. The capacity of the

Lorsch detention basin is 2,616 acre-feet.

The channel will be improved at Weinheim to increase its capacity. Deepening the river bottom makes possible the improvement of the lateral drainage of the agricultural area to provide substantial benefits. A number of roads and field-path bridges have been constructed or reconstructed.

The project is sponsored by the Weschnitz Association, founded in 1958. Construction was started the same year. Members of the association are 3 subassociations, comprising 18 villages, the State of Hesse, and the county of Bergstrasse. The estimated total cost of the project is 5.5 million dollars. It involves large subsidies from the Federal Government and the States.

A second watershed project lies in the State of Baden-Württemberg, about midway between Stuttgart and Nürnberg, in Aalen and Crailsheim Counties. This project is planned for flood control, storage of water for industrial and agricultural use, and improvement of the low flow of the Jagst River to control water quality. The project was undertaken by the Upper Jagst Water Association, comprised of municipalities, owners of hydroelectric plants, and other water users, and the counties of Aalen and Crailsheim.

The first stage of the project is in the upper watershed in Aalen County. Where the Jagst leaves this county, the drainage area is about 81.5 thousand acres.

The plan calls for 17 detention and storage basins in Aalen County. Their aggregate capacity is approximately 10 thousand acre-feet, of which about 4 thousand acre-feet will be in the storage pools and the remainder will be detention capacity. The earthfill dams will be 20 to 50 feet high.

The construction of the Jagst Valley project was started in 1957. Six reservoir structures had been completed in 1962. The completion of the whole project has been set for 1970.

The detention and storage struc-

544 *Yearbook of Agriculture 1963*

tures cost 300 to 600 dollars per acre-foot of total capacity. The project is financed with considerable grants from the Federal Government and from the State of Baden-Württemberg.

THE DURANCE RIVER basin in southeastern France, an area of about 5.5 thousand square miles, has two essential elements for the production of power; namely, slope and runoff. The river runoff is erratic, however. The minimum flow is 1,500 cubic feet per second; the maximum is 212 thousand cubic feet during severely damaging floods.

The lower Durance River Valley, the most important irrigated area in France, has some 173 thousand acres of rich cropland. The river provides municipal and industrial water to many villages and large cities, including Marseilles. Without regulation, the meager summer discharge has not permitted adequate irrigation at the time when the water was needed most. Thus there have been three serious problems: The need for river regulation to provide water for irrigation and municipal and industrial purposes; the need for flood control; and the need for additional electric power to support increases in industrial development.

Improvement of the Durance Basin was authorized by the French Government in January 1955 to include a series of works, of which the Serre-Poncon dam and powerplant is the key structure. Construction of the dam was started in 1955 and was completed in 1960.

The large reservoir created by the Serre-Poncon dam impounds the runoff from about one-third of the basin. The average flow of the river from some 1,400 square miles at this site is about 3 thousand cubic feet per second; during the flood of 1856 the estimated maximum discharge was 63 thousand cubic feet per second. The average annual volume of water that passes the Serre-Poncon site is 2.2 million acre-feet, of which about 811 thousand acre-feet pass during May and June.

The structure is an earthfill dam, with a crest length of 1,970 feet, a height of about 404 feet above the original bed of the river, a top width of 33 feet, and a base width of 2,130 feet. The dam has a total volume of 18.3 million cubic yards and creates a reservoir of 972 thousand acre-feet. The reservoir has a surface area of 7,160 acres and extends 11 miles up the Durance Valley and 5.5 miles up the Ubaye Valley arm of the reservoir.

As is usually the case in the construction of a large reservoir, the problem of right-of-way and the loss of economic development in the reservoir area created a serious situation. Ten hamlets and two large settlements, Savines and Ubaye, were inundated. Four hundred valuable pieces of property, including some 110 farms, had to be abandoned. About 31 miles of main highway and 7 miles of railroad had to be relocated, which involved new construction of 9 miles of railroad and 50 miles of highway.

In connection with the relocation of Savines, Ubaye, and the hamlets, a new village, Savines-le-Lac, was built on the edge of the reservoir. Only about one-half of the displaced persons, however, chose to settle in the village. Those that moved away were indemnified in cash for their property losses. The new village is served by a modern national highway and is becoming a tourist and recreation center and a site for small industries.

THE COST of the Serre-Poncon dam and hydropower facilities was about 110 million dollars—some 44 million dollars for the dam, 13 million for the powerplant, 40 million for purchase of land and relocations, and the rest for investigations and studies.

The powerplant is underground in the left abutment of the dam and is equipped with four vertical shaft turbines, having a discharge of 2,600 cubic feet per second under a 410-foot head. The plant has four 84-thousand-kilowatt generators, producing an average of 700 million kilowatt-hours of energy per year. Considering the cost of production, this generation is not particularly favorable, but regulation of the discharge of the Durance River by this reservoir benefits all the existing and potential downstream hydroelectric powerplants. This can result in an additional 400 million kilowatt-hours of energy a year. After all installations are completed, the cost of power from this overall development delivered at the load centers may approximate 6 mills per kilowatt-hour, which would make it one of the most efficient hydroelectric complexes in France.

Regulation of the river by the Serre-Poncon dam and reservoir insures stabilization of the 80-million-dollar preproject annual agricultural production in the Durance Valley. It also permits an expansion of about 20 percent of irrigated lands. Because of low-cost power for pumping, irrigation has expanded materially above the reservoir. An overall increase of 25 percent in the gross crop value is expected.

The Serre-Poncon dam has provided the needed flood control. The creation of Lake Serre-Poncon has lent encouragement to both summer and winter tourist trade. Recreation thus has become another important element in the economy of the basin.

The development of the Durance River has been the driving force in the economic development of the region and a decisive factor in the expansion of its agricultural wealth. For the first time in France in an undertaking of this size, the interests of industry have been happily allied with those of agriculture. The truly agroindustrial development of the Durance Valley, even before its completion, has had a beneficial influence on the living conditions of the people of the valley.

THE SUCCESS of the Dutch struggle against the sea is due to long and careful planning. One-fifth of their land lies below mean sea level. More than one-half of their land would be subject to flooding at storm tide if there were no protective works.

The defense by diking against the sea and against floods from the rivers Rhine, Meuse, and Scheldt dates from Roman times. The polder, an area ringed by dikes and pumped dry of sea water, is a unique development of the Dutch, dating from the 13th century, when windmills were adapted to pump the water.

As techniques advanced, larger projects were undertaken—the invention of the steam engine permitted the development of the Haarlemmermeer polder of 45 thousand acres in about 1850. As larger and larger plans were conceived, more planning was required. The 20th-century schemes are comprehensive, technically excellent, and specifically related to a national policy of providing living space, employment, and food for their increasing population.

THE TWO major projects of the 1900's are the Zuider Zee plan for reclaiming great areas of agricultural land from the sea and the Delta plan for shortening the shorelines by 453 miles in the area where the Rhine, Maas, and other rivers flow into the sea through a maze of estuaries.

The Delta plan, adopted in 1957 and scheduled for completion in 1978, will protect the most densely populated part of the land from the sea against such a great flood disaster as that of 1953, when nearly 2 thousand people lost their lives. A complex system of dikes, sluices, and locks, besides providing flood protection, will make the estuaries into large, fresh-water reservoirs that will help to solve the problem of soil salinization on the farms and provide water for industry. The system will bring 30 thousand acres of new land into production.

The concept of reclaiming the Zuider Zee had intrigued farsighted men as early as 1667. The modern Zuider Zee plan, not too different from plans of earlier times, became firm in 1918 with the adoption of the proposal of Dr. C. Lely, a well-known engineer and statesman.

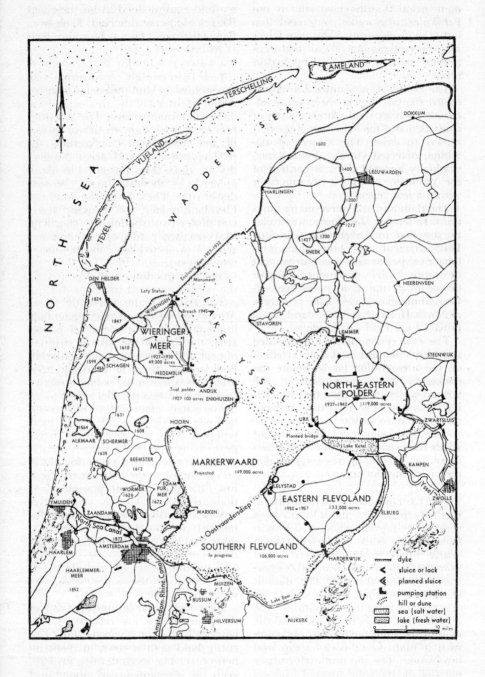

His plan included a 20-mile enclosing dam from Wieringen north to the Frisian coast to make the Zuider Zee into the fresh-water Lake Ysselmeer and the reclamation of five polders of a total area of about 546 thousand acres.

The Board of the Zuider Zee Works closed the last gap in the 20-mile enclosing dam in 1932. After 5 years of construction, the Zuider Zee had ceased to exist. The waters of the Rhine, diverted via the Yssel River, gradually lowered the salt content of the Ysselmeer so that it became fresh within a few years.

The dam and lake serve many functions. In seasons of drought, water can be supplied to surrounding districts. Dikes adjacent to the lake, which is no longer subject to tidal movements, can be more easily maintained. Better drainage of the polders is assured. Communication between the provinces of North Holland and Friesland is improved by a road on the dam.

The conversion of the Zuider Zee into the Ysselmeer had a great effect on the surrounding lands. Before the enclosure, the salt content of the ground water under the lands bordering the sea increased steadily. Because the lands were so low, salinization of the soils was becoming a problem, and yields were dropping. Now that Ysselmeer has become a fresh-water lake, the yields have gone up.

THE ENCLOSING dam is basically an earthen structure, about 100 yards wide at the normal sea level. The sea-facing side is made of boulder-clay, a nearly impervious material dredged from the bottom of the Zuider Zee and transported to the site. The dam is backed up on the lakeside with a fill of sand, also from the sea bottom. The boulder-clay fill on the seaside and the sandfill are protected from storm action with a mattress of rock riprap and brushwood. The top and above-water parts of the dam are covered with ordinary clay to provide for vegetation. If too much fresh water builds up

behind the dam, one or more of the 25 sluices are opened at low tide and then closed as the tide rises. The elevation of the lake thus may be maintained at its best level.

THE DUTCH plan to construct five new polders behind the enclosing dam. About one-third of the area behind the dam will remain a lake. The Wieringermeer polder, 49 thousand acres, became dry in 1930. The Northeastern polder, 119 thousand acres, became dry in 1942. The Eastern Flevoland polder, 133 thousand acres, became dry in 1957. The dike for the Southern Flevoland polder, 106 thousand acres, was under construction in 1963. The Markerwaard polder of 149 thousand acres is projected for construction as resources permit.

The construction of the dike around the polder proceeds much as did the construction of the enclosing dam. After geophysical, soil, and topographic mapping of the underwater polder area, the line of the dike is stripped of peat and other unsuitable material. Boulder-clay then is dredged from under the water in the polder area and laid down in two parallel ridges to an above-water elevation. The trench between the ridges is filled with sand pumped from the line of the main drainage canals in the polder. Brushwood and riprap and a covering of soil on top complete the dike. At the same time, diesel or electric pumping stations are built.

When the dike is finally closed, the polder is pumped dry of sea water. The dikes are constructed so that each polder is surrounded more or less by fresh-water channels, which provide water for controlling the water table and serve boat traffic.

After the polder is pumped dry and the main drains are completed, the land is divided into farm-size lots. The entire land area is sown to reeds by helicopter. The reeds develop rapidly, keep out unwanted vegetation, and accelerate the drying out and conditioning of the soil. After a few years, the reeds are eradicated, and the land is planted to small grains for another year or two. Then trenches are cut across the farm lots to the main drains to increase drainage.

Later, as the land is developed, the drain trenches are replaced by tile drains, which also serve in dry seasons to control the water table. Thus the lands are subirrigated with water from the channels outside the dikes. The system of pumps, drains, and subirrigation is controlled precisely to provide the best water table level for the various types of farming.

In the early years, perhaps the first five or six, the land is entirely under the control of the Dutch Government and is farmed by it. During those years, a land-lease plan is prepared, based on the type of farming for which the soils are best suited, so as to meet national agricultural needs in the best way.

The Northeastern polder, for example, will provide for a population of about 50 thousand, living and farming 17 to 20 feet below sea level. In 1958, farmers occupied about 1,500 arable and mixed farms of 30 to 120 acres and 280 smaller fruit and market-garden farms.

The Government built the town of Emmeloord, which will eventually have a population of about 10 thousand, and 5 villages, each of which will have a population of 800 to 2,500. The government leases the farms and urban properties to private individuals after building the roads, houses, farm buildings, schools, churches, and many of the commercial buildings. Other polders have followed or will follow similar plans.

Occupants for the new land—for each farm there are 20 applicants—are selected on the basis of their skills, the capital they have available for stock and implements, and their ability to contribute to the cultural and social life of the new community. The selection also is coordinated with the land consolidation projects going on in other parts of the Netherlands.

In the new polders, the Government owns the farmland and farm buildings and sets general restrictions on the use of the land. In the older areas, the Government sets maximum land rents and controls further fragmentation of land. Prices for most farm products are guaranteed within certain production limits by the Government.

Farm organizations flourish. Eighty percent of the farmers belong to one of three self-governing farm unions. The farmers successfully operate purchasing, selling, marketing, and credit cooperatives. Drainage and flood control districts are run by the communities, and farm officials—that is, the civil servants—are the sons of the farmers.

The Dutch are master planners, but their skill in planning is exceeded by the success with which they carry out their plans—and that is the ultimate test of a plan. The Netherlands system of farsighted government planning and an energetic and educated farm people is working well.

LAND REFORM is proceeding actively in Western Europe. Adjustments in land are going forward in all six countries we visited as part of the study tour.

Rural development is a major part of the economic development plan in the Netherlands, and structural organization of the resource base for agriculture is considered essential. Objectives include a road network to permit efficient transportation, adjustment of field sizes and locations to simplify management, facilities to discharge and control water efficiently, and farm buildings adapted to a modern way of life. This program is administered through the Government Service for Land and Water Use in cooperation with the Land Registry, the State Forestry Service, the Agricultural Advisory Service, and many rural organizations.

The Dutch believe that a reallotment of agricultural land in older settled areas is necessary in order to increase the size of small farms and consolidate fields into integral farm units. The Land Consolidation Act of 1954 contains provisions facilitating voluntary land consolidation. Consolidation plans had been completed in 1962 on 375 thousand acres, plans for 750 thousand acres were in execution, and 3 million acres had been applied for.

In Western Germany, it is believed that improvement of present farmland holds greater promise for gain in productivity than reclamation of uncultivated areas. The land already being farmed can be used more productively through a better field arrangement, better farmstead planning, and soil improvement.

German farms, cut up in many small plots or compressed into narrow and inconvenient locations, have reflected an unhealthy agriculture. A German word, "Flurbereinigung," describes the process developed to consolidate parcels into efficient farms. Where voluntary land exchanges do not occur, the Federal Republic is in a position to assist. Between 1954 and 1959, more than 2.5 million acres were in need of consolidation to preserve the family farm, which is predominant in West Germany.

IN FRANCE, rural land management has been undertaken as a government program at national and regional levels, beginning in 1946. The national management of rural land is in the direction of expanding productivity, but at the same time reducing the rural labor force by shifts into industrial employment. Consolidation of landholdings is intensified, with help of some compulsion, and financial aid to joint enterprises, such as associations or cooperatives. Public works are provided, including highways, machinery, housing, and electricity.

In the alpine regions of France that we visited, the land adjustment goals include substantial conversion from cultivated crops into grass and forest. Bringing land uses into line with use capabilities is considered essential to restore a balance in watersheds where accelerated erosion occurs.

Land adjustment in Switzerland is represented by developments in the Saas Valley, which is being transformed from a remote subsistence community into a tourist attraction visited at all seasons by people from many countries. After a long decline, the population increased from 1,687 in 1941 to 2,740 in 1962, thanks partly to the development of mountain tourist attractions. Despite the change in the character of employment, the Saas people maintain their traditional respect for natural resources. Most forests belong to the communities, and they are protected carefully.

IN THE ALPINE provinces of Austria, land adjustment has long been viewed as necessary to combat destructive snow avalanches and the heavy sediment flows of mountain torrents. On steep slopes of the Grosse Walsertal (the valley of the Lutz), 125 persons were killed and 491 farm buildings were destroyed by avalanches in January 1954. Reallocation of farmholdings, a part of reconstruction efforts, made possible an increase in average farm size from 14 to 23 acres. Reforestation of high lands with closed, uneven-aged stands was undertaken as a primary protection against avalanches.

Agrarian reform in Italy is typified by the Fucino Basin in the Province of Aquila. The main objective of the reform, under a general law of 1951, was to increase the number of farmers who own the land they cultivate. To that end, land was acquired from absentee owners of large holdings and sold to the farmer tenants on long-term credit. The project, although fairly small, has an integrated approach, which embraces general economic development in the community. Its success has provided impetus for land reform projects in other parts of Italy. The country, however, relies upon general industrial development as the major outlets for rural people where farms are too small.

THE ROOTS of American forestry are in European experience.

Gifford Pinchot learned his forestry in Europe. B. E. Fernow, Filibert Roth, Carl Alwin Schenck, and other foresters came to the United States from Europe in the 19th century to teach aspiring young Americans the new science and art of forestry.

Yet an American forester's first reaction in Europe usually is, "My, what a lot of people are crowded here into a small area—where can there be room for forest lands and forestry?"

In the Netherlands, especially, the newly arrived forester may well think that this crowded country, with an average of 910 persons on a square mile, will have nothing to show in forestry. Quite the opposite. In the reclaimed lands, naturally devoid of trees, people go to considerable expense to provide trees as an addition to the landscape. On the lands being wrested from the Zuider Zee at a cost of nearly 1,500 dollars an acre, the Dutch are setting aside some 7.5 to 10 percent for afforestation.

Tree planting on these new lands is not planned in the Netherlands primarily for the production of merchantable products, even though the country is largely dependent on oversea sources for lumber and woods products.

The planting of trees on reclaimed land is for the "landscape." This term means more to the Dutch than our words "parks" or "recreation areas." It means nesting places and shelter for birds and small animals, shade and shelter for family picnics, and variety in an otherwise monotonous and unvaried landscape across the erstwhile floor of the sea. No favorable monetary benefit-cost ratio led the Dutch to their decision that life for the settlers in the new polders would be more rewarding if up to 10 percent of the reclaimed land was set aside for small forests.

THE DUTCH philosophy could provide a lesson for American urban and rural planners, developers, and Government officials. In our Nation we usually have the wooded areas already in existence. All that is required is that a planned proportion of those areas be spared from the bulldozer.

Dutch planning for their new agricultural lands also includes the establishment of tree plantings on farmsteads. Before new farms reclaimed from the sea are turned over to the settlers, the immediate farmstead area surrounding each combination farm dwelling and barn has been planted to adapted trees and shrubs by the Dutch Forest Service. Again, this is done primarily for the purpose of making life for the settler more agreeable and minimizing the sweep of the cold winds off the North Sea.

A strong effort is being made in Austria and Switzerland as a matter of national policy to keep land in pasture because it had been so used in the past and forms an essential base for the rural population. Only when the control of avalanches or serious gully erosion is involved does there seem to be a disposition to reforest lands that had been cleared of forests two centuries or more ago. When this is done, efforts are made through improvement of remaining pastures to offset pasturage lost to reforestation.

In such areas of hazard, however, strenuous efforts are made to reestablish tree cover to the upper limits of tree growth. Initial efforts to minimize the avalanche hazard consist of structures of rock, steel, concrete, and wood, which are intended to fill the gap until trees can become established once again on the slopes where avalanches start. Tree cover, no matter how hard it is to reestablish it, is considered the ultimate answer to protecting those places.

The United States is fortunate that farsighted American leaders years ago incorporated comparable hazardous areas within our system of national forests. By closing our high-mountain areas to indiscriminate settlement, clearing, and use, we have minimized the exposure of citizens to hazards of snowslides and torrents of mud.

In West Germany, particularly in Hesse, planning for river basins takes into account the management of forest lands. Also noteworthy is the advance planning in West Germany for restoring coal strip-mining areas by reforestation. The lesson for the United States is that the plan for land use and restoration of the mined area is developed *in advance* of the strip mining.

In France, all plans for land use and development of resources relate to a central national plan. The emphasis seems to be on such aspects as the development of hydroelectric power, irrigation, and regulation of waterflow. Not so evident are the aspects that pertain to forest land.

We did not encounter efforts in France to retain land use in the historic pattern, no matter how unsuited the land appeared for that use. As a result, many hilly acres in southern France have been abandoned for cultivation and are growing up to shrubs. We traveled through some of the areas in southern France where abandoned lands are being acquired by the Federal Government to assure future use for forestry and watershed purposes. The acquisition and reforestation efforts that we saw in this part of France have been rather modest. The greatest promise appears to lie in a national program of public acquisition and reforestation of those lands which landowners find they cannot profitably use for tree crops.

A rural redevelopment program in Italy gives strong emphasis to converting tenants to landowners. One way in which that is done is by the employment by the government of unemployed rural workers to reforest steep watershed lands deforested since the days of the Romans. Here forest improvement measures serve a double purpose—to provide food and clothing for low-income landless rural people while arrangements were being made for agrarian reform and to remedy errors in land use made 2,500 years ago.

Italy presents vivid contrasts in planned and unplanned uses of forest land. At the Italian Forest Service Experimental Forest at Vallombosa, for example, one can see well-managed forest and other lands, where planned conservation practices have been applied since the year 1016, when the Dominican Order of Friars established a monastery and concerned themselves with the orderly management of their lands by reforestation, contour plowing, and other conservation practices. Those ancient monks introduced silver fir to Italy and started substantial plantations of this species. One of their members, St. John Gualberto, is reverenced as the patron saint of foresters.

It is an inspiration to visit these long-managed mountain forest lands around Vallombosa and to realize that plans for good land use, adhered to and implemented through the years, carry many benefits.

This example (as do others in Europe) points to need in the United States, as the Nation becomes more densely populated, older, and more demanding as to resources, for sound advance planning of land uses.

Furthermore, sound plans by themselves are not enough. We need also courage and agreement among ourselves to place good plans into effect and keep them in effect.

CARL B. BROWN *was Deputy Assistant Administrator for Watersheds in the Soil Conservation Service. He died May 5, 1963. A native of North Carolina, he joined the Department in 1934 and became internationally known for his work on watershed and flood protection.*

DONALD R. BURNETT *is Chief, Project Development Division, Bureau of Reclamation, the Department of the Interior.*

LUDWIG L. KELLY *is Chief Hydrologist, Soil and Water Conservation Research Division, Agricultural Research Service.*

KARL S. LANDSTROM *is Assistant to the Secretary for Land Utilization, Department of the Interior.*

WARREN T. MURPHY *is Director, Division of Flood Prevention and River Basin Programs, Forest Service.*

H. P. QUADLAND

LET THE COUNTRY
SING WITH BEAUTY

NATURE if left alone probably would make most land beautiful in time. Man largely is responsible for making land ugly. But man also can make land sing with beauty if he wishes to help it flower—whether it is a tiny yard, a street, suburban plot, a farm on the plains, a cutover area in need of reforestation. Ugliness and growth need not be synonymous.

Economic and social benefits come from planting and beautifying the land. Sound conservation practices cannot end at the city or town line without helping to foster slums and endangering the future of the Nation.

I believe that love of our land is necessary for our survival. We will not love our land unless we care for it, and a growing population, which inevitably becomes farther removed from the land, tends to turn aside from natural beauty toward the vulgarities of life.

In cities and suburbs, beautifully planted spaces are needed if urban renewal programs are not to run into the same trouble in the future that cities have run into in the past. One of the biggest threats to the permanency of completed urban renewal projects is the failure of communities to provide for planted and beautified space.

It is preferable if the plantings become part of the long-range improve-

552

ment of cities rather than temporary expedients. Urban renewal presents a great opportunity for planted, open space that is a vital need in many cities.

I see no reason why we should ruin the land in order to build the houses in a subdivision. Often trees that have taken years to grow are destroyed by bulldozers in a day. Emphasis in housing by lending authorities has been on the house; the lot may be ignored.

Some housing developments have become slums in a decade because little thought is given to yards and streets. Other developments, well landscaped, remain livable indefinitely.

An example is the Plant America program, sponsored by the American Association of Nurserymen. It offers a pattern for making our land more productive, beautiful, and livable.

The program was launched on January 5, 1950, in New York by representatives of national organizations.

AN OUTLINE of the original Plant America program, offered in 1950, is applicable today. I quote parts of it:

"The program is predicated on the premise that the land is our most precious heritage. It is believed that the objective of the program in its entirety can only be accomplished by replanting our forests, our farms, our cities, our roadsides, our church and school, our home and factory grounds wherever the need lies. . . .

"For the first time in history our farm population generally is prosperous. But much still needs to be accomplished for a more fruitful and abundant farm home life. Landscaping and improved design of farm homesteads, farm home fruit gardens, landscaping and planting of grange halls, rural schools and rural communities in general are needed. . . .

"Most of our cities and towns have blighted areas that can be made green and beautiful by planting trees, shrubs, and flowers. Much has been accomplished by civic authorities, civic planning groups, park executives, and garden clubs. But here, too, we are just awakening to the task ahead. A consciousness of the fact that the land is our most precious heritage is sorely needed by the general public . . . for its own good. Open spaces, beautifully planted, seriously are needed in all metropolitan areas for recreational as well as conservational purposes; in fact, just for us all to look at, in order to fill our souls with beauty. . . .

"Safety, conservation, beauty as well as happier motoring and recreation enter into the proper development of our roadsides. Despite the great achievements of highway officials and others, general public awakening is needed to prepare for and provide the most efficient use of these roadside facilities for all. . . .

"Beautiful church and school gardens are rare rather than commonplace. Churches and schools can be made more beautiful and inspiring cultural centers through cooperation of educational groups, community improvement groups, garden clubs, parent-teacher associations, etc., in landscaping. This work easily can be accomplished at small expense if public consciousness is awakened to the task. . . .

"Changes are developing in home landscaping and planting. Plantings are more natural, for better living. Outdoor living rooms, indoor-outdoor living on the home property, home fruit and rose gardens, climate control by planting to increase both inside and outside home comfort, are coming to the fore to enable a more enjoyable family home life. There is practical therapy in green growing things— pleasure and health combined. Plant America requires individual as well as group and community cooperation. We need to develop all our land for living, not just the house alone. . . .

"Landscaped and planted industrial sites are important from the viewpoints both of community and employee relations, as well as increased value of the land. . . .

"*Plant America—For More Natural Living* will help to conserve the land and the well-being and health of people. By instilling in the public mind a consciousness of the fact that 'the land is our most precious heritage' and by action in planting in accordance with both need and the proper design, not only will Plant America give Americans greater satisfaction in living, but it will make them more proud of their homes, their factories, their communities and their country."

WHAT HAS BEEN accomplished?

Governors in 39 States have issued proclamations calling for more planting in their States.

The first was issued by Chester Bowles, then Governor of Connecticut.

It stated: "Land in the past has been abundant. Man in those days was able to ravage the land and move on to virgin territory. This led to abuse. . . . Most of these blighted and barren areas can be made green and beautiful if all citizens fully realize their moral obligations to others in the ownership of private, civic, or State land. . . . Much of the future progress of our State and its rare natural beauty rests upon the extent to which we replant and care for all the land. Our State can produce more if we strive to make and keep it beautiful. Everyone will benefit in equal measure."

A highly successful State campaign was conducted in Ohio, as part of the State's sesquicentennial activity. Some 22 million forest seedlings and more than 3 million ornamental trees and shrubs were planted in a year by homeowners and organized groups.

The sesquicentennial's "greatest tribute to the past," Governor Frank J. Lausche pointed out, "would be wise planning for the future." He added: "In this connection, tree planting, for reforestation, beautification, and recreation, is of vital importance. The program encourages farmers to plant waste land; home owners to plant ornamental and shade trees; municipalities to plant trees and shrubs; establishment of school forests, as well as other local programs featuring the Plant Ohio project."

The program in Ohio was efficiently organized. All State departments and 65 private organizations were represented on the Plant Ohio Committee, under the direction of an executive committee, which was headed by the Governor and comprised representatives of the Ohio Department of Natural Resources, the State chamber of commerce, Ohio Nurserymen's Association, forestry associations, garden clubs, the Agricultural Extension Service, and the Federation of Soil Conservation Districts. County and local committees were formed to work on publicity, school and community forests, beautification of factory sites, planting of trees and shrubs around homes, public plantings, industrial reforestation, rural reforestation, and sources of planting materials.

Many community plantings grew out of the effort in Ohio. A Plant Columbus program was a forerunner

for that city's establishment of a large municipal rose garden.

In a natural course of events, the Plant America program expanded into Plant (*State*), Plant (*county*), and Plant (*city or town*) programs.

The Plant America program includes the dissemination of information that will help homeowners upgrade the values of their properties by landscaping and beautifying them. It includes standards for nursery stock and a guide for home landscaping. A movie was produced, "Basic Technique for Home Landscaping." Materials on the pleasures and values of garden living are made available for use in newspapers, magazines, radio, and television.

IN RELATION to cities, schools, highways, and factories, the program attempts to do much the same within the limits of a small budget.

An industrial landscaping competition is conducted with awards for "achievement in industrial and institutional landscaping and beautification contributing to employee and civic pride in our American heritage."

Among the 200-odd winners of awards are the Reader's Digest, Pleasantville, N.Y.; General Motors Corp.; the Washington Water Power Co. in Spokane; the Board of Water Supply, Honolulu; church groups; the little St. Cyprian School in River Grove, Ill.; the Shelburne Museum in Shelburne, Vt.; and the Boscobel Restoration, Garrison, N.Y.

Some striking benefits of industrial landscaping have come to light.

A cement company found that trees and shrubs helped to hold down dust and reduced absenteeism.

Some restaurants have reported that good landscaping increases patronage. Banks, department stores, and shopping centers use landscaping to attract and win the approval of customers.

The Plant America movement took cognizance in 1950 of the need for roadside landscaping. Meetings were arranged with landscape authorities and engineers to find economical methods for functional landscaping. The outgrowth was an illustrated booklet, which outlined 10 purposes of highway landscaping:

To screen out, where necessary, blinding headlight glare of cars in opposing traffic lanes; stop fast-moving cars with little or no damage to their occupants at dangerous intersections; relieve monotony and lessen fatigue; delineate curves and serve as directional traffic guides; restore natural beauty; reduce traffic roar and serve as buffers to adjacent residential areas; screen off unsightly, distracting views; serve as natural snow fencing; control erosion on slopes; and make rest areas.

One development seems particularly interesting. In Tuscaloosa County, Ala., all home grounds bordering on a highway were landscaped to enhance the beauty of the route. The plan has possibilities in improving and beautifying secondary and rural roads after the manner of azalea trails, dogwood trails, and other trails, which attract tourists.

When the Plant America program first was visualized, contact was made with the National Education Association. A great deal of attention is devoted to instruction in planting.

The American Association of School Administrators advises sound recommendations for landscaping and planting school grounds. Annual Arbor Day tree plantings are performed on some school grounds. There is great need, however, for more widespread planting and landscaping of school grounds. It is incongruous that students are taught principles of land conservation and planting, while many of their school grounds and athletic fields are bare, eroded, and ugly.

The planned planting of school grounds affords a basis for practical instruction in the conservation of land and in plantlife. Well-landscaped and planted schools encourage school pride among pupils and teachers. Beautiful school grounds encourage community pride and greater support for education. Landscaped and planted schools

afford a more pleasing recreational environment and are a facility for recreation in themselves.

Landscaping and planting should be a requirement along with the construction of all new schools, as recommended by educational administrators. Where this has not been done, it should be accomplished by local cooperation, along with education by teachers of the reasons behind caring for the land by planting and conserving it.

The Chicago Community Trust gave 10 thousand dollars to the Chicago Horticultural Society to encourage schoolchildren to take up gardening: "We think gardening will make a good long-range hobby that the children will benefit from all their lives. More immediately, we think it will curb vandalism. People who learn to grow things are less likely to destroy trees and flowers or other people's property."

THE FIRST community planting project under the Plant America banner was carried out in Granby, Conn., in August 1951, during Plant Connecticut Week. All public grounds in the town were landscaped and planted, including schools, churches, and the firehouse. Local groups cooperated to serve luncheon to the planters and the nurserymen who supplied the plants. Since this project was completed, the nurserymen each year have landscaped and planted grounds of a public building to commemorate a Plant Connecticut Week.

Another planting project, in Stow Village, Mass., was sponsored by community groups, a garden club, the Extension Service, and New England nurserymen. The grounds of three churches, two schools, the town hall, and the library were landscaped.

Some of the subsequent activities include the planting of dogwood trees given to Morgantown, W. Va., to start a planting project; a tourist arboretum in Tennessee; sample highway plantings in many States; the establishment of municipal rose gardens; and 71 planting projects in Iowa towns through the cooperation of garden clubs, 4–H, Future Farmers of America, Boy Scouts, and others.

Los Angeles planted 296 trees in a 10-block area in downtown streets in 1962. The Textile Association of Los Angeles has a goal to plant 300 trees in the garment area. Living flowers in containers also add color to the area.

New York City's Salute to the Seasons program, in which thousands of trees, shrubs, and bulbs have been donated by business firms, is another example.

The New York City Commerce Department issued a booklet that said: "Massed plantings along major thoroughfares . . . are intended to alleviate this hunger [for green growing things] by bringing greater beauty to our city . . . to make New York a pleasanter place in which to live and work . . . a more attractive place to visit."

Along Lincoln Boulevard in Miami and in Kalamazoo, Mich., where a central mall has been planted, and in other cities, the results of such plantings have been strikingly beneficial. Where they have been made a part of the permanent planning of the city, they have been most successful. Where temporary, they sometimes have failed. Good maintenance is necessary.

A successful program was carried out in Spartanburg, S.C., a city of 45 thousand population, in 1962. Banks, industrial firms, and retail firms cooperated with the Men's Garden Club, the sponsor of the project. In various projects there have been planted: 210 thousand bulbs, 200 thousand azaleas, 1,600 rose bushes, 50 thousand pansies, and 6 thousand petunias. Some of the plants are in a garden in which citizens can choose labeled varieties for their home grounds.

In North Carolina, Charlotte and Winston-Salem have planted roses and trees in expressway medians. Greensboro has appointed a city beautification coordinator.

A Plant America award for landscaping was presented in 1962 to Mayor Melvin T. Matlock for the town of St. James, Mo. Many local trees had lost their vigor in an extended drought. The citizens, helped by the James Foundation, planted 4 thousand sweetgum, flowering crabapple, and holly trees. These plantings gave this small town new beauty and new spirit. Townspeople talk about "the New St. James" and plan to develop a three-block long strip in the center of town into a central plaza, to be planted with grass, shrubs, and trees.

Various community projects have been taken up at times, as recommended in the Plant America program, such as establishment of community gardens; street tree plantings; landscaping and planting around public buildings, including airports; plantings around tourist accommodations, such as gasoline stations and motels and hotels; plantings of highway entrances to the community; developing local parks; cleanup and planting of the banks of local streams; establishment of community forests for recreation; and the planting of flowering plants, or trees, in order to make the city or town known for spectacular azalea, rose, dogwood, lilac, flowering crabapple, cherry, or similar plantings.

As every municipality grows, a long-range program for planting and beautification of land, including acquisition of new park lands, becomes necessary.

Planting America is an extremely rewarding goal for all—individual, community, State, and Nation. With needed and widespread cooperation, our country almost everywhere can be made to "sing with beauty."

H. P. QUADLAND, *owner of a public relations firm in New York, since 1949 has conducted the Plant America program for the American Association of Nurserymen. He is a graduate of the University of Massachusetts and has served as president of the Garden Writers of America and as a member of the Board of Governors of the American Horticultural Council.*

FREDERIC HEUTTE

UNITY, ORIGINALITY, AND SIMPLICITY

ANY community can make itself beautiful if its people are willing to share equally the planning, the work, and the maintenance of a project. A first principle of beauty is unity. Unity takes planning. Unity makes the Champs Élysées in Paris what it is. It is basically no more than a few bands of trees on each side of a broad thoroughfare. (The trees, incidentally, hide quite a few architectural monstrosities.) Yet, because of its rhythmic precision, scale, and classic terminus (the Arch of Triumph), it has become a symbol of beauty throughout the world. Any portion by itself would become insignificant.

But the Champs Élysées or the Grand Canyon—to cite a manmade and a natural wonder—with all their grandeur may be less beautiful to some than the simple play of light and shadow in the arching elms along the main street of an old town in New England. Equally inspiring may be the moss-laden limbs of the sturdy live oak reaching over a southern road. They denote harmony and unity.

A basic error in trying to promote beauty is to copy. It is not wrong to reproduce something through the use of a fundamental text, but in so doing one has to incorporate local atmosphere and radiate self-expression.

The keynote to beauty is simplicity— the simplicity of a Greek temple, the simplicity of the Mall in Washington (at least before ponderous museums were allowed to encroach on it), the simplicity of a greensward anyplace, the simplicity of a Japanese gravel garden, the simplicity of an uncluttered park or lawn or lakeshore or town square.

No community is so poor in natural resources or worldly goods that it cannot evolve a pattern of simple, inspiring self-expression from its soil and surroundings, be it among desert sands or the deposit of a delta. Nature always provides a text, wherever we live.

If we further the philosophy expressed by Aristotle that "Nature has the will but not the power to reach perfection," we are well on the way.

Truly, Nature often fails us, for her local wares are not always the most adaptable, beautiful, or representative of the ultimate potential.

557

Often we can incorporate plants from other lands that will thrive and prosper—in fact, that we may find to be the rule, rather than the exception. The Southeast would be less beautiful without its camellias and azaleas, and the Northeast without its lilacs. In my own section of Norfolk, Va., few people realize that the crapemyrtle is not native but has escaped cultivation.

Water turns deserts into magic expanses of foliage and color. Swamps may be drained or, better, left in their God-made beauty and utility. Snow-covered boughs become classic sculptures in the winter sun. Wherever we live, beautification is a challenge to our ingenuity and determination and appreciation of simplicity, Nature, and unity, where every prospect pleases.

These are broad concepts of design, which can call us to action, whether to make our town the "cleanest community in America," where one would be ashamed to drop even a gum wrapper, or to make it famous for beauty, as people in Rochester have done with lilacs or Portland has done with roses.

IF WE BEAUTIFY with flowers, preference should be given to those that have long lives.

Norfolk, for instance, has adopted the crapemyrtle because it grows so prolifically and has an average lifespan of a century. Crapemyrtles have been planted there since 1900. Now more than 100 thousand flourish in streets, parks, and private yards.

In a community where houses have a uniform setback and only a slight variation of architecture, it is natural and desirable that each owner should want to plant something distinctive or paint his house a different color. That in itself becomes an interesting pattern of self-expression.

Viewed from the street or highway, however, the entire complex may look like a hodgepodge unless it is banded together with a uniform planting; then the text becomes entirely appealing. The feeling of unity might be from the moving shadows of overhanging trees, the uniform placement of distinctive shrubs, or even pink or white petunias in all the window boxes.

Self-perpetuation of plantings is an aim. Self-perpetuation is best expressed by using plants with a long lifespan. We all like to think that what we plant will outlive our own efforts and benefit future generations.

An example: As a member of the Jamestown Beautification Committee for Jamestown's 350th anniversary in 1957, I suggested if everyone within 30 miles of Jamestown could plant crapemyrtles, the approaches to this historical city in Virginia would have bands of beauty that would endure until its 400th anniversary and beyond.

As a result, more than 10 thousand crapemyrtles were planted along the highways and byways. If only 50 percent of them survive, or even 25 percent, these beautiful summer-blooming shrubs will serve their purpose.

As I said, the trees, shrubs, and other plants should be readily adaptable to the environment, beautiful, and easily cared for. Their seasonal climax should be emphasized by some kind of yearly event, no matter how modest its beginning may be. Merchants and newspapers are always responsive to any movement that will focus attention on such an event and will lend their support to any laudable enterprise.

BEAUTIFICATION of a community need not stop at the front door. It can involve several activities to which citizens and officials will lend their support. The best approach is through participation by all. Those who embark on a project should not begin by asking full financial assistance, no matter how good the project may be, for such an attitude defeats the purpose.

Beautifying a schoolyard may begin by planting a tree on some special occasion—or maybe no occasion at all, except that children and teachers want to plant a tree. Modern schoolyards can be made neater and more pleasant in several ways. It is one of the best of all projects.

We underestimate the appreciation of children towards projects of this sort. When we launched a beautification school program in Norfolk at a new high school in 1940, I did not foresee that we would get countless requests from others for plantings. Too many schoolyards had been left barren under the supposition that you cannot expect the children to respect shrubs and flowers.

Of course, the beautification must be well planned, and everybody—from custodian to principal—must be in favor of it. In fact, they must be the main coordinators, or the project will never be a success.

Because spontaneous cleanup and beautification campaigns generally fall short of their objectives, a project should be in the hands of a self-perpetuating committee.

To such a committee I give some advice based on my own experience.

The committee revolves around one person. That person must have ample time to devote to its many details. A retired businessman or teacher or someone without too many other obligations seems to be the best qualified.

Plenty of people will be willing to give advice; they should be well equipped for their assignments. An overall plan and objective cannot be gathered at mass meetings.

The starting point should be to choose what may become the theme—that is, the kind of tree, shrub, or flower that may serve as an emblem.

About that and similar matters, an experienced horticulturist, who may be a member of a park department, a landscape architect, florist, or nurseryman, should be consulted.

Photographs of all stages of the work will help to enlist and maintain support. An investigation of what has been done in other communities is always a good start in planning. Surveys from experts are not always the best source of information, because emphasis should be primarily based on local conditions.

When a simple but effective plan of action has been formed, publicity should be sought that will carry the movement forward. The newspapers, radio, and television are most cooperative, because a well-planned project is news, and news is their business.

I have mentioned no particular organization as a possible sponsor, because communities vary in their leadership. In one section it may be the garden clubs or flower societies; in another, civic leagues, parent-teachers' associations, women's clubs, or men's organizations. Besides, the project does not belong to one organization; everyone should share in it.

THE PARK DEPARTMENT in larger communities often is expected to develop conservation and beautification.

If it does a good job, it naturally stimulates interest in gardening, but the typical park department has too little money and too few workers to undertake the whole work of keeping a community beautiful.

As an example, Norfolk has a population of more than 300 thousand and covers 60 square miles, but its park bureau controls only 1,200 acres of the 38 thousand.

Norfolk residents, however, have reason to think the city is beautiful because of the many groups, especially the garden clubs, who have worked diligently to promote various projects.

EACH YEAR, as more communities adopt this philosophy of self-expression through conservation and beautification, the gaps of ugliness are being eliminated and, with them, I think, many social and economic evils.

FREDERIC HEUTTE *is Superintendent of Parks and Forestry and Director of the Botanical Garden of Norfolk, Va. He was born in France and educated in French and American public schools and served in the American Army in the First World War. He has received the Merite Agricole award and medal from the French Government, the Gold Medal Award of Garden Clubs of America, and many other honors.*

RAYMOND C. ALLEN

EDUCATIONAL
GARDEN CENTERS

NEARLY all metropolitan areas and hundreds of cities and towns have nonprofit garden centers, whose basic purposes are to encourage the growing and use of ornamental and vegetable plants, initiate and support programs of community improvement and beautification, and sponsor activities related to conservation.

The objectives are achieved by making available in various ways information that can be applied to the specific problems of the community and its citizens.

The term "garden center" sometimes is used in connection with commercial enterprises—nursery sales lots, adjuncts to florist shops, special divisions of department and hardware stores, or roadside stands. They are primarily for the sale of plants, garden supplies, equipment, and machinery. They are not operated for the broad public purposes for which the nonprofit, educational garden centers are organized.

For the development of some of the community garden centers we can thank the garden club organizations. A few examples illustrate the scope and importance of their efforts.

The Garden Center of Greater Cleveland was founded by the Garden Club of Cleveland in 1930. It has served as a model for many similar organizations and has an excellent library, staff, and community program. Its emphasis is put on better horticulture, better plant materials, private and civic landscaping, and conservation. It often is called on to help special groups, such as the rose societies and bonsai fanciers in Cleveland. Its influence has been felt in better city and suburban planning, better planting and care of street trees, an outstanding school garden program, and the development of an awareness that gardening is a cultural, recreational, and economic activity.

The Lakeside Park Garden Center, Lakeside Park, Oakland, Calif., sponsors trial gardens for several plants, such as dahlias, fuchsias, rhododendrons, camellias, and succulents and has been effective in furthering their use in home gardens.

560

The Valley Garden Center, 1809 North 15th Avenue, Phoenix, Ariz., has encouraged the planting of roses and other adapted plants by sponsoring a municipal rose garden, offering lecture courses and workshops, and publishing materials, such as "Practical Gardening for Anyone" and "Gardening in the Salt River Valley," for home gardeners.

The Valdosta Garden Center, 904 North Patterson Street, Valdosta, Ga., has done much to widen the planting of hemerocallis throughout the region through its annual hemerocallis festival and emphasis on the merits of the better varieties for the climate. Its test gardens of camellias, azaleas, roses, and hemerocallis are used by the gardening public for observation and study.

The Berkshire Garden Center at Stockbridge, Mass., has brought about a revival of interest in home gardening and the use of the best plant material in its region through practical demonstration plantings, trial gardens, distribution of plants, and activities with children.

The first officially recorded garden center was established in 1929 in Hackensack, N.J.

NATIONAL ORGANIZATIONS of garden clubs, among them the National Council of State Garden Clubs, the Garden Club of America, and the Men's Garden Clubs of America, sponsor educational garden centers through their local clubs and individuals. State and regional gardening organizations also have programs for encouraging the establishment of garden centers. They work through committees, which offer instruction and advice.

The National Council of State Garden Clubs, 4401 Magnolia Avenue, St. Louis 10, Mo., functions through its affiliated State organizations, which in turn work through their affiliated clubs. The members of the State garden center committee are prepared to give assistance are planning the organization, financing, and programs of garden centers through personal consultations and the publications of State and national garden club organizations.

Money to establish a garden center usually is raised locally by memberships, contributions, and projects. Often local agencies, usually the parks and recreation department, may work cooperatively with them in matters of maintenance of garden areas, office space, and possibly personnel.

SOME OTHER types of organizations and institutions perform in varying degrees the functions of garden centers. Several local and State horticultural societies maintain extensive libraries, issue publications, and have a professional staff to give help to members and the general public.

The Massachusetts Horticulture Society, Horticultural Hall, 300 Massachusetts Avenue, Boston 15, has about 9 thousand members and was organized in 1829. It carries on an extensive educational and service program. Its impressive building near the center of Boston has office and auditorium facilities and exhibition space, in which 12 to 15 flower and vegetable shows are held each year.

Its educational activities include courses for amateur gardeners in subjects such as greenhouse gardening, house plants, garden maintenance, and home landscaping. Its staff of 40 answer numberless questions on gardening by mail, telephone, and consultation. The library of about 32 thousand volumes has quite a few rare and valuable works. Some 8 thousand volumes are in the circulating library. Its major publication is a monthly magazine, Horticulture, which goes to about 90 thousand subscribers. It has also published a number of books and bulletins, one of which is *Plant Buyers Guide*, a source list of seeds and plants.

To stimulate achievement in horticulture, it awards medals and other types of recognition to individuals for advancing interest and skill in horticulture, hybridizing and propagation of woody plants, meritorious gardens, and service to horticulture.

The Pennsylvania Horticultural Society, 389 Suburban Station Building, Philadelphia 3, which received its charter in 1831, carries on similar work in serving the amateur gardeners of the Philadelphia vicinage. It has about 5 thousand members. It also sponsors lectures, classes in gardening, flower shows, garden tours, demonstrations of house plantings, and suburban community garden clinics. Its circulating library contains 7,500 volumes.

The Horticultural Society of New York, 157 West 58th Street, New York 19, is primarily an organization for the New York City region, but many of its 4,500 members live in adjoining States. It also has an extensive program of lectures, courses in gardening, home study courses, garden tours, and personal consultation and sponsors monthly flower shows at its headquarters. A circulating library of 15 thousand volumes is maintained, and its collection of rare books numbers 3 thousand. It makes special awards for a wide range of horticultural and gardening achievements. With the New York Florist Club, it sponsors the New York International Flower Show, and some of the income for its support comes from this major enterprise.

The Chicago Horticultural Society, which is not a State society in the usual sense, has undertaken a number of educational projects. It has sponsored a gardening course for schoolteachers in cooperation with the Chicago Teachers College and the Board of Education and has been instrumental in developing a fragrant garden for the blind.

Other State horticultural organizations that have similar but less extensive educational functions than those I have mentioned, are: California Horticultural Society (Golden Gate Park, San Francisco); Connecticut Horticultural Society (199 Griswold Road, Wethersfield 9); Peninsula Horticultural Society (Post Office Box 150, Newark, Del.); Florida State Horticultural Society (Post Office Box 2125, Manatee Station, Bradenton); Iowa State Horticultural Society (State House, Des Moines); Kansas State Horticultural Society (Kansas State College, Manhattan); Kentucky State Horticultural Society (University of Kentucky, Lexington); Michigan Horticultural Society (Dearborn Center, Dearborn); Minnesota State Horticultural Society (University of Minnesota, St. Paul); Rhode Island Horticultural Society (17 Exchange Street, Providence); and South Dakota State Horticultural Society (State College, Brookings).

A FEW PRIVATELY endowed or publicly supported institutions serve as garden centers because they and their staffs have a keen interest in stimulating home gardening. Among them are Longwood Gardens at Kennett Square, Pa., and Kingwood Center at Mansfield, Ohio.

Longwood Gardens is on U.S. Route 1, about 30 miles southwest of Philadelphia and about 12 miles northwest of Wilmington, Del. The late Pierre S. duPont bought the land in 1906 and developed it as his private estate. A part of the acreage was conveyed by William Penn in 1700 to George Peirce, whose descendants in 1800 started a collection of trees and shrubs, a few of which survive.

Mr. duPont opened the gardens and conservatories to the public in 1921. Since his death in 1954, the maintenance and further development have been carried on by the Longwood Foundation, which he created for charitable purposes in 1937. About a thousand acres are included. About 200 persons are employed.

Its educational and scientific program is much broader than that of the usual garden center. It is a combination horticultural showplace, botanic garden, and arboretum. Its various garden-related art forms include what many persons consider the finest fountain display in the country, an abundance of sculpture, an open-air theater, and throughout fine examples of landscape design and plant use and culture.

While Longwood Gardens provides free public lectures and horticultural information like many other institutions, the Longwood Foundation contributes significantly to the development of ornamental horticulture through financial grants for plant exploration, special publications, and other purposes. Longwood Gardens is without equal in the United States for gardening hobbyists to visit and observe, study, and enjoy a wide variety of indoor and outdoor plant material.

KINGWOOD CENTER is located in the north-central part of Ohio, about equidistant from Cleveland and Columbus, near U.S. Routes 30 and 42 and Interstate 71. It was originally the estate of Charles Kelley King, an Ohio industrialist. Before his death in 1952, a trust had been created and endowed for the perpetual maintenance and development of his resident property of 47 acres as a cultural and garden center, with special emphasis on horticulture, nature study, and related subjects. It employs a staff of 25 professional and maintenance workers.

Mr. King had traveled widely and had seen many of the important botanic gardens, arboretums, and private gardens of the United States and Europe, and horticulture was one of his nonbusiness interests.

He became impressed with the importance of gardening as a creative activity that had a close relationship to the health, well-being, and vocational productivity of those participating in it. Because of the rapid industrialization he had seen taking place during his lifetime (1867–1952), he wished to provide through his estate an institution that would actively stimulate interest in gardening, the amateur growing of plants, and an appreciation of native birds, animals, and flowers.

Kingwood Center was opened to the public October 10, 1953. Its educational emphasis is on home gardening, and a full program of workshops, educational exhibits, seasonal indoor flower shows, horticultural meetings, lectures, garden clinics, and short courses are provided for the public. The landscaping of the property serves as a demonstration of good use of trees, shrubs, and herbaceous plants. From the early bulbs of spring through the chrysanthemum display in the fall, special plant groups are featured. Large collections of varieties of daffodils, tulips, iris, peonies, roses, gladiolus, dahlias, annuals and perennials, hemerocallis, and chrysanthemums can be seen in season. A moderate sized greenhouse has displays during the winter to create an interest in growing plants in the home. All plantings and displays are designed to give visitors, including casual observers, as much information as possible.

Kingwood Center maintains close cooperation with national plant organizations, such as the American Iris Society, American Peony Society, and American Hemerocallis Society. Official variety trial grounds are maintained, and other types of research concerned with special cultural problems are carried on. Frequently the facilities are used for national, regional, or State shows and meetings of plant societies.

A PROGRAM of nature study is organized on essentially the same basis. One of its chief attractions is a nature trail, along which can be seen an extensive collection of native Ohio wildflowers.

Several species of native waterfowl, tame enough for visitors to see at close range, inhabit a small pond. A collection of upland game and other species of birds is on display and is used in connection with lectures, demonstrations, and other educational activities of the staff naturalist. Boys and girls in schools, Scout organizations, and other youth groups are eager participants.

Like most garden centers, Kingwood maintains a library on gardening and related subjects and has a monthly publication. It is unique among comparable institutions, however, in being interested primarily in the problems of the small home gardener, and nearly all its activities are slanted toward increasing his interest in plants and nature, helping him to create beauty around his home, and providing him with information on gardening as a hobby.

Kingwood, Longwood, and their sister gardens are alike in one important respect—the cordiality of their welcome to visitors. Countless Americans, from all sections of the country, visit and enjoy them every year and gain new or enlarged love and appreciation of what gardens are and what gardeners can do.

IN THE MODERNIZATION of their educational programs and publications, many of the leading botanic gardens and arboretums have assumed some of the activities often carried on by educational garden centers.

An example is the Los Angeles State and County Arboretum, at Arcadia, Calif., which since its foundation in 1947 has helped greatly in community improvement through its work with individuals, commercial firms, organizations, and departments of the city and county.

It operates as a botanical institution with research facilities and scientific studies, but its objectives are much broader. It is set up to touch and enrich the lives of all citizens by serving as a "horticultural center for Southern California, providing facilities for the promotion of horticulture and floriculture, fostering more extensive and intelligent use of ornamental plants and trees to enhance southern California's gardens, parks, and parkways."

Further, it is "an information center maintaining a complete catalog of all plants cultivated in southern California, where specimens can be readily identified and practical advice given on planting, propagation and cultivation of plants."

Many examples can be pointed out to show how these objectives have contributed to community improvement. The testing and introduction of new plants adapted to local soil and climate conditions has advanced home and civic beautification. Because of the fire hazard of the fast-burning native vegetation on the hillsides of the area, plants have been tested and recommended that offer promise of reducing this danger. Information in lawn improvement has helped solve a number of special problems. Studies of methods of accelerating the growth and flowering of camellias, an important shrub in the region, and the dissemination of information has given impetus to the use of camellias in gardens, parks, and various types of landscape plantings.

Information on the identification of types of injury produced by air pollution and plants that will tolerate the condition has been helpful to home gardeners and professional horticulturists alike.

THROUGHOUT THE 50 States, the staffs of many botanic gardens are working in the field of amateur horticulture and contributing information for the public benefit.

The Missouri Botanical Garden at St. Louis, Mo., established in 1859 and popularly known as Shaw's Garden in honor of the founder, Henry Shaw, has an enviable record of promoting good horticulture through its classes, lectures, and demonstrations.

The New York Botanical Garden in Bronx Park, New York City, established in 1891, has various types of programs for the benefit of amateurs, even though its chief work has been in botanical sciences.

The Brooklyn Botanic Garden, 1000 Washington Avenue, Brooklyn 25, which was established in 1911, has offered popular courses in horticulture for adults and children.

The Morton Arboretum at Lisle, Ill., a few miles west of Chicago, was established in 1922 by Joy Morton,

whose father, J. Sterling Morton, an outstanding agriculturist, served as Secretary of Agriculture in 1893–1897 and originated Arbor Day. It has provided public education in horticulture and nature study through lecture series, tours of the arboretum exhibits, and courses for home gardeners, professional gardeners, and teachers.

THE HOUSING and location of garden centers are as varied as the activities they engage in and the people they serve. Many have their own special buildings on public property or that of another public institution. The Dallas Garden Center uses a splendid enlarged and reconditioned building, formerly one of the buildings of the Texas State Fair. Many centers have offices in public libraries and in buildings in public parks. In some cities space is donated by department stores. A few carry on their activities from a room in private residences.

Nearly all have some library facilities, including good reference sources, current horticultural books, magazines, seed and nursery catalogs, and pamphlets. It is common practice to provide lectures, slide or film programs, classes, workshops, demonstrations, flower shows, and other types of exhibitions. They may sponsor garden tours and excursions to points of horticultural interest. Many have programs for young people. Some sponsor garden therapy programs in cooperation with hospitals. Most of them make awards for special achievements.

Garden centers are financed in various ways—by memberships, the support of local garden clubs, and contributions. Some have moneymaking projects and may charge for some of their programs. A few are endowed or receive grants from philanthropic funds.

The centers touch the lives and interest of many Americans—individuals associated with garden clubs, persons who seek help from the centers, and the many who appreciate the results. This fact suggests their importance in carrying out projects for community betterment that are related to plants, horticulture, and conservation. A great deal remains to be done, and it is fortunate that the number of centers is growing, although not in proportion to the need.

Garden centers perform functions in the modern and progressive community that no other agency is set up to handle.

Even if a garden center did nothing more than to discourage litter and encourage keeping the community picked up and clean, it would be beneficial and important. They are doing much more; their accomplishments, experience, and potential, which has hardly begun to be developed, place them in a strong position to assist in carrying on projects for community improvement.

RAYMOND C. ALLEN *is director of the Kingwood Center in Mansfield, Ohio. Previously he was executive secretary and editor for the American Rose Society. At Cornell University, from which he has a doctor of philosophy degree, he was in charge of the teaching and research work in herbaceous plant materials and supervised the Cornell Test Gardens. He has published a number of scientific papers, articles, and a book,* Roses for Every Garden.

FAY M. MAYES

A SALUTE
TO THE GARDEN CLUBS

A MORE beautiful America is promised if all citizens accept the responsibility that more than one-half million members of garden clubs have accepted since 1930. The promise and the responsibility are to work for cleaner, more attractive communities, conserve and rebuild forests and parks, reclaim neglected natural treasures, and develop roadsides for beauty and safety. People of all ages can share in it.

Members of the National Council of State Garden Clubs, Inc., realize the importance of teaching young people to be guardians of our heritage. Garden clubs, therefore, have junior, high school, and college programs, which start at the fourth grade. The young members learn a great deal about gardening and the importance of using wisely what we have.

The council in 1963 embraced 15 thousand clubs, 500 thousand members, 25 thousand high school and junior high school people, and 100 thousand junior gardeners in 47 States and the District of Columbia. Twenty-five affiliate clubs were mostly outside the continental limits.

Each club initiates and promotes a number of projects, such as the saving of native plants, parks, and natural areas that are being lost through carelessness and exploitation and the

promotion of horticulture by the introduction, propagation, and the study of plants.

The development of roadside parks for use, safety, and beauty is one aim. The "don't-be-a-litterbug" slogan originated in Florida was adopted by the council in 1952, and has become familiar to many Americans. It is a matter of continuing education to convince everyone that "beauty is our duty." It is important to make the landscape beautiful, to use wisely products of the land, and to keep America green; it is important also to keep it clean.

State federations of garden clubs have led the way in the control of billboards and the preservation of scenic beauty. Seventeen States cooperated to support a bill (based on 23 United States Code 131, Section 103 of the Federal-Aid Highway Act of 1961), which provides that billboards be set back 660 feet from highways. States that have the law get 0.5 percent Federal aid for roadside development. The act provides that a State that entered into an agreement with the Federal Government before July 1, 1963, will have its share of Federal funds for highways increased by one-half of 1 percent of the total cost. The increase makes the State's participation 9.5 percent instead of 10 percent of the cost of a Federal highway; the Government then assumes 90.5 percent of the total cost. Each State must pass its own laws to require a setback of 660 feet for billboards on the interstate highways.

Several State federations have a Governor's Committee on Roadside Development and Safety, most of whose members belong to garden clubs. The Florida Highway Department makes funds available to assist clubs in planting and maintaining roadside projects.

Garden clubs have various other interests in highways—preserving natural tracts near them, improving safety, and installing rest and picnic spots. Clubs in many States have undertaken such projects. Alabama, Georgia, South Carolina, Ohio, and Utah are among them.

Members in Colorado landscaped with native plants a site as a Blue Star Memorial at Panoramic Park, part of the Blue Star Memorial highway program, which includes the landscaping of designated sections of highways and placing markers. The project was established in 1944 to honor those who serve in the Armed Forces. Markers are placed in parks, picnic grounds, roadsides, and median strips, all of which present lovely vistas of rivers, valleys, and mountains. The Blue Star Memorial highways crisscross the Nation, and markers may be seen on Highways 1, 11, 29, 41, 90, 70, 380, 80, 190, and others.

THERE ARE AS MANY projects, big and small, as there are clubs. They may include a neglected triangle where Maple Avenue enters Main Street; the care of cemeteries; putting out one tree or several in the drab playground of George Washington Elementary School; cutting weeds down by the railroad tracks; putting in a good word for saving the trees back of the public library.

I cite a few examples of many.

The Ozark Garden Club of Arkansas erected signs to deter vandalism that would destroy natural beauty of the Ozark National Forest.

The Garden Study Club of Marion, Ala., completed a project of cleaning, repairing, and resetting gravestones in the Marion Cemetery, which dates from 1822. The cemetery also was cleared, landscaped, and fenced.

The Garden Club of Georgia relocated a colony of pink ladyslippers (*Cypripedium acaule*) from the Brasstown Bald, the highest mountain in Georgia, to Sosbee Cone, a scenic area 3 miles from Vogel State Park. The cypripediums were in danger of being destroyed by a highway, which was being cut through the mountains on Georgia Highways 180 and 175. The pink ladyslippers grew at an elevation of 3 thousand to 5 thousand feet. The members of the Blairsville Garden Club, Mrs. Charles Hight, State conservation chairman, and Mrs. Claude Carter, president of the Georgia federation, dug the ladyslippers and replanted them in a similar bog 15 miles from where they were growing. The operation took time, work, and knowledge of the ladyslippers' particular requirements, for they are hard to move.

The garden clubs on Signal Mountain, in Tennessee, under the leadership of Mrs. Claude Givens, a past president, succeeded in planting the roads and parks of the mountain with dogwood and other indigenous plants. During the blooming season—usually in April, if the season is favorable—Signal Mountain is truly a garden spot of beauty.

The garden clubs of New York provided a "sitting garden" for the American Field Service in the heart of New York City.

The Garden Club of North Carolina led the way in building and restoring botanic gardens. Six acres of the Daniel Boone Botanical Garden at Boone have been planted with a collection of plants native to North Carolina, and six additional acres were landscaped with flowers and foliage plants. All the plants are labeled as an educational project. The Elizabethan Garden on Roanoke Island was completed after years of effort. The garden was restored to appear as it might have been years ago. The Marcus Franck Fragrance Garden for the Blind in North Carolina is an outstanding contribution in horticultural therapy.

The Rhode Island Federation of Garden Clubs can be proud of the Biblical Garden in the patio of Temple Beth El in Providence.

The Bennington Garden Club of Vermont purchased a 19-acre sphagnum bog in order to preserve a unique plant habitat near Cownal, Vt. It is famous for its variety of plants and illustrations of biological principles.

The Federated Garden Clubs of Connecticut contributed funds to complete the purchase of 40 acres at the Wadsworth Wildlife Sanctuary. It is near Westport and is a perpetual gift to children of Fairfield County.

The Garden Club Federation of Pennsylvania contributed to the preservation of Bewman Hill at Washington's Crossing State Park, a 100-acre woods that has a thousand species of native plants.

Hampton Marsh, a 3,300-acre sea marsh, the second largest in the New England States, is the major project of the New Hampshire Federation of Garden Clubs. In order to get assistance from other organizations and clubs, the Garden Club of Hampton formed a committee, known as the Marsh Conservation Committee. The 350-acre preserve has been one of education, as the members learned much about biology, land use, genealogy, history, title searching, and human nature.

Four garden clubs of the Kalmote district of Oregon worked several years in landscaping Kalmote Park in Kalmote Falls. It is a bird sanctuary with nature trails and a mountain drive. The Oregon federation established a fund in order to plant seeds of wildflowers in favorable areas along highways and on mountainsides. Water was piped 1,200 feet up the mountain to irrigate the dry south side. Along the highways, the first to be planted were timberline and alpine seeds. The historical garden at Champong Pond was developed to preserve native plant materials west of the Cascades. Permanent plant identifications were installed, and perpetual maintenance is assured.

A 15-acre tract of pine plantings near Holly Springs, Miss., on Highway 72 between Memphis and Chattanooga, is a project of the Mississippi federation. Another planting of 15 acres on Highway 84 near Natchez is dedicated to youth. The plantings were made possible by a fund-raising project of the federation, "Pennies for Pines." Another project, "Pennies for Fun," provided a State park.

The largest conservation project of the Colorado Federation of Garden Clubs is replanting the San Juan National Forest, in which fires had destroyed 2,500 acres. The devastation is referred to as the Lime Creek burn. The garden clubs of Colorado adopted the project in 1957; by 1963, 150 acres had been replanted. Other organizations also are active in the reforestation, a continuing project in cooperation with the Forest Service. The replanting with lodgepole pines, which are considered most suitable, may be completed by the year 2000.

Centerville, Utah, is the site of a project on which garden clubs and Boy Scouts worked together in planting trees and grass in a dirt-filled reservoir to stabilize the soil.

The Alma Peterson Azalea Memorial, a 4-acre tract donated by Elmer Peterson in memory of his mother to The Nature Conservancy, is managed and maintained by the Ava Garden Club and the South Central Association of the Federated Garden Clubs of Missouri. The garden clubs contributed the fencing necessary to save the area from encroachment. It contains a native stand of azaleas, a member of the rhododendron family that grows here at the western limits of its range. This living museum also has flowering dogwood, shortleaf pine, black cherry, oak, blackhaw, sassafras, low-bushed huckleberries, and several mosses.

The American Holly Forest, 80 acres of virgin holly near Dexter, Mo., was purchased by The Nature Conservancy. The garden clubs of the Central District are responsible for its maintenance and protection. It is thought that the stand preserved in Missouri is the westernmost stand of this variety in America. Sand-loam soil and spring seepage are vital to holly; it was for this reason that the garden clubs of Missouri were responsible for the purchase of 43 additional acres in order to hold the ground necessary for an ample water supply and proper soil.

The federation in Virginia has launched a campaign to protect our heritage trees, among them the holly. A concentrated effort to plant more trees and to preserve living trees is a project in many States. Memorial forests in West Virginia and Virginia are examples. The Sugar Loaf Garden Club of Roanoke, Va., in a 4-day campaign obtained 460 dogwood trees for its project. The Fernstrom Memorial Forest, in northern Virginia, is a large tract donated in honor of Mrs. Henning Fernstrom, a founder of the Virginia Federation of Garden Clubs. A split-rail fence was placed at the front of the acreage, which has been developed and planted as a beautification and conservation area.

Massachusetts garden clubs cooperated with the Western Forest and Trail Association to save 300 acres at the Hubbard Trail and Wildlife Sanctuary. The Nature Conservancy has secured Black Pond, a true bog at Norwell. The town conservation commissions in Massachusetts are organized by interested individuals, garden clubs, and other organizations. An enabling act gives the city or town governments the power to create a conservation commission, which serves in an advisory capacity and as a coordinating agency of the municipal government. A Massachusetts law provides that land once donated for an original purpose and use cannot be changed without an act of the legislature. It is in cooperation with these conservation commissions and garden clubs that natural areas have been preserved and conservation projects have been carried out.

The Garden Club of New Jersey has cooperated in attemps to save 2,081 acres of the great swamp at the headwaters of the Passaic River from development as an airport. It was deeded to the Department of the Interior. This living museum is 25 miles west of New York City. The purchase of 919 additional acres rounds out the area as a manageable and permanent refuge. The Great Swamp, formed by a glacier 10 thousand years ago, consists of 8 thousand acres of unspoiled wetlands, marshes, wooded swamps, and dry uplands. Its many values include recreational, esthetic, flood control, and educational benefits.

Mrs. Don F. Smith, president of the Federated Garden Clubs of Maryland, in cooperation with The Nature Conservancy, was successful in preserving the Battlecreek Cypress Swamp in Calvert County. The swamp is a laboratory for scientists.

The Elvina Slossom Memorial Redwood Grove in Humboldt County, Calif., is the site of a 130-acre preservation of redwoods. The grove, a project of the California garden clubs, was first established by the National Council of State Garden Clubs.

The Garden Club of North Carolina uses horticulture rating sheets to increase interest in horticulture and to insure well-planned programs and projects. The rating sheets give credit toward a horticultural honor roll and assures the planting of trees, shrubs, and perennials, annuals, and bulbs through projects in the community and home plantings. The data from one report made to Mrs. J. R. Gibson, chairman of the Swainboro Club, revealed that 160 thousand trees were planted by garden club members in a year. Members are urged to replace each tree lost by storms and to plant trees to retard erosion, furnish feed and cover for wildlife, and increase the value of unused land.

The Florida Federation of Garden Clubs has landscaped the highway entrance to Florida at the junction of U.S. Highways 1 and 301. Mrs. Jack Dunlap, president at the time of the landscaping and dedication, obtained a donation of 15 thousand dollars for the project.

The Garden Club of Kentucky cooperated with the State government in building and planting a large clock on the grounds at the capitol in Frankfort. The annual flowers of which the clock is formed are changed with the seasons.

Six garden clubs of La Crosse, Wis., completed a project of landscaping the grounds of the Mary E. Sawyer auditorium. Maple and flowering trees give color and interest to the planting.

The Fox Chapel Garden Club of Pennsylvania donated 300 garden books to establish a garden department at the Shady Side Academy High School library. The nearest garden library was 9 miles away. It is a free, public lending library of books about all phases of gardening.

Because a library is important to those interested in gardening, most garden clubs have a shelf of books on gardening in a public library if they do not maintain their own library in the clubhouse. Some of the shelves have books on a special subject. Memorial books with plates to indicate who was honored by the book, as well as the plates themselves, are used for memorial gifts.

A conservation bookshelf of 150 volumes was established at the Valley Garden Center, Phoenix, Ariz., in memory of Mrs. Lorraine Detterbeck, a former State conservation chairman of the Arizona Federation of Garden Clubs.

THE HELEN KELLER Fragrance Garden for the Blind at the Blind and Deaf School in Talladega, Ala., a garden club project, is a shady plot of 25 thousand square feet. Each plant in it has a small plaque, engraved in ordinary letters and braille, that gives the botanical name and other information.

The garden, named for Miss Keller, a native Alabamian, contains flowers from her garden in Connecticut. A guardrail guides the blind about the garden. The design is informal; there are no sharp corners or any awkward structural features. Curving walks with raised walls enable visitors to stroll through the garden with ease and safety. Rounded concrete benches are conveniently located.

The raised planting beds are placed so that all visitors find the levels of the beds convenient for examining the plants. Low-growing plants were given prominence, so that the stems, the flowers and foliage, and their fragrance may be touched and smelled. Color, texture, and fragrance were considered in the planting.

The garden is maintained through funds derived from garden club dues. A fountain is a gift of members. The Alabama Nurserymen's Association donated 1,100 dollars' worth of shrubs.

A marker in the shape of an open book has an inscription in braille which reads, "Helen Keller Fragrance Garden, established 1960–61, by the Garden Club of Alabama, Mrs. Lewis Easterly, President. In a state where gardens grow, God walks."

The South Dakota Federation of Garden Clubs built a fragrance garden at the School for the Blind at Aberdeen, with funds donated by members and donations from the Sears Foundation. The garden is 108 feet long and 52 feet wide. The flowerbeds in the garden are not raised, because many of the plants grow tall and because it was thought that the children should not have to count the steps as they stroll through the garden. The markers are tall and give the names of the plants in braille. A pool was built at the request of the children.

A touch-and-fragrance garden for the blind was built by the Arizona Federation of Garden Clubs at Scottsdale. The garden, started in 1960, grew out of the realization that blind people usually are unable to use the swimming pools, baseball parks, and playgrounds that sighted people enjoy. The garden provided a guided wall for a stroll where plant materials that could be touched and smelled are listed in braille. They can sit and listen to the waterfall created for them and hear the birds at the feeders and baths. A fountain, 40 feet by 8 feet, with cypress trees in the background, was the last part of the garden to be completed. The garden is 150 feet long and 70 feet wide. Flowerbeds the length of the garden are 5 feet wide.

THE FLORIDA FEDERATION of Garden Clubs began a plant introduction and distribution project in 1948. New and reintroduced plants are grown from seed and distributed statewide to members who grow and keep records

on the development of the plants. Many introduced plants have proved to be of commercial value. The first report printed was "Cold Tolerance Report," which may be obtained from the federation's headquarters, Box 1604, Winter Park.

The Botany Handbook for Florida was printed by the Florida Department of Agriculture in cooperation with the Florida Federation of Garden Clubs. The text was written by Nancy A. Knox and Ethel McSwiney. It contains drawings, pictures in color, and information on the study of plants. Its key to plant names has been used for study in several colleges. A copy of this booklet, Bulletin 187, may be had by writing to the Department of Agriculture, The Capitol, Tallahassee, Fla.

The Delaware federation has prepared *Delaware Looks Ahead*, a handbook on conservation, horticulture, roadside development, and other garden club projects.

SHORT COURSES for gardeners are conducted at colleges and universities in a number of States. These programs are planned jointly by the university staff and garden club members. Nonmembers as well as members may attend a 2- or 3-day course of study.

The National Council and most State federations provide scholarships in horticulture, landscape design, and conservation. The Federated Garden Clubs of Connecticut give four 300-dollar scholarships in horticulture. Clubs in the Garden Club of Kentucky offer scholarships in ornamental horticulture. The Washington State Federation of Garden Clubs makes available scholarships in horticulture, landscape design, and conservation. In addition to a 500-dollar scholarship in tropical horticulture and scholarships in conservation for teachers, the Florida Federation of Garden Clubs provides a 1,800-dollar fellowship in horticulture. The Louisiana Garden Club Federation offers scholarships in horticulture and research grants. The federations of Maine, Massachusetts, Michigan, North Carolina, Ohio, Oklahoma, Tennessee, and Washington provide conservation scholarships.

Conservation camps for young people have been conducted in many States; Wisconsin, South Carolina, Florida, and Virginia are among them.

A nature camp in Virginia used government-owned facilities on Sherando Lake during its first 10 years. A site was selected in 1951 for new camp buildings on Big Mary's Creek in George Washington National Forest. Its brown buildings blend with the beauty of the forest; one building contains a laboratory, museum, and library; there is an attractive outdoor chapel. Each State president of the Virginia federation, beginning with Mrs. C. B. Nettleton, a past president of the National Council, has made the camp her special project. State life memberships were established, and the proceeds go to the permanent camp.

STUDY OF horticulture is not confined to garden club members. Many State federations provide greenhouses for hospitals and other institutions.

The Florida federation built a greenhouse at one of the mental hospitals and one at a tuberculosis hospital. Members devote many hours each week to sharing their knowledge and enthusiasm with patients. The federation provided funds for a greenhouse and slathouse at the Florida State Prison in Raiford and a greenhouse at the Avon Park Institution.

The Delaware Federation of Garden Clubs sponsored a window box project in less privileged areas. Boxes, of an inside measurement of 8 by 12 by 30 inches, are lined with zinc and painted inside and out. The recommended wood for the boxes is cedar, cypress, redwood, or white pine. They are made of 1-inch boards, screwed together, not nailed, with angle irons inside and steel tape outside. The garden clubs furnish the soil and plants for 2 years. The third year, the person may purchase them from the garden clubs at cost. The residents are shown how to plant the boxes and care for the plants. The project was started by the Neighborhood Garden Association of Wilmington.

Clubs in California, Florida, Montana, New York, and Washington have participated in a people-to-people program by making available hundreds of trees to replace those destroyed in wartime in Japan and Korea. Florida sent money to purchase a thousand dogwoods for Nagoya, Japan. New Jersey clubs sent 500 roses to Korea.

Garden club members believe gardening is an international good to be shared as a gesture of friendship that contributes to peace. They are interested also in promoting the art and science of gardening and preserving the natural beauty of America, so our children will enjoy our heritage.

FAY M. MAYES, *who lives in Pompano Beach, Fla., is past publicity chairman of the National Council of State Garden Clubs. The mother of two sons, Mrs. Mayes is an officer and consultant of three corporations, holds a private pilot's license, has edited The Florida Gardener, and has written a number of books and magazine articles. She is the past president of the Florida Federation of Garden Clubs and the awards chairman of the National Council of State Garden Clubs.*

JOHN A. BAKER

WHEN PEOPLE MEET, DISCUSS, AND ACT

A SPEAKER at one of our national conferences on land and people cited a river to make a point about the revitalization of rural America. "In my home State of Wyoming," he said, "there is a historical marker in the Wind River Canyon. It marks the place where the Wind River, which originates in the Wind River Mountains, suddenly changes its name to the Big Horn River, which flows on through the Big Horn Basin and meets the Missouri. The words on the marker read, 'The Wedding of the Waters.'

"That the same river was called by two names came about through a misunderstanding. . . . It was years later that they were found to be one river flowing in the same direction and for the same purpose.

"The time is here for the wedding of the waters of the economic and institutional streams of urban and rural America. For we now know they flow in the same direction and for the same purpose."

The speaker, James W. Fagan, of Casper, Wyo., was one of 10 thousand urban and rural leaders who attended meetings in 1962 in New Orleans, Philadelphia, St. Louis, Denver, and Portland, Oreg., and in Duluth in 1963.

They all had a chance to speak, ask questions, analyze Government programs, tell about experiences in their own communities, and recommend ac-

tion. They examined opportunities, techniques, and methods of developing rural areas—what they thought must and should be done for land and people by people and their governing bodies.

The process of economic growth depends essentially and uniquely on the initiative of local people, they agreed.

Success in rural areas development is keyed to the ability of local people to set their goals in the light of their needs and their realizable potentialities.

Every possible source of technical assistance and service should be considered, and all that can be useful should be drawn on. Usually, no single agency, Federal or State, and no single private enterprise, commercial or cooperative, can supply all of the aids needed to work out the complicated problems of any area.

At the meeting in Denver, Theo-

573

dore Jameison told about activities of the Standing Rock Sioux Indians in South Dakota.

When the tribe received a Government payment of 12.5 million dollars in 1958 to compensate for lands flooded by the Oahe Dam, the people decided to invest the money in enterprises for economic growth. They elected three members from each of their seven districts to talk with the people about plans and gain ideas that might be useful.

When a long list of ideas for improving life on the reservation was submitted to the vote, the people gave first place to new and better schools, second place to improvements in housing, and third place to a livestock program.

Then, as the Indians began these developments, they found new ideas had been stimulated, and new opportunities had been uncovered. One was a cheese factory. Another was a textile mill, which used the talents of Indian artists and weavers and offered employment to more than 100 persons.

Thus, in a few years and through their own initiative and with the catalyst of a payment wisely used, the people of the Standing Rock Sioux tribe had new schools, new homes, and new jobs. They established an industrial development commission to encourage further economic growth.

MANY OTHER examples of the yeastiness of ideas in raising community sights, buttressed with private and public capital resources, were offered as rural areas development projects. The proposals ranged from small farm markets to broad efforts like the regionwide Great Plains conservation program. They were not restricted to enterprises that must draw on nearby farms or forests for supplies of raw materials. Many took large labor resources into account. Proposals were made, for instance, for factories that would recap tires, make pole sockets, produce chemicals, and prefabricate houses.

Among the new endeavors in which rural communities showed keen inter-est were enterprises related to tourism and recreation, which often involve a complex of land and water facilities; the development of specialty crops, such as nursery stock; and the improvement of processing, handling, and marketing facilities for farm and forest products.

Key points made at the conferences included these:

Land, water, timber, and human resources must be put to work systematically for rural America to move all of America ahead more rapidly.

An essential action is to give rural people the motivation and means to solve their problems.

Rural development requires ideas, preparation, and timely action to develop family farms, expand business enterprises, and provide better facilities, such as electric systems and telephones, housing and water and sewer systems, swimming pools, good schools, and tourist attractions.

The Federal and State Governments should cooperate to provide coordinated technical services to help local, private, and government leaders make appropriate, comprehensive, and consistent plans and programs for farm and home, woodlots and forests, soil and water conservation, watersheds, and areawide economic development for the coordinated growth of entire river basins.

People in communities not yet organized for action can get information about rural areas development from local representatives of the Department of Agriculture, who will arrange for the county agent or another leader to call an organizational meeting of people who have a stake in the economic growth of the area.

Many rural areas already have one or more development and planning groups and agencies. Often several such groups may be brought together to develop the broad base of representation and interest essential to action.

AN EXAMPLE is the work in six counties of West Virginia—Braxton, Gilmer, Lewis, Nicholas, Upshur, and Webster—whose residents undertook a study that brought together a score of local committees and local, State, and Federal agencies to develop unified projects.

An initial project was to develop the Sutton and Summerville reservoir areas as outdoor recreation attractions. Another was concerned with training programs for employees in service industries—waitresses, service station attendants, and other workers who meet tourists. A third project in career exploration and youth employment had the goal of reducing unemployment and underemployment, giving youths better training for existing jobs, and cutting the number of school dropouts. A fourth project to boost agricultural income through beef cattle and dairy enterprises was designed to assist producers of beef cattle and dairymen by combining small and idle farms into economic units.

Another project was a survey of water resources to take advantage of opportunities to end floods, abate stream and water pollution, develop multiple-use water impounding reservoirs, and permit the towns and small cities to expand their water facilities. In the sixth project, farm families, whose large houses have room to spare, work with State and Federal agencies to develop vacation farms, where city families with young children may enjoy farm life.

The people of the six counties also joined forces to raise funds for new industries and made plans to consolidate schools, merge hospitals, and build area-wide jails. An Area Resource Center with a staff of 60 was planned to provide continuing education and research.

PROGRAMS to help local governmental and private efforts in rural areas development are administered by several Federal agencies, often as part of regular, ongoing programs.

Among them are the Small Business Administration, the cooperative Federal Farm Credit System, the Federal Reserve System, the land and power developmental and management agencies of the Department of the Interior, Business and Defense Services Administration of the Department of Commerce, the water development program of the Corps of Engineers, the Housing and Home Finance Agency, and the health, education, and welfare services of the newest Department.

The broad, new program of the Area Redevelopment Act, administered by the Department of Commerce, is utilized by the Department of Agriculture in designated low-income, rural counties.

PROGRAMS in the Department of Agriculture include 37 services that offer help in rural development. They are of four types:

Those that contribute to the improvement and stabilization of farm income;

Those that provide technical services and financial resources for the balanced use, development, and conservation of soil, water, forests, and other natural resources;

Those that encourage and facilitate the establishment and expansion of economic enterprises, including family farms, industrial and commercial firms, recreational facilities, and farmers' cooperatives, and

Those that provide leadership, technical services, results of research, and financial resources to stimulate area planning, organization, and action in communities.

Even thus classified, the services do not fit neatly into clear-cut categories, like the pigeonholes of an old-fashioned desk. Rather, they are interrelated and cross-contributing. Each contributes also to other broad national goals.

The Cooperative Federal-State Extension Services provide assistance in organizing and operating rural areas development planning committees and similar local bodies through education for action and organizational leadership for local and State planning activities as well as other specialized technical services.

The Soil Conservation Service administers the program of technical services to members of soil and water conservation districts established under State laws, soil and snow surveys, watershed protection and flood prevention projects programs, the Great Plains conservation program, and a program of special resource conservation and development projects.

The Forest Service applies the multiple-use concept of management to National forests and grasslands with a view to maximum area development and prosperity of rural communities and small cities in adjacent areas. The Forest Service also extends grants-in-aid to State and private forestry activities.

The Farmers Home Administration administers programs of operating loans and real estate loans to family farmers and ranchers, including loans for income-producing recreation facilities and fish farming; loans to associations of rural residents for soil and water conservation and adjustments in land use; and loans to families and groups for rural housing construction and housing purchase or construction for older persons in rural areas and to nonprofit associations to provide housing for migratory farmworkers.

It also administers a loan program for community water systems and assists or administers loans and grants under the Area Redevelopment Act. All types of FHA loans are available only to those who are unable to obtain such credit from normal private cooperative and commercial sources on reasonable terms.

The Rural Electrification Administration administers programs of loans for rural electrification and rural telephone systems and loans to borrowers to extend credit for the purchase and use of electricity-using machinery, appliances, and enterprises. REA also administers the programs of loans for rural industry provided by the Area Redevelopment Administration.

Supporting scientific research for rural areas development activities is conducted by the Agricultural Research Service; Economic Research Service; State agricultural experiment stations, supervised by the Cooperative State Experiment Station Service; the Forest Service; the Agricultural Marketing Service; and the Farmer Cooperative Service.

Farm commodity price support and related programs are administered by the Agricultural Stabilization and Conservation Service. The Federal Crop Insurance Corporation and the production emergency loans of Farmers Home Administration also have leading roles on this stage.

Help also is given in the rural areas development planning process and to rural areas development committees by Technical Action Panels, which include local representatives of agencies of the Department of Agriculture and specialists from the Extension Services, the land-grant universities and other educational institutions, vocational education instructors, scientific personnel of State experiment stations, representatives of State and local governments, and local employees of other Federal Departments.

The county representatives of the Farmers Home Administration, the Soil Conservation Service, and the Agricultural Stabilization and Conservation Service and (when available) local representatives of the Forest Service, Rural Electrification Administration, Agricultural Research Service, Economic Research Service, and other Department agencies comprise the Technical Action Panels. State panels have been established in all States.

The list of Federal services available to rural areas development sounds something like the bill of fare of a cafeteria. In a way it is. The Rural Areas Development program of the Department of Agriculture, however, is not just a vague overall concept. It is a specific, detailed program to bring additional and expanding economic opportunity to rural America.

Some persons have felt that it may be more effective to consolidate into a single Rural Areas Development Administration all the major development, credit, and conservation agencies dealing with farmers, ranchers, and other rural landowners and enterprises with combined units and offices at local, State, and Federal levels.

The more persuasive position, however, has been that greater vigor and stronger technical competence can be brought to the service of county and State rural development committees if the identity of each agency and its tradition and esprit de corps are preserved.

Necessary coordination has been provided by establishing such interagency and staff groups as the Office of Rural Areas Development, the Rural Areas Development Board, Technical Action Panels, and the Land and Water Policy Committee. All of the relevant agencies of the Department are members.

WE CONCEIVE the aims of Rural Areas Development as encompassing activities to obtain the following results:

Preservation and improvement of the family farm pattern of agriculture;

More rapid rate of increase of per person and per family income of people living in rural America, through elimination of the causes of underemployment;

More rapid expansion of the number of remunerative job opportunities in rural America by stimulating a faster growth of rural industry, recreational and other business enterprises of all kinds, both proprietary and cooperative, and expanded income-earning opportunities for those in the service trades and professional pursuits to eliminate the causes of unemployment;

More orderly and rapid development of outdoor recreational opportunities on rural land, private and public, to provide the facilities required by our urban-rural population;

More rapid readjustment towards a better balanced national pattern of land use to the end that each acre and resource will be used in the way for which they are best adapted and for the greatest good of people;

Provision of appropriate services and financial assistance to attain and maintain an adequate level of protection, development, and management of such natural resources as soil, water, forests, fish and wildlife, and open spaces by treating each acre and resource in a manner consistent with its optimum conservation;

More rapid rate of improvement, establishment, and appropriate adaptation of rural community economic and cultural facilities and institutions, including cooperatives, to meet fully the challenges of modern standards and rapid change; and

Increased progress on all other phases of a continuous systematic effort to eliminate all of the complex causes of rural poverty.

METROPOLITAN AMERICA cannot exist without rural America, but, busy with its own growing pains, metropolitan America does not quite understand rural America and tends to overlook it. Meanwhile, rural America, caught up in wrenching global changes neither of its own making nor to its own liking, has some justification for feeling neglected, put upon, and frustrated.

Yet, as the Nation grows it must recapture and improve the sense of unity of simpler times. It must provide a broad opportunity for people in rural America to attain deeply felt aspirations on a parity with urban America. To reach this goal requires higher real incomes and faster economic growth in rural America. Rural Americans need and deserve a higher grade of economic opportunity, more income, more purchasing power, better living.

Americans are generally agreed that poverty and bankruptcy shall not be used as a means to force needed economic adjustments in rural America. Rather, rural America and the whole Nation want prosperous family farms and thriving towns and small cities.

NATIONAL POLICY requires that additional capital and technical resources must be moved to the service of rural

Americans. It should not be a forced movement of additional rural Americans off the land and out of rural areas. Rather the aim is to develop and build for rural Americans of all ages a broad array of attractive alternatives from which to choose where to live and how to make a living.

LET ME EMPHASIZE again that what I have written here reflects not only the thinking and aspirations of people in Washington. Time and again the points were raised in one way or another by men and women who attended the Land and People conferences.

Let me quote a few of their remarks.

The Rev. William H. Stauffer of Stone Creek, Ohio, at the St. Louis Land and People conference, after telling of the differences between steerage and first class on an ocean liner, seemed to sum up the consensus of the aspirations of all for rural America when he said, "We country folks are planning now to start traveling first class."

At the meeting in Philadelphia, Francis A. Pitkin, executive director of the Pennsylvania State Planning Board, said:

"We are now in an era of dramatic and profound change. In such a period, nothing is more crucial than the use of organized foresight to make certain that the direction in which we are traveling is actually the way we want to go. Another name for organized foresight is planning.

"Never before have the destinies of our cities and our countryside been more intimately entwined than they are today."

Dr. Firman E. Bear, of New Brunswick, N.J., editor of the magazine Soil Science, said:

"More and more decisions, covering an ever greater portion of our land, will have to be made by the government—local, county, State, or national as the case may be. Each of these governmental units, at the earliest possible date, should develop carefully detailed plans for the use or uses of all the land under its jurisdiction, even though circumstances may later require that these plans be materially altered. Conflicts of interest among overlapping governmental agencies must be resolved. But this cannot be done until these several units have developed comprehensive plans in the doing of which such conflicts come to light. . . .

"Many more well trained men than are now available will be needed to carry out the programs required to improve the environments under which we are to live."

Emmette Spraker, of Pocatello, Idaho, said:

"Let it never be said that in these years of the scientific revolution we were able to send men into space, but were unable to put bread and milk into the hands of hungry children. It takes more than just dreams to build a community, both urban and rural. It takes plans, then action. Our infinite good fortune, as Americans, is that the dreams we have been given are inexhaustible. Let us activate our dreams to build upon and improve what we have, where we are."

Lathrop E. Smith, secretary-treasurer of the Maryland Association of Soil Conservation Districts, said:

"The President, the Secretary of Agriculture, or his very able staff and assistants cannot do the job for us. They can only assist us—you and me!

"A hundred years ago a strange man lived alone on the shores of a small lake in Massachusetts. He was a victim of tuberculosis and he closed his record of that loneliness with these beautiful words of challenge and hope—'Only that day dawns to which we are awake. There is more day to dawn. The sun is but a morning star.' Henry David Thoreau didn't know about soil conservation districts or about rural areas development, but he knew about people and he loved the land. We will not be found wanting as this new day dawns."

JOHN A. BAKER *was appointed Assistant Secretary of Agriculture for Rural Development and Conservation in 1962.*

INDEX

579